THE PORTABLE HENRY JAMES

The Viking Portable Library

Each Portable Library volume is made up of
representative works of a favorite modern or
classic author, or is a comprehensive anthology
on a special subject. The format is designed
for compactness and for pleasurable reading.
The books average about 700 pages in length.
Each is intended to fill a need not hitherto
met by any single book. Each is edited by
an authority distinguished in his field, who
adds a thoroughgoing introductory essay and
other helpful material. Most "Portables" are
available both in durable cloth and
in stiff paper covers.

****

THE PORTABLE

HENRY JAMES

EDITED, AND WITH AN INTRODUCTION, BY

MORTON DAUWEN ZABEL

*

NEW YORK

THE VIKING PRESS

****

Grateful acknowledgment is made to the following for permission to reprint selections: Charles Scribner's Sons, New York, for "Four Meetings" from Volume XVI of *The Novels and Tales of Henry James,* copyright 1909 by Charles Scribner's Sons, 1937 by Henry James; "The Pupil" from Volume XI of *The Novels and Tales of Henry James* copyright 1908 by Charles Scribner's Sons, 1936 by Henry James; "A Round of Visits" and "The Bench of Desolation" from *The Finer Grain,* copyright 1910 by Charles Scribner's Sons, 1938 by Henry James; "The Beast in the Jungle" from *The Better Sort,* copyright 1903 by Charles Scribner's Sons, 1931 by Henry James; letters from *The Letters of Henry James,* copyright 1920 by Charles Scribner's Sons, 1948 by William James; "The Sense of Glory" from *A Small Boy and Others,* copyright 1913 by Charles Scribner's Sons, 1941 by Henry James; "The End of the Civil War" from *Notes of a Son and Brother,* copyright 1914 by Charles Scribner's Sons, 1942 by Henry James; "The Banquet of Initiation" from *The Middle Years,* copyright 1917, 1945 by Charles Scribner's Sons; Harper & Brothers, New York, for "New York Revisited" and "The Voice of Concord" from *The American Scene,* copyright 1907 by Henry James, 1935 by Henry James; Oxford University Press, Inc., New York, for the excerpt from *The Notebooks of Henry James,* edited by F. O. Matthiessen and Kenneth B. Murdock, copyright 1947 by Oxford University Press, Inc.; John Farquharson, London, for "The Art of Fiction," "Criticism," the excerpt from *Hawthorne,* "Honoré de Balzac," "Gustave Flaubert," "The After-Season in Rome," "Occasional Paris," and "London."

CONTENTS

BIBLIOGRAPHY

*

INTRODUCTION

I

Henry James once spoke of how "the private history of any sincere work . . . looms with its own completeness." In another place he wrote that "the figures in any picture, the agents in any drama, are interesting only in proportion as they feel their respective situations. . . . Their being finely aware—as Hamlet and Lear, say, are finely aware—*makes* absolutely the intensity of their adventure, gives the maximum of sense to what befalls them."

On both occasions James was defining principles for the art to which he devoted his entire life—the art of fiction. But it is safe to say that he also spoke with conscious reference to himself, to his own adventure in the eventful age he witnessed and his own way of turning it to account. The world of readers and critics was slow to admit the intensity of that adventure or to recognize the "maximum of sense" James gave it. His private history was not of the kind that "looms large" with the dramatic capacities in action or passion that have made a whole host of modern writers—from Goethe, Byron, and Dostoevski to Rimbaud, Yeats, Lawrence, and Lorca —vivid figures in the mythology of the human spirit. Outwardly viewed, his career was unspectacular. It was the art and mind by which he enriched it that made it a great life and that continue to make James one of the most interesting figures in the drama of the past century.

Henry James was born on April 15, 1843, in Washington Place in New York City. Fifty years earlier his Irish grandfather had come to America where he established himself in trade in several cities of New York state, prospered handsomely, married three times, and when he died in 1832 left a fortune of three million dollars to his children. By his third wife he had a son called Henry, who rebelled against assuming the family business and devoted himself instead to the study of religion, philosophy, and humanity. This son married at the age of thirty, and four sons and a daughter were born to him and his wife, the oldest son being called William after his grandfather, the second Henry, after his father. In 1843 these two infants were taken across the Atlantic by their parents to spend part of a year in France and England, but the family returned to America and during the next ten years the children received their early schooling in New York and Albany. They were back in Europe in 1855 for three years, and again in 1859 for one. There Henry James went to schools in Switzerland, France, England, and Germany and discovered his passion for books and writing. Back in Newport in 1860 he tried studying painting, gave it up, attended the Harvard Law School briefly, gave it up, lived with his family in Cambridge, began to meet literary men like Charles Eliot Norton, James Russell Lowell, and William Dean Howells, resolved to become a writer, began his public career with a review in the *North American* in 1864 and a story in the *Atlantic Monthly* in 1865, and in another ten years had his first book of tales ready for publication.

Meanwhile his love of travel took him to Europe on his first adult journey in 1869 and on two further trips during the following six years. He studied the French theater at the Comédie Française; he put himself to school among the literary circles of Paris and London, forming friendships with Turgenev, Flaubert, Renan, Zola, Daudet, George Eliot, Ruskin, Morris, Tennyson, Browning, Gladstone, Morley, and other public figures in both countries; he explored Italy, Germany, France, and England. By 1876 he had established himself permanently in London, and he continued to live there and in Sussex for the rest of his life. His books —novels, tales, critical essays, accounts of travel—appeared in increasing numbers year by year. Success came early, and at least twice—with *Daisy Miller* in 1879 and *The Portrait of a Lady* in 1881—he knew public celebrity; but gradually his novels fell into public and critical disfavor. For five years, from 1890 to 1895, he devoted himself to making a success in the theater, but this effort ended in failure. He resumed the writing of fiction; produced a long series of books of increasing subtlety and originality; cultivated a great host of friends; revisited America after an absence of twenty-one years in 1904 and rediscovered his native land as a famous man; revised his major fictions for a handsome collected edition; again tried writing for the theater, again unsuccessfully; came back to America in 1910 with his dying brother William; returned to England; witnessed the outbreak of war in 1914 with shock and anguish; wrote a series of memoirs of his early years; tried to resume the writing of novels; became a British citizen in 1915 as a sign of loyalty to his adopted country; was taken ill in his seventy-third year; received England's Order of Merit on his deathbed; and died in February 1916.

It was a life which, apart from deep family affections, many devoted friendships, many travels, a few high mo-

ments of public celebrity and several of uncomfortable
notoriety, was a record of little except incessant labor
at the desk, many books read and many written, and
finally a quiet death in the fullness of years. It was
committed to a difficult and increasingly thankless kind
of work, and in spite of James's extreme respect for his
calling, his almost sacerdotal conception of the literary
vocation, he was frequently beset by fears that his efforts had come to nothing. More than once he felt that
he had "entered upon evil days," that his finest work
had "reduced the desire, and the demand, of [his] productions to zero," that he was "condemned apparently
to eternal silence." What he called the "complete failure" of the sumptuous New York Edition of his fiction
left him, toward the end of his life, "high and dry"—
"at my age . . . and after my long career, utterly, insurmountably, unsaleable"—and he called that crowning monument of his labors "a sort of miniature Ozy-
mandias of Egypt ('look on my *works*, ye mighty, and
despair!')." He wrote his failure to win popular approval into a remarkable series of tales—"The Author
of Beltraffio," "The Lesson of the Master," "The Death
of the Lion," "The Middle Years," "The Next Time,"
and half a dozen others—which picture art as a tyrannical taskmaster who breaks his devotees when they are
frail, tests them cruelly when they are strong, or grants
them at best a secret victory which the world appears
bound to condemn or ignore. It was with something like
the defiance of a proud desperation that he told William
Dean Howells, at one particularly bleak moment in his
fortunes, that "some day all my buried prose will kick
off its various tombstones at once."

We have seen his prophecy justified. When the hun-
dredth anniversary of James's birth arrived in 1943 it
saw his fame sweeping into the full tide of a revival that

has raised him to a position of supremacy among the novelists of the English-speaking world and given him a rank in the highest company of modern writers. The decade of the nineteen-forties and the years of crisis just preceding it witnessed a crowded procession of centenaries—anniversaries of artists and thinkers who helped to shape a momentous century in the life of Western man. Hardy, Zola, and Nietzsche, Swinburne, Pater, and Butler, Mallarmé, Verlaine, and Anatole France, Cézanne and Renoir, Americans like Mark Twain, Howells, Henry Adams, William James, Bierce, and Lanier— in a time of danger and catastrophe the date of each of them sounded its knell on a darkening age and provided its occasion for revaluing the legacy, heartening or dubious, they left to their inheritors. None of them met a more dramatic recognition than Henry James. As if by a stroke of ironic justice, his own worst fears for his future were dispelled at a time that brought ignominy to much of the civilization he had most valued. "During our current afflictions," said one English tribute, "he has found a greater body of readers than ever before, who discover in him a mirror of the civilized enjoyments now in abeyance, a guardian of the values that war repudiates."

It was an axiom of the aesthetes of the nineties that nature imitates art. James's work makes us believe that history does so also. A great share of the history of his age now appears to find its permanent image in his pages. His books have become a standing example of what he meant when he told H. G. Wells in 1915 that literature *"makes* life, makes interest, makes importance . . . and I know no substitute whatever for the force and beauty of its process." Our present interest in James derives partly, no doubt, from the distrust of history and action that has been bred by the political and moral disorder into which the world has fallen, by the prolonged crisis and sense of disintegrating traditions in which we have come to live. We see in him, by a species of retrospective logic, what men have always seen in their image-makers and heroes of form— what Santayana meant when he said, defining Proust's achievement, that "Life as it flows is so much time wasted, and that nothing can ever be recovered or truly possessed save under the form of eternity, which is also . . . the form of art."

The revival of James has bred its excesses of cult and sanctimony. They come partly from a natural pride— notably an American pride—in reclaiming the books that were for many years disputed or rejected by critics of many schools and prejudices: by realists, by patriots, by skeptics of culture, by reformers of society, by proletarians, all of whom combined to make the public forget that James had his faithful if limited audience through fifty years; that his tales and novels were printed in magazines on a scale that has become incredible in our own boasted age of literary freedom and experiment; that he met positive defeat only once —in his efforts to become a successful dramatist—and turned even that drastic disappointment to the advantage of his real work in fiction; and that his fellow writers had granted him the title of "Master." His critics preferred to charge him with most of the sins in the literary and American calendars—with repudiating his birthright, with being a snob, with falling indecisively between two cultures and finding himself at home in neither, with evading a full commitment to life, with accepting only the values of privilege and aristocracy, with excluding a great share of human misery and injustice from serious consideration. He was accused of being the "culmination of the superficial type," a man

who "doesn't find things out" and so produces "tales of
nothingness"; of being "a fat, wistful remittance man
with a passion for elegance"; of having "never succeeded in coming to grips with life"; of creating "the
impassioned formalism of an art without content"; of
"magnificent pretensions, petty performances!—the fruits
of an irresponsible imagination, of a deranged sense of
values, of a mind working in the void, uncorrected by
any clear consciousness of human cause and effect";
even, finally, of being "simply not interesting: he is
only intelligent; he has no mystery in him, no secret;
no Figure in the Carpet." [1]

This long bill of particulars includes some arguments
with which every serious reader of James must eventually deal, but the verdict is now, on the whole, a very
different one. As early as 1918 one of James's most perceptive followers had made bold to call him "the most
intelligent man of his generation," and today critics of
resolute astuteness and of radically different standards
attest his distinction. "Henry James *is* a great artist, in
ite of everything," says one of them; "his work is
mplete as his experience was; but it is in no respect
se   d-rate, and he can be judged only in the company
of t   reatest." Another, asking only that he be per-
mitte   define the novel in a way "neither difficult
nor illegi ate," has said he would "be inclined to consider James as the greatest novelist in English, as he is
certainly one of the five or six greatest writers of any
variety to be produced in North America." A third has
called James "a man who, if he had never written a
novel, would be considered the first of short-story writ-

[1] The critics quoted are H. G. Wells (in *Boon*, 1915), Bur-
ton Rascoe, Somerset Maugham, J. Middleton Murry, Van
Wyck Brooks (in *The Pilgrimage of Henry James*, 1925), and
André Gide.

ers, and if he had never written a short story, the noblest of letter writers, and if he had never written anything would by his talk alone be known as a great man." A fourth has flatly asked, "What achievement in the art of fiction—fiction as a completely serious art addressed to the adult mind—can we point to in English as surpassing his?" [1]

When controversy, enthusiasm, personal legend, and historic occasion combine in the rediscovery of a writer and make of it a significant episode in the history of taste, it is clear that he constitutes what James himself would have called a "special type"—that he was marked by circumstances as well as genius to play a significant role in the drama of culture. James held a high opinion of the artist's right to such a role. "To do something *great*" of which "the world shall hear" was one of his earliest ambitions. Once, in the earlier days of his conquest of England, he was a guest of Lord Rosebery and his Rothschild wife amid the splendors of Mentmore. "I have retired from the glittering scene, to meditate by my bedroom fire on the fleeting character of earthly possessions," he wrote home to his mother in America. "Tomorrow I return to London and to my personal occupation, always doubly valued after 48 hours among *ces gens-ci*, whose chief effect upon me is to sharpen my desire to distinguish myself by personal achievement, of however limited a character." The desire for fame and power, that "sense of glory" which had struck him in boyhood like a revelation in the Galerie d'Apollon in the Louvre, possessed him even though he felt the

---

[1] The critics quoted here are T. S. Eliot in *The Little Review*, August 1918; Edmund Wilson in *The Triple Thinkers* (1938); Yvor Winters in *Maule's Curse* (1939); Cyril Connolly in *Horizon*, May 1943; F. R. Leavis in *The Great Tradition* (1948).

peril it entailed. He would certainly have agreed with
what one of his contemporaries, Gerard Manley Hopkins,
then wholly unknown to literature, once wrote in a letter to Robert Bridges: that "fame, the being known,
though in itself one of the most dangerous things to
man, is nevertheless the true and appointed air, element, and setting of genius and its works. What are
works of art for? to educate, to be standards. Education
is meant for the many, standards are for public use. To
produce then is of little use unless what we produce is
known, if known widely known, the wider known the
better, for it is by being known it works, it influences,
it does its duty, it does good. We must then try to be
known, aim at it, take means to it."

What James aimed at in his art, what means he took
to provide a standard for the use and education of men,
what tests and scruples he met in the effort, and by
what means his purposes were finally vindicated—all
this makes his career one of the dramatic chapters in
modern literature, and permits him to loom large in a
way that has become a lesson in the persistence and integrity of the writer's vocation. But because James was
a man who, contrary to a still-surviving derogation, did
not live or work unaware of his role in history, it has become something more.

II

James published his first tale in 1865, when he was
twenty-two years old. That date, in the career of an
American, acts as an initial signal. The Civil War had
just ended. The American nation, like James himself,
stood at the threshold of a new age. Her literature had
already passed through its successive formative phases.
Each of them had found a man, some of them several

men, to voice its deciding impulse. Bradford, Mather, Edwards, and Franklin, Jefferson, Irving, Cooper, Emerson, and Whitman brought the republic by clearly defined stages—colonial, religious, revolutionary; frontier, pioneer, and nationalist—to the moment when several talents possessed of a vision more original and searching than any of these crowned the progress of the American spirit with what serious maturity in any ordained course inevitably entails: a moral challenge, a check to self-esteem, a warning to the will, a vision of the tragedy implicit in pride and success. The American mind, rooted in its hereditary conscience, had never escaped its hauntings by darker powers, its stirrings of ancestral guilt, what Howells was presently to call "the slavery implicated in our liberty." Poe had recently imaged them unmistakably. But an enormous confidence in the American destiny allayed them until Hawthorne, Melville, and, in her Amherst seclusion, Emily Dickinson gave them their classic and prophetic definition. The Civil War came as if to certify their presence. An hour of judgment sounded. It called for a new order of intelligence in American life, a critical intelligence; and neither the victory of 1865 nor the prosperity that followed it in the North could disguise the summons.

No writer more than the novelist is so likely to prove, once his work is finished, that he was born at precisely the right moment to become the artist he was intended to be. Stendhal, Balzac, Dickens, Tolstoi, Proust, and Thomas Mann all illustrate the opportunity with which history favors the prose chronicler beyond any other type of artist. The literary novice of 1865 could hardly remain unaware of his special opportunity, particularly when, as in Henry James's case, he saw the end—both triumphant and tragic—of a great national conflict in which a mischance of health had prevented him from taking an active part and whose meaning he was made to feel with a special personal intensity. Already in 1865 James had declared his opposition to Walt Whitman's kind of visionary emotion, but he shared with Whitman the non-participant's sense of the crisis that befell the American nation in the spring of that year.

This is to say that several distinct tasks—two great tasks especially—presented themselves to the young writer of 1865 who was able to see their urgency. One was the problem of defining the point at which America had arrived in her venture of nationhood and of determining her relation to the rival civilization of Europe— a problem which, in spite of the fact that almost every serious American writer had already addressed himself to it, still remained unsettled in the balance-books of history. The other was the re-creation of the art of fiction as a form of critical intelligence by rescuing it from the debris of tradition and the compromises of popularity, and by raising it to the dignity of moral power which novelists like Balzac, Turgenev, and Flaubert had already won for it in Europe, but which only Hawthorne and George Eliot had reached in the novel of the English-speaking world. James saw, with the full insight of his youthful acumen, these two great opportunities at his disposal. He saw he had a major theme to treat, and he saw that a new kind of art was needed to treat it adequately; and he took these as the special tokens of his vocation in literature.

His subject was made inescapable by the family into which he was born. His Irish grandfather had provided the wealth that endowed his heirs with the privileges of comfort, travel, and social affluence. His father, another adventurer but in religion and philosophic speculation instead of trade, had converted those assets to the service of thought and imagination. The James home was a breeding place of curiosity, ideas, and bookish pleasures. Emerson was a familiar guest there—"the divinely pompous rose of the philosophic garden," the elder James called him—and the air was a stir of enthusiasms. Idealism, transcendentalism, and democratic emancipation bred the new faith in humanity whose guides were Emerson and Fourier, and a creative freedom in religion whose prophets were Sandeman and Swedenborg. What a later American,[1] echoing Emerson, has ascribed to the American character as "a heightened sensitivity to the promises of life" was the native emotion of the James home. Man was to be redeemed by society. Society was to be redeemed by a rebirth of moral confidence and a faith in "possibilities." Such ideas implanted in both William and Henry James a religious conviction which, persisting beyond rationality or agnosticism, was to fix its stamp on their ultimate conceptions of science and of art.

But another emotion, balancing and complicating the ardor of emancipation, dominated the family. It was the spell of the past, the call of Europe. "I saw my parents homesick, as I conceived, for the ancient order," Henry James said many years later, "and distressed and inconvenienced by many of the more immediate features of the modern, as the modern pressed about us, and since their theory of our better living was from an early time that we should renew the question of the ancient on the very first possibility I simply grew greater in the faith that somehow to manage that would constitute success in life. I never found myself deterred from this fond view, which was implied in every question I asked, every answer I got, and every plan I formed." In her early essay on James, Rebecca West has said that the essential thing about him was that "he was an American;

[1] F. Scott Fitzgerald.

and that meant, for his type and generation, that he could never feel at home until he was in exile." James himself said it better when he wrote, "It's a complex fate being an American," and better still when he declared it was his function as an artist to be a man "on whom nothing is lost." It was the decree of the elder Henry James that his children should experience their complete fate as Americans by knowing the share Europe played in their lives. By taking his family abroad he enforced the instinct of tradition and cultural complexity in his sons, and he prepared Henry James for the subject that was to tax him throughout his life.

James's Europe, first in boyhood but presently in early manhood, was what Europe is bound to be at some point in the life of every American with any of the emotion or imagination of history in his constitution. It was the "threshold of expectation," the "gate of admirations," a "scene for the reverential spirit." It was "this dear old Europe," a world "immemorial, complex, accumulated"; and he came to it as a "passionate pilgrim," an "heir of all the ages." There he feasted on his "banquet of initiation," experienced "the sense of glory," "looked at history as a still-felt past and a complacently personal future, at society, manners, types, characters, possibilities and prodigies and mysteries of fifty sorts." There he learned that glory meant "ever so many things at once, not only beauty and art and supreme design, but history and fame and power, the world in fine raised to the richest and noblest expression." But though he brought to Europe a good share of his traditional American innocence, he also brought a shrewd curiosity and a divided sympathy. "I still love my country," he wrote his mother in 1869 from his "wondrous England," and that love, tough-rooted and ineradicable, soon defined an attitude that was to assert itself as radical. It

set in motion a debate, a drama of contrasts and oppositions, that was never to subside wholly, either in his
mind or in the tales he created.

What he really had carried to Europe, along with his
native exhilaration and the reverence he had been bred
in in his father's house, was another emotion of which
the Jameses—father, William, Henry, Alice—were all
to become aware in their lives. Henry named it many
years later, in 1896, in a letter to a friend. "I have the
imagination of disaster—and see life indeed as ferocious
and sinister." It was a presentiment that had already
visited his father, as it was to visit his brother and sister, in the form of panic seizure and crises of emotional
illness. In Henry himself it remained controlled by a
strong and vigorous imagination, but it remained none
the less radical to his nature; and it soon added the
force of a tragic vision to his excited responses to the
scene of Europe.

We hear much about the dialectic intelligence in
modern literature. It has come to be regarded as a primary clue to all serious art, a symptom of genuine morality. It is a kind of intelligence of which James is a major
exponent in our literature. He was schooled in it by his
earliest experiences and education. It suffuses all of his
work, serves as fulcrum to his insights and judgments,
and plays its part continuously in the oppositions—
America and Europe, innocence and experience, glory
and disaster, illusion and reality—which are the basic
terms of his drama of morality and culture.

Its workings in his fiction have been variously defined.
One critic, Yvor Winters, has defined them with particular relevance: James's fiction argues that "there is a
moral sense, a sense of decency, inherent in human
character at its best; that this sense of decency, being
only a sense, exists precariously, and may become con-

fused and even hysterical in a crisis; that it may be enriched and cultivated through association with certain environments; that such association may, also, be carried so far as to extinguish the moral sense." And further: that "the moral sense as James conceives it is essentially or at least appears to James most clearly in American character; that it can be cultivated by association with European civilization and manners; that it may be weakened or in some other manner betrayed by an excess of such association." [1]

This is not to say that the American character supplies the invariable norm of virtue or decency in James's tales. The American he pictures in Europe may be innocent, worshipful, honest, or idealistic—may be Daisy Miller, Isabel Archer, Christopher Newman, Milly Theale, Maggie Verver—and thus fall victim through the very fault of his innocence to duplicity or intrigue in the older culture. He may also become perverted by some moral weakness, or by wealth, self-indulgence, and the corruption of cynicism, and thus a doer of evil —Roderick Hudson, Madame Merle, Gilbert Osmond, Charlotte Stant. He may save himself there like Lambert Strether or lose himself like Hudson and Osmond. He will in any case be tested by a complexity he is never likely to have known in his native element; and the test will measure not only his own capacities for intelligence and moral dignity but also the America he came from.

Equally he will act as a test of the culture he encounters, for James's Europe shows a hostility of forces equal to that shown by America or by the two worlds when they meet in conflict. If the America James knew

[1] Yvor Winters, "Maule's Well, or Henry James and the Relation of Morals to Manners," in *Maule's Curse* (1938), p. 169.

in youth gave him a standard of soundness and honesty
(*The American, The Europeans, Washington Square*),
it could also be crude, simple-minded, predatory, and
half-barbaric (*Watch and Ward, Confidence, The Bostonians*); and if the America he rediscovered late in
life revealed unsuspected capacities of energy, inven-
tiveness, and social amenity (*The American Scene*), it
also warned him of a corruption through wealth and
power that could debase its victims and make Europe
in turn assume the virtues of spiritual dignity and maturity ("The Jolly Corner," "A Round of Visits," *The
Ivory Tower*). But when the Jamesian drama shifts to
England and offers a drama exclusively European, as it
does in *The Princess Casamassima, The Tragic Muse,
What Maisie Knew, The Awkward Age, The Spoils of
Poynton,* and *The Sacred Fount*, it may depict the
forces of morality and culture not as stabilized by tradition but as even more dangerous in their workings,
their pregnancy of evil and treachery, than in the
younger and simpler society. There the idealist, the
artist, the innocent, or the child may encounter an immanence of disaster even more "ferocious and sinister"
than America offers, by reason of the cynicism which
time and privilege have bred.

Henry James was incapable of his sister Alice's scathing criticism of European society and politics, as he was
incapable of his brother William's robust confidence in
the American future. But he fully sensed the evil in
what he called "the increasing dehumanization of society"; he knew what threat existed in the "black depths"
and "enormous misery" of "the people"; he dreaded the
advance of the "grossly materialistic"; and he spoke
partly for himself when he made the heroine of *The
Princess Casamassima*, his most ambitious drama of
modern politics, describe English society as "the old

régime again, bristling with every iniquity and every abuse, over which the French Revolution passed like a whirlwind; or perhaps even more a reproduction of Roman society in its decadence, gouty, apoplectic, depraved, gorged and clogged with wealth and spoils, selfishness and scepticism, and waiting for the onset of the barbarians."

James's argument, however rooted in the antithetical values of America and Europe, was never capable of simplicity. He was too deeply implicated in his own divided loyalties to permit it to become so. He was " 'between' countries," as Edna Kenton has rightly said: "There lay his subject and his relation to it, and there was his home"; and "Life is a struggle, wherever we are." But another loyalty claimed him too, another law of moral justice that forbade the rigidities of bias or the simplifications of prejudice. It was the principle of his art, with its standards of detachment, critical lucidity, and mind—that "quality of mind" which he defined as art's crowning virtue because it embodies the fullest possible measure of critical and moral sympathy, "unprejudiced and imperative," and thus insures a value higher than either passion or dogmatism. "I have not the least hesitation," he wrote his brother William in 1888, "in saying that I aspire to write in such a way that it would be impossible to an outsider to say whether I am at a given moment an American writing about England or an Englishman writing about America (dealing as I do with both countries), and so far from being ashamed of such an ambiguity I should be exceedingly proud of it, for it would be highly civilized."

III

The worth of an art "civilized" in James's sense was not a matter of common acceptance when James wrote those sentences, and it is ceasing to be so in various quarters today. Literature, like life itself, is again being reclaimed by prejudice and force. Having passed through a great period of experiment and sophistication, it is once more called upon to declare positions, judgments, decisions; to revert to crudity or didacticism in order to serve the uses of social justice; to become partisan, political, or *engagé*. That demand continues to support the argument that James's work is a symptom of the casuistry, ambiguity, and equivocation that have undermined society and incurred its disasters. Thus the long-standing complaints about "a mind working in the void, uncorrected by any clear consciousness of human cause and effect," "an art without content," an inability "to come to grips with life."

They are complaints which, lodged against a minor part of his work, have a certain relevance, but they cannot stand against the weight and solidity of his whole achievement. James must be read, and read in his entirety; read not with the demand that he be another Tolstoi, Dostoevski, or Melville, or even a Balzac or Dickens, but because he had his own unique contribution to make to the art of fiction and made it in a way that proves him as much a moral historian as any of these, even when he fell short of their final range and eloquence.

It may be allowed that the lengths of subtlety, analysis, and density to which James carried his craft can, if we do not follow him far enough, obscure the laws on which he based it. A factor of contrivance or calculation does figure in his workmanship. The ideas or "germs" for his tales, which he compiled in his notebooks—those germs which illustrate the "odd law which somehow always makes the minimum of valid suggestion serve the man of imagination better than the maximum" —sometimes take on the appearance of theorems in moral algebra or exercises in dramatic calculus. Occasionally his stories—slighter tales like "The Solution," "The Real Right Thing," and "The Great Condition"; intricate parables like "The Figure in the Carpet"; elaborate studies in social morality like *The Tragic Muse* and *The Awkward Age;* dramas of obsession or hallucination like *The Other House* and *The Sacred Fount*—will show a virtuosity that results in sheer intellection or a disembodiment of sensibility. Most of James's plays for the theater, lacking his narrative and stylistic body, expose their skeletons of pure contrivance and lapse into theatrical formulae. H. G. Wells, hostile as a social and scientific realist to James's art, complained that James's exhaustive analysis of motives becomes "psychologizing" rather than genuine psychology; but even some of James's greatest admirers have found in the novels of his final period—*The Ambassadors, The Golden Bowl, The Sense of the Past*—an "unhealthy vitality of undernourishment and etiolation," a failure in the "sense of human solidarity," an excess of expression over "what is actually felt." Is *The Ambassadors*, for instance, what James himself and a large body of recent readers consider it, "the best 'all round'" of his novels, or is F. R. Leavis justified in thinking it "to be not only *not* one of his great books, but to be a bad one"? Is *The Awkward Age*, as Leavis insists, "one of James's major achievements," or does it, as Edmund Wilson believes, combine "a lifeless trickery of logic with the equivocal subjectivity of a nightmare"? James was always fasci-

nated by the difference between "a given appearance
and a taken meaning," and obviously this difference,
pushed far enough, can produce a disproportion between fact and illusion, substance and ratiocination,
manners and morals, which is likely to end in casuistry
and moral enigma.

These are the serious grounds of Jamesian criticism.
What seems clear to the present writer is that James
established his certain mastery in the books of his so-
called "middle period." That great sequence begins with
the concise perfection of *Washington Square*, continues
through *The Portrait of a Lady* (possibly the touchstone of his entire achievement, with its shapeliness and
movement as of fine music and its superbly controlled
sympathy and justice) and his two masterpieces of social drama, *The Bostonians* and *The Princess Casamassima*, and is rounded out by the brilliant *nouvelles* of
the nineties, to reach its climax in such searching studies
of human and ethical values as *What Maisie Knew* and
The Spoils of Poynton.

Yet given James's gifts and purpose, it is impossible
to expect him to have rested with the achievements
of those astonishing twenty years. The momentum of
his vision was incapable of stopping at that point. He
had earned his right to carry his art into the poetic
and metaphysical risks of his final period, particularly
when that period produced the rich qualities of *The
Wings of the Dove* (whatever the dramatic frailty of
its nebulous heroine, certainly his highest point in delicacy of moral criticism), the profound ethical reverberation of *The Golden Bowl*, and that phenomenal revival of his powers as a critic of society, *The Ivory
Tower*. *The Ambassadors* may show too arbitrary a
schematization; *The Outcry* and *The Sense of the Past*
may err in the direction of abstraction; but the final

phase of James's work brought the modern novel into a greater sense of its moral and imaginative possibilities than any other work of the early twentieth century. And in spite of his increasing addiction to obsessive themes and subjective treatment, the vigorous recuperation of realism in *The Ivory Tower* shows how genuinely he was sustained to the end of his life by the principles he adopted in early maturity and how these gave him a creative longevity, a persistence in imaginative invention, that is virtually unique in the history of fiction.

Those principles animate his work as a critic; they are condensed in his most famous essay, "The Art of Fiction." James was not a formal critic, and it is doubtless true that he wrote brilliant criticism without being a "great" critic. He never formulated an organic aesthetic; he did not investigate classical literature, not even English and French; he had little skill in the theory and appreciation of poetry. R. P. Blackmur has said that he never arrived at "a relation to the whole body of literature" such as we find in Johnson, Coleridge, Sainte-Beuve, Arnold, and Eliot. Instead he worked empirically, pursuing consistently only his special interests in fiction and drama. But within these limits he showed an integrity of interest that was tireless, and he produced the most coherent study of a chosen craft by a practicing craftsman that we have in English. His essays rival Baudelaire's in their continuous relevance to actual creation and to the origins of such creation in the artist's mind and sensibility.

His emphasis is often on devices, on what he called "doing," at that time a major problem in his craft. Thus the attention he gave to the "grammar" of fiction—to such matters as "the point of view," "scene" and "dramatizing" ("Dramatize! dramatize!"), plotting and motivation, *ficelles* and *disponibles*, problems of inclusion and exclusion, form and structure, distancing and perspective, structure and selection. This may appear to be an exaggeration of method for method's sake. But James's practice always proves more than his theory, and there he succeeds in proving that technique of any valid kind is always an instrument of values. He never lets us forget what his primary values are, for they emerge from his books—from their complex craftsmanship, their subtleties and ironies, their wit and ambiguities—bearing the short and simple names he insisted on giving them. One is "truth"; the other is "life."

Truth was, for James, the basic law of realism. It means honesty, first of all, but it also means justice to the writer's material. It takes precedence over conscious morality. It is the single test of all genuinely valid morality. He defined it in an early essay: "When once a work of fiction may be classed as a novel, its foremost claim to merit, and indeed the measure of its merit, is its *truth*—its truth to something, however questionable that thing may be in point of morals or of taste." The something to which it refers is wide, various, and illimitable; it is, in fact, life itself—not Whitman's life of enraptured abstraction; not Zola's life in its raw and "unprejudiced identity," a phenomenon for scientific dissection; not the life lyrically idealized by Emerson and the naturalistic mystics. It is life "felt," "realized," "penetrated," "understood." In one of his prefaces James said that there is "no more nutritive or suggestive truth" than that of "the perfect dependence of the 'moral' sense of a work of art on the amount of felt life concerned in producing it." And when he said that "just in proportion as he is sentient and restless, just in proportion as he reacts and reciprocates and penetrates, is the critic a valuable instrument," he formulated a law that applies as much to the novelist as to the critic.

To lend himself, to project himself and steep himself, to feel and feel till he understands and to understand so well that he can say, to have perception at the pitch of passion and expression as embracing as the air, to be infinitely curious and incorrigibly patient, and yet plastic and inflammable and determinable, stooping to conquer and serving to direct— these are fine chances for an active mind, chances to add the idea of independent beauty to the conception of success.

These are the elements that make art great—feeling, passion, curiosity, patience; above all, understanding. They are the only basis of a valid realism. They tell us why James, in Paris in the seventies, believed *l'art pour l'art* to be an "absurdity" and naturalism a "treacherous ideal." They alone, incorruptibly exercised, can make of the novel "a living thing, all one and continuous, like any other organism"; give it the "air of reality," "solidity of specification," "illusion of life." They are "the beginning and the end of the art of the novelist"—"his inspiration, his despair, his reward, his torment, his delight."

When, in the summer of 1889, James was asked to participate in a summer school on the novel in Massachusetts, he sent his doctrine from England to "the nymphs and swains who propose to converse about it under the great trees at Deerfield," and he put it in his most generous and inspired terms.

Oh, do something from your point of view; an ounce of example is worth a ton of generalities; do something with the great art and the great form; do something with life. Any point of view is interesting that is a direct impression of life. You each have an impression coloured by your individual conditions; make that into a picture, a picture framed by your own personal wisdom, your glimpse of the American world. The field is vast for freedom, for study, for observation, for satire, for truth. . . . I have only two little words for the matter remotely approaching to rule or doctrine; one is life and the other freedom.

The two words are our best clues to everything James said as a critic or achieved as an artist. He made them imperative as principles among his disciples and fellow craftsmen. Conrad, for one, was only speaking the Jamesian language when he said that the artist "cannot be faithful to any one of the temporary formulas of his craft." All of these will "abandon him—even on the very threshold of the temple—to the stammerings of his conscience and to the outspoken consciousness of the difficulties of his work," leaving him to descend "within himself, and in that lonely region of stress and strife, if he be deserving and fortunate, [to find] the terms of his appeal."

IV

James staked his appeal on the "quality of mind" he sought to make his art embody, but quality of mind is only another name for the quality of the life art gives us when it achieves its essential purpose. Merely to live is not enough. Strether's words to little Bilham in *The Ambassadors*—"Live all you can; it's a mistake not to. It doesn't so much matter what you do in particular, so long as you have your life. . . . Live!"—can, if taken too literally, be mistaken as the whole moral teaching of James's work. The exhortation strikes one of his deepest convictions, but it was never intended as an argument for self-sufficient living or for the cults of personality and experience which, whether among optimists or aesthetes, became popular doctrines of James's age. Strether himself qualified his advice when he said, "What it comes to is that it's not, that it's never, a happiness at all, to *take*. The only safe thing is to give. It's what plays you least false."

The essence of mediocrity for James was selfishness, as the essence of baseness was treachery and the essence of failure a denial of the spiritual quality of life—of the wisdom that comes through suffering or privation, the fulfillment that comes through generosity and love. To deny these is to face at last the real "beast in the jungle" and to meet the worst of damnations, which is negation. Isabel Archer, in *The Portrait of a Lady*, voiced another of James's deepest convictions. She first came to Europe with the theory that one "should move in a realm of light, of natural wisdom, of happy impulse, of inspiration fully chronic," and with "a fixed determination to regard the world as a place of brightness, of free expansion, of irresistible action." Yet she also brought a bolder sense of the human fate. One of her suitors, Lord Warburton, on being rejected by her, views her assertion that she "can't escape unhappiness" with skepticism and accuses her of fostering a romantic view of misery. "I'm not bent on a life of misery," Isabel answers. "I've always been intensely determined to be happy, and I've often believed I should be. . . . But it comes over me every now and then that I can never be happy in any extraordinary way; not by turning away, by separating myself." "By separating yourself from what?" he asks. "From life," she answers. "From the usual chances and dangers, from what most people know and suffer."

The ideal of consciousness she implies was the basis of James's morality as an artist. It has been called his religion. He refused to make it a means merely of spiritual luxury or happy self-extension. He shows it to be a much harder thing than that. It is a principle of real-

ization, of self-knowledge, of moral limitation and recognition. And this is what permitted him to make it a
principle of sanity and of tragedy. When he named
Hamlet and Lear as examples of the kind of living that
endows life with intensity and gives it a maximum of
sense, he took his examples from tragic drama. By doing so he assented to the classical doctrine that it is
the denials and privations of life that must be made to
enrich it; its capacity for tragedy that gives it its final
value. Yeats was one poet who agreed with him: "Hamlet and Lear are gay."

When James, in 1910, wrote his essay "Is There a Life
After Death?" he gave his belief in "the unlimited vision of being" the appealing accents of a Platonic idea.
Death offers the possibility of "a renewal of the interest,
the appreciation, the passion, the large and consecrated
consciousness" of life itself. But when he wrote closer
to the actual conditions of living he found a stricter
language. He used it in the magnificent letter he sent
his old Cambridge friend Grace Norton in 1883, at a
time when she was passing through an ordeal of suffering:

I am determined not to speak to you except with the
voice of stoicism. I don't know *why* we live—the gift of life
comes to us from I don't know what source or for what purpose; but I believe we can go on living for the reason that
(always of course up to a certain point) life is the most valuable thing we know anything about, and it is therefore presumptively a great mistake to surrender it while there is any
yet left in the cup. In other words consciousness is an illimitable power, and though at times it may seem to be all
consciousness of misery, yet in the way it propagates itself
from wave to wave, so that we never cease to feel, and
though at moments we appear to, try to, pray to, there is
something that holds one in one's place, makes it a standpoint in the universe which it is probably good not to for-

sake. . . . Only don't, I beseech you, *generalize* too much in these sympathies and tendernesses—remember that every life is a special problem which is not yours but another's, and content yourself with the terrible algebra of your own. Don't melt too much into the universe, but be as solid and dense and fixed as you can. We all live together, and those of us who love and know, live so most. We help each other— even unconsciously, each in our own effort, we lighten the effort of others, we contribute to the sum of success, make it possible for others to live. Sorrow comes in great waves. . . . It wears us, uses us, but we wear it and use it in return; and it is blind, whereas we after a manner see.

What James here phrased as a precept of experience he made the guiding principle of his vision as an artist. He had already recognized it as such early in his career, in 1874, when he first discovered the wisdom of Turgenev. Turgenev crystallized a reading of life James had already traced in his chosen models of seriousness in the craft of fiction—Hawthorne, George Eliot, Balzac— but he gave it a quality of "charm," of spiritual force, which lent a particular intensity to James's statement of it:

Life *is,* in fact, a battle. On this point optimists and pessimists agree. Evil is insolent and strong; beauty enchanting but rare; goodness very apt to be weak; folly very apt to be defiant; wickedness to carry the day; imbeciles to be in great places, people of sense in small, and mankind generally, unhappy. But the world as it stands is no illusion, no phantasm, no evil dream of a night; we wake up to it again for ever and ever; we can neither forget it nor deny it nor dispense with it. We can welcome experience as it comes, and give it what it demands, in exchange for something which it is idle to pause to call much or little so long as it contributes to swell the volume of consciousness. In this there is mingled pain and delight, but over the mysterious mixture there hovers a visible rule, that bids us learn to will and seek to understand.

James carried his conviction of that rule into the great scene of his age—carried it out of the simpler world of his youth in America into the *Imperium* of pride and vanity which he made the special stage of his complex drama of cultures and moralities. There he traced the rule in all its conditions of humor and pathos, success and hardship, virtue and evil; and to its workings he brought a wit, compassion, and inexhaustible moral curiosity which not only give his work its depth and richness of imagination but establish its authority as a historical document that comes close to being unique of its kind in English fiction. No one who reads James seriously today is likely to miss the bearing of his insight and prophetic vision on the present circumstances of our lives. As much as Balzac or Stendhal, Tolstoi or Proust, he saw his age in the perspective of the future. He seized his special opportunity as a citizen of two worlds to create a classic drama of their rivalries and oppositions; but before he had finished his work he also achieved an art that transcends the international drama and becomes capable of analyzing the forces in men or societies which the moral vision defines as comedy or tragedy.

To his task he brought a large fund of the faith, idealism, and capacity for confidence that was natural to his American generation; but the realism of vision that accompanied these, while it kept him from remaining an idealist, enforced in his character something of much greater importance to a novelist: a sense of the inescapable value of life and a responsibility, equally inescapable, to its moral necessities. It was these instincts that permitted him to show in his books what T. S. Eliot, in one of the most famous remarks ever made about James, once called "his mastery over, his baffling escape from, Ideas"—"a mind so fine that no idea could violate it." His personal character, as we come to know it through his work, exemplifies what his art embodies as a principle. His last secretary, Theodora Bosanquet, speaking as an intimate witness, has said that it became a passion with James "not to exercise any tyrannical power over other people"; that his "Utopia was an anarchy where nobody would be responsible for any other human being only for his own civilized character." That passion is what finally gives James the terms of his appeal. It ensures both his authority as an artist and his responsible seriousness as an intelligence. In taking as his supreme ambition the achievement of an art fully civilized, he assumed the difficult task of reconciling knowledge with beauty, of holding "in a single thought reality and justice." That is why his work has reasserted its value for us in a tragic and ominous time, and that is why, the prospects for justice and intelligence being what they are in the modern world, it must remain valuable to the future.

HENRY JAMES: A CHRONOLOGY

WITH A LIST OF HIS PRINCIPAL WORKS ON THEIR FIRST PUBLICATION IN BOOK FORM

1793   William James, grandfather (1775-1832), comes from Ireland to the United States. Settles in Albany; conducts tobacco, salt, express, and land businesses in Albany, Utica, Syracuse, and New York City, thus laying the basis of the family fortune of three million dollars—with John Jacob Astor's and Stephen Van Rensselaer's, one of the three largest fortunes in the state.

1811   Henry James, fourth son of the ten children (seven sons and three daughters) of William James and his third wife, Catherine Barber, born in Albany. Educated at Union College, Schenectady, and Princeton Theological Seminary, he declined to assume the family business in order to study philosophy and religion and to become a follower of Sandeman, Emerson, Fourier, and Swedenborg.

1840   Henry James, Sr., marries Mary Robertson Walsh.

1842   William James, son of the above, born in New York City.

1843   April 15: HENRY JAMES, their second son, born at 2 Washington Place, New York City.

1843-44   Mr. and Mrs. James go to Europe, taking their two infant sons with them, and making extended sojourns in Paris and at Windsor, near London.

1845   Garth Wilkinson James, their third son, born (dies 1883).

1846   Robertson James, their fourth son, born (dies 1910).

1848   Alice James, their daughter, born.

1845-55   Family lives in New York City and Albany. H.J. and other children educated by governesses and in day schools in both cities.

1855-58   Family travels and lives in Switzerland (Geneva), England (London), France (Paris, Boulogne-sur-Mer). H.J. attends schools in Geneva, Paris (Institution Fezandié), and Boulogne. Begins youthful writing (Henry James, Sr., to Mrs. James, Boulogne, October 15, 1857: "Harry is not so fond of study, properly so-called, as of reading. He is a devourer of libraries, and an immense writer of novels and dramas.")

1858   Family returns to America; lives at Newport, Rhode Island.

1859   Family returns to Europe. H.J. studies at Geneva (Institution Rochette) and in Bonn, Germany. Friendship with John LaFarge and Thomas Sergeant Perry.

1860   They return to Newport. H.J. studies art in the studio of William Morris Hunt there. Translates Alfred de Musset's *Lorenzaccio* and Merimée's *La Vénus d'Ille*.

1861   Receives injury—"a horrid even if an obscure hurt"—while helping extinguish a fire at Newport. Goes through a period of ill health. The brothers Wilkinson and Robertson James join the Union Army of the Civil War.

1862-63   H.J. studies law at Harvard Law School but abandons it.

1864   Family moves from Newport to Boston (Ashburton Place). H.J. begins friendships with Charles Eliot Norton, James Russell Lowell, William Dean Howells. Begins reviewing books in October for *The North American Review*.

1865   His first tale, "The Story of a Year," appears in March issue of *The Atlantic Monthly*. Begins reviewing books for E. L. Godkin's new magazine *The Nation*.

1866   Family settles in Cambridge, Massachusetts.

1869   H.J. makes first adult trip to Europe: England, France, Switzerland, Italy.

1870   Hears while in England of the death in America of Mary ("Minny") Temple, beloved cousin of the Jameses, later to be commemorated in a number of H.J.'s heroines, notably Milly Theale in *The Wings of the Dove*. Returns to Cambridge home.

1871   *Watch and Ward*, his first novel, serialized in *The Atlantic Monthly*.

1872   Goes to Europe with sister Alice and Aunt Katherine Walsh, traveling in Switzerland, Italy, Bavaria.

1872-74   Travels in England, Holland, Belgium, Germany, Switzerland; lives in Paris, Rome, Florence. Writes reviews and travel articles for *The Nation, The North American Review, The Galaxy, The Atlantic, The Independent*. Studies French theater in Paris.

1874-75   Spends winter in New York. Continues writing for above magazines and presently for *The New York Tribune, Scribner's Monthly, Lippincott's*, and other journals.

1875   First book: *A Passionate Pilgrim and Other Tales* ("The Last of the Valerii," "Eugene Pickering," "The Madonna of the Future," "The Romance of Certain Old Clothes," "Madame de Mauves"). *Transatlantic Sketches* (essays of travel in England, Switzerland, France, Italy, Germany, Holland, Belgium).

1876   *Roderick Hudson*, his first novel to appear in book form. Spends year in France, meeting Turgenev, Flaubert, Edmond de Goncourt, Renan, Maupassant, Daudet, Zola in Paris. Begins living in London (Bolton Street) in December, and meeting the literary and political leaders of England: Tennyson, Browning, Ruskin, George Eliot, Lewes, Leslie Stephen, William Morris, Herbert Spencer, Gladstone, Morley, and others.

1877   Revisits Paris; winters in Rome. *The American* (novel).

1878   Visits Scotland. *Watch and Ward* published in book form. First book of criticism: *French Poets and Novelists* (essays on Musset, Gautier, Baudelaire, Balzac, George Sand, Flaubert, Turgenev, Mérimée, and "The Théâtre Français"). *The Europeans* (novel).

1879   Travels in Italy; spends three months in Paris. *Daisy Miller*, his first tale to gain international celebrity. *An International Episode; "Four Meetings"* (tales). *Hawthorne* (critical biography in the English Men of Letters series). *The Madonna of the Future and Other Tales* (earlier tales collected, with "Longstaff's Marriage," "The Diary of a Man of Fifty," and "Benvolio" added). Continues his "siege" of English life and society, dining out 107 times in a single winter.

1880   *Confidence* (novel). Travels in Italy.

1881   *Washington Square* (novel; later reprinted with "The Pension Beaurepas" and "A Bundle of Letters"). *The Portrait of a Lady* (novel). Returns to the United States, visiting New York, Boston, Cambridge, Washington.

1882   Mother dies in Cambridge in February. H.J. writes dramatization of *Daisy Miller*, later rejected in both New York and London. Returns to England in May; visits France in autumn. Father dies in Cambridge in December. H.J. returns briefly to America.

1883   Returns to England. First collected edition of novels and tales published in 14 volumes in London. *The Siege of London* (with "The Pension Beaurepas" and "The Point of View"). *Portraits of Places* (essays of travel in Italy, France, England, United States, Canada).

1884   Visits Paris. *Tales of Three Cities* ("The Impressions of a Cousin," "Lady Barbarina," "A New England Winter"). Sojourns in Italy.

1885   *A Little Tour of France* (essays of travel in France). *Stories Revived* (collected in three volumes, with "The Author of 'Beltraffio,'" "Pandora," "The Path of Duty," "A Light Man," "A Day of Days," "Georgina's Reasons," "A Landscape Painter," "Rose-Agathe," "Poor Richard," "Master Eustace," "A Most Extraordinary Case" added to stories from earlier books). Sister Alice, now an invalid, comes to live in England, in London, Bournemouth, Leamington. Friendship with Robert Louis Stevenson begins.

1886   *The Bostonians* (novel). *The Princess Casamassima* (novel). Takes flat in De Vere Mansions (later De Vere Gardens), Kensington, London.

1887   Long sojourn in Italy.

1888   *Partial Portraits* (critical essays on Emerson, George Eliot, Trollope, Stevenson, Constance Fenimore Woolson, Daudet, Maupassant, Turgenev, George du Maurier, and "The Art of Fiction"). *The Aspern Papers* (with "Louisa Pallant" and "The Modern Warning"). *The Reverberator* (short novel). Travels in Switzerland, northern Italy, France. Returns to London.

1889   *A London Life* (with "The Patagonia," "The Liar," "Mrs. Temperley").

1890   *The Tragic Muse* (novel). Revisits Italy. Determines seriously to write plays.

1891   A dramatization of *The American* produced in provinces and London by Edward Compton.

1892   *The Lesson of the Master* (with "The Marriages," "The Pupil," "Brooksmith," "The Solution," "Sir Edmund Orme"). Alice James dies at Campden Hill, London, in March. H.J. summers in Italy. Continues writing plays.

1893   *The Private Life* (with "Lord Beaupré" and "The Visits"). *The Wheel of Time* (with "Collaboration" and "Owen Wingrave"). *The Real Thing and Other Tales* ("Sir Dominick Ferrand," "Nona Vincent," "The Chaperon," "Greville Fane"). *Picture and Text* (essays on artists: Edwin Austin Abbey, Charles S. Reinhart, Alfred Parsons, John S. Sargent, Daumier; and "After the Play"). *Essays in London and Elsewhere* (on London, James Russell Lowell, Frances Anne Kemble, Flaubert, Loti, the Goncourts, Browning, Ibsen, Mrs. Humphry Ward, "Criticism"). Visits Paris and Switzerland. Writes the play *Guy Domville*.

1894   *Theatricals* (two unproduced comedies for the theater: "Tenants" and "Disengaged").

1894-95 Contributes "The Death of the Lion," "The Coxon Fund," and "The Next Time" to *The Yellow Book*.

1895   January 5: *Guy Domville* produced at St. James's Theatre, London, by George Alexander; disastrous first night at which H.J. is jeered at the final curtain; it runs a month. *Theatri-*

cals: Second Series (two more unproduced comedies: "The Album" and "The Reprobate"). *Terminations* (tales: "The Death of the Lion," "The Coxon Fund," "The Middle Years," "The Altar of the Dead").

1896 *Embarrassments* (tales: "The Figure in the Carpet," "Glasses," "The Next Time," "The Way It Came"). *The Other House* (novel). Spends summer at Playden, near Rye, in Sussex; autumn in the "Old Vicarage" at Rye, where he discovers Lamb House and takes a lease on it.

1897 *The Spoils of Poynton* (novel). *What Maisie Knew* (novel).

1898 *The Two Magics* ("The Turn of the Screw" and "Covering End"). *In the Cage* (short novel). Begins living in Lamb House, Rye.

1899 *The Awkward Age* (novel). Summers in Italy.

1900 *The Soft Side* (tales: "The Great Good Place," " 'Europe,' " "Paste," "The Real Right Thing," "The Great Condition," "The Tree of Knowledge," "The Abasement of the Northmores," "The Given Case," "John Delavoy," "The Third Person," "Maud-Evelyn," "Miss Gunton of Poughkeepsie").

1901 *The Sacred Fount* (novel).

1902 *The Wings of the Dove* (novel).

1903 *The Ambassadors* (novel). *William Wetmore Story and His Friends* (memoir). *The Better Sort* (tales: "Broken Wings," "The Beldonald Holbein," "The Two Faces," "The Tone of Time," "The Special Type," "Mrs. Medwin," "Flickerbridge," "The Story in It," "The Beast in the Jungle," "The Birthplace," "The Papers").

1904 *The Golden Bowl* (novel). September: returns to the United States for the first time since 1883; spends autumn with William James and family at Chocorua, New Hampshire, and in Cambridge; revisits New York.

1905 Travels in the United States, south to Florida, west across continent to California, lecturing on "The Lesson of Balzac" and "The Question of Our Speech." Returns to England and Lamb House in August. *English Hours* (old and new essays of travel in England).

1906 Lamb House: begins revising his fiction and writing the critical prefaces for the definitive collection (New York Edition), which begins to appear in 1907.

1907 *The American Scene* (essays of travel in the United States). Resumes writing plays after 12 years: *The High Bid* (three acts) and *The Saloon* (one act, based on "Owen Wingrave").

1908 *The High Bid* produced in Edinburgh, March 26, by Forbes-Robertson and Gertrude Elliott (again in London, February 18, 1909). Writes play *The Other House*. *Views and Reviews* (early critical essays and reviews of the years 1865-91 now collected by LeRoy Phillips).

1909 *Julia Bride* (short novel). *Italian Hours* (collected essays of travel in Italy). Writes play *The Outcry*. Long nervous illness.

1910   Continued illness. Goes with William James, now ill, to Nauheim, Germany; then back to Lamb House and thence with Mr. and Mrs. W.J. to New Hampshire, where W.J. dies on August 26. *The Finer Grain* (tales: "The Velvet Glove," "Mora Montravers," "A Round of Visits," "Crapy Cornelia," "The Bench of Desolation").

1911   Honorary degree from Harvard. Returns to England and Lamb House. *The Outcry* (novel). *The Saloon* produced January 17 by Gertrude Kingston in London.

1912   Takes flat at 21 Carlyle Mansions, Cheyne Walk, Chelsea, London. Receives honorary degree from Oxford (*fecundissimus et facundissimus scriptor*).

1913   *A Small Boy and Others* (first autobiographical memoir).

1914   *Notes on Novelists with Some Other Notes* (essays on Stevenson, Zola, Flaubert, Balzac, George Sand, D'Annunzio, Dumas, Browning, "The New Novel," etc.). *Notes of a Son and Brother* (second autobiographical memoir). Outbreak of war in Europe. H.J., greatly disturbed, begins war work, visits hospitals, writes for war charities, aids Belgian refugees, works for American ambulance corps.

1915   July 26: H.J. naturalized a British subject. December 2: his last illness, a stroke, followed by pneumonia, begins ("So here it is at last, the distinguished thing!").

1916   Awarded Order of Merit by King George V. February 28: dies in Chelsea, aged 72 years, 10 months. Funeral service in Chelsea Old Church, London; ashes interred in family plot in cemetery at Cambridge, Mass.

1917   *The Ivory Tower* (novel, unfinished). *The Sense of the Past* (novel, unfinished). *The Middle Years* (third autobiographical memoir, unfinished).

1918   *Within the Rim* (wartime papers written in England). *Gabrielle de Bergerac* (early tale of 1869, now published as book).

1919   *A Landscape Painter* (four early tales of 1866-68 now re-collected by Albert Mordell: "A Landscape Painter," "Poor Richard," "A Day of Days," "A Most Extraordinary Case"). *Travelling Companions* (seven early tales of 1868-74, never published by James in book form, now collected from magazines by Albert Mordell: "Travelling Companions," "The Sweetheart of M. Briseux," "Professor Fargo," "At Isella," "Guest's Confession," "Adina," "DeGrey: A Romance").

1920   *The Letters of Henry James*, selected and edited by Percy Lubbock. *Master Eustace* (five early tales of 1869-78, now re-collected by Albert Mordell: "Master Eustace," "Longstaff's Marriage," "Théodolinde," "A Light Man," "Benvolio").

1921   *Notes and Reviews* (early contributions to *The North American Review* and *The Nation*, 1864-86, collected by Pierre de Chaignon la Rose).

1921-23 *The Novels and Stories of Henry James* (collected edition in 35 volumes, London).

1930   *A Bibliography of the Writings of Henry James,* by LeRoy
        Phillips (a revision and enlargement of the first edition,
        which appeared in 1906).

1934   *The Art of the Novel* (the critical prefaces collected from
        the New York Edition of 1907-1909, with a preface by Rich-
        ard P. Blackmur).

1947   *The Notebooks of Henry James,* edited by F. O. Matthiessen
        and Kenneth B. Murdock.

1948   *The Scenic Art: Notes on Acting and the Drama, 1872-1901,*
        edited by Allan Wade.

1949   *The Complete Plays of Henry James,* edited by Leon Edel
        [contains the long plays: "Daisy Miller" (1882), "The
        American" (1890), "Tenants" (1890), "Disengaged" (1892),
        "The Album" (1891), "The Reprobate" (1891), "Guy
        Domville" (1893), "The Other House" (1908); and the
        shorter plays and dramatic sketches: "Pyramus and Thisbe"
        (1869), "Still Waters" (1871), "A Change of Heart"
        (1872), "Summersoft" (1895), "The High Bid" (1907),
        the project of "The Chaperon" (1893, 1907), "The Saloon"
        (1908), "The Outcry" (1909), and a monologue written
        for Ruth Draper (1913), together with lengthy biographi-
        cal and textual notes by Leon Edel].

1950   *Eight Uncollected Tales of Henry James,* edited by Edna
        Kenton (early tales of 1865-76 never collected by James in
        book form: "The Story of a Year," "My Friend Bingham,"
        "The Story of a Masterpiece," "A Problem," "Osborne's
        Revenge," "Gabrielle de Bergerac," "Crawford's Consist-
        ency," "The Ghostly Rental"). With *Travelling Companions*
        (see 1919) this volume completes the book publication of
        the 15 early tales not collected from magazines by James.

NOTE AND ACKNOWLEDGMENTS

   The aim of this book is to show as fully as space permits the scope
and variety of Henry James's writings from his earliest work in the
1860s to the last year of his life. The examples cover fifty years, from
1865 to 1915, and represent selections from twenty of his books. My
choices are based on a total reading of the work published by James
or his editors in book form, and on a copious reading of the still uncollected contributions he made to magazines, newspapers, and books
during his lifetime. No experienced reader of James need be told the
acute problems an editor encounters when he attempts to represent in
a limited space an author of such bulk and diversity. For every inclusion there must be a score of omissions that appeal insistently to be
included; and no one knows better than the present editor how many
favorite items have had to be excluded or how final decisions are
bound to remain personal and arbitrary. While it has been impossible

to include one of James's full-length novels—these being in most cases now procurable in recent reprint editions—his work is shown in all its other major kinds: short stories, longer tales or *nouvelles*, essays and reviews in literary criticism and biography, travel writings, excerpts from his three autobiographical memoirs, one of the longest and most important personal journals from his notebooks, and his letters. A particular point has been made of showing James's *range*—range of production from early to late, range of themes, range of stylistic development and artistry. Room has not been found for any of his plays or dramatic criticisms (though the essay on Paris offers a glimpse of the latter in its paragraphs on Sarah Bernhardt and the Comédie Française), his random articles on art, or the prefaces for the New York Edition of his fiction; but to these more specialized sides of his work the reader will soon be led.

I have tried to strike something of a balance between familiar or celebrated writings, for which some readers will inevitably look, and those less familiar. Four of the eight tales, for instance, are recognized Jamesian classics; the other four will, I hope, suggest the riches that exist among the lesser-known stories. There was a strong temptation to include more of the uncollected work that still exists only in the files of newspapers and periodicals—book reviews, critical essays, travel and political reports from Europe, art notices, etc.—but this wish has been necessarily curbed. (I leave the student to explore these writings with the help of LeRoy Phillips's invaluable *Bibliography of the Writings of Henry James* in its revised edition of 1930.) The majority of the selections—including, of course, all the fiction—are printed complete. Where excerpts from long books or essays have been unavoidable, these are indicated in the editor's notes, and care has been taken to make such excerpts as self-contained as possible. The Bibliography gives suggestions for the further reading of James's work, as well as a selective account of biography and criticism on James.

I wish to thank a number of Jamesians whose advice has been helpful: first and particularly, Mr. Leon Edel, who has generously offered his expert knowledge of the biography and writings of Henry James in checking and amending the Chronology, Bibliography, and notes, and in making other valuable suggestions about the contents. I have also had the advantage of discussing my selections with other students of James—F. W. Dupee, the late F. O. Matthiessen, Philip Rahv, Lionel Trilling, Edmund Wilson, and Napier Wilt. All of them gave me valuable suggestions, and while their choices inevitably differed widely and could not all be included, I have profited greatly by their advice and trust that something survives of the recommendations of each of them.

A Note on the Texts: The spelling and punctuation in James's books show many changes and inconsistencies over a space of fifty years, and they also vary between the English and American editions. The sources of the present texts are indicated in the editor's notes. Those of the nonfiction are first editions unless otherwise noted. Spellings have been made as consistent as possible within individual items but not in the book as a whole; thus such variants as *connection—connexion, realize —realise, enquire—inquire, today—to-day, humor—humour, unmistakable—unmistakeable,* etc., have been allowed to stand. The six tales taken from the New York Edition of 1907-1909 follow that text as James revised and supervised it. The two tales which did not appear in that edition—"A Round of Visits" and "The Bench of Desolation," both from *The Finer Grain* of 1910—offer special difficulties, since they show both verbal and technical differences between the London and New York first editions and again in the form in which they appeared in the *Novels and Stories of Henry James* edited by Percy Lubbock in 35 volumes (London, 1921-23). "A Round of Visits" is here based on the first edition of *The Finer Grain* published by Scribner (New York, 1910), though it has been collated with the London edition (Methuen, 1910). "The Bench of Desolation" is based on a collation of all three of the above-named editions in order to secure the greatest consistency and exactness possible. One liberty has been taken in the items printed in Parts III, IV, and V: titles of books or whole works, variously printed by James, have been set in italics; titles of shorter works and pictures have been set in Roman type inside quotation marks. The letters in Part VI preserve the inconsistent orthography and punctuation which Percy Lubbock followed in his edition of *The Letters of Henry James* (New York: Scribner, 1920). Acknowledgment to publishers and holders of copyright appears on the copyright page.

ADDENDA, 1956

A new edition of this book permits certain additions to the Bibliography (pp. 687-96) as prepared in 1951.

The most important of these is the first volume of a full biography of Henry James which Leon Edel is writing. This appeared in 1953 as *Henry James: The Untried Years* (Philadelphia and New York: J. B. Lippincott Co.), covering James's life from 1843 to 1870. It will be followed by a second volume, *Henry James: The Middle Years* (1870-95), and finally by a third, *Henry James: The Master* (1895-1916). Robert C. LeClair's *The Young Henry James* (New York: Bookman Associates, 1955) covers much the same ground as Mr. Edel's *The Untried Years*, but with less biographical and critical interpretation.

One of Mr. Edel's discoveries concerns James's first appearance as a writer of fiction. In the present book, "The Story of a Year," in *The Atlantic Monthly*, March 1865, is described as James's first published work in fiction (see p. 30, under the date 1865; also pp. 2, 9, 39, 688). As such it had hitherto figured in all discussions of James's work; in LeRoy Phillips' *Bibliography* of James (1906, 1930); in F. O. Matthiessen's *The American Novels and Stories of Henry James* (1947); and in Edna Kenton's *Eight Uncollected Tales of Henry James* (1950). Mr. Edel found that this story had been preceded by one called "A Tragedy of Error" in *The Continental Monthly*, February 1864, which must now be called James's first appearance as an author of fiction.

To the collections of James's letters listed on pp. 631-32 may now be added Leon Edel's *Selected Letters of Henry James* (New York: Farrar, Straus, and Cudahy, 1955), containing some 120 letters, half of them not previously published, with a critical introduction. James's letters on crime to William Roughead, the Edinburgh historian of crime, are included in Roughead's *Tales of the Criminous*, edited by W. N. Roughead (London: Cassell, 1956). Carl J. Weber and Burdett

Gardner have published letters of James to Vernon Lee (Violet Paget) in *PMLA*, LXVIII, pp. 672-95 (September 1953); and Michael Swan those of James to Hendrik Andersen, the American sculptor in Rome, in *The London Magazine*, II, pp. 78-86 (May 1955).

James's writings on art have been collected for the first time by John L. Sweeney as *The Painter's Eye: Notes and Essays on Pictorial Art* by Henry James (London: Rupert Hart-Davis; Cambridge, Mass.: Harvard University Press, 1956).

LeRoy Phillips' pioneer *Bibliography of the Writings of Henry James* (1906, revised 1930), mentioned on pp. 35, 36, 689, and 696, is to be superseded by a more complete inventory of all of James's writings in *A Bibliography of Henry James* by Leon Edel and Dan H. Laurence. in the Soho Bibliographies series (London: Rupert Hart-Davis). Oscar Cargill is preparing a critical and bibliographical guide, to be called *A Henry James Handbook*, for early publication by Hendricks House, New York.

Critical discussion of James's work has continued to appear in many periodicals, and in prefaces to various reprints of his fiction, but these cannot be listed here. Marius Bewley's studies of James and Hawthorne, here listed on p. 694, are now included in his book *The Complex Fate* (New York: Grove Press, 1953). Joseph Warren Beach's early study of 1918, *The Method of Henry James*, has been reissued with additional material (Philadelphia: Albert Saifer, 1954). Michael Swan has written a brief study, *Henry James*, seriously disfigured by numerous errors (London: Arthur Barker, Ltd., 1952). Quentin Anderson's *The American Henry James: The Novelist as Moralist* appears from the Rutgers University Press (New Brunswick, N. J., 1956). F. W. Dupee's *Henry James* in the American Men of Letters series, 1951, has been republished with revisions (New York: Doubleday–Anchor Books, 1956). Among new editions of James's writings are a collection of his personal memoirs, *Henry James's Autobiography*, edited by F. W. Dupee (Criterion Books, 1956); a collection of James's critical essays, *The Future of the Novel*, and one of his *American Essays*, both edited by Leon Edel (New York: Knopf–Vintage Books, 1956); a collection of James's *Major Critical Essays*, edited by Morton Dauwen Zabel (New York: Doubleday–Anchor Books, 1956); and the correspondence of James and H. G. Wells, edited by Gordon Ray and Leon Edel, planned for publication in 1957.

One remarkable discovery about James's fiction should be mentioned. In its first American edition by Harper and Brothers, 1903, two chapters of the novel *The Ambassadors*—XXVIII and XXIX—were accidentally reversed and have so persisted in all subsequent American editions, including the New York Edition (Scribner, 1907-1909). They were correctly printed in the London edition by Methuen, 1903, and in later English editions. This discovery was made by Robert E. Young in the quarterly *American Literature*, XXII, pp. 246-53 (November 1950), and was further discussed by Leon Edel and Mr. Young in that journal, XXIII, pp. 128-30 (March 1951); XXIII, pp. 487-90 (January 1952); and XXIV, pp. 370-72 (November 1952); and in *Notes and Queries*, New Series, II, pp. 37-38 (January 1, 1955). It is planned that future American editions of *The Ambassadors* by Harper and Brothers will restore these two chapters to their proper sequence.

January 15, 1956

I

FIVE TALES

EDITOR'S NOTE

From his first published tale, "The Story of a Year" in *The Atlantic Monthly* for March 1865, to his final collection of fiction, *The Finer Grain* in 1910, Henry James wrote, in addition to his twenty book-length novels, about 106 shorter works in fiction. They range in length from fairly brief stories to the longer tales or *nouvelles* which became for him a favored form of fiction. In their subject matter these tales cover the entire range of James's themes and preoccupations: his moral drama, his "international subject," his criticism of culture and society, his explorations of character and situation, his studies of writers and artists, his fantasy and "ghostly" themes, his comedy and tragedy. They relate continuously to the full-scale treatment he gave these subjects in his novels, and the finest rank with the most powerful and original work he achieved.

The five tales chosen out of many urgent possibilities for inclusion here show as far as possible James's scope and maturing artistry in the shorter forms of fiction. They date from 1877 to 1910, and thus reveal something of the development in style and treatment which makes a continuous drama of his growth as an artist. "Four Meetings" (1877) is one of his early and most felicitous versions of the international theme, and a flawless example of his art in the pathos of privation. "The Marriages" (1891) shows his comedy of society and character, a comedy which insistently advances, in his work, toward tragedy. "Greville Fane" (1892) presents the theme of the literary life which he made peculiarly his own, in a style marked by the wit and epigram favored in the nineties; I think it one of his wittiest pieces of writing. That theme and style become more explicit in "The Real Thing" (1892), a key story and one of his keenest parables of the conflict of art and life, and thus to be coupled with tales like "The Aspern Papers," "The Author of Beltraffio," "The Lesson of the Master," "The Death of the Lion," "The Next Time," "The Middle Years," and "The Figure in the Carpet." "A Round of Visits" (1910) reverts to the international theme; it derived—like its two companion stories, "The Jolly Corner" and "Crapy Cornelia" —from James's momentous return to America in 1904 after an absence of twenty-one years; I include it here in preference to the more famous "Jolly Corner" (which has been frequently reprinted) not only because it is less well known and accessibly published, but because, like "The Jolly Corner," it adds to its complexity of treatment and tragic insight the force of one of the most personal subjects James ever presented—his own judgment, on encountering a new age of money and power, on his decision to spend his life and do his work in Europe.

"Four Meetings" first appeared in *Scribner's Monthly* for November 1877, and was first published in book form in *Daisy Miller: A Study, and Other Tales* in 1879. "The Marriages" first appeared in *The Atlantic Monthly* for August 1891, and was included in *The Lesson of the Master and Other Tales* in 1892. "Greville Fane" first appeared in the *Illustrated London News* of September 17 and 24, 1892, and "The Real Thing" in *Black and White* for April 16, 1892; and both these stories—whose first magazine appearance has been discovered by Mr. Allan Wade—were collected in *The Real Thing and Other Tales* in 1893. All four of these tales were revised for the New York Edition of James's *Novels and Tales*, 1907-1909, and the texts here printed were taken from it. "A Round of Visits" is the last story James published in his lifetime: it was first printed in *The English Review* for April and May 1910, and was included in *The Finer Grain* of 1910. For suggestions on the further reading of James's stories and tales, the reader is referred to the Bibliography.

FOUR MEETINGS

I saw her but four times, though I remember them vividly; she made her impression on me. I thought her very pretty and very interesting—a touching specimen of a type with which I had had other and perhaps less charming associations. I'm sorry to hear of her death, and yet when I think of it why *should* I be? The last time I saw her she was certainly not—! But it will be of interest to take our meetings in order.

I

The first was in the country, at a small tea-party, one snowy night some seventeen years ago. My friend Latouche, going to spend Christmas with his mother, had insisted on my company, and the good lady had given in our honour the entertainment of which I speak. To me it was really full of savour—it had all the right marks: I had never been in the depths of New England at that season. It had been snowing all day and the drifts were knee-high. I wondered how the ladies had made their way to the house; but I inferred that just those general rigours rendered any assembly offering the attraction of two gentlemen from New York worth a desperate effort.

Mrs. Latouche in the course of the evening asked me

if I "didn't want to" show the photographs to some of the young ladies. The photographs were in a couple of great portfolios, and had been brought home by her son, who, like myself, was lately returned from Europe. I looked round and was struck with the fact that most of the young ladies were provided with an object of interest more absorbing than the most vivid sun-picture. But there was a person alone near the mantelshelf who looked round the room with a small vague smile, a discreet, a disguised yearning, which seemed somehow at odds with her isolation. I looked at her a moment and then chose. "I should like to show them to that young lady."

"Oh yes," said Mrs. Latouche, "she's just the person. She doesn't care for flirting—I'll speak to her." I replied that if she didn't care for flirting she wasn't perhaps just the person; but Mrs. Latouche had already, with a few steps, appealed to her participation. "She's delighted," my hostess came back to report; "and she's just the person—so quiet and so bright." And she told me the young lady was by name Miss Caroline Spencer—with which she introduced me.

Miss Caroline Spencer was not quite a beauty, but was none the less, in her small odd way, formed to please. Close upon thirty, by every presumption, she was made almost like a little girl and had the complexion of a child. She had also the prettiest head, on which her hair was arranged as nearly as possible like the hair of a Greek bust, though indeed it was to be doubted if she had ever seen a Greek bust. She was "artistic," I suspected, so far as the polar influences of North Verona could allow for such yearnings or could minister to them. Her eyes were perhaps just too round and too inveterately surprised, but her lips had a certain mild decision and her teeth, when she showed them, were charming.

About her neck she wore what ladies call, I believe, a "ruche" fastened with a very small pin of pink coral, and in her hand she carried a fan made of plaited straw and adorned with pink ribbon. She wore a scanty black silk dress. She spoke with slow soft neatness, even without smiles showing the prettiness of her teeth, and she seemed extremely pleased, in fact quite fluttered, at the prospect of my demonstrations. These went forward very smoothly after I had moved the portfolios out of their corner and placed a couple of chairs near a lamp. The photographs were usually things I knew—large views of Switzerland, Italy and Spain, landscapes, reproductions of famous buildings, pictures and statues. I said what I could for them, and my companion, looking at them as I held them up, sat perfectly still, her straw fan raised to her under-lip and gently, yet, as I could feel, almost excitedly, rubbing it. Occasionally, as I laid one of the pictures down, she said without confidence, which would have been too much: "Have you seen that place?" I usually answered that I had seen it several times—I had been a great traveller, though I was somehow particularly admonished not to swagger— and then I felt her look at me askance for a moment with her pretty eyes. I had asked her at the outset whether she had been to Europe; to this she had answered "No, no, no"—almost as much below her breath as if the image of such an event scarce, for solemnity, brooked phrasing. But after that, though she never took her eyes off the pictures, she said so little that I feared she was at last bored. Accordingly when we had finished one portfolio I offered, if she desired it, to desist. I rather guessed the exhibition really held her, but her reticence puzzled me and I wanted to make her speak. I turned round to judge better and then saw a faint flush in each of her cheeks. She kept waving her little fan to and fro.

Instead of looking at me she fixed her eyes on the remainder of the collection, which leaned, in its receptacle, against the table.

"Won't you show me that?" she quavered, drawing the long breath of a person launched and afloat but conscious of rocking a little.

"With pleasure," I answered, "if you're really not tired."

"Oh I'm not tired a bit. I'm just fascinated." With which as I took up the other portfolio she laid her hand on it, rubbing it softly. "And have you been here too?"

On my opening the portfolio it appeared I had indeed been there. One of the first photographs was a large view of the Castle of Chillon by the Lake of Geneva. "Here," I said, "I've been many a time. Isn't it beautiful?" And I pointed to the perfect reflexion of the rugged rocks and pointed towers in the clear still water. She didn't say "Oh enchanting!" and push it away to see the next picture. She looked a while and then asked if it weren't where Bonnivard, about whom Byron wrote, had been confined. I assented, trying to quote Byron's verses, but not quite bringing it off.

She fanned herself a moment and then repeated the lines correctly, in a soft flat voice but with charming conviction. By the time she had finished, she was nevertheless blushing. I complimented her and assured her she was perfectly equipped for visiting Switzerland and Italy. She looked at me askance again, to see if I might be serious, and I added that if she wished to recognise Byron's descriptions she must go abroad speedily— Europe was getting sadly dis-Byronised. "How soon must I go?" she thereupon enquired.

"Oh I'll give you ten years."

"Well, I guess I can go in *that* time," she answered as if measuring her words.

"Then you'll enjoy it immensely," I said; "you'll find it of the highest interest." Just then I came upon a photograph of some nook in a foreign city which I had been very fond of and which recalled tender memories. I discoursed (as I suppose) with considerable spirit; my companion sat listening breathless.

"Have you been *very* long over there?" she asked some time after I had ceased.

"Well, it mounts up, put all the times together."

"And have you travelled everywhere?"

"I've travelled a good deal. I'm very fond of it and happily have been able."

Again she turned on me her slow shy scrutiny. "Do you know the foreign languages?"

"After a fashion."

"Is it hard to speak them?"

"I don't imagine you'd find it so," I gallantly answered.

"Oh I shouldn't want to speak—I should only want to listen." Then on a pause she added: "They say the French theatre's so beautiful."

"Ah the best in the world."

"Did you go there very often?"

"When I was first in Paris I went every night."

"Every night!" And she opened her clear eyes very wide. "That to me is"—and her expression hovered— "as if you tell me a fairy-tale." A few minutes later she put to me: "And which country do you prefer?"

"There's one I love beyond any. I think you'd do the same."

Her gaze rested as on a dim revelation and then she breathed "Italy?"

"Italy," I answered softly too; and for a moment we communed over it. She looked as pretty as if instead of showing her photographs I had been making love to her.

To increase the resemblance she turned off blushing. It made a pause which she broke at last by saying: "That's the place which—in particular—I thought of going to."

"Oh that's the place—that's the place!" I laughed.

She looked at two or three more views in silence. "They say it's not very dear."

"As some other countries? Well, one gets back there one's money. That's not the least of the charms."

"But it's *all* very expensive, isn't it?"

"Europe, you mean?"

"Going there and travelling. That has been the trouble. I've very little money. I teach, you know," said Miss Caroline Spencer.

"Oh of course one must have money," I allowed; "but one can manage with a moderate amount judiciously spent."

"I think I should manage. I've saved and saved up, and I'm always adding a little to it. It's all for that." She paused a moment, and then went on with suppressed eagerness, as if telling me the story were a rare, but possibly an impure satisfaction. "You see it hasn't been only the money—it has been everything. Everything has acted against it. I've waited and waited. It has been my castle in the air. I'm almost afraid to talk about it. Two or three times it has come a little nearer, and then I've talked about it and it has melted away. I've talked about it too much," she said hypocritically—for I saw such talk was now a small tremulous ecstasy. "There's a lady who's a great friend of mine—she doesn't want to go, but I'm always at her about it. I think I must tire her dreadfully. She told me just the other day she didn't know what would become of me. She guessed I'd go crazy if I didn't sail, and yet certainly I'd go crazy if I did."

"Well," I laughed, "you haven't sailed up to now—so I suppose you *are* crazy."

She took everything with the same seriousness. "Well, I guess I must be. It seems as if I couldn't think of anything else—and I don't require photographs to work me up! I'm always right *on* it. It kills any interest in things nearer home—things I ought to attend to. That's a kind of craziness."

"Well then the cure for it's just to go," I smiled—"I mean the cure for this kind. Of course you may have the other kind worse," I added—"the kind you get over there."

"Well, I've a faith that I'll go *some* time all right!" she quite elatedly cried. "I've a relative right there on the spot," she went on, "and I guess he'll know how to control me." I expressed the hope that he would, and I forget whether we turned over more photographs; but when I asked her if she had always lived just where I found her, "Oh no sir," she quite eagerly replied; "I've spent twenty-two months and a half in Boston." I met it with the inevitable joke that in this case foreign lands might prove a disappointment to her, but I quite failed to alarm her. "I know more about them than you might think"—her earnestness resisted even that. "I mean by reading—for I've really read considerable. In fact I guess I've prepared my mind about as much as you *can* —in advance. I've not only read Byron—I've read histories and guide-books and articles and lots of things. I know I shall rave about everything."

" 'Everything' is saying much, but I understand your case," I returned. "You've the great American disease, and you've got it 'bad'—the appetite, morbid and monstrous, for colour and form, for the picturesque and the romantic at any price. I don't know whether we come into the world with it—with the germs implanted and antecedent to experience; rather perhaps we catch it early, almost before developed consciousness—we *feel*, as we look about, that we're going (to save our souls, or at least our senses) to be thrown back on it hard. We're like travellers in the desert—deprived of water and subject to the terrible mirage, the torment of illusion, of the thirst-fever. They hear the plash of fountains, they see green gardens and orchards that are hundreds of miles away. So we with *our* thirst—except that with us it's *more* wonderful: we have before us the beautiful old things we've never seen at all, and when we do at last see them—if we're lucky!—we simply recognise them. What experience does is merely to confirm and consecrate our confident dream."

She listened with her rounded eyes. "The way you express it's too lovely, and I'm sure it will be just like that. I've dreamt of everything—I'll know it all!"

"I'm afraid," I pretended for harmless comedy, "that you've wasted a great deal of time."

"Oh yes, that has been my great wickedness!" The people about us had begun to scatter; they were taking their leave. She got up and put out her hand to me, timidly, but as if quite shining and throbbing.

"I'm going back there—one *has* to," I said as I shook hands with her. "I shall look out for you."

Yes, she fairly glittered with her fever of excited faith. "Well, I'll tell you if I'm disappointed." And she left me, fluttering all expressively her little straw fan.

II

A few months after this I crossed the sea eastward again and some three years elapsed. I had been living in Paris and, toward the end of October, went from that city to the Havre, to meet a pair of relatives who had written me they were about to arrive there. On reaching the

Havre I found the steamer already docked—I was two or three hours late. I repaired directly to the hotel, where my travellers were duly established. My sister had gone to bed, exhausted and disabled by her voyage; she was the unsteadiest of sailors and her sufferings on this occasion had been extreme. She desired for the moment undisturbed rest and was able to see me but five minutes—long enough for us to agree to stop over, restoratively, till the morrow. My brother-in-law, anxious about his wife, was unwilling to leave her room; but she insisted on my taking him a walk for aid to recovery of his spirits and his land-legs.

The early autumn day was warm and charming, and our stroll through the bright-coloured busy streets of the old French seaport beguiling enough. We walked along the sunny noisy quays and then turned into a wide pleasant street which lay half in sun and half in shade—a French provincial street that resembled an old water-colour drawing: tall grey steep-roofed red-gabled many-storied houses; green shutters on windows and old scroll-work above them; flower-pots in balconies and white-capped women in doorways. We walked in the shade; all this stretched away on the sunny side of the vista and made a picture. We looked at it as we passed along; then suddenly my companion stopped—pressing my arm and staring. I followed his gaze and saw that we had paused just before reaching a café where, under an awning, several tables and chairs were disposed upon the pavement. The windows were open behind; half a dozen plants in tubs were ranged beside the door; the pavement was besprinkled with clean bran. It was a dear little quiet old-world café; inside, in the comparative dusk, I saw a stout handsome woman, who had pink ribbons in her cap, perched up with a mirror behind her back and smiling at some one placed out of

sight. This, to be exact, I noted afterwards; what I
first observed was a lady seated alone, outside, at one
of the little marble-topped tables. My brother-in-law
had stopped to look at her. Something had been put
before her, but she only leaned back, motionless and
with her hands folded, looking down the street and
away from us. I saw her but in diminished profile;
nevertheless I was sure I knew on the spot that we must
already have met.

"The little lady of the steamer!" my companion cried.

"Was she on your steamer?" I asked with interest.

"From morning till night. She was never sick. She
used to sit perpetually at the side of the vessel with her
hands crossed that way, looking at the eastward horizon."

"And are you going to speak to her?"

"I don't know her. I never made acquaintance with
her. I wasn't in form to make up to ladies. But I used
to watch her and—I don't know why—to be interested
in her. She's a dear little Yankee woman. I've an idea
she's a school-mistress taking a holiday—for which her
scholars have made up a purse."

She had now turned her face a little more into profile,
looking at the steep grey house-fronts opposite. On this
I decided. "I shall speak to her myself."

"I wouldn't—she's very shy," said my brother-in-law.

"My dear fellow, I know her. I once showed her
photographs at a tea-party." With which I went up to
her, making her, as she turned to look at me, leave me
in no doubt of her identity. Miss Caroline Spencer had
achieved her dream. But she was less quick to recognise
me and showed a slight bewilderment. I pushed a chair
to the table and sat down. "Well," I said, "I hope you're
not disappointed!"

She stared, blushing a little—then gave a small jump

and placed me. "It was you who showed me the photographs—at North Verona."

"Yes, it was I. This happens very charmingly, for isn't it quite proper for me to give you a formal reception here—the official welcome? I talked to you so much about Europe."

"You didn't say too much. I'm so intensely happy!" she declared.

Very happy indeed she looked. There was no sign of her being older; she was gravely, decently, demurely pretty as before. If she had struck me then as a thin-stemmed, mild-hued flower of Puritanism it may be imagined whether in her present situation this clear bloom was less appealing. Beside her an old gentleman was drinking absinthe; behind her the *dame de comptoir* in the pink ribbons called "Alcibiade, Alcibiade!" to the long-aproned waiter. I explained to Miss Spencer that the gentleman with me had lately been her shipmate, and my brother-in-law came up and was introduced to her. But she looked at him as if she had never so much as seen him, and I remembered he had told me her eyes were always fixed on the eastward horizon. She had evidently not noticed him, and, still timidly smiling, made no attempt whatever to pretend the contrary. I stayed with her on the little terrace of the café while he went back to the hotel and to his wife. I remarked to my friend that this meeting of ours at the first hour of her landing partook, among all chances, of the miraculous, but that I was delighted to be there and receive her first impressions.

"Oh I can't tell you," she said—"I feel so much in a dream. I've been sitting here an hour and I don't want to move. Everything's so delicious and romantic. I don't know whether the coffee has gone to my head—it's *so* unlike the coffee of my dead past."

"Really," I made answer, "if you're so pleased with this poor prosaic Havre you'll have no admiration left for better things. Don't spend your appreciation all the first day—remember it's your intellectual letter of credit. Remember all the beautiful places and things that are waiting for you. Remember that lovely Italy we talked about."

"I'm not afraid of running short," she said gaily, still looking at the opposite houses. "I could sit here all day —just saying to myself that here I am at last. It's so dark and strange—so old and different."

"By the way then," I asked, "how come you to be encamped in this odd place? Haven't you gone to one of the inns?" For I was half-amused, half-alarmed at the good conscience with which this delicately pretty woman had stationed herself in conspicuous isolation on the edge of the sidewalk.

"My cousin brought me here and—a little while ago —left me," she returned. "You know I told you I had a relation over here. He's still here—a real cousin. Well," she pursued with unclouded candour, "he met me at the steamer this morning."

It was absurd—and the case moreover none of my business; but I felt somehow disconcerted. "It was hardly worth his while to meet you if he was to desert you so soon."

"Oh he has only left me for half an hour," said Caroline Spencer. "He has gone to get my money."

I continued to wonder. "Where *is* your money?"

She appeared seldom to laugh, but she laughed for the joy of this. "It makes me feel very fine to tell you! It's in circular notes."

"And where are your circular notes?"

"In my cousin's pocket."

This statement was uttered with such clearness of

candour that—I can hardly say why—it gave me a sensible chill. I couldn't at all at the moment have justified my lapse from ease, for I knew nothing of Miss Spencer's cousin. Since he stood in that relation to her—dear respectable little person—the presumption was in his favour. But I found myself wincing at the thought that half an hour after her landing her scanty funds should have passed into his hands. "Is he to travel with you?" I asked.

"Only as far as Paris. He's an art-student in Paris—I've always thought that so splendid. I wrote to him that I was coming, but I never expected him to come off to the ship. I supposed he'd only just meet me at the train in Paris. It's very kind of him. But he *is*," said Caroline Spencer, "very kind—and very bright."

I felt at once a strange eagerness to see this bright kind cousin who was an art-student. "He's gone to the banker's?" I enquired.

"Yes, to the banker's. He took me to an hotel—such a queer quaint cunning little place, with a court in the middle and a gallery all round, and a lovely landlady in such a beautifully fluted cap and such a perfectly fitting dress! After a while we came out to walk to the banker's, for I hadn't any French money. But I was very dizzy from the motion of the vessel and I thought I had better sit down. He found this place for me here—then he went off to the banker's himself. I'm to wait here till he comes back."

Her story was wholly lucid and my impression perfectly wanton, but it passed through my mind that the gentleman would never come back. I settled myself in a chair beside my friend and determined to await the event. She was lost in the vision and the imagination of everything near us and about us—she observed, she recognised and admired, with a touching intensity. She noticed everything that was brought before us by the movement of the street—the peculiarities of costume, the shapes of vehicles, the big Norman horses, the fat priests, the shaven poodles. We talked of these things, and there was something charming in her freshness of perception and the way her book-nourished fancy sallied forth for the revel.

"And when your cousin comes back what are you going to do?" I went on.

For this she had, a little oddly, to think. "We don't quite know."

"When do you go to Paris? If you go by the four o'clock train I may have the pleasure of making the journey with you."

"I don't think we shall do that." So far she was prepared. "My cousin thinks I had better stay here a few days."

"Oh!" said I—and for five minutes had nothing to add. I was wondering what our absentee was, in vulgar parlance, "up to." I looked up and down the street, but saw nothing that looked like a bright and kind American art-student. At last I took the liberty of observing that the Havre was hardly a place to choose as one of the æsthetic stations of a European tour. It was a place of convenience, nothing more; a place of transit, through which transit should be rapid. I recommended her to go to Paris by the afternoon train and meanwhile to amuse herself by driving to the ancient fortress at the mouth of the harbour—that remarkable circular structure which bore the name of Francis the First and figured a sort of small Castle of Saint Angelo. (I might really have foreknown that it was to be demolished.)

She listened with much interest—then for a moment looked grave. "My cousin told me that when he returned he should have something particular to say to me, and that we could do nothing or decide nothing till I should have heard it. But I'll make him tell me right off, and then we'll go to the ancient fortress. Francis the First, did you say? Why, that's lovely. There's no hurry to get to Paris; there's plenty of time."

She smiled with her softly severe little lips as she spoke those last words, yet, looking at her with a purpose, I made out in her eyes, I thought, a tiny gleam of apprehension. "Don't tell me," I said, "that this wretched man's going to give you bad news!"

She coloured as if convicted of a hidden perversity, but she was soaring too high to drop. "Well I guess it's a *little* bad, but I don't believe it's *very* bad. At any rate I must listen to it."

I usurped an unscrupulous authority. "Look here; you didn't come to Europe to listen—you came to *see!*" But now I was sure her cousin would come back; since he had something disagreeable to say to her he'd infallibly turn up. We sat a while longer and I asked her about her plans of travel. She had them on her fingers' ends and told over the names as solemnly as a daughter of another faith might have told over the beads of a rosary: from Paris to Dijon and to Avignon, from Avignon to Marseilles and the Cornice road; thence to Genoa, to Spezia, to Pisa, to Florence, to Rome. It apparently had never occurred to her that there could be the least incommodity in her travelling alone; and since she was unprovided with a companion I of course civilly abstained from disturbing her sense of security.

At last her cousin came back. I saw him turn toward us out of a side-street, and from the moment my eyes rested on him I knew he could but be the bright, if not the kind, American art-student. He wore a slouch hat and a rusty black velvet jacket, such as I had often encountered in the Rue Bonaparte. His shirt-collar displayed a stretch of throat that at a distance wasn't strikingly statuesque. He was tall and lean, he had red hair and freckles. These items I had time to take in while he approached the café, staring at me with natural surprise from under his romantic brim. When he came up to us I immediately introduced myself as an old acquaintance of Miss Spencer's, a character she serenely permitted me to claim. He looked at me hard with a pair of small sharp eyes, then he gave me a solemn wave, in the "European" fashion, of his rather rusty sombrero.

"You weren't on the ship?" he asked.

"No, I wasn't on the ship. I've been in Europe these several years."

He bowed once more, portentously, and motioned me to be seated again. I sat down, but only for the purpose of observing him an instant—I saw it was time I should return to my sister. Miss Spencer's European protector was, by my measure, a very queer quantity. Nature hadn't shaped him for a Raphaelesque or Byronic attire, and his velvet doublet and exhibited though not columnar throat weren't in harmony with his facial attributes. His hair was cropped close to his head; his ears were large and ill-adjusted to the same. He had a lackadaisical carriage and a sentimental droop which were peculiarly at variance with his keen conscious strange-coloured eyes—of a brown that was almost red. Perhaps I was prejudiced, but I thought his eyes too shifty. He said nothing for some time; he leaned his hands on his stick and looked up and down the street. Then at last, slowly lifting the stick and pointing with it, "That's a very nice bit," he dropped with a certain flatness. He had his head to one side—he narrowed his ugly lids. I followed the direction of his stick; the object it indicated was a red cloth hung out of an old window. "Nice bit of colour," he continued; and without moving his head transferred his half-closed gaze to me. "Composes well. Fine old tone. Make a nice thing." He spoke in a charmless vulgar voice.

"I see you've a great deal of eye," I replied. "Your cousin tells me you're studying art." He looked at me in the same way, without answering, and I went on with deliberate urbanity: "I suppose you're at the studio of one of those great men." Still on this he continued to fix me, and then he named one of the greatest of that day; which led me to ask him if he liked his master.

"Do you understand French?" he returned.

"Some kinds."

He kept his little eyes on me; with which he remarked: "Je suis fou de la peinture!"

"Oh I understand that kind!" I replied. Our companion laid her hand on his arm with a small pleased and fluttered movement; it was delightful to be among people who were on such easy terms with foreign tongues. I got up to take leave and asked her where, in Paris, I might have the honour of waiting on her. To what hotel would she go?

She turned to her cousin enquiringly and he favoured me again with his little languid leer. "Do you know the Hôtel des Princes?"

"I know where it is."

"Well, that's the shop."

"I congratulate you," I said to Miss Spencer. "I believe it's the best inn in the world; but, in case I should still have a moment to call on you here, where are you lodged?"

"Oh it's such a pretty name," she returned gleefully. "À la Belle Normande."

"I guess I know my way round!" her kinsman threw in; and as I left them he gave me with his swaggering head-cover a great flourish that was like the wave of a banner over a conquered field.

III

My relative, as it proved, was not sufficiently restored to leave the place by the afternoon train; so that as the autumn dusk began to fall I found myself at liberty to call at the establishment named to me by my friends. I must confess that I had spent much of the interval in wondering what the disagreeable thing was that the less attractive of these had been telling the other. The *auberge* of the Belle Normande proved an hostelry in a shady by-street, where it gave me satisfaction to think Miss Spencer must have encountered local colour in abundance. There was a crooked little court, where much of the hospitality of the house was carried on; there was a staircase climbing to bedrooms on the outer side of the wall; there was a small trickling fountain with a stucco statuette set in the midst of it; there was a little boy in a white cap and apron cleaning copper vessels at a conspicuous kitchen door; there was a chattering landlady, neatly laced, arranging apricots and grapes into an artistic pyramid upon a pink plate. I looked about, and on a green bench outside of an open door labelled Salle-à-Manger, I distinguished Caroline Spencer. No sooner had I looked at her than I was sure something had happened since the morning. Supported by the back of her bench, with her hands clasped in her lap, she kept her eyes on the other side of the court, where the landlady manipulated the apricots.

But I saw that, poor dear, she wasn't thinking of apricots or even of landladies. She was staring absently, thoughtfully; on a nearer view I could have certified she had been crying. I had seated myself beside her before she was aware; then, when she had done so, she simply turned round without surprise and showed me her sad face. Something very bad indeed had happened; she was completely changed, and I immediately charged her with it. "Your cousin has been giving you bad news. You've had a horrid time."

For a moment she said nothing, and I supposed her afraid to speak lest her tears should again rise. Then it came to me that even in the few hours since my leaving her she had shed them all—which made her now intensely, stoically composed. "My poor cousin has been having one," she replied at last. "He has had great worries. His news was bad." Then after a dismally conscious wait: "He was in dreadful want of money."

"In want of yours, you mean?"

"Of any he could get—honourably of course. Mine *is* all—well, that's available."

Ah it was as if I had been sure from the first! "And he has taken it from you?"

Again she hung fire, but her face meanwhile was pleading. "I gave him what I had."

I recall the accent of those words as the most angelic human sound I had ever listened to—which is exactly why I jumped up almost with a sense of personal outrage. "Gracious goodness, madam, do you call that his getting it 'honourably'?"

I had gone too far—she coloured to her eyes. "We won't speak of it."

"We *must* speak of it," I declared as I dropped beside her again. "I'm your friend—upon my word I'm your protector; it seems to me you need one. What's the matter with this extraordinary person?"

She was perfectly able to say. "He's just badly in debt."

"No doubt he is! But what's the special propriety of your—in such tearing haste!—paying for that?"

"Well, he has told me all his story. I *feel* for him so much."

"So do I, if you come to that! But I hope," I roundly added, "he'll give you straight back your money."

As to this she was prompt. "Certainly he will—as soon as ever he can."

"And when the deuce will that be?"

Her lucidity maintained itself. "When he has finished his great picture."

It took me full in the face. "My dear young lady, damn his great picture! Where is this voracious man?"

It was as if she must let me feel a moment that I did push her!—though indeed, as appeared, he was just where he'd naturally be. "He's having his dinner."

I turned about and looked through the open door into the salle-à-manger. There, sure enough, alone at the end of a long table, was the object of my friend's compassion—the bright, the kind young art-student. He was dining too attentively to notice me at first, but in the act of setting down a well-emptied wineglass he caught sight of my air of observation. He paused in his repast and, with his head on one side and his meagre jaws slowly moving, fixedly returned my gaze. Then the landlady came brushing lightly by with her pyramid of apricots.

"And that nice little plate of fruit is for him?" I wailed.

Miss Spencer glanced at it tenderly. "They seem to arrange everything so nicely!" she simply sighed.

I felt helpless and irritated. "Come now, really," I said; "do you think it right, do you think it decent, that that long strong fellow should collar your funds?" She looked away from me—I was evidently giving her pain.

The case was hopeless; the long strong fellow had "interested" her.

"Pardon me if I speak of him so unceremoniously," I said. "But you're really too generous, and he hasn't, clearly, the rudiments of delicacy. He made his debts himself—he ought to pay them himself."

"He has been foolish," she obstinately said—"of course I know that. He has told me everything. We had a long talk this morning—the poor fellow threw himself on my charity. He has signed notes to a large amount."

"The more fool he!"

"He's in real distress—and it's not only himself. It's his poor young wife."

"Ah he has a poor young wife?"

"I didn't know—but he made a clean breast of it. He married two years since—secretly."

"Why secretly?"

My informant took precautions as if she feared listeners. Then with low impressiveness: "She was a Countess!"

"Are you very sure of that?"

"She has written me the most beautiful letter."

"Asking you—whom she has never seen—for money?"

"Asking me for confidence and sympathy"—Miss Spencer spoke now with spirit. "She has been cruelly treated by her family—in consequence of what she has done for him. My cousin has told me every particular, and she appeals to me in her own lovely way in the letter, which I've here in my pocket. It's such a wonderful old-world romance," said my prodigious friend. "She was a beautiful young widow—her first husband was a Count, tremendously high-born, but really most wicked, with whom she hadn't been happy and whose death had left her ruined after he had deceived her in all sorts of

ways. My poor cousin, meeting her in that situation and
perhaps a little too recklessly pitying her and charmed
with her, found her, don't you see?"—Caroline's appeal
on this head was amazing!—"but too ready to trust a
better man after all she had been through. Only when
her 'people,' as he says—and I do like the word!—understood she *would* have him, poor gifted young American art-student though he simply was, because she just
adored him, her great-aunt, the old Marquise, from
whom she had expectations of wealth which she could
yet sacrifice for her love, utterly cast her off and
wouldn't so much as speak to her, much less to *him,* in
their dreadful haughtiness and pride. They *can* be
haughty over here, it seems," she ineffably developed—
"there's no mistake about that! It's like something in
some famous old book. The family, my cousin's wife's,"
she by this time almost complacently wound up, "are of
the oldest Provençal noblesse."

I listened half-bewildered. The poor woman positively
found it so interesting to be swindled by a flower of that
stock—if stock or flower or solitary grain of truth was
really concerned in the matter—as practically to have
lost the sense of what the forfeiture of her hoard meant
for her. "My dear young lady," I groaned, "you don't
want to be stripped of every dollar for such a rigmarole!"

She asserted, at this, her dignity—much as a small
pink shorn lamb might have done. "It isn't a rigmarole,
and I shan't be stripped. I shan't live any worse than I
have lived, don't you see? And I'll come back before
long to stay with them. The Countess—he still gives her,
he says, her title, as they do to noble widows, that is to
'dowagers,' don't you know? in England—insists on a
visit from me *some* time. So I guess for *that* I can start

afresh—and meanwhile I'll have recovered my money."

It was all too heart-breaking. "You're going home then at once?"

I felt the faint tremor of voice she heroically tried to stifle. "I've nothing left for a tour."

"You gave it *all* up?"

"I've kept enough to take me back."

I uttered, I think, a positive howl, and at this juncture the hero of the situation, the happy proprietor of my little friend's sacred savings and of the infatuated *grande dame* just sketched for me, reappeared with the clear consciousness of a repast bravely earned and consistently enjoyed. He stood on the threshold an instant, extracting the stone from a plump apricot he had fondly retained; then he put the apricot into his mouth and, while he let it gratefully dissolve there, stood looking at us with his long legs apart and his hands thrust into the pockets of his velvet coat. My companion got up, giving him a thin glance that I caught in its passage and which expressed at once resignation and fascination— the last dregs of her sacrifice and with it an anguish of upliftedness. Ugly vulgar pretentious dishonest as I thought him, and destitute of every grace of plausibility, he had yet appealed successfully to her eager and tender imagination. I was deeply disgusted, but I had no warrant to interfere, and at any rate felt that it would be vain. He waved his hand meanwhile with a breadth of appreciation. "Nice old court. Nice mellow old place. Nice crooked old staircase. Several pretty things."

Decidedly I couldn't stand it, and without responding I gave my hand to my friend. She looked at me an instant with her little white face and rounded eyes, and as she showed her pretty teeth I suppose she meant to smile. "Don't be sorry for me," she sublimely pleaded;

"I'm very sure I shall see something of this dear old Europe yet."

I refused however to take literal leave of her—I should find a moment to come back next morning. Her awful kinsman, who had put on his sombrero again, flourished it off at me by way of a bow—on which I hurried away.

On the morrow early I did return, and in the court of the inn met the landlady, more loosely laced than in the evening. On my asking for Miss Spencer, *"Partie, monsieur,"* the good woman said. "She went away last night at ten o'clock, with her—her—not her husband, eh?—in fine her Monsieur. They went down to the American ship." I turned off—I felt the tears in my eyes. The poor girl had been some thirteen hours in Europe.

IV

I myself, more fortunate, continued to sacrifice to opportunity as I myself met it. During this period—of some five years—I lost my friend Latouche, who died of a malarious fever during a tour in the Levant. One of the first things I did on my return to America was to go up to North Verona on a consolatory visit to his poor mother. I found her in deep affliction and sat with her the whole of the morning that followed my arrival—I had come in late at night—listening to her tearful descant and singing the praises of my friend. We talked of nothing else, and our conversation ended only with the arrival of a quick little woman who drove herself up to the door in a "carry-all" and whom I saw toss the reins to the horse's back with the briskness of a startled sleeper throwing off the bedclothes. She jumped out of the carry-all and she jumped into the room. She proved to be the minister's wife and the great town-gossip, and she had evidently, in the latter capacity, a choice morsel to communicate. I was as sure of this as I was that poor Mrs. Latouche was not absolutely too bereaved to listen to her. It seemed to me discreet to retire, and I described myself as anxious for a walk before dinner.

"And by the way," I added, "if you'll tell me where my old friend Miss Spencer lives, I think I'll call on her."

The minister's wife immediately responded. Miss Spencer lived in the fourth house beyond the Baptist church; the Baptist church was the one on the right, with that queer green thing over the door; they called it a portico, but it looked more like an old-fashioned bedstead swung in the air. "Yes, do look up poor Caroline," Mrs. Latouche further enjoined. "It will refresh her to see a strange face."

"I should think she had had enough of strange faces!" cried the minister's wife.

"To see, I mean, a charming visitor"—Mrs. Latouche amended her phrase.

"I should think she had had enough of charming visitors!" her companion returned. "But *you* don't mean to stay ten years," she added with significant eyes on me.

"Has she a visitor of that sort?" I asked in my ignorance.

"You'll make out the sort!" said the minister's wife "She's easily seen; she generally sits in the front yard. Only take care what you say to her, and be very sure you're polite."

"Ah she's so sensitive?"

The minister's wife jumped up and dropped me a curtsey—a most sarcastic curtsey. "That's what she is, if you please. 'Madame la Comtesse!'"

And pronouncing these titular words with the most

scathing accent, the little woman seemed fairly to laugh
in the face of the lady they designated. I stood staring,
wondering, remembering.

"Oh I shall be very polite!" I cried; and, grasping
my hat and stick, I went on my way.

I found Miss Spencer's residence without difficulty.
The Baptist church was easily identified, and the small
dwelling near it, of a rusty white, with a large central
chimney-stack and a Virginia creeper, seemed naturally
and properly the abode of a withdrawn old maid with
a taste for striking effects inexpensively obtained. As I
approached I slackened my pace, for I had heard that
some one was always sitting in the front yard, and I
wished to reconnoitre. I looked cautiously over the low
white fence that separated the small garden-space from
the unpaved street, but I descried nothing in the shape
of a Comtesse. A small straight path led up to the
crooked door-step, on either side of which was a little
grass-plot fringed with currant-bushes. In the middle
of the grass, right and left, was a large quince-tree, full
of antiquity and contortions, and beneath one of the
quince-trees were placed a small table and a couple of
light chairs. On the table lay a piece of unfinished embroidery and two or three books in bright-coloured
paper covers. I went in at the gate and paused halfway
along the path, scanning the place for some further token
of its occupant, before whom—I could hardly have said
why—I hesitated abruptly to present myself. Then I
saw the poor little house to be of the shabbiest and felt
a sudden doubt of my right to penetrate, since curiosity
had been my motive and curiosity here failed of confidence. While I demurred a figure appeared in the
open doorway and stood there looking at me. I immediately recognised Miss Spencer, but she faced me as
if we had never met. Gently, but gravely and timidly,

I advanced to the door-step, where I spoke with an attempt at friendly banter.

"I waited for you over there to come back, but you never came."

"Waited where, sir?" she quavered, her innocent eyes rounding themselves as of old. She was much older; she looked tired and wasted.

"Well," I said, "I waited at the old French port."

She stared harder, then recognised me, smiling, flushing, clasping her two hands together. "I remember you now—I remember that day." But she stood there, neither coming out nor asking me to come in. She was embarrassed.

I too felt a little awkward while I poked at the path with my stick. "I kept looking out for you year after year."

"You mean in Europe?" she ruefully breathed.

"In Europe of course! Here apparently you're easy enough to find."

She leaned her hand against the unpainted door-post and her head fell a little to one side. She looked at me thus without speaking, and I caught the expression visible in women's eyes when tears are rising. Suddenly she stepped out on the cracked slab of stone before her threshold and closed the door. Then her strained smile prevailed and I saw her teeth were as pretty as ever. But there had been tears too. "Have you been there ever since?" she lowered her voice to ask.

"Until three weeks ago. And you—you never came back?"

Still shining at me as she could, she put her hand behind her and reopened the door. "I'm not very polite," she said. "Won't you come in?"

"I'm afraid I incommode you."

"Oh no!"—she wouldn't hear of it now. And she

pushed back the door with a sign that I should enter.

I followed her in. She led the way to a small room on the left of the narrow hall, which I supposed to be her parlour, though it was at the back of the house, and we passed the closed door of another apartment which apparently enjoyed a view of the quince-trees. This one looked out upon a small wood-shed and two clucking hens. But I thought it pretty until I saw its elegance to be of the most frugal kind; after which, presently, I thought it prettier still, for I had never seen faded chintz and old mezzotint engravings, framed in varnished autumn leaves, disposed with so touching a grace. Miss Spencer sat down on a very small section of the sofa, her hands tightly clasped in her lap. She looked ten years older, and I needn't now have felt called to insist on the facts of her person. But I still thought them interesting, and at any rate I was moved by them. She was peculiarly agitated. I tried to appear not to notice it; but suddenly, in the most inconsequent fashion—it was an irresistible echo of our concentrated passage in the old French port—I said to her: "I do incommode you. Again you're in distress."

She raised her two hands to her face and for a moment kept it buried in them. Then taking them away, "It's because you remind me," she said.

"I remind you, you mean, of that miserable day at the Havre?"

She wonderfully shook her head. "It wasn't miserable. It was delightful."

Ah was it? my manner of receiving this must have commented. "I never was so shocked as when, on going back to your inn the next morning, I found you had wretchedly retreated."

She waited an instant, after which she said: "Please let us not speak of that."

"Did you come straight back here?" I nevertheless went on.

"I was back here just thirty days after my first start."

"And here you've remained ever since?"

"Every minute of the time."

I took it in; I didn't know what to say, and what I presently said had almost the sound of mockery. "When then are you going to make that tour?" It might be practically aggressive; but there was something that irritated me in her depths of resignation, and I wished to extort from her some expression of impatience.

She attached her eyes a moment to a small sun-spot on the carpet; then she got up and lowered the window-blind a little to obliterate it. I waited, watching her with interest—as if she had still something more to give me. Well, presently, in answer to my last question, she gave it. "Never!"

"I hope at least your cousin repaid you that money," I said.

At this again she looked away from me. "I don't care for it now."

"You don't care for your money?"

"For ever going to Europe."

"Do you mean you wouldn't go if you could?"

"I can't—I can't," said Caroline Spencer. "It's all over. Everything's different. I never think of it."

"The scoundrel never repaid you then!" I cried.

"Please, please—!" she began.

But she had stopped—she was looking toward the door. There had been a rustle and a sound of steps in the hall.

I also looked toward the door, which was open and now admitted another person—a lady who paused just within the threshold. Behind her came a young man. The lady looked at me with a good deal of fixedness—

long enough for me to rise to a vivid impression of herself. Then she turned to Caroline Spencer and, with a smile and a strong foreign accent, *"Pardon, ma chère!* I didn't know you had company," she said. "The gentleman came in so quietly." With which she again gave me the benefit of her attention. She was very strange, yet I was at once sure I had seen her before. Afterwards I rather put it that I had only seen ladies remarkably like her. But I had seen them very far away from North Verona, and it was the oddest of all things to meet one of them in that frame. To what quite other scene did the sight of her transport me? To some dusky landing before a shabby Parisian *quatrième*—to an open door revealing a greasy ante-chamber and to Madame leaning over the banisters while she holds a faded wrapper together and bawls down to the portress to bring up her coffee. My friend's guest was a very large lady, of middle age, with a plump dead-white face and hair drawn back *à la chinoise*. She had a small penetrating eye and what is called in French *le sourire agréable*. She wore an old pink cashmere dressing-gown covered with white embroideries, and, like the figure in my momentary vision, she confined it in front with a bare and rounded arm and a plump and deeply-dimpled hand.

"It's only to spick about my café," she said to her hostess with her *sourire agréable*. "I should like it served in the garden under the leetle tree."

The young man behind her had now stepped into the room, where he also stood revealed, though with rather less of a challenge. He was a gentleman of few inches but a vague importance, perhaps the leading man of the world of North Verona. He had a small pointed nose and a small pointed chin; also, as I observed, the most diminutive feet and a manner of no point at all. He looked at me foolishly and with his mouth open.

"You shall have your coffee," said Miss Spencer as if an army of cooks had been engaged in the preparation of it.

"C'est bien!" said her massive inmate. "Find your bouk"—and this personage turned to the gaping youth.

He gaped now at each quarter of the room. "My grammar, d' ye mean?"

The large lady however could but face her friend's visitor while persistently engaged with a certain laxity in the flow of her wrapper. "Find your bouk," she more absently repeated.

"My poetry, d' ye mean?" said the young man, who also couldn't take his eyes off me.

"Never mind your bouk"—his companion reconsidered. "To-day we'll just talk. We'll make some conversation. But we mustn't interrupt Mademoiselle's. Come, come"—and she moved off a step. "Under the leetle tree," she added for the benefit of Mademoiselle. After which she gave me a thin salutation, jerked a measured "Monsieur!" and swept away again with her swain following.

I looked at Miss Spencer, whose eyes never moved from the carpet, and I spoke, I fear, without grace. "Who in the world's that?"

"The Comtesse—that *was:* my *cousine* as they call it in French."

"And who's the young man?"

"The Countess's pupil, Mr. Mixter." This description of the tie uniting the two persons who had just quitted us must certainly have upset my gravity; for I recall the marked increase of my friend's own as she continued to explain. "She gives lessons in French and music, the simpler sorts—"

"The simpler sorts of French?" I fear I broke in.

But she was still impenetrable, and in fact had now an

intonation that put me vulgarly in the wrong. "She has had the worst reverses—with no one to look to. She's prepared for any exertion—and she takes her misfortunes with gaiety."

"Ah well," I returned—no doubt a little ruefully, "that's all I myself am pretending to do. If she's determined to be a burden to nobody, nothing could be more right and proper."

My hostess looked vaguely, though I thought quite wearily enough, about: she met this proposition in no other way. "I must go and get the coffee," she simply said.

"Has the lady many pupils?" I none the less persisted.

"She has only Mr. Mixter. She gives him all her time." It might have set me off again, but something in my whole impression of my friend's sensibility urged me to keep strictly decent. "He pays very well," she at all events inscrutably went on. "He's not very bright—as a pupil; but he's very rich and he's very kind. He has a buggy—with a back, and he takes the Countess to drive."

"For good long spells I hope," I couldn't help interjecting—even at the cost of her so taking it that she had still to avoid my eyes. "Well, the country's beautiful for miles," I went on. And then as she was turning away: "You're going for the Countess's coffee?"

"If you'll excuse me a few moments."

"Is there no one else to do it?"

She seemed to wonder who there should be. "I keep no servants."

"Then can't I help?" After which, as she but looked at me, I bettered it. "Can't she wait on herself?"

Miss Spencer had a slow headshake—as if that too had ·been a strange idea. "She isn't used to *manual* labour."

The discrimination was a treat, but I cultivated decorum. "I see—and you *are*." But at the same time I couldn't abjure curiosity. "Before you go, at any rate, please tell me this: who *is* this wonderful lady?"

"I told you just who in France—that extraordinary day. She's the wife of my cousin, whom you saw there."

"The lady disowned by her family in consequence of her marriage?"

"Yes; they've never seen her again. They've completely broken with her."

"And where's her husband?"

"My poor cousin's dead."

I pulled up, but only a moment. "And where's your money?"

The poor thing flinched—I kept her on the rack. "I don't know," she woefully said.

I scarce know what it didn't prompt me to—but I went step by step. "On her husband's death this lady at once came to you?"

It was as if she had had too often to describe it. "Yes, she arrived one day."

"How long ago?"

"Two years and four months."

"And has been here ever since?"

"Ever since."

I took it all in. "And how does she like it?"

"Well, not *very* much," said Miss Spencer divinely.

That too I took in. "And how do *you*—?"

She laid her face in her two hands an instant as she had done ten minutes before. Then, quickly, she went to get the Countess's coffee.

Left alone in the little parlour I found myself divided between the perfection of my disgust and a contrary wish to see, to learn more. At the end of a few minutes the young man in attendance on the lady in question reappeared as for a fresh gape at me. He was inordinately grave—to be dressed in such parti-coloured flannels; and he produced with no great confidence on his own side the message with which he had been charged. "She wants to know if you won't come right out."

"Who wants to know?"

"The Countess. That French lady."

"She has asked you to bring me?"

"Yes sir," said the young man feebly—for I may claim to have surpassed him in stature and weight.

I went out with him, and we found his instructress seated under one of the small quince-trees in front of the house; where she was engaged in drawing a fine needle with a very fat hand through a piece of embroidery not remarkable for freshness. She pointed graciously to the chair beside her and I sat down. Mr. Mixter glanced about him and then accommodated himself on the grass at her feet; whence he gazed upward more gapingly than ever and as if convinced that between us something wonderful would now occur.

"I'm sure you spick French," said the Countess, whose eyes were singularly protuberant as she played over me her agreeable smile.

"I do, madam—*tant bien que mal,*" I replied, I fear, more dryly.

"Ah voilà!" she cried as with delight. "I knew it as soon as I looked at you. You've been in my poor dear country."

"A considerable time."

"You love it then, *mon pays de France?*"

"Oh it's an old affection." But I wasn't exuberant.

"And you know Paris well?"

"Yes, *sans me vanter,* madam, I think I really do."

And with a certain conscious purpose I let my eyes meet her own.

She presently, hereupon, moved her own and glanced down at Mr. Mixter. "What are we talking about?" she demanded of her attentive pupil.

He pulled his knees up, plucked at the grass, stared, blushed a little. "You're talking French," said Mr. Mixter.

"La belle découverte!" mocked the Countess. "It's going on ten months," she explained to me, "since I took him in hand. Don't put yourself out not to say he's *la bêtise même,*" she added in fine style. "He won't in the least understand you."

A moment's consideration of Mr. Mixter, awkwardly sporting at our feet, quite assured me that he wouldn't. "I hope your other pupils do you more honour," I then remarked to my entertainer.

"I have no others. They don't know what French— or what anything else—is in this place; they don't want to know. You may therefore imagine the pleasure it is to me to meet a person who speaks it like yourself." I could but reply that my own pleasure wasn't less, and she continued to draw the stitches through her embroidery with an elegant curl of her little finger. Every few moments she put her eyes, near-sightedly, closer to her work—this as if for elegance too. She inspired me with no more confidence than her late husband, if husband he was, had done, years before, on the occasion with which this one so detestably matched: she was coarse, common, affected, dishonest—no more a Countess than I was a Caliph. She had an assurance— based clearly on experience; but this couldn't have been the experience of "race." Whatever it was indeed it did now, in a yearning fashion, flare out of her. "Talk to me of Paris, *mon beau Paris* that I'd give my eyes to see. The very name of it *me fait languir*. How long since you were there?"

"A couple of months ago."

"*Vous avez de la chance!* Tell me something about it. What were they doing? Oh for an hour of the Boulevard!"

"They were doing about what they're always doing—amusing themselves a good deal."

"At the theatres, *hein?*" sighed the Countess. "At the cafés-concerts? *sous ce beau ciel*—at the little tables before the doors? *Quelle existence!* You know I'm a Parisienne, monsieur," she added, "to my finger-tips."

"Miss Spencer was mistaken then," I ventured to return, "in telling me you're a Provençale."

She stared a moment, then put her nose to her embroidery, which struck me as having acquired even while we sat a dingier and more desultory air. "Ah I'm a Provençale by birth, but a Parisienne by—inclination." After which she pursued: "And by the saddest events of my life—as well as by some of the happiest, hélas!"

"In other words by a varied experience!" I now at last smiled.

She questioned me over it with her hard little salient eyes. "Oh experience!—I could talk of that, no doubt, if I wished. *On en a de toutes les sortes*—and I never dreamed that mine, for example, would ever have *this* in store for me." And she indicated with her large bare elbow and with a jerk of her head all surrounding objects; the little white house, the pair of quince-trees, the rickety paling, even the rapt Mr. Mixter.

I took them all bravely in. "Ah if you mean you're decidedly in exile—!"

"You may imagine what it is. These two years of my *épreuve*—*elles m'en ont données, des heures, des heures!* One gets used to things"—and she raised her shoulders to the highest shrug ever accomplished at North Verona; "so that I sometimes think I've got used to this. But there are some things that are always beginning again. For example my coffee."

I so far again lent myself. "Do you always have coffee at this hour?"

Her eyebrows went up as high as her shoulders had done. "At what hour would you propose to me to have it? I must have my little cup after breakfast."

"Ah you breakfast at this hour?"

"At mid-day—*comme cela se fait.* Here they breakfast at a quarter past seven. That 'quarter past' is charming!"

"But you were telling me about your coffee," I observed sympathetically.

"My *cousine* can't believe in it; she can't understand it. C'est une fille charmante, but that little cup of black coffee with a drop of '*fine,*' served at this hour—they exceed her comprehension. So I have to break the ice each day, and it takes the coffee the time you see to arrive. And when it does arrive, monsieur—! If I don't press it on *you*—though monsieur here sometimes joins me!—it's because you've drunk it on the Boulevard."

I resented extremely so critical a view of my poor friend's exertions, but I said nothing at all—the only way to be sure of my civility. I dropped my eyes on Mr. Mixter, who, sitting cross-legged and nursing his knees, watched my companion's foreign graces with an interest that familiarity had apparently done little to restrict. She became aware, naturally, of my mystified view of him and faced the question with all her boldness. "He adores me, you know," she murmured with her nose again in her tapestry—"he dreams of becoming *mon amoureux.* Yes, *il me fait une cour acharnée*—such as you see him. That's what we've come to. He has read some French novel—it took him six months. But ever since that he has thought himself a hero and me—such as I am, monsieur—*je ne sais quelle dévergondée!*"

Mr. Mixter may have inferred that he was to that extent the object of our reference; but of the manner in which he was handled he must have had small suspicion—preoccupied as he was, as to my companion, with the ecstasy of contemplation. Our hostess moreover at this moment came out of the house, bearing a coffee-pot and three cups on a neat little tray. I took from her eyes, as she approached us, a brief but intense appeal—the mute expression as I felt, conveyed in the hardest little look she had yet addressed me, of her longing to know what, as a man of the world in general and of the French world in particular, I thought of these allied forces now so encamped on the stricken field of her life. I could only "act" however, as they said at North Verona, quite impenetrably—only make no answering sign. I couldn't intimate, much less could I frankly utter, my inward sense of the Countess's probable past, with its measure of her virtue, value and accomplishments, and of the limits of the consideration to which she could properly pretend. I couldn't give my friend a hint of how I myself personally "saw" her interesting pensioner—whether as the runaway wife of a too-jealous hair-dresser or of a too-morose pastry-cook, say; whether as a very small bourgeoise, in fine, who had vitiated her case beyond patching up, or even as some character, of the nomadic sort, less edifying still. I couldn't let in, by the jog of a shutter, as it were, a hard informing ray and then, washing my hands of the business, turn my back for ever. I could on the contrary but save the situation, my own at least, for the moment, by pulling myself together with a master hand and appearing to ignore everything but that the dreadful per-

son between us *was* a "grande dame." This effort was
possible indeed but as a retreat in good order and with
all the forms of courtesy. If I couldn't speak, still less
could I stay, and I think I must, in spite of everything,
have turned black with disgust to see Caroline Spencer
stand there like a waiting-maid. I therefore won't answer for the shade of success that may have attended
my saying to the Countess, on my feet and as to leave
her: "You expect to remain some time in these *parages?*"

What passed between us, as from face to face, while
she looked up at me, *that* at least our companion may
have caught, that at least may have sown, for the aftertime, some seed of revelation. The Countess repeated
her terrible shrug. "Who knows? I don't see my way—!
It isn't an existence, but when one's in misery—! *Chère
belle,*" she added as an appeal to Miss Spencer, "you've
gone and forgotten the '*fine*'!"

I detained that lady as, after considering a moment in
silence the small array, she was about to turn off in
quest of this article. I held out my hand in silence—I
had to go. Her wan set little face, severely mild and
with the question of a moment before now quite cold
in it, spoke of extreme fatigue, but also of something
else strange and conceived—whether a desperate patience still, or at last some other desperation, being
more than I can say. What was clearest on the whole
was that she was glad I was going. Mr. Mixter had risen
to his feet and was pouring out the Countess's coffee.
As I went back past the Baptist church I could feel how
right my poor friend had been in her conviction at the
other, the still intenser, the now historic crisis, that she
should still see something of that dear old Europe.

1877

*

THE MARRIAGES

I

"Won't you stay a little longer?" the hostess asked while she held the girl's hand and smiled. "It's too early for every one to go—it's too absurd." Mrs. Churchley inclined her head to one side and looked gracious; she flourished about her face, in a vaguely protecting sheltering way, an enormous fan of red feathers. Everything in her composition, for Adela Chart, was enormous. She had big eyes, big teeth, big shoulders, big hands, big rings and bracelets, big jewels of every sort and many of them. The train of her crimson dress was longer than any other; her house was huge; her drawing-room, especially now that the company had left it, looked vast, and it offered to the girl's eyes a collection of the largest sofas and chairs, pictures, mirrors, clocks, that she had ever beheld. Was Mrs. Churchley's fortune also large, to account for so many immensities? Of this Adela could know nothing, but it struck her, while she smiled sweetly back at their entertainer, that she had better try to find out. Mrs. Churchley had at least a high-hung carriage drawn by the tallest horses, and in the Row she was to be seen perched on a mighty hunter. She was high and extensive herself, though not exactly fat; her bones were big, her limbs were long, and her loud hurrying voice resembled the bell of a steamboat. While she spoke to his daughter she had the air of hiding from Colonel Chart, a little shyly, behind the wide ostrich fan. But Colonel Chart was not a man to be either ignored or eluded.

"Of course every one's going on to something else," he said. "I believe there are a lot of things to-night."

"And where are *you* going?" Mrs. Churchley asked, dropping her fan and turning her bright hard eyes on the Colonel.

"Oh I don't do that sort of thing!"—he used a tone of familiar resentment that fell with a certain effect on his daughter's ear. She saw in it that he thought Mrs. Churchley might have done him a little more justice. But what made the honest soul suppose her a person to look to for a perception of fine shades? Indeed the shade was one it might have been a little difficult to seize—the difference between "going on" and coming to a dinner of twenty people. The pair were in mourning; the second year had maintained it for Adela, but the Colonel hadn't objected to dining with Mrs. Churchley, any more than he had objected at Easter to going down to the Millwards', where he had met her and where the girl had her reasons for believing him to have known he should meet her. Adela wasn't clear about the occasion of their original meeting, to which a certain mystery attached. In Mrs. Churchley's exclamation now there was the fullest concurrence in Colonel Chart's idea; she didn't say "Ah yes, dear friend, I understand!" but this was the note of sympathy she plainly wished to sound. It immediately made Adela say to her "Surely you must be going on somewhere yourself."

"Yes, you must have a lot of places," the Colonel concurred, while his view of her shining raiment had an invidious directness. Adela could read the tacit implication: "You're not in sorrow, in desolation."

Mrs. Churchley turned away from her at this and just waited before answering. The red fan was up again, and this time it sheltered her from Adela. "I'll give everything up—for *you*," were the words that issued from behind it. "*Do* stay a little. I always think this is such a nice hour. One can really talk," Mrs. Churchley went on. The Colonel laughed; he said it wasn't fair. But their hostess pressed his daughter. "Do sit down; it's the only time to have any talk." The girl saw her father sit down, but she wandered away, turning her back and pretending to look at a picture. She was so far from agreeing with Mrs. Churchley that it was an hour she particularly disliked. She was conscious of the queerness, the shyness, in London, of the gregarious flight of guests after a dinner, the general *sauve qui peut* and panic fear of being left with the host and hostess. But personally she always felt the contagion, always conformed to the rush. Besides, she knew herself turn red now, flushed with a conviction that had come over her and that she wished not to show.

Her father sat down on one of the big sofas with Mrs. Churchley; fortunately he was also a person with a presence that could hold its own. Adela didn't care to sit and watch them while they made love, as she crudely imaged it, and she cared still less to join in their strange commerce. She wandered further away, went into another of the bright "handsome," rather nude rooms— they were like women dressed for a ball—where the displaced chairs, at awkward angles to each other, seemed to retain the attitudes of bored talkers. Her heart beat as she had seldom known it, but she continued to make a pretence of looking at the pictures on the walls and the ornaments on the tables, while she hoped that, as she preferred it, it would be also the course her father would like best. She hoped "awfully," as she would have said, that he wouldn't think her rude. She was a person of courage, and he was a kind, an intensely good-natured man; nevertheless she went in some fear of him. At home it had always been a religion with them to be nice to the people he liked. How, in the old days, her mother, her incomparable mother, so clever, so unerring, so perfect, how in the precious days her mother had practised that art! Oh her mother, her irrecoverable mother! One of the pictures she was looking at swam before her eyes. Mrs. Churchley, in the natural course, would have begun immediately to climb staircases. Adela could see the high bony shoulders and the long crimson tail and the universal coruscating nod wriggle their horribly practical way through the rest of the night. Therefore she *must* have had her reasons for detaining them. There were mothers who thought every one wanted to marry their eldest son, and the girl sought to be clear as to whether she herself belonged to the class of daughters who thought every one wanted to marry their father. Her companions left her alone; and though she didn't want to be near them it angered her that Mrs. Churchley didn't call her. That proved she was conscious of the situation. She would have called her, only Colonel Chart had perhaps dreadfully murmured "Don't, love, don't." This proved he also was conscious. The time was really not long—ten minutes at the most elapsed—when he cried out gaily, pleasantly, as if with a small jocular reproach, "I say, Adela, we must release this dear lady!" He spoke of course as if it had been Adela's fault that they lingered. When they took leave she gave Mrs. Churchley, without intention and without defiance, but from the simple sincerity of her pain, a longer look into the eyes than she had ever given her before. Mrs. Churchley's onyx pupils reflected the question as distant dark windows reflect the sunset; they seemed to say: "Yes, I *am*, if that's what you want to know!"

What made the case worse, what made the girl more sure, was the silence preserved by her companion in the brougham on their way home. They rolled along in the June darkness from Prince's Gate to Seymour Street, each looking out of a window in conscious prudence; watching but not seeing the hurry of the London night, the flash of lamps, the quick roll on the wood of hansoms and other broughams. Adela had expected her father would say something about Mrs. Churchley; but when he said nothing it affected her, very oddly, still more as if he had spoken. In Seymour Street he asked the footman if Mr. Godfrey had come in, to which the servant replied that he had come in early and gone straight to his room. Adela had gathered as much, without saying so, from a lighted window on the second floor; but she contributed no remark to the question. At the foot of the stairs her father halted as if he had something on his mind; but what it amounted to seemed only the dry "Good-night" with which he presently ascended. It was the first time since her mother's death that he had bidden her good-night without kissing her. They were a kissing family, and after that dire event the habit had taken a fresh spring. She had left behind her such a general passion of regret that in kissing each other they felt themselves a little to be kissing her. Now, as, standing in the hall, with the stiff watching footman—she could have said to him angrily "Go away!" —planted near her, she looked with unspeakable pain at her father's back while he mounted, the effect was of his having withheld from another and a still more slighted cheek the touch of his lips.

He was going to his room, and after a moment she heard his door close. Then she said to the servant "Shut

up the house"—she tried to do everything her mother
had done, to be a little of what she had been, conscious
only of falling woefully short—and took her own way
upstairs. After she had reached her room she waited, listening, shaken by the apprehension that she should
hear her father come out again and go up to Godfrey.
He would go up to tell him, to have it over without delay, precisely because it would be so difficult. She asked
herself indeed why he should tell Godfrey when he
hadn't taken the occasion—their drive home being an
occasion—to tell herself. However, she wanted no
announcing, no telling; there was such a horrible clearness in her mind that what she now waited for was only
to be sure her father wouldn't proceed as she had imagined. At the end of the minutes she saw this particular danger was over, upon which she came out and
made her own way to her brother. Exactly what she
wanted to say to him first, if their parent counted on the
boy's greater indulgence, and before he could say anything, was: "Don't forgive him; don't, don't!"

He was to go up for an examination, poor lad, and
during these weeks his lamp burned till the small hours.
It was for the Foreign Office, and there was to be some
frightful number of competitors; but Adela had great
hopes of him—she believed so in his talents and saw
with pity how hard he worked. This would have made
her spare him, not trouble his night, his scanty rest,
if anything less dreadful had been at stake. It was a
blessing however that one could count on his coolness,
young as he was—his bright good-looking discretion,
the thing that already made him half a man of the world.
Moreover he was the one who would care most. If
Basil was the eldest son—he had as a matter of course
gone into the army and was in India, on the staff, by
good luck, of a governor-general—it was exactly this

that would make him comparatively indifferent. His life was elsewhere, and his father and he had been in a measure military comrades, so that he would be deterred by a certain delicacy from protesting; he wouldn't have liked any such protest in an affair of *his*. Beatrice and Muriel would care, but they were too young to speak, and this was just why her own responsibility was so great.

Godfrey was in working-gear—shirt and trousers and slippers and a beautiful silk jacket. His room felt hot, though a window was open to the summer night; the lamp on the table shed its studious light over a formidable heap of text-books and papers, the bed moreover showing how he had flung himself down to think out a problem. As soon as she got in she began. "Father's going to marry Mrs. Churchley, you know."

She saw his poor pink face turn pale. "How do you know?"

"I've seen with my eyes. We've been dining there— we've just come home. He's in love with her. She's in love with *him*. They'll arrange it."

"Oh I say!" Godfrey exclaimed, incredulous.

"He will, he will, he will!" cried the girl; and with it she burst into tears.

Godfrey, who had a cigarette in his hand, lighted it at one of the candles on the mantelpiece as if he were embarrassed. As Adela, who had dropped into his armchair, continued to sob, he said after a moment: "He oughtn't to—he oughtn't to."

"Oh think of mamma—think of mamma!" she wailed almost louder than was safe.

"Yes, he ought to think of mamma." With which Godfrey looked at the tip of his cigarette.

"To such a woman as that—after *her!*"

"Dear old mamma!" said Godfrey while he smoked.

Adela rose again drying her eyes. "It's like an insult to her; it's as if he denied her." Now that she spoke of it she felt herself rise to a height. "He rubs out at a stroke all the years of their happiness."

"They were awfully happy," Godfrey agreed.

"Think what she was—think how no one else will ever again be like her!" the girl went on.

"I suppose he's not very happy now," her brother vaguely contributed.

"Of course he isn't, any more than you and I are; and it's dreadful of him to want to be."

"Well, don't make yourself miserable till you're sure," the young man said.

But Adela showed him confidently that she *was* sure, from the way the pair had behaved together and from her father's attitude on the drive home. If Godfrey had been there he would have seen everything; it couldn't be explained, but he would have felt. When he asked at what moment the girl had first had her suspicion she replied that it had all come at once, that evening; or that at least she had had no conscious fear till then. There had been signs for two or three weeks, but she hadn't understood them—ever since the day Mrs. Churchley had dined in Seymour Street. Adela had on that occasion thought it odd her father should have wished to invite her, given the quiet way they were living; she was a person they knew so little. He had said something about her having been very civil to him, and that evening, already, she had guessed that he must have frequented their portentous guest herself more than there had been signs of. To-night it had come to her clearly that he would have called on her every day since the time of her dining with them; every afternoon about the hour he was ostensibly at his club. Mrs. Churchley *was* his club—she was for all the world just like one. At this Godfrey laughed; he wanted to know what his sister knew about clubs. She was slightly disappointed in his laugh, even wounded by it, but she knew perfectly what she meant: she meant that Mrs. Churchley was public and florid, promiscuous and mannish.

"Oh I dare say she's all right," he said as if he wanted to get on with his work. He looked at the clock on the mantel-shelf; he would have to put in another hour.

"All right to come and take darling mamma's place— to sit where *she* used to sit, to lay her horrible hands on *her* things?" Adela was appalled—all the more that she hadn't expected it—at her brother's apparent acceptance of such a prospect.

He coloured; there was something in her passionate piety that scorched him. She glared at him with tragic eyes—he might have profaned an altar. "Oh I mean that nothing will come of it."

"Not if we do our duty," said Adela. And then as he looked as if he hadn't an idea of what that could be: "You must speak to him—tell him how we feel; that we shall never forgive him, that we can't endure it."

"He'll think I'm cheeky," her brother returned, looking down at his papers with his back to her and his hands in his pockets.

"Cheeky to plead for *her* memory?"

"He'll say it's none of my business."

"Then you believe he'll do it?" cried the girl.

"Not a bit. Go to bed!"

"*I'll* speak to him"—she had turned as pale as a young priestess.

"Don't cry out till you're hurt; wait till he speaks to *you.*"

"He won't, he won't!" she declared. "He'll do it without telling us.

Her brother had faced round to her again; he started
a little at this, and again, at one of the candles, lighted
his cigarette, which had gone out. She looked at him
a moment; then he said something that surprised her.
"Is Mrs. Churchley very rich?"

"I haven't the least idea. What on earth has that to
do with it?"

Godfrey puffed his cigarette. "Does she live as if she
were?"

"She has a lot of hideous showy things."

"Well, we must keep our eyes open," he concluded.
"And now you *must* let me get on." He kissed his visitor
as if to make up for dismissing her, or for his failure to
take fire; and she held him a moment, burying her head
on his shoulder.

A wave of emotion surged through her, and again she
quavered out: "Ah why did she leave us? Why did
she leave us?"

"Yes, why indeed?" the young man sighed, disengaging himself with a movement of oppression.

II

Adela was so far right as that by the end of the week,
though she remained certain, her father had still not
made the announcement she dreaded. What convinced
her was the sense of her changed relations with him—
of there being between them something unexpressed,
something she was aware of as she would have been of
an open wound. When she spoke of this to Godfrey he
said the change was of her own making—also that she
was cruelly unjust to the governor. She suffered even
more from her brother's unexpected perversity; she had
had so different a theory about him that her disappointment was almost an humiliation and she needed all her
fortitude to pitch her faith lower. She wondered what

had happened to him and why he so failed her. She
would have trusted him to feel right about anything,
above all about such a question. Their worship of their
mother's memory, their recognition of her sacred place
in their past, her exquisite influence in their father's life,
his fortune, his career, in the whole history of the family
and welfare of the house—accomplished clever gentle
good beautiful and capable as she had been, a woman
whose quiet distinction was universally admired, so
that on her death one of the Princesses, the most august
of her friends, had written Adela such a note about her
as princesses were understood very seldom to write:
their hushed tenderness over all this was like a religion,
and was also an attributive honour, to fall away from
which was a form of treachery. This wasn't the way
people usually felt in London, she knew; but strenuous ardent observant girl as she was, with secrecies of
sentiment and dim originalities of attitude, she had
already made up her mind that London was no treas-
ure-house of delicacies. Remembrance there was ham-
mered thin—to be faithful was to make society gape.
The patient dead were sacrificed; they had no shrines,
for people were literally ashamed of mourning. When
they had hustled all sensibility out of their lives they
invented the fiction that they felt too much to utter.
Adela said nothing to her sisters; this reticence was part
of the virtue it was her idea to practise for them. *She*
was to be their mother, a direct deputy and representative. Before the vision of that other woman parading
in such a character she felt capable of ingenuities, of
deep diplomacies. The essence of these indeed was just
tremulously to watch her father. Five days after they
had dined together at Mrs. Churchley's he asked her
if she had been to see that lady.

"No indeed, why should I?" Adela knew that he knew

she hadn't been, since Mrs. Churchley would have told him.

"Don't you call on people after you dine with them?" said Colonel Chart.

"Yes, in the course of time. I don't rush off within the week."

Her father looked at her, and his eyes were colder than she had ever seen them, which was probably, she reflected, just the way hers appeared to himself. "Then you'll please rush off to-morrow. She's to dine with us on the 12th, and I shall expect your sisters to come down."

Adela stared. "To a dinner-party?"

"It's not to be a dinner-party. I want them to know Mrs. Churchley."

"Is there to be nobody else?"

"Godfrey of course. A family party," he said with an assurance before which she turned cold.

The girl asked her brother that evening if *that* wasn't tantamount to an announcement. He looked at her queerly and then said: "*I've* been to see her."

"What on earth did you do that for?"

"Father told me he wished it."

"Then he *has* told you?"

"Told me what?" Godfrey asked while her heart sank with the sense of his making difficulties for her.

"That they're engaged, of course. What else can all this mean?"

"He didn't tell me that, but I like her."

"*Like* her!" the girl shrieked.

"She's very kind, very good."

"To thrust herself upon us when we hate her? Is that what you call kind? Is that what you call decent?"

"Oh *I* don't hate her"—and he turned away as if she bored him.

She called the next day on Mrs. Churchley, designing
to break out somehow, to plead, to appeal—"Oh spare
us! have mercy on us! let him alone! go away!" But that
wasn't easy when they were face to face. Mrs. Churchley
had every intention of getting, as she would have said—
she was perpetually using the expression—into touch;
but her good intentions were as depressing as a tailor's
misfits. She could never understand that they had no
place for her vulgar charity, that their life was filled
with a fragrance of perfection for which she had no
sense fine enough. She was as undomestic as a shop-front
and as out of tune as a parrot. She would either make
them live in the streets or bring the streets into their life
—it was the same thing. She had evidently never read
a book, and she used intonations that Adela had never
heard, as if she had been an Australian or an American.
She understood everything in a vulgar sense; speaking
of Godfrey's visit to her and praising him according to
her idea, saying horrid things about him—that he was
awfully good-looking, a perfect gentleman, the kind she
liked. How could her father, who was after all in everything else such a dear, listen to a woman, or endure her,
who thought she pleased him when she called the son
of his dead wife a perfect gentleman? What would he
have been, pray? Much she knew about what any of
them were! When she told Adela she wanted her to like
her the girl thought for an instant her opportunity had
come—the chance to plead with her and beg her off.
But she presented such an impenetrable surface that it
would have been like giving a message to a varnished
door. She wasn't a woman, said Adela; she was an address.

When she dined in Seymour Street the "children,"
as the girl called the others, including Godfrey, liked
her. Beatrice and Muriel stared shyly and silently at the

wonders of her apparel (she was brutally overdressed) without of course guessing the danger that tainted the air. They supposed her in their innocence to be amusing, and they didn't know, any more than she did herself, how she patronised them. When she was upstairs with them after dinner Adela could see her look round the room at the things she meant to alter—their mother's things, not a bit like her own and not good enough for her. After a quarter of an hour of this our young lady felt sure she was deciding that Seymour Street wouldn't do at all, the dear old home that had done for their mother those twenty years. Was she plotting to transport them all to her horrible Prince's Gate? Of one thing at any rate Adela was certain: her father, at that moment alone in the dining-room with Godfrey, pretending to drink another glass of wine to make time, was coming to the point, was telling the news. When they reappeared they both, to her eyes, looked unnatural: the news had been told.

She had it from Godfrey before Mrs. Churchley left the house, when, after a brief interval, he followed her out of the drawing-room on her taking her sisters to bed. She was waiting for him at the door of her room. Her father was then alone with his *fiancée*—the word was grotesque to Adela; it was already as if the place were her home.

"What did you say to him?" our young woman asked when her brother had told her.

"I said nothing." Then he added, colouring—the expression of her face was such—"There was nothing to say."

"Is that how it strikes you?"—and she stared at the lamp.

"He asked me to speak to her," Godfrey went on.

"In what hideous sense?"

"To tell her I was glad."

"And did you?" Adela panted.

"I don't know. I said something. She kissed me."

"Oh how *could* you?" shuddered the girl, who covered her face with her hands.

"He says she's very rich," her brother returned.

"Is that why you kissed her?"

"I didn't kiss her. Good-night." And the young man, turning his back, went out.

When he had gone Adela locked herself in as with the fear she should be overtaken or invaded, and during a sleepless feverish memorable night she took counsel of her uncompromising spirit. She saw things as they were, in all the indignity of life. The levity, the mockery, the infidelity, the ugliness, lay as plain as a map before her; it was a world of gross practical jokes, a world *pour rire;* but she cried about it all the same. The morning dawned early, or rather it seemed to her there had been no night, nothing but a sickly creeping day. But by the time she heard the house stirring again she had determined what to do. When she came down to the breakfast-room her father was already in his place with newspapers and letters; and she expected the first words he would utter to be a rebuke to her for having disappeared the night before without taking leave of Mrs. Churchley. Then she saw he wished to be intensely kind, to make every allowance, to conciliate and console her. He knew she had heard from Godfrey, and he got up and kissed her. He told her as quickly as possible, to have it over, stammering a little, with an "I've a piece of news for you that will probably shock you," yet looking even exaggeratedly grave and rather pompous, to inspire the respect he didn't deserve. When he kissed her she melted, she burst into tears. He held her against him, kissing her again and again, saying tenderly "Yes, yes,

I know, I know." But he didn't know—else he couldn't have done it. Beatrice and Muriel came in, frightened when they saw her crying, and still more scared when she turned to them with words and an air that were terrible in their comfortable little lives: "Papa's going to be married; he's going to marry Mrs. Churchley!" After staring a moment and seeing their father look as strange, on his side, as Adela, though in a different way, the children also began to cry, so that when the servants arrived with tea and boiled eggs these functionaries were greatly embarrassed with their burden, not knowing whether to come in or hang back. They all scraped together a decorum, and as soon as the things had been put on table the Colonel banished the men with a glance. Then he made a little affectionate speech to Beatrice and Muriel, in which he described Mrs. Churchley as the kindest, the most delightful of women, only wanting to make them happy, only wanting to make *him* happy, and convinced that he would be if they were and that they would be if he was.

"What do such words mean?" Adela asked herself. She declared privately that they meant nothing, but she was silent, and every one was silent, on account of the advent of Miss Flynn the governess, before whom Colonel Chart preferred not to discuss the situation. Adela recognised on the spot that if things were to go as he wished his children would practically never again be alone with him. He would spend all his time with Mrs. Churchley till they were married, and then Mrs. Churchley would spend all her time with him. Adela was ashamed of him, and that was horrible—all the more that every one else would be, all his other friends, every one who had known her mother. But the public dishonour to that high memory shouldn't be enacted; he shouldn't do as he wished.

After breakfast her father remarked to her that it would give him pleasure if in a day or two she would take her sisters to see their friend, and she replied that he should be obeyed. He held her hand a moment, looking at her with an argument in his eyes which presently hardened into sternness. He wanted to know that she forgave him, but also wanted to assure her that he expected her to mind what she did, to go straight. She turned away her eyes; she was indeed ashamed of him.

She waited three days and then conveyed her sisters to the *repaire,* as she would have been ready to term it, of the lioness. That queen of beasts was surrounded with callers, as Adela knew she would be; it was her "day" and the occasion the girl preferred. Before this she had spent all her time with her companions, talking to them about their mother, playing on their memory of her, making them cry and making them laugh, reminding them of blest hours of their early childhood, telling them anecdotes of her own. None the less she confided to them that she believed there was no harm at all in Mrs. Churchley, and that when the time should come she would probably take them out immensely. She saw with smothered irritation that they enjoyed their visit at Prince's Gate; they had never been at anything so "grown-up," nor seen so many smart bonnets and brilliant complexions. Moreover they were considered with interest, quite as if, being minor elements, yet perceptible ones, of Mrs. Churchley's new life, they had been described in advance and were the heroines of the occasion. There were so many ladies present that this personage didn't talk to them much; she only called them her "chicks" and asked them to hand about teacups and bread and butter. All of which was highly agreeable and indeed intensely exciting to Beatrice and Muriel, who had little round red spots in *their* cheeks

when they came away. Adela quivered with the sense
that her mother's children were now Mrs. Churchley's
"chicks" and a part of the furniture of Mrs. Churchley's
dreadful consciousness.

It was one thing to have made up her mind, however;
it was another thing to make her attempt. It was when
she learned from Godfrey that the day was fixed, the
20th of July, only six weeks removed, that she felt the
importance of prompt action. She learned everything
from Godfrey now, having decided it would be hypoc-
risy to question her father. Even her silence was hypo-
critical, but she couldn't weep and wail. Her father
showed extreme tact; taking no notice of her detachment, treating it as a moment of *bouderie* he was bound
to allow her and that would pout itself away. She
debated much as to whether she should take Godfrey
into her confidence; she would have done so without
hesitation if he hadn't disappointed her. He was so little
what she might have expected, and so perversely preoccupied that she could explain it only by the high pressure at which he was living, his anxiety about his
"exam." He was in a fidget, in a fever, putting on a spurt
to come in first; sceptical moreover about his success
and cynical about everything else. He appeared to agree
to the general axiom that they didn't want a strange
woman thrust into their life, but he found Mrs. Churchley "very jolly as a person to know." He had been to see
her by himself—he had been to see her three times. He
in fact gave it out that he would make the most of her
now; he should probably be so little in Seymour Street
after these days. What Adela at last determined to give
him was her assurance that the marriage would never
take place. When he asked what she meant and who
was to prevent it she replied that the interesting couple
would abandon the idea of themselves, or that Mrs.

Churchley at least would after a week or two back out of it.

"That will be really horrid then," Godfrey pronounced. "The only respectable thing, at the point they've come to, is to put it through. Charming for poor Dad to have the air of being 'chucked'!"

This made her hesitate two days more, but she found answers more valid than any objections. The many-voiced answer to everything—it was like the autumn wind round the house—was the affront that fell back on her mother. Her mother was dead, but it killed her again. So one morning at eleven o'clock, when she knew her father was writing letters, she went out quietly and, stopping the first hansom she met, drove to Prince's Gate. Mrs. Churchley was at home, and she was shown into the drawing-room with the request that she would wait five minutes. She waited without the sense of breaking down at the last, and the impulse to run away, which were what she had expected to have. In the cab and at the door her heart had beat terribly, but now suddenly, with the game really to play, she found herself lucid and calm. It was a joy to her to feel later that this was the way Mrs. Churchley found her; not confused, not stammering nor prevaricating, only a little amazed at her own courage, conscious of the immense responsibility of her step and wonderfully older than her years. Her hostess sounded her at first with suspicious eyes, but eventually, to Adela's surprise, burst into tears. At this the girl herself cried, and with the secret happiness of believing they were saved. Mrs. Churchley said she would think over what she had been told, and she promised her young friend, freely enough and very firmly, not to betray the secret of the latter's step to the Colonel. They were saved—they were saved: the words sung themselves in the girl's soul as she came downstairs.

When the door opened for her she saw her brother on the step, and they looked at each other in surprise, each finding it on the part of the other an odd hour for Prince's Gate. Godfrey remarked that Mrs. Churchley would have enough of the family, and Adela answered that she would perhaps have too much. None the less the young man went in while his sister took her way home.

III

She saw nothing of him for nearly a week; he had more and more his own times and hours, adjusted to his tremendous responsibilities, and he spent whole days at his crammer's. When she knocked at his door late in the evening he was regularly not in his room. It was known in the house how much he was worried; he was horribly nervous about his ordeal. It was to begin on the 23d of June, and his father was as worried as himself. The wedding had been arranged in relation to this; they wished poor Godfrey's fate settled first, though they felt the nuptials would be darkened if it shouldn't be settled right.

Ten days after that performance of her private undertaking Adela began to sniff, as it were, a difference in the general air; but as yet she was afraid to exult. It wasn't in truth a difference for the better, so that there might be still a great tension. Her father, since the announcement of his intended marriage, had been visibly pleased with himself, but that pleasure now appeared to have undergone a check. She had the impression known to the passengers on a great steamer when, in the middle of the night, they feel the engines stop. As this impression may easily sharpen to the sense that something serious has happened, so the girl asked herself what had actually occurred. She had expected something serious;

but it was as if she couldn't keep still in her cabin—she wanted to go up and see. On the 20th, just before breakfast, her maid brought her a message from her brother. Mr. Godfrey would be obliged if she would speak to him in his room. She went straight up to him, dreading to find him ill, broken down on the eve of his formidable week. This was not the case however—he rather seemed already at work, to have been at work since dawn. But he was very white and his eyes had a strange and new expression. Her beautiful young brother looked older; he looked haggard and hard. He met her there as if he had been waiting for her, and he said at once: "Please tell me this, Adela—what was the purpose of your visit the other morning to Mrs. Churchley, the day I met you at her door?"

She stared—she cast about. "The purpose? What's the matter? Why do you ask?"

"They've put it off—they've put it off a month."

"Ah thank God!" said Adela.

"Why the devil do you thank God?" Godfrey asked with a strange impatience.

She gave a strained intense smile. "You know I think it all wrong."

He stood looking at her up and down. "What did you do there? How did you interfere?"

"Who told you I interfered?" she returned with a deep flush.

"You said something—you did something. I knew you had done it when I saw you come out."

"What I did was my own business."

"Damn your own business!" cried the young man.

She had never in her life been so spoken to, and in advance, had she been given the choice, would have said that she'd rather die than be so handled by Godfrey. But her spirit was high, and for a moment she was

as angry as if she had been cut with a whip. She escaped
the blow but felt the insult. "And *your* business then?"
she asked. "I wondered what that was when I saw *you.*"

He stood a moment longer scowling at her; then with
the exclamation "You've made a pretty mess!" he turned
away from her and sat down to his books.

They had put it off, as he said; her father was dry and
stiff and official about it. "I suppose I had better let you
know we've thought it best to postpone our marriage
till the end of the summer—Mrs. Churchley has so many
arrangements to make": he was not more expansive than
that. She neither knew nor greatly cared whether she
but vainly imagined or correctly observed him to watch
her obliquely for some measure of her receipt of these
words. She flattered herself that, thanks to Godfrey's
forewarning, cruel as the form of it had been, she was
able to repress any crude sign of elation. She had a perfectly good conscience, for she could now judge what
odious elements Mrs. Churchley, whom she had not
seen since the morning in Prince's Gate, had already
introduced into their dealings. She gathered without
difficulty that her father hadn't concurred in the post-
ponement, for he was more restless than before, more
absent and distinctly irritable. There was naturally still
the question of how much of this condition was to be
attributed to his solicitude about Godfrey. That young
man took occasion to say a horrible thing to his sister:
"If I don't pass it will be your fault." These were dreadful days for the girl, and she asked herself how she could
have borne them if the hovering spirit of her mother
hadn't been at her side. Fortunately she always felt it
there, sustaining, commending, sanctifying. Suddenly
her father announced to her that he wished her to go
immediately, with her sisters, down to Brinton, where
there was always part of a household and where for a

few weeks they would manage well enough. The only explanation he gave of this desire was that he wanted them out of the way. "Out of the way of what?" she queried, since there were to be for the time no preparations in Seymour Street. She was willing to take it for out of the way of his nerves.

She never needed urging however to go to Brinton, the dearest old house in the world, where the happiest days of her young life had been spent and the silent nearness of her mother always seemed greatest. She was happy again, with Beatrice and Muriel and Miss Flynn, with the air of summer and the haunted rooms and her mother's garden and the talking oaks and the nightingales. She wrote briefly to her father, giving him, as he had requested, an account of things; and he wrote back that since she was so contented—she didn't recognise having told him that—she had better not return to town at all. The fag-end of the London season would be unimportant to her, and he was getting on very well. He mentioned that Godfrey had passed his tests, but, as she knew, there would be a tiresome wait before news of results. The poor chap was going abroad for a month with young Sherard—he had earned a little rest and a little fun. He went abroad without a word to Adela, but in his beautiful little hand he took a chaffing leave of Beatrice. The child showed her sister the letter, of which she was very proud and which contained no message for any one else. This was the worst bitterness of the whole crisis for that somebody—its placing in so strange a light the creature in the world whom, after her mother, she had loved best.

Colonel Chart had said he would "run down" while his children were at Brinton, but they heard no more about it. He only wrote two or three times to Miss Flynn on matters in regard to which Adela was surprised he shouldn't have communicated with herself. Muriel accomplished an upright little letter to Mrs. Churchley —her eldest sister neither fostered nor discouraged the performance—to which Mrs. Churchley replied, after a fortnight, in a meagre and, as Adela thought, illiterate fashion, making no allusion to the approach of any closer tie. Evidently the situation had changed; the question of the marriage was dropped, at any rate for the time. This idea gave our young woman a singular and almost intoxicating sense of power; she felt as if she were riding a great wave of confidence. She had decided and acted —the greatest could do no more than that. The grand thing was to see one's results, and what else was she doing? These results were in big rich conspicuous lives; the stage was large on which she moved her figures. Such a vision was exciting, and as they had the use of a couple of ponies at Brinton she worked off her excitement by a long gallop. A day or two after this however came news of which the effect was to rekindle it. Godfrey had come back, the list had been published, he had passed first. These happy tidings proceeded from the young man himself; he announced them by a telegram to Beatrice, who had never in her life before received such a missive and was proportionately inflated. Adela reflected that she herself ought to have felt snubbed, but she was too happy. They were free again, they were themselves, the nightmare of the previous weeks was blown away, the unity and dignity of her father's life restored, and, to round off her sense of success, Godfrey had achieved his first step toward high distinction. She wrote him the next day as frankly and affectionately as if there had been no estrangement between them, and besides telling him how she rejoiced in his triumph begged him in charity to let them know exactly how the case stood with regard to Mrs. Churchley.

Late in the summer afternoon she walked through the park to the village with her letter, posted it and came back. Suddenly, at one of the turns of the avenue, half-way to the house, she saw a young man hover there as if awaiting her—a young man who proved to be Godfrey on his pedestrian progress over from the station. He had seen her as he took his short cut, and if he had come down to Brinton it wasn't apparently to avoid her. There was nevertheless none of the joy of his triumph in his face as he came a very few steps to meet her; and although, stiffly enough, he let her kiss him and say "I'm so glad—I'm so glad!" she felt this tolerance as not quite the mere calm of the rising diplomatist. He turned toward the house with her and walked on a short distance while she uttered the hope that he had come to stay some days.

"Only till to-morrow morning. They're sending me straight to Madrid. I came down to say good-bye; there's a fellow bringing my bags."

"To Madrid? How awfully nice! And it's awfully nice of you to have come," she said as she passed her hand into his arm.

The movement made him stop, and, stopping, he turned on her in a flash a face of something more than suspicion—of passionate reprobation. "What I really came for—you might as well know without more delay —is to ask you a question."

"A question?"—she echoed it with a beating heart.

They stood there under the old trees in the lingering light, and, young and fine and fair as they both were, formed a complete superficial harmony with the peaceful English scene. A near view, however, would have shown that Godfrey Chart hadn't taken so much trouble only to skim the surface. He looked deep into his sister's eyes. "What was it you said that morning to Mrs. Churchley?"

She fixed them on the ground a moment, but at last met his own again. "If she has told you, why do you ask?"

"She has told me nothing. I've seen for myself."

"What have you seen?"

"She has broken it off. Everything's over. Father's in the depths."

"In the depths?" the girl quavered.

"Did you think it would make him jolly?" he went on.

She had to choose what to say. "He'll get over it. He'll be glad."

"That remains to be seen. You interfered, you invented something, you got round her. I insist on knowing what you did."

Adela felt that if it was a question of obstinacy there was something within her she could count on; in spite of which, while she stood looking down again a moment she said to herself "I could be dumb and dogged if I chose, but I scorn to be." She wasn't ashamed of what she had done, but she wanted to be clear. "Are you absolutely certain it's broken off?"

"He is, and she is; so that's as good."

"What reason has she given?"

"None at all—or half a dozen; it's the same thing. She has changed her mind—she mistook her feelings—she can't part with her independence. Moreover he has too many children."

"Did he tell you this?" the girl asked.

"Mrs. Churchley told me. She has gone abroad for a year."

"And she didn't tell you what I said to her?"

Godfrey showed an impatience. "Why should I take this trouble if she had?"

"You might have taken it to make me suffer," said Adela. "That appears to be what you want to do."

"No, I leave that to *you*—it's the good turn you've done me!" cried the young man with hot tears in his eyes.

She stared, aghast with the perception that there was some dreadful thing she didn't know; but he walked on, dropping the question angrily and turning his back to her as if he couldn't trust himself. She read his disgust in his averted face, in the way he squared his shoulders and smote the ground with his stick, and she hurried after him and presently overtook him. She kept by him for a moment in silence; then she broke out: "What do you mean? What in the world have I done to you?"

"She would have helped me. She was all ready to help me," Godfrey portentously said.

"Helped you in what?" She wondered what he meant; if he had made debts that he was afraid to confess to his father and—of all horrible things—had been looking to Mrs. Churchley to pay. She turned red with the mere apprehension of this and, on the heels of her guess, exulted again at having perhaps averted such a shame.

"Can't you just see I'm in trouble? Where are your eyes, your senses, your sympathy, that you talk so much about? Haven't you seen these six months that I've a curst worry in my life?"

She seized his arm, made him stop, stood looking up at him like a frightened little girl. "What's the matter, Godfrey?—what *is* the matter?"

"You've gone against me so—I could strangle you!" he growled. This image added nothing to her dread; her dread was that he had done some wrong, was stained with some guilt. She uttered it to him with clasped hands, begging him to tell her the worst; but, still more passionately, he cut her short with his own cry: "In

God's name, satisfy me! What infernal thing did you do?"

"It wasn't infernal—it was right. I told her mamma had been wretched," said Adela.

"Wretched? You told her such a lie?"

"It was the only way, and she believed me."

"Wretched how? — wretched when? — wretched where?" the young man stammered.

"I told her papa had made her so, and that *she* ought to know it. I told her the question troubled me unspeakably, but that I had made up my mind it was my duty to initiate her." Adela paused, the light of bravado in her face, as if, though struck while the words came with the monstrosity of what she had done, she was incapable of abating a jot of it. "I notified her that he had faults and peculiarities that made mamma's life a long worry— a martyrdom that she hid wonderfully from the world, but that we saw and that I had often pitied. I told her what they were, these faults and peculiarities; I put the dots on the *i's*. I said it wasn't fair to let another person marry him without a warning. I warned her; I satisfied my conscience. She could do as she liked. My responsibility was over."

Godfrey gazed at her; he listened with parted lips, incredulous and appalled. "You invented such a tissue of falsities and calumnies, and you talk about your conscience? You stand there in your senses and proclaim your crime?"

"I'd have committed any crime that would have rescued us."

"You insult and blacken and ruin your own father?" Godfrey kept on.

"He'll never know it; she took a vow she wouldn't tell him."

"Ah I'll be damned if *I* won't tell him!" he rang out.

Adela felt sick at this, but she flamed up to resent the treachery, as it struck her, of such a menace. "I did right —I did right!" she vehemently declared. "I went down on my knees to pray for guidance, and I saved mamma's memory from outrage. But if I hadn't, if I hadn't"—she faltered an instant—"I'm not worse than you, and I'm not so bad, for you've done something that you're ashamed to tell me."

He had taken out his watch; he looked at it with quick intensity, as if not hearing nor heeding her. Then, his calculating eyes raised, he fixed her long enough to exclaim with unsurpassable horror and contempt: "You raving maniac!" He turned away from her; he bounded down the avenue in the direction from which they had come, and, while she watched him, strode away, across the grass, toward the short cut to the station.

IV

His bags, by the time she got home, had been brought to the house, but Beatrice and Muriel, immediately informed of this, waited for their brother in vain. Their sister said nothing to them of her having seen him, and she accepted after a little, with a calmness that surprised herself, the idea that he had returned to town to denounce her. She believed this would make no difference now—she had done what she had done. She had somehow a stiff faith in Mrs. Churchley. Once that so considerable mass had received its impetus it wouldn't, it couldn't pull up. It represented a heavy-footed person, incapable of further agility. Adela recognised too how well it might have come over her that there were too many children. Lastly the girl fortified herself with the reflexion, grotesque in the conditions and conducing to prove her sense of humour not high, that her father was after all not a man to be played with. It seemed to her at any rate that if she *had* baffled his unholy purpose she could bear anything—bear imprisonment and bread and water, bear lashes and torture, bear even his lifelong reproach. What she could bear least was the wonder of the inconvenience she had inflicted on Godfrey. She had time to turn this over, very vainly, for a succession of days—days more numerous than she had expected, which passed without bringing her from London any summons to come up and take her punishment. She sounded the possible, she compared the degrees of the probable; feeling however that as a cloistered girl she was poorly equipped for speculation. She tried to imagine the calamitous things young men might do, and could only feel that such things would naturally be connected either with borrowed money or with bad women. She became conscious that after all she knew almost nothing about either of those interests. The worst woman she knew was Mrs. Churchley herself. Meanwhile there was no reverberation from Seymour Street —only a sultry silence.

At Brinton she spent hours in her mother's garden, where she had grown up, where she considered that she was training for old age, since she meant not to depend on whist. She loved the place as, had she been a good Catholic, she would have loved the smell of her parish church; and indeed there was in her passion for flowers something of the respect of a religion. They seemed to her the only things in the world that really respected themselves, unless one made an exception for Nutkins, who had been in command all through her mother's time, with whom she had had a real friendship and who had been affected by their pure example. He was the person left in the world with whom on the whole she could speak most intimately of the dead. They never had to name her together—they only said "she"; and

Nutkins freely conceded that she had taught him every-thing he knew. When Beatrice and Muriel said "she" they referred to Mrs. Churchley. Adela had reason to believe she should never marry, and that some day she should have about a thousand a year. This made her see in the far future a little garden of her own, under a hill, full of rare and exquisite things, where she would spend most of her old age on her knees with an apron and stout gloves, with a pair of shears and a trowel, steeped in the comfort of being thought mad.

One morning ten days after her scene with Godfrey, on coming back into the house shortly before lunch, she was met by Miss Flynn with the notification that a lady in the drawing-room had been waiting for her for some minutes. "A lady" suggested immediately Mrs. Church-ley. It came over Adela that the form in which her pen-alty was to descend would be a personal explanation with that misdirected woman. The lady had given no name, and Miss Flynn hadn't seen Mrs. Churchley; nevertheless the governess was certain Adela's surmise was wrong.

"Is she big and dreadful?" the girl asked.

Miss Flynn, who was circumspection itself, took her time. "She's dreadful, but she's not big." She added that she wasn't sure she ought to let Adela go in alone; but this young lady took herself throughout for a heroine, and it wasn't in a heroine to shrink from any encounter. Wasn't she every instant in transcendent contact with her mother? The visitor might have no connexion what-ever with the drama of her father's frustrated marriage; but everything to-day for Adela was part of that.

Miss Flynn's description had prepared her for a con-siderable shock, but she wasn't agitated by her first glimpse of the person who awaited her. A youngish well-dressed woman stood there, and silence was be-

tween them while they looked at each other. Before
either had spoken however Adela began to see what
Miss Flynn had intended. In the light of the drawing-
room window the lady was five-and-thirty years of age
and had vivid yellow hair. She also had a blue cloth suit
with brass buttons, a stick-up collar like a gentleman's,
a necktie arranged in a sailor's knot, a golden pin in the
shape of a little lawn-tennis racket, and pearl-grey gloves
with big black stitchings. Adela's second impression was
that she was an actress, and her third that no such
person had ever before crossed that threshold.

"I'll tell you what I've come for," said the apparition.
"I've come to ask you to intercede." She wasn't an
actress; an actress would have had a nicer voice.

"To intercede?" Adela was too bewildered to ask her
to sit down.

"With your father, you know. He doesn't know, but
he'll have to." Her "have" sounded like "ave." She
explained, with many more such sounds, that she was
Mrs. Godfrey, that they had been married seven mortal
months. If Godfrey was going abroad she must go with
him, and the only way she could go with him would
be for his father to do something. He was afraid of his
father—that was clear; he was afraid even to tell him.
What she had come down for was to see some other
member of the family face to face—"fice to fice" Mrs.
Godfrey called it—and try if he couldn't be approached
by another side. If no one else would act then she would
just have to act herself. The Colonel would have to do
something—that was the only way out of it.

What really happened Adela never quite understood;
what seemed to be happening was that the room went
round and round. Through the blur of perception ac-
companying this effect the sharp stabs of her visitor's
revelation came to her like the words heard by a patient

"going off" under ether. She afterwards denied passionately even to herself that she had done anything so
abject as to faint; but there was a lapse in her consciousness on the score of Miss Flynn's intervention. This intervention had evidently been active, for when they
talked the matter over, later in the day, with bated
breath and infinite dissimulation for the school-room
quarter, the governess had more lurid truths, and still
more, to impart than to receive. She was at any rate
under the impression that she had athletically contended, in the drawing-room, with the yellow hair—this
after removing Adela from the scene and before induc-
ing Mrs. Godfrey to withdraw. Miss Flynn had never
known a more thrilling day, for all the rest of it too was
pervaded with agitations and conversations, precautions
and alarms. It was given out to Beatrice and Muriel that
their sister had been taken suddenly ill, and the governess ministered to her in her room. Indeed Adela had
never found herself less at ease, for this time she had
received a blow that she couldn't return. There was
nothing to do but to take it, to endure the humiliation
of her wound.

At first she declined to take it—having, as might appear, the much more attractive resource of regarding
her visitant as a mere masquerading person, an impudent
impostor. On the face of the matter moreover it wasn't
fair to believe till one heard; and to hear in such a case
was to hear Godfrey himself. Whatever she had tried
to imagine about him she hadn't arrived at anything so
belittling as an idiotic secret marriage with a dyed and
painted hag. Adela repeated this last word as if it gave
her comfort; and indeed where everything was so bad
fifteen years of seniority made the case little worse. Miss
Flynn was portentous, for Miss Flynn had had it out
with the wretch. She had cross-questioned her and had

not broken her down. This was the most uplifted hour of Miss Flynn's life; for whereas she usually had to content herself with being humbly and gloomily in the right she could now be magnanimously and showily so. Her only perplexity was as to what she ought to do—write to Colonel Chart or go up to town to see him. She bloomed with alternatives—she resembled some dull garden-path which under a copious downpour has begun to flaunt with colour. Toward evening Adela was obliged to recognise that her brother's worry, of which he had spoken to her, had appeared bad enough to consist even of a low wife, and to remember that, so far from its being inconceivable a young man in his position should clandestinely take one, she had been present, years before, during her mother's lifetime, when Lady Molesley declared gaily, over a cup of tea, that this was precisely what she expected of her eldest son. The next morning it was the worst possibilities that seemed clearest; the only thing left with a tatter of dusky comfort being the ambiguity of Godfrey's charge that her own action had "done" for him. That was a matter by itself, and she racked her brains for a connecting link between Mrs. Churchley and Mrs. Godfrey. At last she made up her mind that they were related by blood; very likely, though differing in fortune, they were cousins or even sisters. But even then what did the wretched boy mean?

Arrested by the unnatural fascination of opportunity, Miss Flynn received before lunch a telegram from Colonel Chart—an order for dinner and a vehicle; he and Godfrey were to arrive at six o'clock. Adela had plenty of occupation for the interval, since she was pitying her father when she wasn't rejoicing that her mother had gone too soon to know. She flattered herself she made out the providential reason of that cruelty now. She found time however still to wonder for what purpose, given the situation, Godfrey was to be brought down. She wasn't unconscious indeed that she had little general knowledge of what usually was done with young men in that predicament. One talked about the situation, but the situation was an abyss. She felt this still more when she found, on her father's arrival, that nothing apparently was to happen as she had taken for granted it would. There was an inviolable hush over the whole affair, but no tragedy, no publicity, nothing ugly. The tragedy had been in town—the faces of the two men spoke of it in spite of their other perfunctory aspects; and at present there was only a family dinner, with Beatrice and Muriel and the governess—with almost a company tone too, the result of the desire to avoid publicity. Adela admired her father; she knew what he was feeling if Mrs. Godfrey had been at him, and yet she saw him positively gallant. He was mildly austere, or rather even —what was it?—august; just as, coldly equivocal, he never looked at his son, so that at moments he struck her as almost sick with sadness. Godfrey was equally inscrutable and therefore wholly different from what he had been as he stood before her in the park. If he was to start on his career (with such a wife!—wouldn't she utterly blight it?) he was already professional enough to know how to wear a mask.

Before they rose from table she felt herself wholly bewildered, so little were such large causes traceable in their effects. She had nerved herself for a great ordeal, but the air was as sweet as an anodyne. It was perfectly plain to her that her father was deadly sore—as pathetic as a person betrayed. He was broken, but he showed no resentment; there was a weight on his heart, but he had lightened it by dressing as immaculately as usual for dinner. She asked herself what immensity of a row there could have been in town to have left his anger so spent.

He went through everything, even to sitting with his son after dinner. When they came out together he invited Beatrice and Muriel to the billiard-room, and as Miss Flynn discreetly withdrew Adela was left alone with Godfrey, who was completely changed, and not now in the least of a rage. He was broken too, but not so pathetic as his father. He was only very correct and apologetic; he said to his sister: "I'm awfully sorry *you* were annoyed—it was something I never dreamed of."

She couldn't think immediately what he meant; then she grasped the reference to her extraordinary invader. She was uncertain, however, what tone to take; perhaps his father had arranged with him that they were to make the best of it. But she spoke her own despair in the way she murmured "Oh Godfrey, Godfrey, is it true?"

"I've been the most unutterable donkey—you can say what you like to me. You can't say anything worse than I've said to myself."

"My brother, my brother!"—his words made her wail it out. He hushed her with a movement and she asked: "What has father said?"

He looked very high over her head. "He'll give her six hundred a year."

"Ah the angel!"—it was too splendid.

"On condition"—Godfrey scarce blinked—"she never comes near me. She has solemnly promised, and she'll probably leave me alone to get the money. If she doesn't —in diplomacy—I'm lost." He had been turning his eyes vaguely about, this way and that, to avoid meeting hers; but after another instant he gave up the effort and she had the miserable confession of his glance. "I've been living in hell."

"My brother, my brother!" she yearningly repeated.

"I'm not an idiot; yet for her I've behaved like one. Don't ask me—you mustn't know. It was all done in a day, and since then fancy my condition; fancy my work in such a torment; fancy my coming through at all."

"Thank God you passed!" she cried. "You were wonderful!"

"I'd have shot myself if I hadn't been. I had an awful day yesterday with the governor; it was late at night before it was over. I leave England next week. He brought me down here for it to look well—so that the children shan't know."

"*He's* wonderful too!" Adela murmured.

"Wonderful too! Godfrey echoed.

"Did *she* tell him?" the girl went on.

"She came straight to Seymour Street from here. She saw him alone first; then he called me in. *That* luxury lasted about an hour."

"Poor, poor father!" Adela moaned at this; on which her brother remained silent. Then after he had alluded to it as the scene he had lived in terror of all through his cramming, and she had sighed forth again her pity and admiration for such a mixture of anxieties and such a triumph of talent, she pursued: "Have you told him?"

"Told him what?"

"What you said you would—what *I* did."

Godfrey turned away as if at present he had very little interest in that inferior tribulation. "I was angry with you, but I cooled off. I held my tongue."

She clasped her hands. "You thought of mamma!"

"Oh don't speak of mamma!" he cried as in rueful tenderness.

It was indeed not a happy moment, and she murmured: "No; if you *had* thought of her—!"

This made Godfrey face her again with a small flare in his eyes. "Oh *then* it didn't prevent. I thought that woman really good. I believed in her."

"Is she *very* bad?"

"I shall never mention her to you again," he returned with dignity.

"You may believe *I* won't speak of her! So father doesn't know?" the girl added.

"Doesn't know what?"

"That I said what I did to Mrs. Churchley."

He had a momentary pause. "I don't think so, but you must find out for yourself."

"I shall find out," said Adela. "But what had Mrs. Churchley to do with it?"

"With *my* misery? I told her. I had to tell some one."

"Why didn't you tell me?"

He appeared—though but after an instant—to know exactly why. "Oh you take things so beastly hard—you make such rows." Adela covered her face with her hands and he went on: "What I wanted was comfort—not to be lashed up. I thought I should go mad. I wanted Mrs. Churchley to break it to father, to intercede for me and help him to meet it. She was awfully kind to me, she listened and she understood; she could fancy how it had happened. Without her I shouldn't have pulled through. She liked me, you know," he further explained, and as if it were quite worth mentioning —all the more that it was pleasant to him. "She said she'd do what she could for me. She was full of sympathy and resource. I really leaned on her. But when *you* cut in of course it spoiled everything. That's why I was so furious with you. She couldn't do anything then."

Adela dropped her hands, staring; she felt she had walked in darkness. "So that he had to meet it alone?"

"*Dame!*" said Godfrey, who had got up his French tremendously.

Muriel came to the door to say papa wished the two

others to join them, and the next day Godfrey returned to town. His father remained at Brinton, without an intermission, the rest of the summer and the whole of the autumn, and Adela had a chance to find out, as she had said, whether he knew she had interfered. But in spite of her chance she never found out. He knew Mrs. Churchley had thrown him over and he knew his daughter rejoiced in it, but he appeared not to have divined the relation between the two facts. It was strange that one of the matters he was clearest about—Adela's secret triumph—should have been just the thing which from this time on justified less and less such a confidence. She was too sorry for him to be consistently glad. She watched his attempts to wind himself up on the subject of shorthorns and drainage, and she favoured to the utmost of her ability his intermittent disposition to make a figure in orchids. She wondered whether they mightn't have a few people at Brinton; but when she mentioned the idea he asked what in the world there would be to attract them. It was a confoundedly stupid house, he remarked—with all respect to *her* cleverness. Beatrice and Muriel were mystified; the prospect of going out immensely had faded so utterly away. They were apparently not to go out at all. Colonel Chart was aimless and bored; he paced up and down and went back to smoking which was bad for him, and looked drearily out of windows as if on the bare chance that something might arrive. Did he expect Mrs. Churchley to arrive, did he expect her to relent on finding she couldn't live without him? It was Adela's belief that she gave no sign. But the girl thought it really remarkable of her not to have betrayed her ingenious young visitor. Adela's judgement of human nature was perhaps harsh, but she believed that most women, given the various facts, wouldn't have been so forbearing. This lady's conception of the point of honour placed her there in a finer and purer light than had at all orginally promised to shine about her.

She meanwhile herself could well judge how heavy her father found the burden of Godfrey's folly and how he was incommoded at having to pay the horrible woman six hundred a year. Doubtless he was having dreadful letters from her; doubtless she threatened them all with hideous exposure. If the matter should be bruited Godfrey's prospects would collapse on the spot. He thought Madrid very charming and curious, but Mrs. Godfrey was in England, so that his father had to face the music. Adela took a dolorous comfort in her mother's being out of *that*—it would have killed her; but this didn't blind her to the fact that the comfort for her father would perhaps have been greater if he had had some one to talk to about his trouble. He never dreamed of doing so to her, and she felt she couldn't ask him. In the family life he wanted utter silence about it. Early in the winter he went abroad for ten weeks, leaving her with her sisters in the country, where it was not to be denied that at this time existence had very little savour. She half-expected her sister-in-law would again descend on her; but the fear wasn't justified, and the quietude of the awful creature seemed really to vibrate with the ring of gold-pieces. There were sure to be extras. Adela winced at the extras. Colonel Chart went to Paris and to Monte Carlo and then to Madrid to see his boy. His daughter had the vision of his perhaps meeting Mrs. Churchley somewhere, since, if she had gone for a year, she would still be on the Continent. If he should meet her perhaps the affair would come on again: she caught herself musing over this. But he brought back no such appearance, and, seeing him after an interval, she was struck afresh with his jilted and wasted air. She didn't like it—she resented it. A little more and she would have said that that was no way to treat so faithful a man.

They all went up to town in March, and on one of the first days of April she saw Mrs. Churchley in the Park. She herself remained apparently invisible to that lady—she herself and Beatrice and Muriel, who sat with her in their mother's old bottle-green landau. Mrs. Churchley, perched higher than ever, rode by without a recognition; but this didn't prevent Adela's going to her before the month was over. As on her great previous occasion she went in the morning, and she again had the good fortune to be admitted. This time, however, her visit was shorter, and a week after making it—the week was a desolation—she addressed to her brother at Madrid a letter containing these words: "I could endure it no longer—I confessed and retracted; I explained to her as well as I could the falsity of what I said to her ten months ago and the benighted purity of my motives for saying it. I besought her to regard it as unsaid, to forgive me, not to despise me too much, to take pity on poor *perfect* papa and come back to him. She was more good-natured than you might have expected—indeed she laughed extravagantly. She had never believed me —it was too absurd; she had only, at the time, disliked me. She found me utterly false—she was very frank with me about this—and she told papa she really thought me horrid. She said she could never live with such a girl, and as I would certainly never marry I must be sent away—in short she quite loathed me. Papa defended me, he refused to sacrifice me, and this led practically to their rupture. Papa gave her up, as it were, for *me*. Fancy the angel, and fancy what I must try to be to him

for the rest of his life! Mrs. Churchley can never come
back—she's going to marry Lord Dovedale."

1891

∗

GREVILLE FANE

Coming in to dress for dinner I found a telegram: "Mrs.
Stormer dying; can you give us half a column for to-
morrow evening? Let her down easily, but not too easily." I was late; I was in a hurry; I had very little time
to think; but at a venture I despatched a reply: "Will
do what I can." It was not till I had dressed and was
rolling away to dinner that, in the hansom, I bethought
myself of the difficulty of the condition attached. The
difficulty was not of course in letting her down easily
but in qualifying that indulgence. "So I simply won't
qualify it," I said. I didn't admire but liked her, and had
known her so long that I almost felt heartless in sitting
down at such an hour to a feast of indifference. I must
have seemed abstracted, for the early years of my acquaintance with her came back to me. I spoke of her
to the lady I had taken down, but the lady I had taken
down had never heard of Greville Fane. I tried my other
neighbour, who pronounced her books "too vile." I had
never thought them very good, but I should let her
down more easily than that.

I came away early, for the express purpose of driving
to ask about her. The journey took time, for she lived
in the northwest district, in the neighbourhood of Primrose Hill. My apprehension that I should be too late was
justified in a fuller sense than I had attached to it—I

had only feared that the house would be shut up. There were lights in the windows, and the temperate tinkle of my bell brought a servant immediately to the door; but poor Mrs. Stormer had passed into a state in which the resonance of no earthly knocker was to be feared. A lady hovering behind the servant came forward into the hall when she heard my voice. I recognised Lady Luard, but she had mistaken me for the doctor.

"Pardon my appearing at such an hour," I said; "it was the first possible moment after I heard."

"It's all over," Lady Luard replied. "Dearest mamma!"

She stood there under the lamp with her eyes on me; she was very tall, very stiff, very cold, and always looked as if these things, and some others beside, in her dress, in her manner and even in her name, were an implication that she was very admirable. I had never been able to follow the argument, but that's a detail. I expressed briefly and frankly what I felt, while the little mottled maidservant flattened herself against the wall of the narrow passage and tried to look detached without looking indifferent. It was not a moment to make a visit, and I was on the point of retreating when Lady Luard arrested me with a queer casual drawling "Would you —a—would you perhaps be *writing* something?" I felt for the instant like an infamous interviewer, which I wasn't. But I pleaded guilty to this intention, on which she returned: "I'm so very glad—but I think my brother would like to see you." I detested her brother, but it wasn't an occasion to act this out; so I suffered myself to be inducted, to my surprise, into a small back room which I immediately recognised as the scene, during the later years, of Mrs. Stormer's imperturbable industry. Her table was there, the battered and blotted accessory to innumerable literary lapses, with its contracted space for the arms (she wrote only from the elbow down) and the confusion of scrappy scribbled sheets which had already become literary remains. Leolin was also there, smoking a cigarette before the fire and looking impudent even in his grief, sincere as it well might have been.

To meet him, to greet him, I had to make a sharp effort; for the air he wore to me as he stood before me was quite that of his mother's murderer. She lay silent for ever upstairs—as dead as an unsuccessful book, and his swaggering erectness was a kind of symbol of his having killed her. I wondered if he had already, with his sister, been calculating what they could get for the poor papers on the table; but I hadn't long to wait to learn, since in reply to the few words of sympathy I addressed him he puffed out: "It's miserable, miserable, yes; but she has left three books complete." His words had the oddest effect; they converted the cramped little room into a seat of trade and made the "book" wonderfully feasible. He would certainly get all that could be got for the three. Lady Luard explained to me that her husband had been with them, but had had to go down to the House. To her brother she mentioned that I was going to write something, and to me again made it clear that she hoped I would "do mamma justice." She added that she didn't think this had ever been done. She said to her brother: "Don't you think there are some things he ought thoroughly to understand?" and on his instantly exclaiming "Oh thoroughly, thoroughly!" went on rather austerely: "I mean about mamma's birth."

"Yes and her connexions," Leolin added.

I professed every willingness, and for five minutes I listened; but it would be too much to say I clearly understood. I don't even now, but it's not important. My vision was of other matters than those they put before me, and while they desired there should be no mistake about their ancestors I became keener and keener about themselves. I got away as soon as possible and walked home through the great dusky empty London—the best of all conditions for thought. By the time I reached my door my little article was practically composed—ready to be transferred on the morrow from the polished plate of fancy. I believe it attracted some notice, was thought "graceful" and was said to be by some one else. I had to be pointed without being lively, and it took some doing. But what I said was much less interesting than what I thought—especially during the half-hour I spent in my armchair by the fire, smoking the cigar I always light before going to bed. I went to sleep there, I believe; but I continued to moralise about Greville Fane. I'm reluctant to lose that retrospect altogether, and this is a dim little memory of it, a document not to "serve." The dear woman had written a hundred stories, but none so curious as her own.

When first I knew her she had published half a dozen fictions, and I believe I had also perpetrated a novel. She was more than a dozen years my elder, but a person who always acknowledged her comparative state. It wasn't so very long ago, but in London, amid the big waves of the present, even a near horizon gets hidden. I met her at some dinner and took her down, rather flattered at offering my arm to a celebrity. She didn't look like one, with her matronly mild inanimate face, but I supposed her greatness would come out in her conversation. I gave it all the opportunities I could, but was nevertheless not disappointed when I found her only a dull kind woman. This was why I liked her—she rested me so from literature. To myself literature was an irritation, a torment; but Greville Fane slumbered in the intellectual part of it even as a cat on a hearthrug or a Creole in a hammock. She wasn't a woman of genius, but her faculty was so special, so much a gift out of hand, that

I've often wondered why she fell below that distinction. This was doubtless because the transaction, in her case, had remained incomplete; genius always pays for the gift, feels the debt, and she was placidly unconscious of a call. She could invent stories by the yard, but couldn't write a page of English. She went down to her grave without suspecting that though she had contributed volumes to the diversion of her contemporaries she hadn't contributed a sentence to the language. This hadn't prevented bushels of criticism from being heaped on her head; she was worth a couple of columns any day to the weekly papers, in which it was shown that her pictures of life were dreadful but her style superior. She asked me to come and see her and I complied. She lived then in Montpellier Square; which helped me to see how dissociated her imagination was from her character.

An industrious widow, devoted to her daily stint, to meeting the butcher and baker and making a home for her son and daughter, from the moment she took her pen in her hand she became a creature of passion. She thought the English novel deplorably wanting in that element, and the task she had cut out for herself was to supply the deficiency. Passion in high life was the general formula of this work, for her imagination was at home only in the most exalted circles. She adored in truth the aristocracy, and they constituted for her the romance of the world or what is more to the point, the prime material of fiction. Their beauty and luxury, their loves and revenges, their temptations and surrenders, their immoralities and diamonds were as familiar to her as the blots on her writing-table. She was not a belated producer of the old fashionable novel, but, with a cleverness and a modernness of her own, had freshened up the fly-blown tinsel. She turned off plots by the hundred and—so far as her flying quill could convey her—was perpetually going abroad. Her types, her illustrations, her tone were nothing if not cosmopolitan. She recognised nothing less provincial than European society, and her fine folk knew each other and made love to each other from Doncaster to Bucharest. She had an idea that she resembled Balzac, and her favourite historical characters were Lucien de Rubempré and the Vidame de Pamiers. I must add that when I once asked her who the latter personage was she was unable to tell me. She was very brave and healthy and cheerful, very abundant and innocent and wicked. She was expert and vulgar and snobbish, and never so intensely British as when she was particularly foreign.

This combination of qualities had brought her early success, and I remember having heard with wonder and envy of what she "got," in those days, for a novel. The revelation gave me a pang: it was such a proof that, practising a totally different style, I should never make my fortune. And yet when, as I knew her better she told me her real tariff and I saw how rumour had quadrupled it, I liked her enough to be sorry. After a while I discovered too that if she got less it was not that *I* was to get any more. My failure never had what Mrs. Stormer would have called the banality of being relative—it was always admirably absolute. She lived at ease however in those days—ease is exactly the word, though she produced three novels a year. She scorned me when I spoke of difficulty—it was the only thing that made her angry. If I hinted at the grand licking into shape that a work of art required she thought it a pretension and a *pose*. She never recognised the "torment of form"; the furthest she went was to introduce into one of her books (in satire her hand was heavy) a young poet who was always talking about it. I couldn't quite understand her irritation on this score, for she had nothing at stake in the matter. She had a shrewd perception that form, in prose at least, never recommended any one to the public we were condemned to address; according to which she lost nothing (her private humiliation not counted) by having none to show. She made no pretence of producing works of art, but had comfortable tea-drinking hours in which she freely confessed herself a common pastrycook, dealing in such tarts and puddings as would bring customers to the shop. She put in plenty of sugar and of cochineal, or whatever it is that gives these articles a rich and attractive colour. She had a calm independence of observation and opportunity which constituted an inexpugnable strength and would enable her to go on indefinitely. It's only real success that wanes, it's only solid things that melt. Greville Fane's ignorance of life was a resource still more unfailing than the most approved receipt. On her saying once that the day would come when she should have written herself out I answered: "Ah you open straight into fairyland, and the fairies love you and *they* never change. Fairyland's always there; it always was from the beginning of time and always will be to the end. They've given you the key and you can always open the door. With me it's different; I try, in my clumsy way, to be in some direct relation to life." "Oh bother your direct relation to life!" she used to reply, for she was always annoyed by the phrase—which wouldn't in the least prevent her using it as a note of elegance. With no more prejudices than an old sausage-mill, she would give forth again with patient punctuality any poor verbal scrap that had been dropped into her. I cheered her with saying that the dark day, at the end, would be for the "likes" of *me;* since, proceeding in our small way by experience and study—priggish we!—we depended not on a revelation but on a little tiresome process. Attention depended on occasion, and where should we be when occasion failed?

One day she told me that as the novelist's life was so delightful and, during the good years at least, such a comfortable support—she had these staggering optimisms—she meant to train up her boy to follow it. She took the ingenious view that it was a profession like another and that therefore everything was to be gained by beginning young and serving an apprenticeship. Moreover the education would be less expensive than any other special course, inasmuch as she could herself administer it. She didn't profess to keep a school, but she could at least teach her own child. It wasn't that she had such a gift, but—she confessed to me as if she were afraid I should laugh at her—that *he* had. I didn't laugh at her for that, because I thought the boy sharp— I had seen him sundry times. He was well-grown and good-looking and unabashed, and both he and his sister made me wonder about their defunct papa, concerning whom the little I knew was that he had been a country vicar and brother to a small squire. I explained them to myself by suppositions and imputations possibly unjust to the departed; so little were they—superficially at least—the children of their mother. There used to be on an easel in her drawing-room an enlarged photograph of her husband, done by some horrible posthumous "process" and draped, as to its florid frame, with a silken scarf which testified to the candour of Greville Fane's bad taste. It made him look like an unsuccessful tragedian, but it wasn't a thing to trust. He may have been a successful comedian. Of the two children the girl was the elder, and struck me in all her younger years as singularly colourless. She was only long, very long, like an undecipherable letter. It wasn't till Mrs. Stormer

came back from a protracted residence abroad that Ethel
(which was this young lady's name) began to produce
the effect, large and stiff and afterwards eminent in her,
of a certain kind of resolution, something as public and
important as if a meeting and a chairman had passed it.
She gave one to understand she meant to do all she
could for herself. She was long-necked and near-sighted
and striking, and I thought I had never seen sweet
seventeen in a form so hard and high and dry. She was
cold and affected and ambitious, and she carried an eye-
glass with a long handle, which she put up whenever
she wanted not to see. She had come out, as the phrase
is, immensely; and yet I felt as if she were surrounded
with a spiked iron railing. What she meant to do for
herself was to marry, and it was the only thing, I think,
that she meant to do for any one else; yet who would
be inspired to clamber over that bristling barrier? What
flower of tenderness or of intimacy would such an adventurer conceive as his reward?

This was for Sir Baldwin Luard to say; but he naturally never confided me the secret. He was a joyless
jokeless young man, with the air of having other secrets
as well, and a determination to get on politically that
was indicated by his never having been known to commit himself—as regards any proposition whatever—
beyond an unchallengeable "Oh!" His wife and he must
have conversed mainly in prim ejaculations, but they
understood sufficiently that they were kindred spirits.
I remember being angry with Greville Fane when she
announced these nuptials to me as magnificent; I remember asking her what splendour there was in the
union of the daughter of a woman of genius with an
irredeemable mediocrity. "Oh he has immense ability,
she said; but she blushed for the maternal fib. What she
meant was that though Sir Baldwin's estates were not

vast—he had a dreary house in South Kensington and a still drearier "Hall' somewhere in Essex, which was let—the connexion was a "smarter" one than a child of hers could have aspired to form. In spite of the social bravery of her novels she took a very humble and dingy view of herself, so that of all her productions "my daughter Lady Luard" was quite the one she was proudest of. That personage thought our authoress vulgar and was distressed and perplexed by the frequent freedoms of her pen, but had a complicated attitude for this indirect connexion with literature. So far as it was lucrative her ladyship approved of it and could compound with the inferiority of the pursuit by practical justice to some of its advantages. I had reason to know—my reason was simply that poor Mrs. Stormer told me—how she suffered the inky fingers to press an occasional banknote into her palm. On the other hand she deplored the "peculiar style" to which Greville Fane had devoted herself, and wondered where a spectator with the advantage of so ladylike a daughter could have picked up such views about the best society. "She might know better, with Leolin and me," Lady Luard had been heard to remark; but it appeared that some of Greville Fane's superstitions were incurable. She didn't live in Lady Luard's society, and the best wasn't good enough for her—she must improve on it so prodigiously.

I could see this necessity increase in her during the years she spent abroad, when I had glimpses of her in the shifting sojourns that lay in the path of my annual ramble. She betook herself from Germany to Switzerland and from Switzerland to Italy; she favoured cheap places and set up her desk in the smaller capitals. I took a look at her whenever I could, and I always asked how Leolin was getting on. She gave me beautiful accounts of him, and, occasion favouring, the boy was produced for my advantage. I had entered from the first into the joke of his career—I pretended to regard him as a consecrated child. It had been a joke for Mrs. Stormer at first, but the youth himself had been shrewd enough to make the matter serious. If his parent accepted the principle that the intending novelist can't begin too early to see life, Leolin wasn't interested in hanging back from the application of it. He was eager to qualify himself and took to cigarettes at ten on the highest literary grounds. His fond mother gazed at him with extravagant envy and, like Desdemona, wished heaven had made *her* such a man. She explained to me more than once that in her profession she had found her sex a dreadful drawback. She loved the story of Madame George Sand's early rebellion against this hindrance, and believed that if she had worn trousers she could have written as well as that lady. Leolin had for the career at least the qualification of trousers, and as he grew older he recognised its importance by laying in ever so many pair. He grew up thus in gorgeous apparel, which was his way of interpreting his mother's system. Whenever I met her, accordingly, I found her still under the impression that she was carrying this system out and that the sacrifices made him were bearing heavy fruit. She was giving him experience, she was giving him impressions, she was putting a *gagne-pain* into his hand. It was another name for spoiling him with the best conscience in the world. The queerest pictures come back to me of this period of the good lady's life and of the extraordinarily virtuous muddled bewildering tenor of it. She had an idea she was seeing foreign manners as well as her petticoats would allow; but in reality she wasn't seeing anything, least of all, fortunately, how much she was laughed at. She drove her whimsical pen at Dresden and at Florence—she produced in all places and at all times the

same romantic and ridiculous fictions. She carried about
her box of properties, tumbling out promptly the familiar tarnished old puppets. She believed in them when
others couldn't, and as they were like nothing that was
to be seen under the sun it was impossible to prove by
comparison that they were wrong. You can't compare
birds and fishes; you could only feel that, as Greville
Fane's characters had the fine plumage of the former
species, human beings must be of the latter.

It would have been droll if it hadn't been so exem-
plary to see her tracing the loves of the duchesses beside the innocent cribs of her children. The immoral and
the maternal lived together, in her diligent days, on the
most comfortable terms, and she stopped curling the
moustaches of her Guardsmen to pat the heads of her
babes. She was haunted by solemn spinsters who came
to tea from Continental pensions, and by unsophisticated
Americans who told her she was just loved in *their* country. "I had rather be just paid there," she usually replied; for this tribute of transatlantic opinion was the
only thing that galled her. The Americans went away
thinking her coarse; though as the author of so many
beautiful love-stories she was disappointing to most of
these pilgrims, who hadn't expected to find a shy stout
ruddy lady in a cap like a crumbled pyramid. She wrote
about the affections and the impossibility of controlling
them, but she talked of the price of pension and the
convenience of an English chemist. She devoted much
thought and many thousands of francs to the education
of her daughter, who spent three years at a very superior school at Dresden, receiving wonderful instruction in sciences, arts and tongues, and who, taking a
different line from Leolin, was to be brought up wholly
as a *femme du monde*. The girl was musical and philo-
logical; she went in for several languages and learned

enough about them to be inspired with a great contempt for her mother's artless accents. Greville Fane's French and Italian were droll; the imitative faculty had been denied her, and she had an unequalled gift, especially pen in hand, of squeezing big mistakes into small opportunities. She knew it but didn't care; correctness was the virtue in the world that, like her heroes and heroines, she valued least. Ethel, who had noted in her pages some remarkable lapses, undertook at one time to revise her proofs; but I remember her telling me a year after the girl had left school that this function had been very briefly exercised. "She can't read me," said Mrs. Stormer; "I offend her taste. She tells me that at Dresden—at school—I was never allowed." The good lady seemed surprised at this, having the best conscience in the world about her lucubrations. She had never meant to fly in the face of anything, and considered that she grovelled before the Rhadamanthus of the English literary tribunal, the celebrated and awful Young Person. I assured her, as a joke, that she was frightfully indecent—she had in fact that element of truth as little as any other—my purpose being solely to prevent her guessing that her daughter had dropped her not because she was immoral but because she was vulgar. I used to figure her children closeted together and putting it to each other with a gaze of dismay: "Why should she *be* so—and so *fearfully* so—when she has the advantage of our society? Shouldn't *we* have taught her better?" Then I imagined their recognising with a blush and a shrug that she was unteachable, irreformable. Indeed she was, poor lady, but it's never fair to read by the light of taste things essentially not written in it. Greville Fane kept through all her riot of absurdity a witless confidence that should have been as safe from criticism as a stutter or a squint.

She didn't make her son ashamed of the profession to which he was destined, however; she only made him ashamed of the way she herself exercised it. But he bore his humiliation much better than his sister, being ready to assume he should one day restore the balance. A canny and far-seeing youth, with appetites and aspirations, he hadn't a scruple in his composition. His mother's theory of the happy knack he could pick up deprived him of the wholesome discipline required to prevent young idlers from becoming cads. He enjoyed on foreign soil a casual tutor and the common snatch or two of a Swiss school, but addressed himself to no consecutive study nor to any prospect of a university or a degree. It may be imagined with what zeal, as the years went on, he entered into the pleasantry of there being no manual so important to him as the massive book of life. It was an expensive volume to peruse, but Mrs. Stormer was willing to lay out a sum in what she would have called her *premiers frais*. Ethel disapproved—she found this education irregular for an English gentleman. Her voice was for Eton and Oxford or for any public school—she would have resigned herself to one of the scrubbier—with the army to follow. But Leolin never was afraid of his sister, and they visibly disliked, though they sometimes agreed to assist, each other. They could combine to work the oracle—to keep their mother at her desk.

When she reappeared in England, telling me she had "secured" all the Continent could give her, Leolin was a broad-shouldered red-faced young man with an immense wardrobe and an extraordinary assurance of manner. She was fondly, quite aggressively certain she had taken the right course with him, and addicted to boasting of all he knew and had seen. He was now quite ready to embark on the family profession, to commence author, as they used to say, and a little while later she told me he had started. He had written something tremendously clever which was coming out in the *Cheapside*. I believe it came out; I had no time to look for it; I never heard anything about it. I took for granted that if this contribution had passed through his mother's hands it would virtually rather illustrate *her* fine facility, and it was interesting to consider the poor lady's future in the light of her having to write her son's novels as well as her own. This wasn't the way she looked at it herself—she took the charming ground that he'd help her to write hers. She used to assure me he supplied passages of the greatest value to these last—all sorts of telling technical things, happy touches about hunting and yachting and cigars and wine, about City slang and the way men talk at clubs—that she couldn't be expected to get very straight. It was all so much practice for him and so much alleviation for herself. I was unable to identify such pages, for I had long since ceased to "keep up" with Greville Fane; but I could quite believe at least that the wine-question had been put by Leolin's good offices on a better footing, for the dear woman used to mix her drinks—she was perpetually serving the most splendid suppers—in the queerest fashion. I could see him quite ripe to embrace regularly that care. It occurred to me indeed, when she settled in England again, that she might by a shrewd use of both her children be able to rejuvenate her style. Ethel had come back to wreak her native, her social yearning, and if she couldn't take her mother into company would at least go into it herself. Silently, stiffly, almost grimly, this young lady reared her head, clenched her long teeth, squared her lean elbows and found her way up the staircases she had marked. The only communication she ever made, the only effusion of confidence with which she ever honoured me, was when she said "I don't want to know the people mamma knows, I mean to know others." I took due note of the remark, for I wasn't one of the "others." I couldn't trace therefore the steps and stages of her climb; I could only admire it at a distance and congratulate her mother in due course on the results. The results, the gradual, the final, the wonderful, were that Ethel went to "big" parties and got people to take her. Some of them were people she had met abroad, and others people the people she had met abroad had met. They ministered alike to Miss Ethel's convenience, and I wondered how she extracted so many favours without the expenditure of a smile. Her smile was the dimmest thing in nature, diluted, unsweetened, inexpensive lemonade, and she had arrived precociously at social wisdom, recognising that if she was neither pretty enough nor rich enough nor clever enough, she could at least, in her muscular youth, be rude enough. Therefore, so placed to give her parent tips, to let her know what really occurred in the mansions of the great, to supply her with local colour, with *data* to work from, she promoted the driving of the well-worn quill, over the brave old battered blotting book, to a still lustier measure and precisely at the moment when most was to depend on this labour. But if she became a great critic it appeared that the labourer herself was constitutionally inapt for the lesson. It was late in the day for Greville Fane to learn, and I heard nothing of her having developed a new manner. She was to have had only one manner, as Leolin would have said, from start to finish.

She was weary and spent at last, but confided to me that she couldn't afford to pause. She continued to speak of her son's work as the great hope of their future—she had saved no money—though the young man wore to my sense an air more and more professional if you like,

but less and less literary. There was at the end of a couple of years something rare in the impudence of his playing of his part in the comedy. When I wondered how
she could play hers it was to feel afresh the fatuity of
her fondness, which was proof, I believed—I indeed
saw to the end—against any interference of reason.
She loved the young impostor with a simple blind benighted love, and of all the heroes of romance who had
passed before her eyes he was by far the brightest. He
was at any rate the most real—she could touch him, pay
for him, suffer for him, worship him. He made her
think of her princes and dukes, and when she wished to
fix these figures in her mind's eye she thought of her
boy. She had often told me she was herself carried away
by her creations, and she was certainly carried away by
Leolin. He vivified—by what romantically might have
been at least—the whole question of youth and passion. She held, not unjustly, that the sincere novelist
should feel the whole flood of life; she acknowledged
with regret that she hadn't had time to feel it herself,
and the lapse in her history was in a manner made up
by the sight of its rush through this magnificent young
man. She exhorted him, I suppose, to encourage the
rush; she wrung her own flaccid little sponge into the
torrent. What passed between them in her pedagogic
hours was naturally a blank to me, but I gathered that
she mainly impressed on him that the great thing was to
live, because that gave you material. He asked nothing
better; he collected material, and the recipe served as a
universal pretext. You had only to look at him to see
that, with his rings and breastpins, his crossbarred jackets, his early *embonpoint*, his eyes that looked like
imitation jewels, his various indications of a dense full-
blown temperament, his idea of life was singularly vulgar; but he was so far auspicious as that his response to

his mother's expectations was in a high degree practical.
If she had imposed a profession on him from his tenderest years it was exactly a profession that he followed.
The two were not quite the same, inasmuch as the one
he had adopted was simply to live at her expense; but at
least she couldn't say he hadn't taken a line. If she insisted on believing in him he offered himself to the sacrifice. My impression is that her secret dream was that
he should have a *liaison* with a countess, and he persuaded her without difficulty that he had one. I don't
know what countesses are capable of, but I've a clear
notion of what Leolin was.

He didn't persuade his sister, who despised him—she
wished to work her mother in her own way; so that I
asked myself why the girl's judgment of him didn't
make me like her better. It was because it didn't save her
after all from the mute agreement with him to go halves.
There were moments when I couldn't help looking hard
into his atrocious young eyes, challenging him to confess
his fantastic fraud and give it up. Not a little tacit conversation passed between us in this way, but he had
always the best of the business. If I said: "Oh come
now, with *me* you needn't keep it up; plead guilty and
I'll let you off," he wore the most ingenuous, the most
candid expression, in the depths of which I could read:
"Ah yes, I know it exasperates you—that's just why I
do it." He took the line of earnest enquiry, talked about
Balzac and Flaubert, asked me if I thought Dickens
did exaggerate and Thackeray *ought* to be called a
pessimist. Once he came to see me, at his mother's suggestion he declared, on purpose to ask me how far, in
my opinion, in the English novel, one really might venture to "go." He wasn't resigned to the usual pruderies,
the worship of childish twaddle; he suffered already
from too much bread and butter. He struck out the bril-

liant idea that nobody knew how far we might go, since nobody had ever tried. Did I think *he* might safely try—would it injure his mother if he did? He would rather disgrace himself by his timidities than injure his mother, but certainly some one ought to try. Wouldn't *I* try—couldn't I be prevailed upon to look at it as a duty? Surely the ultimate point ought to be fixed—he was worried, haunted by the question. He patronised me unblushingly, made me feel a foolish amateur, a helpless novice, inquired into my habits of work and conveyed to me that I was utterly *vieux jeu* and hadn't had the advantage of an early training. I hadn't been brought up from the egg, I knew nothing of life—didn't go at it on *his* system. He had dipped into French feuilletons and picked up plenty of phrases, and he made a much better show in talk than his poor mother, who never had time to read anything and could only be showy with her pen. If I didn't kick him downstairs it was because he would have landed on her at the bottom.

When she went to live at Primrose Hill I called there and found her wasted and wan. It had visibly dropped, the elation caused the year before by Ethel's marriage; the foam on the cup had subsided and there was bitterness in the draught. She had had to take a cheaper house—and now had to work still harder to pay even for that. Sir Baldwin was obliged to be close; his charges were fearful, and the dream of her living with her daughter—a vision she had never mentioned to me—must be renounced. "I'd have helped them with things, and could have lived perfectly in one room," she said; "I'd have paid for everything, and—after all—I'm some one, ain't I? But I don't fit in, and Ethel tells me there are tiresome people she *must* receive. I can help them from here, no doubt, better than from there. She told me once, you know, what she thinks of my picture of life. 'Mamma, your picture of life's preposterous!' No doubt it is, but she's vexed with me for letting my prices go down; and I had to write three novels to pay for all her marriage cost me. I did it very well—I mean the outfit and the wedding; but that's why I'm here. At any rate she doesn't want a dingy old woman at Blicket. I should give the place an atmosphere of literary prestige, but literary prestige is only the eminence of nobodies. Besides, she knows what to think of my glory— she knows I'm glorious only at Peckham and Hackney. She doesn't want her friends to ask if I've never known nice people. She can't tell them I've never been in society. She tried to teach me better once, but I couldn't catch on. It would seem too as if Peckham and Hackney had had enough of me; for (don't tell any one) I've had to take less for my last than I ever took for anything." I asked her how little this had been, not from curiosity, but in order to upbraid her, more disinterestedly than Lady Luard had done, for such concessions. She answered "I'm ashamed to tell you" and then began to cry.

I had never seen her break down and I was proportionately moved; she sobbed like a frightened child over the extinction of her vogue and the exhaustion of her vein. Her little workroom seemed indeed a barren place to grow flowers for the market, and I wondered in the after years (for she continued to produce and publish) by what desperate and heroic process she dragged them out of the soil. I remember asking her on that occasion what had become of Leolin and how much longer she intended to allow him to amuse himself at her cost. She retorted with spirit, wiping her eyes, that he was down at Brighton hard at work—he was in the midst of a novel—and that he *felt* life so, in all its misery and mystery, that it was cruel to speak of such experiences as a pleasure. "He goes beneath the surface," she said, "and he *forces* himself to look at things from which he'd rather turn away. Do you call that amusing yourself? You should see his face sometimes! And he does it for me as much as for himself. He tells me everything— he comes home to me with his *trouvailles*. We're artists together, and to the artist all things are pure. I've often heard you say so yourself." The novel Leolin was engaged in at Brighton never saw the light, but a friend of mine and of Mrs. Stormer's who was staying there happened to mention to me later that he had seen the young apprentice to fiction driving, in a dog-cart, a young lady with a very pink face. When I suggested that she was perhaps a woman of title with whom he was conscientiously flirting my informant replied: "She is indeed, but do you know what her title is?" He pronounced it—it was familiar and descriptive—but I won't reproduce it here. I don't know whether Leolin mentioned it to his mother: she would have needed all the purity of the artist to forgive him. I hated so to come across him that in the very last years I went rarely to see her, though I knew she had come pretty well to the end of her rope. I didn't want her to tell me she had fairly to give her books away; I didn't want to see her old and abandoned and derided; I didn't want, in a word, to see her terribly cry. She still, however, kept it up amazingly, and every few months, at my club, I saw three new volumes, in green, in crimson, in blue, on the booktable that groaned with light literature. Once I met her at the Academy soirée, where you meet people you thought were dead, and she vouchsafed the information, as if she owed it to me in candour, that Leolin had been obliged to recognise the insuperable difficulties of the question of *form*—he was so fastidious; but that she had now arrived at a definite understanding with him (it was such a comfort!)

that *she* would do the form if he would bring home the substance. That was now his employ—he foraged for her in the great world at a salary. "He's my 'devil,' don't you see? as if I were a great lawyer: he gets up the case and I argue it." She mentioned further that in addition to his salary he was paid by the piece: he got so much for a striking character, so much for a pretty name, so much for a plot, so much for an incident, and had so much promised him if he would invent a new crime.

"He *has* invented one," I said, "and he's paid every day of his life."

"What is it?" she asked, looking hard at the picture of the year, "Baby's Tub," near which we happened to be standing.

I hesitated a moment. "I myself will write a little story about it, and then you'll see."

But she never saw; she had never seen anything, and she passed away with her fine blindness unimpaired. Her son published every scrap of scribbled paper that could be extracted from her table-drawers, and his sister quarrelled with him mortally about the proceeds, which showed her only to have wanted a pretext, for they can't have been great. I don't know what Leolin lives on unless on a queer lady many years older than himself, whom he lately married. The last time I met him he said to me with his infuriating smile: "Don't you think we can go a little further still—just a little?" *He* really—with me at least—goes too far.

1892

*

THE REAL THING

I

When the porter's wife, who used to answer the house-bell, announced "A gentleman and a lady, sir," I had, as I often had in those days—the wish being father to the thought—an immediate vision of sitters. Sitters my visitors in this case proved to be; but not in the sense I should have preferred. There was nothing at first however to indicate that they mightn't have come for a portrait. The gentleman, a man of fifty, very high and very straight, with a moustache slightly grizzled and a dark grey walking-coat admirably fitted, both of which I noted professionally—I don't mean as a barber or yet as a tailor—would have struck me as a celebrity if celebrities often were striking. It was a truth of which I had for some time been conscious that a figure with a good deal of frontage was, as one might say, almost never a public institution. A glance at the lady helped to remind me of this paradoxical law: she also looked too distinguished to be a "personality." Moreover one would scarcely come across two variations together.

Neither of the pair immediately spoke—they only prolonged the preliminary gaze suggesting that each wished to give the other a chance. They were visibly shy; they stood there letting me take them in—which, as I afterwards perceived, was the most practical thing they could have done. In this way their embarrassment served their cause. I had seen people painfully reluctant to mention that they desired anything so gross as to be represented on canvas; but the scruples of my new friends appeared almost insurmountable. Yet the gentleman might have said "I should like a portrait of my wife, and the lady might have said "I should like a portrait of my husband." Perhaps they weren't husband and wife—this naturally would make the matter more delicate. Perhaps they wished to be done together— in which case they ought to have brought a third person to break the news.

"We come from Mr. Rivet," the lady finally said with a dim smile that had the effect of a moist sponge passed over a "sunk" piece of painting, as well as of a vague allusion to vanished beauty. She was as tall and straight, in her degree, as her companion, and with ten years less to carry. She looked as sad as a woman could look whose face was not charged with expression; that is her tinted oval mask showed waste as an exposed surface shows friction. The hand of time had played over her freely, but to an effect of elimination. She was slim and stiff, and so well-dressed, in dark blue cloth, with lappets and pockets and buttons, that it was clear she employed the same tailor as her husband. The couple had an indefinable air of prosperous thrift —they evidently got a good deal of luxury for their money. If I was to be one of their luxuries it would behoove me to consider my terms.

"Ah Claude Rivet recommended me?" I echoed; and I added that it was very kind of him, though I could reflect that, as he only painted landscape, this wasn't a sacrifice.

The lady looked very hard at the gentleman, and the gentleman looked round the room. Then staring at the floor a moment and stroking his moustache, he rested his pleasant eyes on me with the remark: "He said you were the right one."

"I try to be, when people want to sit."

"Yes, we should like to," said the lady anxiously.

"Do you mean together?"

My visitors exchanged a glance. "If you could do anything with *me* I suppose it would be double," the gentleman stammered.

"Oh yes, there's naturally a higher charge for two figures than for one."

"We should like to make it pay," the husband confessed.

"That's very good of you," I returned, appreciating so unwonted a sympathy—for I supposed he meant pay the artist.

A sense of strangeness seemed to dawn on the lady. "We mean for the illustrations—Mr. Rivet said you might put one in."

"Put in—an illustration?" I was equally confused.

"Sketch her off, you know," said the gentleman, colouring.

It was only then that I understood the service Claude Rivet had rendered me; he had told them how I worked in black-and-white, for magazines, for story-books, for sketches of contemporary life, and consequently had copious employment for models. These things were true, but it was not less true—I may confess it now; whether because the aspiration was to lead to everything or to nothing I leave the reader to guess—that I couldn't get the honours, to say nothing of the emoluments, of a great painter of portraits out of my head. My "illustrations" were my pot-boilers; I looked to a different branch of art—far and away the most interesting it had always seemed to me—to perpetuate my fame. There was no shame in looking to it also to make my fortune; but that fortune was by so much further from being made from the moment my visitors wished to be "done" for nothing. I was disappointed; for in the pictorial sense I had immediately *seen* them. I had seized their type—I had already settled what I would do with it. Something that wouldn't absolutely have pleased them, I afterwards reflected.

"Ah you're—you're—a?" I began as soon as I had mastered my surprise. I couldn't bring out the dingy word "models": it seemed so little to fit the case.

"We haven't had much practice," said the lady.

"We've got to *do* something, and we've thought that an artist in your line might perhaps make something of us," her husband threw off. He further mentioned that they didn't know many artists and that they had gone first, on the off-chance—he painted views of course, but sometimes put in figures; perhaps I remembered—to Mr. Rivet, whom they had met a few years before at a place in Norfolk where he was sketching.

"We used to sketch a little ourselves," the lady hinted.

"It's very awkward, but we absolutely *must* do something," her husband went on.

"Of course we're not so *very* young," she admitted with a wan smile.

With the remark that I might as well know something more about them the husband had handed me a card extracted from a neat new pocket-book—their appurtenances were all of the freshest—and inscribed with the words "Major Monarch." Impressive as these words were they didn't carry my knowledge much further; but my visitor presently added: "I've left the army and we've had the misfortune to lose our money. In fact our means are dreadfully small."

"It's awfully trying—a regular strain," said Mrs. Monarch.

They evidently wished to be discreet—to take care not to swagger because they were gentlefolk. I felt them willing to recognise this as something of a draw-back, at the same time that I guessed at an underlying sense—their consolation in adversity—that they *had* their points. They certainly had; but these advantages struck me as preponderantly social; such for instance as would help to make a drawing-room look well. How-ever, a drawing-room was always, or ought to be, a picture.

In consequence of his wife's allusion to their age Major Monarch observed: "Naturally it's more for the figure that we thought of going in. We can still hold ourselves up." On the instant I saw that the figure was indeed their strong point. His "naturally" didn't sound vain, but it lighted up the question. "*She* has the best one," he continued, nodding at his wife with a pleasant after-dinner absence of circumlocution. I could only reply, as if we were in fact sitting over our wine, that this didn't prevent his own from being very good; which led him in turn to make answer: "We thought that if you ever have to do people like us we might be something like it. *She* particularly—for a lady in a book, you know."

I was so amused by them that, to get more of it, I did my best to take their point of view; and though it was an embarrassment to find myself appraising physically, as if they were animals on hire or useful blacks, a pair whom I should have expected to meet only in one of the relations in which criticism is tacit, I looked at Mrs. Monarch judicially enough to be able to exclaim after a moment with conviction: "Oh yes, a lady in a book!" She was singularly like a bad illustration.

"We'll stand up, if you like," said the Major; and he raised himself before me with a really grand air.

I could take his measure at a glance—he was six feet two and a perfect gentleman. It would have paid any club in process of formation and in want of a stamp to engage him at a salary to stand in the principal window. What struck me at once was that in coming to me they had rather missed their vocation; they could surely have been turned to better account for advertising purposes. I couldn't of course see the thing in detail, but I could see them make somebody's fortune—I don't mean their own. There was something in them for a waistcoat-maker, an hotel-keeper or a soap-vendor. I could imagine "We always use it" pinned on their bosoms with the greatest effect; I had a vision of the brilliancy with which they would launch a table d'hôte.

Mrs. Monarch sat still, not from pride but from shyness, and presently her husband said to her: "Get up, my dear, and show how smart you are." She obeyed, but she had no need to get up to show it. She walked to the end of the studio and then came back blushing, her fluttered eyes on the partner of her appeal. I was reminded of an incident I had accidentally had a glimpse of in Paris—being with a friend there, a dramatist about to produce a play, when an actress came to him to ask to be entrusted with a part. She went through her paces before him, walked up and down as Mrs. Monarch was doing. Mrs. Monarch did it quite as well, but I abstained from applauding. It was very odd to see such people apply for such poor pay. She looked as if she had ten thousand a year. Her husband had used the word that described her: she was in the London current jargon essentially and typically "smart." Her figure was, in the same order of ideas, conspicuously and irreproachably "good." For a woman of her age her waist was surprisingly small; her elbow moreover had the orthodox crook. She held her head at the conventional angle, but why did she come to *me*? She ought to have tried on jackets at a big shop. I feared my visitors were not only destitute but "artistic"—which would be a great complication. When she sat down again I thanked her, observing that what a draughtsman most valued in his model was the faculty of keeping quiet.

"Oh *she* can keep quiet," said Major Monarch. Then he added jocosely: "I've always kept her quiet."

"I'm not a nasty fidget, am I?" It was going to wring tears from me, I felt, the way she hid her head, ostrichlike, in the other broad bosom.

The owner of this expanse addressed his answer to me. "Perhaps it isn't out of place to mention—because we ought to be quite business-like, oughtn't we?—that when I married her she was known as the Beautiful Statue."

"Oh dear!" said Mrs. Monarch ruefully.

"Of course I should want a certain amount of expression," I rejoined.

"Of *course!*"—and I had never heard such unanimity.

"And then I suppose you know that you'll get awfully tired."

"Oh we *never* get tired!" they eagerly cried.

"Have you had any kind of practice?"

They hesitated—they looked at each other. "We've been photographed—*immensely*," said Mrs. Monarch.

"She means the fellows have asked us themselves," added the Major.

"I see—because you're so good-looking."

"I don't know what they thought, but they were always after us."

"We always got our photographs for nothing," smiled Mrs. Monarch.

"We might have brought some, my dear," her husband remarked.

"I'm not sure we have any left. We've given quantities away," she explained to me.

"With our autographs and that sort of thing," said the Major.

"Are they to be got in the shops?" I enquired as a harmless pleasantry.

"Oh yes, *hers*—they used to be."

"Not now," said Mrs. Monarch with her eyes on the floor.

II

I could fancy the "sort of thing" they put on the presentation copies of their photographs, and I was sure they wrote a beautiful hand. It was odd how quickly I was sure of everything that concerned them. If they were now so poor as to have to earn shillings and pence they could never have had much of a margin. Their good looks had been their capital, and they had good-humouredly made the most of the career that this resource marked out for them. It was in their faces, the blankness, the deep intellectual repose of the twenty years of country-house visiting that had given them pleasant intonations. I could see the sunny drawing-rooms, sprinkled with periodicals she didn't read, in which Mrs. Monarch had continuously sat; I could see the wet shrubberies in which she had walked, equipped to admiration for either exercise. I could see the rich covers the Major had helped to shoot and the wonderful garments in which, late at night, he repaired to the smoking-room to talk about them. I could imagine their leggings and waterproofs, their knowing tweeds and rugs, their rolls of sticks and cases of tackle and neat umbrellas; and I could evoke the exact appearance of their servants and the compact variety of their luggage on the platforms of country stations.

They gave small tips, but they were liked; they didn't do anything themselves, but they were welcome. They looked so well everywhere; they gratified the general relish for stature, complexion and "form." They knew it without fatuity or vulgarity, and they respected themselves in consequence. They weren't superficial; they were thorough and kept themselves up—it had been their line. People with such a taste for activity had to have some line. I could feel how even in a dull house they could have been counted on for the joy of life. At present something had happened—it didn't matter what, their little income had grown less, it had grown least—and they had to do something for pocket-money. Their friends could like them, I made out, without liking to support them. There was something about them that represented credit—their clothes, their manners, their type; but if credit is a large empty pocket in which an occasional chink reverberates, the chink at least must be audible. What they wanted of me was to help to make it so. Fortunately they had no children—I soon divined that. They would also perhaps wish our relations to be kept secret: this was why it was "for the figure"—the reproduction of the face would betray them.

I liked them—I felt, quite as their friends must have done—they were so simple; and I had no objection to them if they would suit. But somehow with all their perfections I didn't easily believe in them. After all they were amateurs, and the ruling passion of my life was the detestation of the amateur. Combined with this was another perversity—an innate preference for the represented subject over the real one: the defect of the real one was so apt to be a lack of representation. I like things that appeared; then one was sure. Whether they *were* or not was a subordinate and almost always a profitless question. There were other considerations, the first of which was that I already had two or three recruits in use, notably a young person with big feet, in alpaca, from Kilburn, who for a couple of years had come to me regularly for my illustrations and with whom I was still—perhaps ignobly—satisfied. I frankly explained to my visitors how the case stood, but they had taken more precautions than I supposed. They had reasoned out their opportunity, for Claude Rivet had told them of the projected *édition de luxe* of one of the writers of our day—the rarest of the novelists—who, long neglected by the multitudinous vulgar and dearly prized by the attentive (need I mention Philip Vincent?) had had the happy fortune of seeing, late in life, the dawn and then the full light of a higher criticism; an estimate in which on the part of the public there was something really of expiation. The edition preparing, planned by a publisher of taste, was practically an act of high reparation; the wood-cuts with which it was to be enriched were the homage of English art to one of the most independent representatives of English letters. Major and Mrs. Monarch confessed to me they had hoped I might be able to work *them* into my branch of the enterprise. They knew I was to do the first of the books, "Rutland Ramsay," but I had to make clear to them that my participation in the rest of the affair—this first book was to be a test—must depend on the satisfaction I should give. If this should be limited my employers would drop me with scarce common forms. It was therefore a crisis for me, and naturally I was making special preparations, looking about for new people, should they be necessary, and securing the best types. I admitted however that I should like to settle down to two or three good models who would do for everything.

"Should we have often to—a—put on special clothes?" Mrs. Monarch timidly demanded.

"Dear yes—that's half the business."

"And should we be expected to supply our own costumes?"

"Oh no; I've got a lot of things. A painter's models put on—or put off—anything he likes."

"And you mean—a—the same?"

"The same?"

Mrs. Monarch looked at her husband again.

"Oh she was just wondering," he explained, "if the costumes are in *general* use." I had to confess that they were, and I mentioned further that some of them—I had a lot of genuine greasy last-century things—had served their time, a hundred years ago, on living world-stained men and women; on figures not perhaps so far removed, in that vanished world, from *their* type, the Monarchs', *quoi!* of a breeched and bewigged age. "We'll put on anything that *fits*," said the Major.

"Oh I arrange that—they fit in the pictures."

"I'm afraid I should do better for the modern books. I'd come as you like," said Mrs. Monarch.

"She has got a lot of clothes at home: they might do for contemporary life," her husband continued.

"Oh I can fancy scenes in which you'd be quite natural." And indeed I could see the slipshod rearrangements of stale properties—the stories I tried to produce pictures for without the exasperation of reading them—whose sandy tracts the good lady might help to people. But I had to return to the fact that for this sort of work —the daily mechanical grind—I was already equipped: the people I was working with were fully adequate.

"We only thought we might be more like *some* characters," said Mrs. Monarch mildly, getting up.

Her husband also rose; he stood looking at me with a dim wistfulness that was touching in so fine a man. "Wouldn't it be rather a pull sometimes to have—a—to have—?" He hung fire; he wanted me to help him by phrasing what he meant. But I couldn't—I didn't know. So he brought it out awkwardly: "The *real* thing; a gentleman, you know, or a lady." I was quite ready to give a general assent—I admitted that there was a great deal in that. This encouraged Major Monarch to say, following up his appeal with an unacted gulp: "It's awfully hard—we've tried everything." The gulp was communicative; it proved too much for his wife. Before I knew it Mrs. Monarch had dropped again upon a divan and burst into tears. Her husband sat down beside her, holding one of her hands; whereupon she quickly dried her eyes with the other, while I felt embarrassed as she looked up at me. "There isn't a confounded job I haven't applied for—waited for—prayed for. You can fancy we'd be pretty bad first. Secretaryships and that sort of thing? You might as well ask for a peerage. I'd be *anything*—I'm strong; a messenger or a coalheaver. I'd put on a gold-laced cap and open carriage-doors in front of the haberdasher's; I'd hang about a station to carry portmanteaux; I'd be a postman. But they won't *look* at you; there are thousands as good as yourself already on the ground. *Gentlemen,* poor beggars, who've drunk their wine, who've kept their hunters!"

I was as reassuring as I knew how to be, and my visitors were presently on their feet again while, for the experiment, we agreed on an hour. We were discussing it when the door opened and Miss Churm came in with a wet umbrella. Miss Churm had to take the omnibus to Maida Vale and then walk half a mile. She looked a trifle blowsy and slightly splashed. I scarcely ever saw her come in without thinking afresh how odd it was that, being so little in herself, she should yet be so much in others. She was a meagre little Miss Churm, but was such an ample heroine of romance. She was only a freckled cockney, but she could represent everything, from a fine lady to a shepherdess; she had the faculty as she might have had a fine voice or long hair. She couldn't spell and she loved beer, but she had two or three "points," and practice, and a knack, and mother-wit, and a whimsical sensibility, and a love of the theatre, and seven sisters, and not an ounce of respect, especially for the *h*. The first thing my visitors saw was that her umbrella was wet, and in their spotless perfection they visibly winced at it. The rain had come on since their arrival.

"I'm all in a soak; there *was* a mess of people in the 'bus. I wish you lived near a styttion," said Miss Churm. I requested her to get ready as quickly as possible, and she passed into the room in which she always changed her dress. But before going out she asked me what she was to get into this time.

"It's the Russian princess, don't you know?" I answered; "the one with the 'golden eyes,' in black velvet, for the long thing in the *Cheapside*."

"Golden eyes? I *say!*" cried Miss Churm, while my companions watched her with intensity as she withdrew. She always arranged herself, when she was late, before I could turn round; and I kept my visitors a little on purpose, so that they might get an idea, from seeing her, what would be expected of themselves. I mentioned that she was quite my notion of an excellent model—she was really very clever.

"Do you think she looks like a Russian princess?" Major Monarch asked with lurking alarm.

"When I make her, yes."

"Oh if you have to *make* her—!" he reasoned, not without point.

"That's the most you can ask. There are so many who are not makeable."

"Well now, *here's* a lady"—and with a persuasive smile he passed his arm into his wife's—"who's already made!"

"Oh I'm not a Russian princess," Mrs. Monarch protested a little coldly. I could see she had known some and didn't like them. There at once was a complication of a kind I never had to fear with Miss Churm.

This young lady came back in black velvet—the gown was rather rusty and very low on her lean shoulders— and with a Japanese fan in her red hands. I reminded her that in the scene I was doing she had to look over some one's head. "I forget whose it is; but it doesn't matter. Just look over a head."

"I'd rather look over a stove," said Miss Churm; and she took her station near the fire. She fell into position, settled herself into a tall attitude, gave a certain backward inclination to her head and a certain forward droop to her fan, and looked, at least to my prejudiced sense, distinguished and charming, foreign and dangerous. We left her looking so while I went downstairs with Major and Mrs. Monarch.

"I believe I could come about as near it as that," said Mrs. Monarch.

"Oh you think she's shabby, but you must allow for the alchemy of art."

However, they went off with an evident increase of comfort founded on their demonstrable advantage in being the real thing. I could fancy them shuddering over Miss Churm. She was very droll about them when I went back, for I told her what they wanted.

"Well, if *she* can sit I'll tyke to book-keeping," said my model.

"She's very ladylike," I replied as an innocent form of aggravation.

"So much the worse for *you*. That means she can't turn round."

"She'll do for the fashionable novels."

"Oh yes, she'll *do* for them!" my model humorously declared. "Ain't they bad enough without her?" I had often sociably denounced them to Miss Churm.

III

It was for the elucidation of a mystery in one of these works that I first tried Mrs. Monarch. Her husband came with her, to be useful if necessary—it was sufficiently clear that as a general thing he would prefer to come with her. At first I wondered if this were for "propriety's" sake—if he were going to be jealous and meddling. The idea was too tiresome, and if it had been confirmed it would speedily have brought our acquaintance to a close. But I soon saw there was nothing in it and that if he accompanied Mrs. Monarch it was—in addition to the chance of being wanted—simply because he had nothing else to do. When they were separate his occupation was gone and they never *had* been separate. I judged rightly that in their awkward situation their close union was their main comfort and that this union had no weak spot. It was a real marriage, an encouragement to the hesitating, a nut for pessimists to crack. Their address was humble—I remember afterwards thinking it had been the only thing about them that was really professional—and I could fancy the lamentable lodgings in which the Major would have been left alone. He could sit there more or less grimly with his wife—he couldn't sit there anyhow without her.

He had too much tact to try and make himself agreeable when he couldn't be useful; so when I was too
absorbed in my work to talk he simply sat and waited.
But I liked to hear him talk—it made my work, when
not interrupting it, less mechanical, less special. To
listen to him was to combine the excitement of going
out with the economy of staying at home. There was
only one hindrance—that I seemed not to know any of
the people this brilliant couple had known. I think he
wondered extremely, during the term of our intercourse,
whom the deuce I *did* know. He hadn't a stray sixpence
of an idea to fumble for, so we didn't spin it very fine;
we confined ourselves to questions of leather and even
of liquor—saddlers and breeches-makers and how to get
excellent claret cheap—and matters like "good trains"
and the habits of small game. His lore on these last subjects was astonishing—he managed to interweave the
station-master with the ornithologist. When he couldn't
talk about greater things he could talk cheerfully about
smaller, and since I couldn't accompany him into reminiscences of the fashionable world he could lower the
conversation without a visible effort to my level.

So earnest a desire to please was touching in a man
who could so easily have knocked one down. He looked
after the fire and had an opinion on the draught of the
stove without my asking him, and I could see that he
thought many of my arrangements not half knowing. I
remember telling him that if I were only rich I'd offer
him a salary to come and teach me how to live. Sometimes he gave a random sigh of which the essence might
have been: "Give me even such a bare old barrack as
this, and I'd do something with it!" When I wanted to
use him he came alone; which was an illustration of the
superior courage of women. His wife could bear her

solitary second floor, and she was in general more discreet; showing by various small reserves that she was
alive to the propriety of keeping our relations markedly
professional—not letting them slide into sociability. She
wished it to remain clear that she and the Major were
employed, not cultivated, and if she approved of me as
a superior, who could be kept in his place, she never
thought me quite good enough for an equal.

She sat with great intensity, giving the whole of her
mind to it, and was capable of remaining for an hour
almost as motionless as before a photographer's lens. I
could see she had been photographed often, but somehow the very habit that made her good for that purpose unfitted her for mine. At first I was extremely
pleased with her ladylike air, and it was a satisfaction,
on coming to follow her lines, to see how good they
were and how far they could lead the pencil. But after a
little skirmishing I began to find her too insurmountably
stiff; do what I would with it my drawing looked like a
photograph or a copy of a photograph. Her figure had
no variety of expression—she herself had no sense of
variety. You may say that this was my business and was
only a question of placing her. Yet I placed her in every
conceivable position and she managed to obliterate their
differences. She was always a lady certainly, and into
the bargain was always the same lady. She was the real
thing, but always the same thing. There were moments
when I rather writhed under the serenity of her confidence that she *was* the real thing. All her dealings with
me and all her husband's were an implication that this
was lucky for *me*. Meanwhile I found myself trying to
invent types that approached her own, instead of making her own transform itself—in the clever way that was
not impossible for instance to poor Miss Churm. Arrange

as I would and take the precautions I would, she always
came out, in my pictures, too tall—landing me in the
dilemma of having represented a fascinating woman as
seven feet high, which (out of respect perhaps to my
own very much scantier inches) was far from my idea
of such a personage.

The case was worse with the Major—nothing I could
do would keep *him* down, so that he became useful only
for the representation of brawny giants. I adored variety
and range, I cherished human accidents, the illustrative
note; I wanted to characterise closely, and the thing in
the world I most hated was the danger of being ridden
by a type. I had quarrelled with some of my friends
about it; I had parted company with them for maintain-
ing that one *had* to be, and that if the type was beautiful—witness Raphael and Leonardo—the servitude was
only a gain. I was neither Leonardo nor Raphael—I
might only be a presumptuous young modern searcher;
but I held that everything was to be sacrificed sooner
than character. When they claimed that the obsessional
form could easily *be* character I retorted, perhaps superficially, "Whose?" It couldn't be everybody's—it might
end in being nobody's.

After I had drawn Mrs. Monarch a dozen times I felt
surer even than before that the value of such a model as
Miss Churm resided precisely in the fact that she had no
positive stamp, combined of course with the other fact
that what she did have was a curious and inexplicable
talent for imitation. Her usual appearance was like a
curtain which she could draw up at request for a capital performance. This performance was simply suggestive; but it was a word to the wise—it was vivid
and pretty. Sometimes even I thought it, though she
was plain herself, too insipidly pretty; I made it a reproach to her that the figures drawn from her were

monotonously (*bêtement,* as we used to say) graceful.
Nothing made her more angry; it was so much her pride
to feel she could sit for characters that had nothing in
common with each other. She would accuse me at such
moments of taking away her "reputytion."

It suffered a certain shrinkage, this queer quantity,
from the repeated visits of my new friends. Miss Churm
was greatly in demand, never in want of employment,
so I had no scruple in putting her off occasionally, to
try them more at my ease. It was certainly amusing at
first to do the real thing—it was amusing to do Major
Monarch's trousers. They *were* the real thing, even if
he did come out colossal. It was amusing to do his wife's
back hair—it was so mathematically neat—and the particular "smart" tension of her tight stays. She lent herself especially to positions in which the face was somewhat averted or blurred; she abounded in ladylike back
views and *profils perdus.* When she stood erect she took
naturally one of the attitudes in which court-painters
represent queens and princesses; so that I found myself
wondering whether, to draw out this accomplishment,
I couldn't get the editor of the *Cheapside* to publish a
really royal romance, "A Tale of Buckingham Palace."
Sometimes however the real thing and the make-believe
came into contact; by which I mean that Miss Churm,
keeping an appointment or coming to make one on days
when I had much work in hand, encountered her invidious rivals. The encounter was not on their part,
for they noticed her no more than if she had been the
housemaid; not from intentional loftiness, but simply
because as yet, professionally, they didn't know how to
fraternise, as I could imagine they would have liked—or
at least that the Major would. They couldn't talk about
the omnibus—they always walked; and they didn't
know what else to try—she wasn't interested in good

trains or cheap claret. Besides, they must have felt—in the air—that she was amused at them, secretly derisive of their ever knowing how. She wasn't a person to conceal the limits of her faith if she had had a chance to show them. On the other hand Mrs. Monarch didn't think her tidy; for why else did she take pains to say to me—it was going out of the way, for Mrs. Monarch—that she didn't like dirty women?

One day when my young lady happened to be present with my other sitters—she even dropped in, when it was convenient, for a chat—I asked her to be so good as to lend a hand in getting tea, a service with which she was familiar and which was one of a class that, living as I did in a small way, with slender domestic resources, I often appealed to my models to render. They liked to lay hands on my property, to break the sitting, and sometimes the china—it made them feel Bohemian. The next time I saw Miss Churm after this incident she surprised me greatly by making a scene about it—she accused me of having wished to humiliate her. She hadn't resented the outrage at the time, but had seemed obliging and amused, enjoying the comedy of asking Mrs. Monarch, who sat vague and silent, whether she would have cream and sugar, and putting an exaggerated simper into the question. She had tried intonations—as if she too wished to pass for the real thing—till I was afraid my other visitors would take offence.

Oh they were determined not to do this, and their touching patience was the measure of their great need. They would sit by the hour, uncomplaining, till I was ready to use them; they would come back on the chance of being wanted and would walk away cheerfully if it failed. I used to go to the door with them to see in what magnificent order they retreated. I tried to find other employment for them—I introduced them to several artists. But they didn't "take," for reasons I could appreciate, and I became rather anxiously aware that after such disappointments they fell back upon me with a heavier weight. They did me the honour to think me most *their* form. They weren't romantic enough for the painters, and in those days there were few serious workers in black-and-white. Besides, they had an eye to the great job I had mentioned to them—they had secretly set their hearts on supplying the right essence for my pictorial vindication of our fine novelist. They knew that for this undertaking I should want no costume-effects, none of the frippery of past ages—that it was a case in which everything would be contemporary and satirical and presumably genteel. If I could work them into it their future would be assured, for the labour would of course be long and the occupation steady.

One day Mrs. Monarch came without her husband—she explained his absence by his having had to go to the City. While she sat there in her usual relaxed majesty there came at the door a knock which I immediately recognised as the subdued appeal of a model out of work. It was followed by the entrance of a young man whom I at once saw to be a foreigner and who proved in fact an Italian acquainted with no English word but my name, which he uttered in a way that made it seem to include all others. I hadn't then visited his country, nor was I proficient in his tongue; but as he was not so meanly constituted—what Italian is?—as to depend only on that member for expression he conveyed to me, in familiar but graceful mimicry, that he was in search of exactly the employment in which the lady before me was engaged. I was not struck with him at first, and while I continued to draw I dropped few signs of interest or encouragement. He stood his ground however—not importunately, but with a dumb dog-like fidelity in his eyes that amounted to innocent impudence, the manner of a devoted servant—he might have been in the house for years—unjustly suspected. Suddenly it struck me that this very attitude and expression made a picture; whereupon I told him to sit down and wait till I should be free. There was another picture in the way he obeyed me, and I observed as I worked that there were others still in the way he looked wonderingly, with his head thrown back, about the high studio. He might have been crossing himself in Saint Peter's. Before I finished I said to myself "The fellow's a bankrupt orange-monger, but a treasure."

When Mrs. Monarch withdrew he passed across the room like a flash to open the door for her, standing there with the rapt pure gaze of the young Dante spellbound by the young Beatrice. As I never insisted, in such situations, on the blankness of the British domestic, I reflected that he had the making of a servant—and I needed one, but couldn't pay him to be only that—as well as of a model; in short I resolved to adopt my bright adventurer if he would agree to officiate in the double capacity. He jumped at my offer, and in the event my rashness—for I had really known nothing about him—wasn't brought home to me. He proved a sympathetic though a desultory ministrant, and had in a wonderful degree the *sentiment de la pose*. It was uncultivated, instinctive, a part of the happy instinct that had guided him to my door and helped him to spell out my name on the card nailed to it. He had had no other introduction to me than a guess, from the shape of my high north window, seen outside, that my place was a studio and that as a studio it would contain an artist. He had wandered to England in search of fortune, like other itinerants, and had embarked, with a partner

and a small green hand-cart, on the sale of penny ices.
The ices had melted away and the partner had dis-
solved in their train. My young man wore tight yellow
trousers with reddish stripes and his name was Oronte.
He was sallow but fair, and when I put him into some
old clothes of my own he looked like an Englishman. He
was as good as Miss Churm, who could look, when requested, like an Italian.

IV

I thought Mrs. Monarch's face slightly convulsed when,
on her coming back with her husband, she found Oronte
installed. It was strange to have to recognise in a scrap
of a lazzarone a competitor to her magnificent Major. It
was she who scented danger first, for the Major was an-
ecdotically unconscious. But Oronte gave us tea, with a
hundred eager confusions—he had never been concerned in so queer a process—and I think she thought
better of me for having at last an "establishment." They
saw a couple of drawings that I had made of the establishment, and Mrs. Monarch hinted that it never would
have struck her he had sat for them. "Now the drawings you make from *us*, they look exactly like us," she
reminded me, smiling in triumph; and I recognised that
this was indeed just their defect. When I drew the
Monarchs I couldn't anyhow get away from them—get
into the character I wanted to represent; and I hadn't
the least desire my model should be discoverable in my
picture. Miss Churm never was, and Mrs. Monarch
thought I hid her, very properly, because she was vulgar; whereas if she was lost it was only as the dead who
go to heaven are lost—in the gain of an angel the more.

By this time I had got a certain start with "Rutland
Ramsay," the first novel in the great projected series;
that is I had produced a dozen drawings, several with

the help of the Major and his wife, and I had sent them in for approval. My understanding with the publishers, as I have already hinted, had been that I was to be left to do my work, in this particular case, as I liked, with the whole book committed to me; but my connexion with the rest of the series was only contingent. There were moments when, frankly, it *was* a comfort to have the real thing under one's hand; for there were characters in "Rutland Ramsay" that were very much like it. There were people presumably as erect as the Major and women of as good a fashion as Mrs. Monarch. There was a great deal of country-house life— treated, it is true, in a fine fanciful ironical generalised way—and there was a considerable implication of knickerbockers and kilts. There were certain things I had to settle at the outset; such things for instance as the exact appearance of the hero and the particular bloom and figure of the heroine. The author of course gave me a lead, but there was a margin for interpretation. I took the Monarchs into my confidence, I told them frankly what I was about, I mentioned my embarrassments and alternatives. "Oh take *him!*" Mrs. Monarch murmured sweetly, looking at her husband; and "What could you want better than my wife?" the Major enquired with the comfortable candour that now prevailed between us.

I wasn't obliged to answer these remarks—I was only obliged to place my sitters. I wasn't easy in mind, and I postponed a little timidly perhaps the solving of my question. The book was a large canvas, the other figures were numerous, and I worked off at first some of the episodes in which the hero and the heroine were not concerned. When once I had set *them* up I should have to stick to them—I couldn't make my young man seven feet high in one place and five feet nine in another. I inclined on the whole to the latter measurement, though the Major more than once reminded me that *he* looked about as young as any one. It was indeed quite possible to arrange him, for the figure, so that it would have been difficult to detect his age. After the spontaneous Oronte had been with me a month, and after I had given him to understand several times over that his native exuberance would presently constitute an insurmountable barrier to our further intercourse, I waked to a sense of his heroic capacity. He was only five feet seven, but the remaining inches were latent. I tried him almost secretly at first, for I was really rather afraid of the judgement my other models would pass on such a choice. If they regarded Miss Churm as little better than a snare what would they think of the representation by a person so little the real thing as an Italian street-vendor of a protagonist formed by a public school?

If I went a little in fear of them it wasn't because they bullied me, because they had got an oppressive foothold, but because in their really pathetic decorum and mysteriously permanent newness they counted on me so intensely. I was therefore very glad when Jack Hawley came home: he was always of such good counsel. He painted badly himself, but there was no one like him for putting his finger on the place. He had been absent from England for a year; he had been somewhere—I don't remember where—to get a fresh eye. I was in a good deal of dread of any such organ, but we were old friends; he had been away for months and a sense of emptiness was creeping into my life. I hadn't dodged a missile for a year.

He came back with a fresh eye, but with the same old black velvet blouse, and the first evening he spent in my studio we smoked cigarettes till the small hours.

He had done no work himself, he had only got the eye; so the field was clear for the production of my little things. He wanted to see what I had produced for the *Cheapside,* but he was disappointed in the exhibition. That at least seemed the meaning of two or three comprehensive groans which, as he lounged on my big divan, his leg folded under him, looking at my latest drawings, issued from his lips with the smoke of the cigarette.

"What's the matter with you?" I asked.

"What's the matter with *you?*"

"Nothing save that I'm mystified."

"You are indeed. You're quite off the hinge. What's the meaning of this new fad?" And he tossed me, with visible irreverence, a drawing in which I happened to have depicted both my elegant models. I asked if he didn't think it good, and he replied that it struck him as execrable, given the sort of thing I had always represented myself to him as wishing to arrive at; but I let that pass—I was so anxious to see exactly what he meant. The two figures in the picture looked colossal, but I supposed this was *not* what he meant, inasmuch as, for aught he knew to the contrary, I might have been trying for some such effect. I maintained that I was working exactly in the same way as when he last had done me the honour to tell me I might do something some day. "Well, there's a screw loose somewhere," he answered; "wait a bit and I'll discover it." I depended upon him to do so: where else was the fresh eye? But he produced at last nothing more luminous than "I don't know—I don't like your types." This was lame for a critic who had never consented to discuss with me anything but the question of execution, the direction of strokes and the mystery of values.

"In the drawings you've been looking at I think my types are very handsome."

"Oh they won't do!"

"I've been working with new models."

"I see you have. *They* won't do."

"Are you very sure of that?"

"Absolutely—they're stupid."

"You mean *I* am—for I ought to get round that."

"You *can't*—with such people. Who are they?"

I told him, so far as was necessary, and he concluded heartlessly: "Ce sont des gens qu'il faut mettre à la porte."

"You've never seen them; they're awfully good"—I flew to their defence.

"Not seen them? Why all this recent work of yours drops to pieces with them. It's all I want to see of them."

"No one else has said anything against it—the *Cheapside* people are pleased."

"Every one else is an ass, and the *Cheapside* people the biggest asses of all. Come, don't pretend at this time of day to have pretty illusions about the public, especially about publishers and editors. It's not for *such* animals you work—it's for those who know, *coloro che sanno;* so keep straight for *me* if you can't keep straight for yourself. There was a certain sort of thing you used to try for—and a very good thing it was. But this twaddle isn't *in* it." When I talked with Hawley later about "Rutland Ramsay" and its possible successors he declared that I must get back into my boat again or I should go to the bottom. His voice in short was the voice of warning.

I noted the warning, but I didn't turn my friends out of doors. They bored me a good deal; but the very fact that they bored me admonished me not to sacrifice them—if there was anything to be done with them—simply to irritation. As I look back at this phase they seem to me to have pervaded my life not a little. I have a vision of them as most of the time in my studio, seated against the wall on an old velvet bench to be out of the way, and resembling the while a pair of patient courtiers in a royal ante-chamber. I'm convinced that during the coldest weeks of the winter they held their ground because it saved them fire. Their newness was losing its gloss, and it was impossible not to feel them objects of charity. Whenever Miss Churm arrived they went away, and after I was fairly launched in "Rutland Ramsay" Miss Churm arrived pretty often. They managed to express to me tacitly that they supposed I wanted her for the low life of the book, and I let them suppose it, since they had attempted to study the work—it was lying about the studio—without discovering that it dealt only with the highest circles. They had dipped into the most brilliant of our novelists without deciphering many passages. I still took an hour from them, now and again, in spite of Jack Hawley's warning: it would be time enough to dismiss them, if dismissal should be necessary, when the rigour of the season was over. Hawley had made their acquaintance—he had met them at my fireside—and thought them a ridiculous pair. Learning that he was a painter they tried to approach him, to show him too that they were the real thing; but he looked at them, across the big room, as if they were miles away: they were a compendium of everything he most objected to in the social system of his country. Such people as that, all convention and patent-leather, with ejaculations that stopped conversation, had no business in a studio. A studio was a place to learn to see, and how could you see through a pair of feather-beds?

The main inconvenience I suffered at their hands was that at first I was shy of letting it break upon them that my artful little servant had begun to sit to me for "Rutland Ramsay." They knew I had been odd enough— they were prepared by this time to allow oddity to artists—to pick a foreign vagabond out of the streets when I might have had a person with whiskers and credentials; but it was some time before they learned how high I rated his accomplishments. They found him in an attitude more than once, but they never doubted I was doing him as an organ-grinder. There were several things they never guessed, and one of them was that for a striking scene in the novel, in which a footman briefly figured, it occurred to me to make use of Major Monarch as the menial. I kept putting this off, I didn't like to ask him to don the livery—besides the difficulty of finding a livery to fit him. At last, one day late in the winter, when I was at work on the despised Oronte, who caught one's idea on the wing, and was in the glow of feeling myself go very straight, they came in, the Major and his wife, with their society laugh about nothing (there was less and less to laugh at); came in like country-callers —they always reminded me of that—who have walked across the park after church and are presently persuaded to stay to luncheon. Luncheon was over, but they could stay to tea—I knew they wanted it. The fit was on me, however, and I couldn't let my ardour cool and my work wait, with the fading daylight, while my model prepared it. So I asked Mrs. Monarch if she would mind laying it out—a request which for an instant brought all the blood to her face. Her eyes were on her husband's for a second, and some mute telegraphy passed between them. Their folly was over the next instant; his cheerful shrewdness put an end to it. So far from pitying their wounded pride, I must add, I was

moved to give it as complete a lesson as I could. They
bustled about together and got out the cups and saucers
and made the kettle boil. I know they felt as if they were
waiting on my servant, and when the tea was prepared
I said: "He'll have a cup, please—he's tired." Mrs. Monarch brought him one where he stood, and he took it
from her as if he had been a gentleman at a party
squeezing a crush-hat with an elbow.

Then it came over me that she had made a great effort
for me—made it with a kind of nobleness—and that I
owed her a compensation. Each time I saw her after
this I wondered what the compensation could be. I
couldn't go on doing the wrong thing to oblige them.
Oh it *was* the wrong thing, the stamp of the work for
which they sat—Hawley was not the only person to say
it now. I sent in a large number of the drawings I had
made for "Rutland Ramsay," and I received a warning
that was more to the point than Hawley's. The artistic
adviser of the house for which I was working was of
opinion that many of my illustrations were not what had
been looked for. Most of these illustrations were the
subjects in which the Monarchs had figured. Without
going into the question of what *had* been looked for, I
had to face the fact that at this rate I shouldn't get the
other books to do. I hurled myself in despair on Miss
Churm—I put her through all her paces. I not only
adopted Oronte publicly as my hero, but one morning
when the Major looked in to see if I didn't require him
to finish a *Cheapside* figure for which he had begun to
sit the week before, I told him I had changed my mind
—I'd do the drawing from my man. At this my visitor
turned pale and stood looking at me. "Is *he* your idea of
an English gentleman?" he asked.

I was disappointed, I was nervous, I wanted to get

on with my work; so I replied with irritation: "Oh my dear Major—I can't be ruined for *you!*"

It was a horrid speech, but he stood another moment —after which, without a word, he quitted the studio. I drew a long breath, for I said to myself that I shouldn't see him again. I hadn't told him definitely that I was in danger of having my work rejected, but I was vexed at his not having felt the catastrophe in the air, read with me the moral of our fruitless collaboration, the lesson that in the deceptive atmosphere of art even the highest respectability may fail of being plastic.

I didn't owe my friends money, but I did see them again. They reappeared together three days later, and, given all the other facts, there was something tragic in that one. It was a clear proof they could find nothing else in life to do. They had threshed the matter out in a dismal conference—they had digested the bad news that they were not in for the series. If they weren't useful to me even for the *Cheapside* their function seemed difficult to determine, and I could only judge at first that they had come, forgivingly, decorously, to take a last leave. This made me rejoice in secret that I had little leisure for a scene; for I had placed both my other models in position together and I was pegging away at a drawing from which I hoped to derive glory. It had been suggested by the passage in which Rutland Ramsay, drawing up a chair to Artemisia's piano-stool, says extraordinary things to her while she ostensibly fingers out a difficult piece of music. I had done Miss Churm at the piano before—it was an attitude in which she knew how to take on an absolutely poetic grace. I wished the two figures to "compose" together with intensity, and my little Italian had entered perfectly into my conception. The pair were vividly before me, the piano had been pulled out; it was a charming show of blended youth and murmured love, which I had only to catch and keep. My visitors stood and looked at it, and I was friendly to them over my shoulder.

They made no response, but I was used to silent company and went on with my work, only a little disconcerted—even though exhilarated by the sense that *this* was at least the ideal thing—at not having got rid of them after all. Presently I heard Mrs. Monarch's sweet voice beside or rather above me: "I wish her hair were a little better done." I looked up and she was staring with a strange fixedness at Miss Churm, whose back was turned to her. "Do you mind my just touching it?" she went on—a question which made me spring up for an instant as with the instinctive fear that she might do the young lady a harm. But she quieted me with a glance I shall never forget—I confess I should like to have been able to paint *that*—and went for a moment to my model. She spoke to her softly, laying a hand on her shoulder and bending over her; and as the girl, understanding, gratefully assented, she disposed her rough curls, with a few quick passes, in such a way as to make Miss Churm's head twice as charming. It was one of the most heroic personal services I've ever seen rendered. Then Mrs. Monarch turned away with a low sigh and, looking about her as if for something to do, stooped to the floor with a noble humility and picked up a dirty rag that had dropped out of my paint-box.

The Major meanwhile had also been looking for something to do, and, wandering to the other end of the studio, saw before him my breakfast-things neglected, unremoved. "I say, can't I be useful *here?*" he called out to me with an irrepressible quaver. I assented with a laugh that I fear was awkward, and for the next ten minutes, while I worked, I heard the light clatter of china and the tinkle of spoons and glass. Mrs. Monarch assisted her husband—they washed up my crockery, they put it away. They wandered off into my little scullery, and I afterwards found that they had cleaned my knives and that my slender stock of plate had an unprecedented surface. When it came over me, the latent eloquence of what they were doing, I confess that my drawing was blurred for a moment—the picture swam. They had accepted their failure, but they couldn't accept their fate. They had bowed their heads in bewilderment to the perverse and cruel law in virtue of which the real thing could be so much less precious than the unreal; but they didn't want to starve. If my servants were my models, then my models might be my servants. They would reverse the parts—the others would sit for the ladies and gentlemen and *they* would do the work. They would still be in the studio—it was an intense dumb appeal to me not to turn them out. "Take us on," they wanted to say—"we'll do *anything*."

My pencil dropped from my hand; my sitting was spoiled and I got rid of my sitters, who were also evidently rather mystified and awestruck. Then, alone with the Major and his wife I had a most uncomfortable moment. He put their prayer into a single sentence: "I say, you know—just let *us* do for you, can't you?" I couldn't —it was dreadful to see them emptying my slops; but I pretended I could, to oblige them, for about a week. Then I gave them a sum of money to go away, and I never saw them again. I obtained the remaining books, but my friend Hawley repeats that Major and Mrs. Monarch did me a permanent harm, got me into false ways. If it be true I'm content to have paid the price—for the memory.

A ROUND OF VISITS

I

He had been out but once since his arrival, Mark Monteith; that was the next day after—he had disembarked by night on the previous; then everything had come at once, as he would have said, everything had changed. He had got in on Tuesday; he had spent Wednesday for the most part down town, looking into the dismal subject of his anxiety—the anxiety that, under a sudden decision, had brought him across the unfriendly sea at midwinter, and it was through information reaching him on Wednesday evening that he had measured his loss, measured above all his pain. These were two distinct things, he felt, and, though both bad, one much worse than the other. It wasn't till the next three days had pretty well ebbed, in fact, that he knew himself for so badly wounded. He had waked up on Thursday morning, so far as he had slept at all, with the sense, together, of a blinding New York blizzard and of a deep sore inward ache. The great white savage storm would have kept him at the best within doors, but his stricken state was by itself quite reason enough.

He so felt the blow indeed, so gasped, before what had happened to him, at the ugliness, the bitterness, and, beyond these things, the sinister strangeness, that, the matter of his dismay little by little detaching and projecting itself, settling there face to face with him as something he must now live with always, he might have been in charge of some horrid alien thing, some violent, scared, unhappy creature whom there was small joy, of a truth, in remaining with, but whose behaviour wouldn't perhaps bring him under notice, nor otherwise compromise him, so long as he should stay to watch it. A young jibbering ape of one of the more formidable sorts, or an ominous infant panther, smuggled into the great gaudy hotel and whom it might yet be important he shouldn't advertise, couldn't have affected him as needing more domestic attention. The great gaudy hotel—The Pocahontas, but carried out largely on "Du Barry" lines— made all about him, beside, behind, below, above, in blocks and tiers and superpositions, a sufficient defensive hugeness; so that, between the massive labyrinth and the New York weather, life in a lighthouse during a gale would scarce have kept him more apart. Even when in the course of that worse Thursday it had occurred to him for vague relief that the odious certified facts couldn't be all his misery, and that, with his throat and a probable temperature, a brush of the epidemic, which was for ever brushing him, accounted for something, even then he couldn't resign himself to bed and broth and dimness, but only circled and prowled the more within his high cage, only watched the more from his tenth story the rage of the elements.

In the afternoon he had a doctor—the caravanserai, which supplied everything in quantities, had one for each group of so many rooms—just in order to be assured that he was *grippé* enough for anything. What his visitor, making light of his attack, perversely told him was that he was, much rather, "blue" enough, and from causes doubtless known to himself—which didn't come to the same thing; but he "gave him something," prescribed him warmth and quiet and broth and courage, and came back the next day as to readminister this last dose. He then pronounced him better, and on Satur-

day pronounced him well—all the more that the storm
had abated and the snow had been dealt with as New
York, at a push, knew how to deal with things. Oh, how
New York knew how to deal—to deal, that is, with other
accumulations lying passive to its hand—was exactly
what Mark now ached with his impression of; so that,
still threshing about in this consciousness, he had on the
Saturday come near to breaking out as to what was
the matter with him. The Doctor brought in somehow
the air of the hotel—which, cheerfully and conscientiously, by his simple philosophy, the good man wished
to diffuse; breathing forth all the echoes of other woes
and worries and pointing the honest moral that, especially with such a thermometer, there were enough of
these to go round. Our sufferer, by that time, would
have liked to tell some one; extracting, to the last acid
strain of it, the full strength of his sorrow, taking it all in
as he could only do by himself and with the conditions
favourable at least to this, had been his natural first
need. But now, he supposed, he *must* be better; there
was something of his heart's heaviness he wanted so to
give out.

He had rummaged forth on the Thursday night half
a dozen old photographs stuck into a leather frame,
a small show-case that formed part of his usual equipage
of travel—he mostly set it up on a table when he stayed
anywhere long enough; and in one of the neat gilt-edged
squares of this convenient portable array, as familiar as
his shaving-glass or the hair-brushes, of backs and mono-
grams now so beautifully toned and wasted, long ago
given him by his mother, Phil Bloodgood handsomely
faced him. Not contemporaneous, and a little faded, but
so saying what it said only the more dreadfully, the
image seemed to sit there, at an immemorial window,
like some long effective and only at last exposed "decoy"

of fate. It was *because* he was so beautifully good-looking, because he was so charming and clever and frank—
besides being one's third cousin, or whatever it was,
one's early school-fellow and one's later college classmate
—that one had abjectly trusted him. To live thus with
his unremoved, undestroyed, engaging, treacherous face,
had been, as our traveller desired, to live with all of the
felt pang; had been to consume it in such a single hot,
sore mouthful as would so far as possible dispose of it
and leave but cold dregs. Thus, if the Doctor, casting
about for pleasantness, had happened to notice him
there, salient since he was, and possibly by the same
stroke even to know him, as New York—and more or
less to its cost now, mightn't one say?—so abundantly
and agreeably had, the cup would have overflowed and
Monteith, for all he could be sure of the contrary, would
have relieved himself positively in tears.

"Oh *he's* what's the matter with me—that, looking
after some of my poor dividends, as he for the ten years
of my absence had served me by doing, he has simply
jockeyed me out of the whole little collection, such as it
was, and taken the opportunity of my return, inevitably
at last bewildered and uneasy, to 'sail,' ten days ago,
for parts unknown and as yet unguessable. It isn't the
beastly values themselves, however; that's only awkward and I can still live, though I don't quite know how
I shall turn round; it's the horror of *his* having done it,
and done it to *me*—without a mitigation or, so to speak,
a warning or an excuse." That, at a hint or a jog, is what
he would have brought out—only to feel afterward,
no doubt, that he had wasted his impulse and profaned
even a little his sincerity. The Doctor didn't in the event
so much as glance at his cluster of portraits—which fact
quite put before our friend the essentially more vivid
range of imagery that a pair of eyes transferred from

room to room and from one queer case to another, in
such a place as that, would mainly be adjusted to. It
wasn't for *him* to relieve himself touchingly, strikingly
or whatever, to such a man: such a man might much
more pertinently—save for professional discretion—
have emptied out there his own bag of wonders; prodigies of observation, flowers of oddity, flowers of misery,
flowers of the monstrous, gathered in current hotel practice. Countless possibilities, making doctors perfunctory,
Mark felt, swarmed and seethed at their doors; it showed
for an incalculable world, and at last, on Sunday, he
decided to leave his room.

II

Everything, as he passed through the place, went on—
all the offices of life, the whole bustle of the market,
and withal, surprisingly, scarce less that of the nursery
and the playground; the whole sprawl in especial of the
great gregarious fireside: it was a complete social scene
in itself, on which types might figure and passions rage
and plots thicken and dramas develop, without reference
to any other sphere, or perhaps even to anything at all
outside. The signs of this met him at every turn as
he threaded the labyrinth, passing from one extraordinary masquerade of expensive objects, one portentous
"period" of decoration, one violent phase of publicity,
to another: the heavy heat, the luxuriance, the extravagance, the quantity, the colour, gave the impression
of some wondrous tropical forest, where vociferous,
bright-eyed, and feathered creatures, of every variety
of size and hue, were half smothered between under-
growths of velvet and tapestry and ramifications of marble and bronze. The fauna and the flora startled him
alike, and among them his bruised spirit drew in and
folded its wings. But he roamed and rested, exploring

and in a manner enjoying the vast rankness—in the
depth of which he suddenly encountered Mrs. Folliott,
whom he had last seen, six months before, in London,
and who had spoken to him then, precisely, of Phil
Bloodgood, for several years previous her confidential
American agent and factotum too, as she might say, but
at that time so little in her good books, for the extraordinary things he seemed to be doing, that she was just
hurrying home, she had made no scruple of mentioning,
to take everything out of his hands.

Mark remembered how uneasy she had made him—
how that very talk with her had wound him up to fear,
as so acute and intent a little person she affected him;
though he had affirmed with all emphasis and flourish
his own confidence and defended, to iteration, his old
friend. This passage had remained with him for a certain
pleasant heat of intimacy, his partner, of the charming
appearance, being what she was; he liked to think how
they had fraternised over their difference and called
each other idiots, or almost, without offence. It was
always a link to have scuffled, failing a real scratch, with
such a character; and he had at present the flutter of
feeling that something of this would abide. *He* hadn't
been hurrying home, at the London time, in any case;
he was doing nothing then, and had continued to do it;
he would want, before showing suspicion—that had
been his attitude—to have more, after all, to go upon.
Mrs. Folliott also, and with a great actual profession
of it, remembered and rejoiced; and, also staying in the
house as she was, sat with him, under a spreading palm,
in a wondrous rococo salon, surrounded by the pinkest,
that is the fleshiest, imitation Boucher panels, and wanted
to know if he *now* stood up for his swindler. She would
herself have tumbled on a cloud, very passably, in a
fleshy Boucher manner, hadn't she been over-dressed

for such an exercise; but she was quite realistically aware of what had so naturally happened—she was prompt about Bloodgood's "flight."

She had acted with energy, on getting back—she had saved what she could; which hadn't, however, prevented her losing all disgustedly some ten thousand dollars. She was lovely, lively, friendly, interested, she connected Monteith perfectly with their discussion that day during the water-party on the Thames; but, sitting here with him half an hour, she talked only of her peculiar, her cruel sacrifice—since she should never get a penny back. He had felt himself, on their meeting, quite yearningly reach out to her—so decidedly, by the morning's end, and that of his scattered sombre stations, had he been sated with meaningless contacts, with the sense of people all about him intensely, though harmlessly, animated, yet at the same time raspingly indifferent. *They* would have, he and she at least, their common pang—through which fact, somehow, he should feel less stranded. It wasn't that he wanted to be pitied— he fairly didn't pity himself; he winced, rather, and even to vicarious anguish, as it rose again, for poor shamed Bloodgood's doom-ridden figure. But he wanted, as with a desperate charity, to give some easier turn to the mere ugliness of the main facts; to work off his obsession from them by mixing with it some other blame, some other pity, it scarce mattered what—if it might be some other experience; as an effect of which larger ventilation it would have, after a fashion and for a man of free sensibility, a diluted and less poisonous taste.

By the end of five minutes of Mrs. Folliott, however, he felt his dry lips seal themselves to a makeshift simper. She could *take* nothing—no better, no broader perception of anything than fitted her own small faculty; so that though she must have recalled or imagined that he

had still, up to lately, had interests at stake, the rapid
result of her egotistical little chatter was to make him
wish he might rather have conversed with the French
waiter dangling in the long vista that showed the orien-
tal café as a climax, or with the policeman, outside, the
top of whose helmet peeped above the ledge of a window. She bewailed her wretched money to excess—
she who, he was sure, had quantities more; she pawed
and tossed her bare bone, with her little extraordinarily gemmed and manicured hands, till it acted on his
nerves; she rang all the changes on the story, the dire
fatality, of her having wavered and muddled, thought
of this and but done that, of her stupid failure to have
pounced, when she had first meant to, in season. She
abused the author of their wrongs—recognising thus too
Monteith's right to loathe him—for the desperado he
assuredly had proved, but with a vulgarity of analysis
and an incapacity for the higher criticism, as her listener
felt it to be, which made him determine resentfully,
almost grimly, that she shouldn't have the benefit of a
grain of *his* vision or *his* version of what had befallen
them, and of how, in particular, it had come; and should
never dream thereby (though much would she suffer
from that!) of how interesting he might have been. She
had, in a finer sense, no manners, and to be concerned
with her in any retrospect was—since their discourse
was of losses—to feel the dignity of history incur the
very gravest. It was true that such fantasies, or that
any shade of inward irony, would be Greek to Mrs.
Folliott.

It was also true, however, and not much more
strange, when she had presently the comparatively
happy thought of "Lunch with *us*, you poor dear!" and
mentioned three or four of her "crowd"—a new crowd,
rather, for her, all great Sunday lunchers there and im-

mense fun, who would in a moment be turning up—
that this seemed to him as easy as anything else; so that
after a little, deeper in the jungle and while, under
the temperature as of high noon, with the crowd complete and "ordering," he wiped the perspiration from
his brow, he felt he was letting himself go. He did that
certainly to the extent of leaving far behind any question of Mrs. Folliott's manners. They didn't matter there
—nobody's did; and if she ceased to lament her ten
thousand it was only because, among higher voices, she
couldn't make herself heard. Poor Bloodgood didn't
have a show, as they might have said, didn't get through
at any point; the crowd was so new that—there either
having been no hue and cry for him, or having been
too many others, for other absconders, in the intervals—
they had never so much as heard of him and would have
no more of Mrs. Folliott's true inwardness, on that subject at least, than she had lately cared to have of Monteith's.

There was nothing like a crowd, this unfortunate
knew, for making one feel lonely, and he felt so increasingly during the meal; but he got thus at least in a measure away from the terrible little lady; after which, and
before the end of the hour, he wanted still more to get
away from every one else. He was in fact about to perform this manœuvre when he was checked by the jolly
young woman he had been having on his left and who
had more to say about the Hotels, up and down the
town, than he had ever known a young woman to have
to say on any subject at all; she expressed herself in
hotel terms exclusively, the names of those establishments playing through her speech as the *leit-motif* might
have recurrently flashed and romped through a piece
of profane modern music. She wanted to present him
to the pretty girl she had brought with her, and who

had apparently signified to her that she must do so.

"I think you know my brother-in-law, Mr. Newton Winch," the pretty girl had immediately said; she moved her head and shoulders together, as by a common spring, the effect of a stiff neck or of something loosened in her back hair; but becoming, queerly enough, all the prettier for doing so. He had seen in the papers, her brother-in-law, Mr. Monteith's arrival —Mr. Mark P. Monteith, wasn't it?—and where he was, and she had been with him, three days before, at the time; whereupon he had said, "Hullo, what can have brought old Mark back?" He seemed to have believed—Newton had seemed—that that shirker, as he called him, never *would* come; and she guessed that if she had known she was going to meet such a former friend ("Which he claims you are, sir," said the pretty girl) he would have asked her to find out what the trouble could be. But the real satisfaction would just be, she went on, if his former friend would himself go and see him and tell him; he had appeared of late so down.

"Oh, I remember him"—Mark didn't repudiate the friendship, placing him easily; only then he wasn't married and the pretty girl's sister must have come in later: which showed, his not knowing such things, how they had lost touch. The pretty girl was sorry to have to say in return to this that her sister wasn't living—had died two years after marrying; so that Newton was up there in Fiftieth Street alone; where (in explanation of his being "down") he had been shut up for days with bad *grippe;* though now on the mend, or she wouldn't have gone to him, not she, who had had it nineteen times and didn't want to have it again. But the horrid poison just seemed to have entered into poor Newton's soul.

"That's the way it *can* take you, don't you know?" And then as, with her single twist, she just charmingly hunched her eyes at our friend, "Don't you want to go to see him?"

Mark bethought himself: "Well, I'm going to see a lady——"

She took the words from his mouth. "Of course you're going to see a lady—every man in New York is. But Newton isn't a lady, unfortunately for him, to-day; and Sunday afternoon in this place, in this weather, alone——!"

"Yes, isn't it awful?"—he was quite drawn to her.

"Oh, *you've* got your lady!"

"Yes, I've got my lady, thank goodness!" The fervour of which was his sincere tribute to the note he had had on Friday morning from Mrs. Ash, the only thing that had a little tempered his gloom.

"Well then, feel for others. Fit him in. Tell him why!"

"Why I've come back? I'm glad I *have*—since it was to see *you!*" Monteith made brave enough answer, promising to do what he could. He liked the pretty girl, with her straight attack and her free awkwardness— also with her difference from the others through something of a sense and a distinction given her by so clearly having Newton on her mind. Yet it was odd to him, and it showed the lapse of the years, that Winch—as he had known him of old—could *be* to that degree on any one's mind.

III

Outside in the intensity of the cold—it was a jump from the Tropics to the Pole—he felt afresh the force of what he had just been saying; that if it weren't for the fact of Mrs. Ash's good letter of welcome, despatched, characteristically, as soon as she had, like the faithful sufferer in Fiftieth Street, observed his name, in a newspaper, on one of the hotel-lists, he should verily, for want of a

connection and an abutment, have scarce dared to face
the void and the chill together, but have sneaked back
into the jungle and there tried to lose himself. He made,
as it was, the opposite effort, resolute to walk, though
hovering now and then at vague crossways, radiations
of roads to nothing, or taking cold counsel of the long
but still sketchy vista, as it struck him, of the northward
Avenue, bright and bleak, fresh and harsh, rich and evident somehow, a perspective like a page of florid modern
platitudes. He didn't quite know what he had expected
for his return—not certainly serenades and deputations;
but without Mrs. Ash his mail would have quite lacked
geniality, and it was as if Phil Bloodgood had gone off
not only with so large a slice of his small *peculium,* but
with all the broken bits of the past, the loose ends of old
relationships, that he had supposed he might pick up
again. Well, perhaps he should still pick up a few—by
the sweat of his brow; no motion of their own at least,
he by this time judged, would send them fluttering into
his hand.

Which reflections but quickened his forecast of
this charm of the old Paris inveteracy renewed—
the so-prized custom of nine years before, when he
still believed in results from his fond frequentation of
the Beaux Arts; that of walking over the river to the
Rue de Marignan, precisely, every Sunday without exception, and sitting at her fireside, and often all offensively, no doubt, outstaying every one. How he had
used to want those hours then, and how again, after
a little, at present, the Rue de Marignan might have
been before him! He had gone to her there at that time
with his troubles, such as they were, and they had always worked for her amusement—which had been her
happy, her clever way of taking them: she couldn't have
done anything better for them in that phase, poor inno-

cent things compared with what they might have been, than be amused by them. Perhaps that was what she would still be—with those of his present hour; now too they might inspire her with the touch she best applied and was most instinctive mistress of: this didn't at all events strike him as what he should most resent. It wasn't as if Mrs. Folliott, to make up for boring him with her own plaint, for example, had had so much as a gleam of conscious diversion over his.

"I'm *so* delighted to see you, I've such immensities to tell you!"—it began with the highest animation twenty minutes later, the very moment he stood there, the sense of the Rue de Marignan in the charming room and in the things about all reconstituted, regrouped, wonderfully preserved, down to the very sitting-places in the same relations, and down to the faint sweet mustiness of generations of cigarettes; but everything else different, and even vaguely alien, and by a measure still other than that of their own stretched interval and of the dear delightful woman's just a little pathetic alteration of face. He had allowed for the nine years, and so, it was to be hoped, had she; but the last thing, otherwise, that would have been touched, he immediately felt, was the quality, the intensity, of her care to see him. She cared, oh so visibly and touchingly and almost radiantly—save for her being, yes, distinctly, a little *more* battered than from even a good nine years' worth; nothing could in fact have perched with so crowning an impatience on the heap of what she had to "tell" as that special shade of revived consciousness of having him in particular to tell it to. It wasn't perhaps much to matter how soon she brought out and caused to ring, as it were, on the little recognised marqueterie table between them (such an anciently envied treasure), the heaviest gold-piece of current history she was to pay him with for having

just so felicitously come back: he knew already, without
the telling, that intimate domestic tension must lately,
within those walls, have reached a climax and that he
could serve supremely—oh how he was going to serve!
—as the most sympathetic of all pairs of ears.

The whole thing was upon him, in any case, with the
minimum of delay: Bob had had it from her, definitely,
the first of the week, and it was absolutely final now,
that they must set up avowedly separate lives—without
horrible "proceedings" of any sort, but with her own
situation, her independence, secured to her once for all.
She had been coming to it, taking her time, and she had
gone through—well, so old a friend would guess enough
what; but she was at the point, oh blessedly now, where
she meant to stay, he'd see if she didn't; with which,
in this wonderful way, he himself had arrived for the
cream of it and she was just selfishly glad. Bob had gone
to Washington—ostensibly on business, but really to
recover breath; she had, speaking vulgarly, knocked the
wind out of him and was allowing him time to turn
round. Mrs. Folliott moreover, she was sure, would have
gone—was certainly believed to have been seen there
five days ago; and of course his first necessity, for
public use, would be to patch up something with Mrs.
Folliott. Mark knew about Mrs. Folliott?—who was
only, for that matter, one of a regular "bevy." Not that
it signified, however, if he didn't: she would tell him
about *her* later.

He took occasion from the first fraction of a break
not quite to know what he knew about Mrs. Folliott—
though perhaps he could imagine a little; and it was
probably at this minute that, having definitely settled
to a position, and precisely in his very own tapestry
bergère, the one with the delicious little spectral "subjects" on the back and seat, he partly exhaled, and yet

managed partly to keep to himself, the deep resigned sigh of a general comprehension. He knew what he was "in" for, he heard her go on—she said it again and again, seemed constantly to be saying it while she smiled at him with her peculiar fine charm, her positive gaiety of sensibility, scarce dimmed: "I'm just selfishly glad, just selfishly glad!" Well, she was going to have reason to be; she was going to put the whole case to him, all her troubles and plans, and each act of the tragi-comedy of her recent existence, as to the dearest and safest sympathiser in all the world. There would be no chance for *his* case, though it was so much for his case he had come; yet there took place within him but a mild, dumb convulsion, the momentary strain of his substituting, by the turn of a hand, one prospect of interest for another.

Squaring himself in his old *bergère,* and with his lips, during the effort, compressed to the same passive grimace that had an hour or two before operated for the encouragement of Mrs. Folliott—just as it was to clear the stage completely for the present more prolonged performance—he shut straight down, as he even in the act called it to himself, on any personal claim for social consideration and rendered a perfect little agony of justice to the grounds of his friend's vividness. For it was all the justice that could be expected of him that, though, secretly, he wasn't going to be interested in her being interesting, she was yet going to be so, all the same, by the very force of her lovely material (Bob Ash *was* such a pure pearl of a donkey!) and he was going to keep on knowing she was—yes, to the very end. When after the lapse of an hour he rose to go, the rich fact that she *had* been was there between them, and with an effect of the frankly, fearlessly, harmlessly intimate fireside passage for it that went beyond even the best memories of the pleasant past. He hadn't "amused" her, no, in quite the same way as in the Rue de Marignan time—it had then been he who for the most part took frequent turns, emphatic, explosive, elocutionary, over that wonderful waxed parquet while she laughed as for the young perversity of him from the depths of the second, the matching *bergère*. To-day she herself held and swept the floor, putting him merely to the trouble of his perpetual "Brava!" But that was all through the change of basis—the amusement, another name only for the thrilled absorption, having been inevitably for *him;* as how could it have failed to be with such a regular "treat" to his curiosity? With the tea-hour now other callers were turning up, and he got away on the plea of his wanting so to think it all over. He hoped again he hadn't too queer a grin with his assurance to her, as if she would quite know what he meant, that he had been thrilled to the core. But she returned, quite radiantly, that he had carried *her* completely away; and her sincerity was proved by the final frankness of their temporary parting. "My pleasure of you is selfish, horribly, I admit; so that if *that* doesn't suit you—!" Her faded beauty flushed again as she said it.

IV

In the street again, as he resumed his walk, he saw how perfectly it would *have* to suit him and how he probably for a long time wouldn't be suited otherwise. Between them and that time, however, what mightn't, for him, poor devil, on his new basis, have happened? She wasn't at any rate within any calculable period going to care so much for anything as for the so quaintly droll terms in which her rearrangement with her husband—thanks to that gentleman's inimitable fatuity—would have to be made. This was what it was to own, exactly, her

special grace—the brightest gaiety in the finest sensibility; *such* a display of which combination, Mark felt
as he went (if he could but have done it still more justice) she must have regaled him with! That exquisite
last flush of her fadedness could only remain with him;
yet while he presently stopped at a street-corner in a
district redeemed from desolation but by the passage
just then of a choked trolley-car that howled, as he
paused for it, beneath the weight of its human accre-
tions, he seemed to know the inward "sinking" that had
been determined in a hungry man by some extravagant
sight of the preparation of somebody else's dinner. Florence Ash was dining, so to speak, off the feast of appreciation, appreciation of what she had to "tell" him, that
he had left her seated at; and she was welcome, assuredly—welcome, welcome, welcome, he musingly, he
wistfully, and yet at the same time a trifle mechanically,
repeated, stayed as he was a moment longer by the suffering shriek of another public vehicle and a sudden odd
automatic return of his mind to the pretty girl, the flower
of Mrs. Folliott's crowd, who had spoken to him of Newton Winch. It was extraordinarily as if, on the instant,
she reminded him, from across the town, that *she* had
offered him dinner: it was really quite strangely, while
he stood there, as if she had told him where he could
go and get it. With which, none the less, it was apparently where he wouldn't find her—and what was there,
after all, of nutritive in the image of Newton Winch?
He made up his mind in a moment that it owed that
property, which the pretty girl had somehow made imputable, to the fact of its simply being just then the one
image of anything known to him that the terrible place
had to offer. Nothing, he a minute later reflected, could
have been so "rum" as that, sick and sore, of a bleak

New York eventide, he should have had nowhere to
turn if not to the said Fiftieth Street.

That was the direction he accordingly took, for when
he found the number given him by the same remarkable
agent of fate also present to his memory he recognised
the direct intervention of Providence and how it absolutely required a miracle to explain his so precipitately
embracing this loosest of connections. The miracle indeed soon grew clearer: Providence had, on some obscure system, chosen this very ridiculous hour to save
him from cultivation of the sin of selfishness, the obsession of egotism, and was breaking him to its will by constantly directing his attention to the claims of others.
Who could say what at that critical moment mightn't
have become of Mrs. Folliott (otherwise too then so
sadly embroiled!) if she hadn't been enabled to air to
him her grievance and her rage?—just as who could
deny that it must have done Florence Ash a world of
good to have put her thoughts of Bob in order by
the aid of a person to whom the vision of Bob in the
light of those thoughts (or in other words to whom *her*
vision of Bob and nothing else) would mean so delightfully much? It was on the same general lines that poor
Newton Winch, bereft, alone, ill, perhaps dying, and
with the drawback of a not very sympathetic personality
—as Mark remembered it at least—to contend against
in almost any conceivable appeal to human furtherance,
it was on these lines, very much, that the luckless case
in Fiftieth Street was offered him as a source of salutary
discipline. The moment for such a lesson might strike
him as strange, in view of the quite special and independent opportunity for exercise that his spirit had during the last three days enjoyed there in his hotel bedroom; but evidently his languor of charity needed some

admonition finer than any it might trust to chance for, and by the time he at last, Winch's residence recognised, was duly elevated to his level and had pressed the electric button at his door, he felt himself acting indeed as under stimulus of a sharp poke in the side.

V

Within the apartment to which he had been admitted, moreover, the fine intelligence we have imputed to him was in the course of three minutes confirmed; since it took him no longer than that to say to himself, facing his old acquaintance, that he had never seen any one so improved. The place, which had the semblance of a high studio light as well as a general air of other profusions and amplitudes, might have put him off a little by its several rather glaringly false accents, those of contemporary domestic "art" striking a little wild. The scene was smaller, but the rich confused complexion of the Pocahontas, showing through Du Barry paint and patches, might have set the example—which had been followed with the costliest candour—so that, clearly, Winch was in these days rich, as most people in New York seemed rich; as, in spite of Bob's depredations, Florence Ash was, as even Mrs. Folliott was in spite of Phil Bloodgood's, as even Phil Bloodgood himself must have been for reasons too obvious; as in fine every one had a secret for being, or for feeling, or for looking, every one at least but Mark Monteith.

These facts were as nothing, however, in presence of his quick and strong impression that his pale, nervous, smiling, clean-shaven host had undergone since their last meeting some extraordinary process of refinement. He had been ill, unmistakably, and the effects of a plunge into plain clean living, where any fineness had remained, were often startling, sometimes almost charming. But independently of this, and for a much longer time, some principle of intelligence, some art of life, would discernibly have worked in him. Remembered from college years and from those two or three luckless and faithless ones of the Law School as constitutionally common, as consistently and thereby doubtless even rather powerfully coarse, clever only for uncouth and questionable things, he yet presented himself now as if he had suddenly and mysteriously been educated. There was a charm in his wide, "drawn," convalescent smile, in the way his fine fingers—had he anything like fine fingers of old?—played, and just fidgeted, over the prompt and perhaps a trifle incoherent offer of cigars, cordials, ash-trays, over the question of his visitor's hat, stick, fur coat, general best accommodation and ease; and how the deuce, accordingly, had charm, for coming out so on top, Mark wondered, "squared" the other old elements? For the short interval so to have dealt with him what force had it turned on, what patented process, of the portentous New York order in which there were so many, had it skilfully applied? Were these the things New York did when you just gave her *all* her head, and that he himself then had perhaps too complacently missed? Strange almost to the point of putting him positively off at first—quite as an exhibition of the uncanny —this sense of Newton's having all the while neither missed nor muffed anything, and having, as with an eye to the *coup de théâtre* to come, lowered one's expectations, at the start, to that abject pitch. It might have been taken verily for an act of bad faith—really for such a rare stroke of subtlety as could scarce have been achieved by a straight or natural aim.

So much as this at least came and went in Monteith's agitated mind; the oddest intensity of apprehension, admiration, mystification, which the high northlight of the March afternoon and the quite splendidly vulgar appeal of fifty overdone decorative effects somehow fostered and sharpened. Everything had already gone, however, the next moment, for wasn't the man he had come so much too intelligently himself to patronise absolutely bowling him over with the extraordinary speech: "See here, you know—you must be ill, or have had a bad shock, or some beastly upset: are you very sure you ought to have come out?" Yes, he after an instant believed his ears; coarse common Newton Winch, whom he had called on because he could, as a gentleman, after all afford to, coarse common Newton Winch, who had had troubles and been epidemically poisoned, lamentably sick, who bore in his face and in the very tension, quite exactly the "charm," of his manner, the traces of his late ordeal, and, for that matter, of scarce completed gallant emergence—this astonishing ex-comrade was simply writing himself at a stroke (into our friend's excited imagination at all events) the most distinguished of men. Oh, *he* was going to be interesting, if Florence Ash had been going to be; but Mark felt how, under the law of a lively present difference, that would be as an effect of one's having one's self thoroughly rallied. He knew within the minute that the tears stood in his eyes; he stared through them at his friend with a sharp "Why, how do you know? How *can* you?" To which he added before Winch could speak: "I met your charming sister-in-law a couple of hours since—at luncheon, at the Pocahontas; and heard from her that you were badly laid up and had spoken of me. So I came to minister to you."

The object of this design hovered there again, considerably restless, shifting from foot to foot, changing his place, beginning and giving up motions, striking matches for a fresh cigarette, offering them again, redundantly, to his guest and then not lighting himself—

but all the while with the smile of another creature than
the creature known to Mark; all the while with the history of something that had happened to him ever so
handsomely shining out. Mark was conscious within
himself from this time on of two quite distinct processes
of notation—that of his practically instant surrender to
the consequences of the act of perception in his host
of which the two women trained supposably in the art
of pleasing had been altogether incapable; and that of
some other condition on Newton's part that left his own
poor power of divination nothing less than shamed. This
last was signally the case on the former's saying, ever
so responsively, almost radiantly, in answer to his account of how he happened to come: "Oh then it's very
interesting!" *That* was the astonishing note, after what
he had been through: neither Mrs. Folliott nor Florence
Ash had so much as hinted or breathed to him that *he*
might have incurred that praise. No wonder therefore
he was now taken—with this fresh party's instant suspicion and imputation of it; though it was indeed for
some minutes next as if each tried to see which could
accuse the other of the greater miracle of penetration.
Mark was so struck, in a word, with the extraordinarily
straight guess Winch had had there in reserve for him
that, other quick impressions helping, there was nothing
for him but to bring out, himself: "There must be, my
dear man, something rather wonderful the matter with
you!" The quite more intensely and more irresistibly
drawn grin, the quite unmistakably deeper consciousness
in the dark, wide eye, that accompanied the not quite
immediate answer to which remark he was afterward
to remember.

"How do you know that—or why do you think it?"

"Because there *must* be—for you to see! I shouldn't
have expected it."

"Then you take me for a damned fool?" laughed wonderful Newton Winch.

VI

He could say nothing that, whether as to the sense of it or as to the way of it, didn't so enrich Mark's vision of him that our friend, after a little, as this effect proceeded, caught himself in the act of almost too curiously gaping. Everything, from moment to moment, fed his curiosity; such a question, for instance, as whether the quite ordinary peepers of the Newton Winch of their earlier youth could have looked, under any provocation, either dark or wide; such a question, above all, as how *this* incalculable apparition came by the whole startling power of play of its extravagantly sensitive labial connections—expose, so to its advantage (he now jumped at one explanation) by the removal of what had probably been one of the vulgarest of moustaches. With this, at the same time, the oddity of that particular consequence was vivid to him; the glare of his curiosity fairly lasting while he remembered how he had once noted the very opposite turn of the experiment for Phil Bloodgood. He would have said in advance that poor Winch couldn't have afforded to risk showing his "real" mouth; just as he would have said that in spite of the fine ornament that so considerably muffled it Phil could only have gained by showing his. But to have seen Phil shorn —as he once had done—was earnestly to pray that he might promptly again bristle; beneath Phil's moustache lurked nothing to "make up" for it in case of removal. While he thought of which things the line of grimace, as he could only have called it, the mobile, interesting, ironic line the great double curve of which connected, in the face before him, the strong nostril with the lower cheek, became the very key to his first idea of Newton's capture of refinement. He had shaved and was happily transfigured. Phil Bloodgood had shaved and been well-nigh lost; though why should he just now too precipitately drag the reminiscence in?

That question too, at the queer touch of association, played up for Mark even under so much proof that the state of his own soul was being with the lapse of every instant registered. Phil Bloodgood had brought about the state of his soul—there was accordingly that amount of connection; only it became further remarkable that from the moment his companion had sounded him, and sounded him, he knew, down to the last truth of things, his disposition, his necessity to talk, the desire that had in the morning broken the spell of his confinement, the impulse that had thrown him so defeatedly into Mrs. Folliott's arms and into Florence Ash's, these forces seemed to feel their impatience ebb and their discretion suddenly grow. His companion was talking again, but just then, incongruously, made his need to communicate lose itself. It was as if his personal case had already been touched by some tender hand—and that, after all, was the modest limit of its greed. "I know now why you came back—did Lottie mention how I had wondered? But sit down, sit down—only let me, nervous beast as I am, take it standing!—and believe me when I tell you that I've now ceased to wonder. My dear chap, I *have* it! It can't but have been for poor Phil Bloodgood. He sticks out of you, the brute—as how, with what he has done to you, shouldn't he? There was a man to see me yesterday—Tim Slater, whom I don't think you know, but who's 'on' everything within about two minutes of its happening (I never saw such a fellow!) and who confirmed my supposition, all my own, however, mind you, at first, that you're one of the sufferers. So how the devil can you *not* feel knocked? Why *should* you look

as if you were having the time of your life? What a hog
to have played it on *you*, on *you*, of all his friends!" So
Newton Winch continued, and so the air between the
two men might have been, for a momentary watcher
—which is indeed what I can but invite the reader to
become—that of a nervously displayed, but all considerate, as well as most acute, curiosity on the one side,
and that on the other, after a little, of an eventually fascinated acceptance of so much free and in especial of so
much right attention. "Do you *mind* my asking you?
Because if you do I won't press; but as a man whose own
responsibilities, some of 'em at least, don't differ much,
I gather, from some of his, one would like to know how
he was ever allowed to get to the point—! But I *do*
plough you up?"

Mark sat back in his chair, moved but holding himself, his elbows squared on each arm, his hands a bit
convulsively interlocked across him—very much in fact
as he had appeared an hour ago in the old tapestry
bergère; but as his rigour was all then that of the grind-
ing effort to profess and to give, so it was considerably
now for the fear of too hysterically gushing. Somehow
too—since his wound was to that extent open—he
winced at hearing the author of it branded. He hadn't
so much minded the epithets Mrs. Folliott had applied,
for they were to the appropriator of *her* securities. As
the appropriator of his own he didn't so much want to
brand him as—just more "amusingly" even, if one
would!—to make out, perhaps, with intelligent help,
how such a man, in such a relation, *could* come to tread
such a path: which was exactly the interesting light that
Winch's curiosity and sympathy were there to assist
him to. He pleaded at any rate immediately his advertising no grievance. "I feel sore, I admit, and it's a horrid
sort of thing to have had happen; but when you call

him a brute and a hog I rather squirm, for brutes and hogs never live, I guess, in the sort of hell in which he now must be."

Newton Winch, before the fireplace, his hands deep in his pockets, where his guest could see his long fingers beat a tattoo on his thighs, Newton Winch dangled and swung himself, and threw back his head and laughed. "Well, I must say you take it amazingly!—all the more that to see you again this way is to feel that if, all along, there was a man whose delicacy and confidence and general attitude might have marked him for a particular consideration, you'd have been the man." And they were more directly face to face again; with Newton smiling and smiling *so* appreciatively; making our friend in fact almost ask himself when before a man had ever grinned from ear to ear to the effect of its so becoming him. What he replied, however, was that Newton described in those flattering terms a client temptingly fatuous; after which, and the exchange of another protest or two in the interest of justice and decency, and another plea or two in that of the still finer contention that even the basest misdeeds had always somewhere or other, could one get at it, their propitiatory side, our hero found himself on his feet again, under the influence of a sudden failure of everything but horror—a horror determined by some turn of their talk and indeed by the very fact of the freedom of it. It was as if a far-borne sound of the hue and cry, a vision of his old friend hunted and at bay, had suddenly broken in—this other friend's, this irresistibly intelligent other companion's, practically vivid projection of that making the worst ugliness real. "Oh, it's just making my wry face to somebody, and your letting me and caring and wanting to know: that," Mark said, "is what does me good; not any other hideous question. I mean I don't take any interest in *my* case—what one wonders about, you see, is what can be done for him. I mean, that is"—for he floundered a little, not knowing at last quite what he did mean, a great rush of mere memories, a great humming sound as of thick, thick echoes, rising now to an assault that he met with his face indeed contorted. If he didn't take care he should howl; so he more or less successfully took care—yet with his host vividly watching him while he shook the danger temporarily off. "I don't mind—though it's rather *that;* my having felt this morning, after three dismal dumb bad days, that one's friends perhaps would be thinking of one. All I'm conscious of now—I give you my word—is that I'd like to see him."

"You'd like to see him?"

"Oh, I don't say," Mark ruefully smiled, "that I should like him to see *me*——!"

Newton Winch, from where he stood—and they were together now, on the great hearth-rug that was a triumph of modern orientalism—put out one of the noted find hands and, with an expressive headshake, laid it on his shoulder. "Don't wish him that, Monteith—don't wish him that!"

"Well, but,"—and Mark raised his eyebrows still higher—"he'd see I bear up; pretty well!"

"God forbid he should see, my dear fellow!" Newton cried as for the pang of it.

Mark had for his idea, at any rate, the oddest sense of an exaltation that grew by this use of frankness. "I'd go to him. Hanged if I wouldn't—anywhere!"

His companion's hand still rested on him. "You'd go to him?"

Mark stood up to it—though trying to sink solemnity as pretentious. "I'd go like a shot." And then he added: "And it's probably what—when we've turned round— I *shall* do."

"When 'we' have turned round?"

"Well"—he was a trifle disconcerted at the tone—
"I say that because you'll have helped me."

"Oh, I do nothing but want to help you!" Winch
replied—which made it right again; especially as our
friend still felt himself reassuringly and sustainingly
grasped. But Winch went on: "You *would* go to him—
in kindness?"

"Well—to understand."

"To understand how he could swindle you?"

"Well," Mark kept on, "to try and make out with him
how, after such things—!" But he stopped; he couldn't
name them.

It was as if his companion knew. "Such things as
you've done for him of course—such services as you've
rendered him."

"Ah, from far back. If I could tell you," our friend
vainly wailed—"if I could tell you!"

Newton Winch patted his shoulder. "Tell me—tell
me!"

"The sort of relation, I mean; ever so many things of
a kind—!" Again, however, he pulled up; he felt the
tremor of his voice.

"Tell me, tell me," Winch repeated with the same
movement.

The tone in it now made their eyes meet again, and
with this presentation of the altered face Mark measured
as not before, for some reason, the extent of the recent
ravage. "You must have been ill indeed."

"Pretty bad. But I'm better. And you do me good"—
with which the light of convalescence came back.

"I don't awfully bore you?"

Winch shook his head. "You keep me up—and you
see how no one else comes near me."

Mark's eyes made out that he *was* better—though it

wasn't yet that nothing was the matter with him. If there was ever a man with whom there was still something the matter—! Yet one couldn't insist on that, and meanwhile he clearly did want company. "Then there we are. I myself had no one to go to."

"You save my life," Newton renewedly grinned.

VII

"Well, it's your own fault," Mark replied to that, "if you make me take advantage of you." Winch had withdrawn his hand, which was back, violently shaking keys or money, in his trousers pocket; and in this position he had abruptly a pause, a sensible, absence, that might have represented either some odd drop of attention, some turn-off to another thought, or just simply the sudden act of listening. His guest had indeed himself— under suggestion—the impression of a sound. "Mayn't you perhaps—if you hear something—have a call?"

Mark had said it so lightly, however, that he was the more struck with his host's appearing to turn just paler; and, with it, the latter now *was* listening. "You hear something?"

"I thought *you* did." Winch himself, on Mark's own pressure of the outside bell, had opened the door of the apartment—an indication then, it sufficiently appeared, that Sunday afternoons were servants', or attendants', or even trained nurses' holidays. It had also marked the stage of his convalescence, and to that extent—after his first flush of surprise—had but smoothed Monteith's way. At present he barely gave further attention; detaching himself as under some odd cross-impulse, he had quitted the spot and then taken, in the wide room, a restless turn—only, however, to revert in a moment to his friend's just-uttered deprecation of the danger of boring him. "If I make you take advantage of me—

that is blessedly talk to me—it's exactly what I want to do. Talk to me—talk to me!" He positively waved it on; pulling up again, however, in his own talk, to say with a certain urgency: "Hadn't you better sit down?"

Mark, who stayed before the fire, couldn't but excuse himself. "Thanks—I'm very well so. I think of things and I fidget."

Winch stood a moment with his eyes on the ground. "Are you very sure?"

"Quite—I'm all right if you don't mind."

"Then as you like!" With which, shaking to extravagance again his long legs, Newton had swung off—only with a movement that, now his back was turned, affected his visitor as the most whimsical of all the forms of his rather unnatural manner. He was curiously different with his back turned, as Mark now for the first time saw it—dangling and somewhat wavering, as from an excess of uncertainty of gait; and this impression was so strange, it created in our friend, uneasily and on the spot, such a need of explanation, that his speech was stayed long enough to give Winch time to turn round again. The latter had indeed by this moment reached one of the limits of the place, the wide studio bay, where he paused, his back to the light and his face afresh presented, to let his just passingly depressed and quickened eyes take in as much as possible of the large floor, range over it with such brief freedom of search as the disposition of the furniture permitted. He was looking for something, though the betrayed reach of vision was but of an instant. Mark caught it, however, and with his own sensibility all in vibration, found himself feeling at once that it meant something and that what it meant was connected with his entertainer's slightly marked appeal to him, the appeal of a moment before, not to remain standing. Winch knew by this time quite easily enough that

he was hanging fire; which meant that they were suddenly facing each other across the wide space with a
new consciousness.

Everything had changed—changed extraordinarily
with the mere turning of that gentleman's back, the
treacherous aspect of which its owner couldn't surely
have suspected. If the question was of the pitch of their
sensibility, at all events, it wouldn't be Mark's that
should vibrate to least purpose. Visibly it had come to
his host that something had within the few instants remarkably happened, but there glimmered on him an
induction that still made him keep his own manner.
Newton himself might now resort to any manner he
liked. His eyes had raked the floor to recover the position
of something dropped or misplaced, and something,
above all, awkward or compromising; and he had
wanted his companion not to command this scene from
the hearth-rug, the hearth-rug where he had been just
before holding him, hypnotising him to blindness, *because* the object in question would there be most exposed to sight. Mark embraced this with a further drop
—while the apprehension penetrated—of his power to
go on, and with an immense desire at the same time that
his eyes should seem only to look at his friend; who
broke out now, for that matter, with a fresh appeal.
"Aren't you going to take advantage of me, man—aren't
you going to *take* it?"

Everything had changed, we have noted, and nothing
could more have proved it than the fact that, by
the same turn, sincerity of desire had dropped out of
Winch's chords, while irritation, sharp and almost im-
perious, had come in. "That's because he sees I see
something!" Mark said to himself; but he had no need
to add that it shouldn't prevent his seeing more—for the
simple reason that, in a miraculous fashion, this was ex-

actly what he did do in glaring out the harder. It was beyond explanation, but the very act of blinking thus in an attempt at showy steadiness became one and the same thing with an optical excursion lasting the millionth of a minute and making him aware that the edge of a rug, at the point where an arm-chair, pushed a little out of position, over-straddled it, happened just not wholly to have covered in something small and queer, neat and bright, crooked and compact, in spite of the strong toe-tip surreptitiously applied to giving it the right lift. Our gentleman, from where he hovered, and while looking straight at the master of the scene, yet saw, as by the tiny flash of a reflection from fine metal, *under* the chair. What he recognised, or at least guessed at, as sinister, made him for a moment turn cold, and that chill was on him while Winch again addressed him —as differently as possible from any manner yet used. "I beg of you in God's name to talk to me—to *talk* to me!"

It had the ring of pure alarm and anguish, but was by this turn at least more human than the dazzling glitter of intelligence to which the poor man had up to now been treating him. "It's you, my good friend, who are in deep trouble," Mark was accordingly quick to reply, "and I ask your pardon for being so taken up with my own sorry business."

"Of course I'm in deep trouble"—with which Winch came nearer again; "but turning you on was exactly what I wanted."

Mark Monteith, at this, couldn't, for all his rising dismay, but laugh out; his sense of the ridiculous so swallowed up, for that brief convulsion, his sense of the sinister. Of such convenience in pain, it seemed, was the fact of another's pain, and of so much worth again disinterested sympathy! "Your interest was then——?"

"My interest was in your being interesting. For you *are!* And my nerves——!" said Newton Winch with a face from which the mystifying smile had vanished, yet in which distinction, as Mark so persistently appreciated it, still sat in the midst of ravage.

Mark wondered and wondered—he made strange things out. "Your nerves have needed company." He could lay his hand on him now, even as shortly before he had felt Winch's own pressure of possession and detention. "As good for you yourself, that—or still better," he went on—"than I and my grievance were to have found you. Talk to *me*, talk to *me*, Newton Winch!" he added with an immense inspiration of charity.

"That's a different matter—that others but too much can do! But I'll say this. If you want to go to Phil Blood-good——!"

"Well?" said Mark as he stopped. He stopped, and Mark had now a hand on each of his shoulders and held him at arm's-length, held him with a fine idea that was not disconnected from the sight of the small neat weapon he had been fingering in the low luxurious morocco chair—it was of the finest orange colour—and then had laid beside him on the carpet; where, after he had admitted his visitor, his presence of mind coming back to it and suggesting that he couldn't pick it up without making it more conspicuous, he had thought, by some swing of the foot or other casual manœuvre, to dissimulate its visibility.

They were at close quarters now as not before and Winch perfectly passive, with eyes that somehow had no shadow of a secret left and with the betrayal to the sentient hands that grasped him of an intense, an extraordinary general tremor. To Mark's challenge he opposed afresh a brief silence, but the very quality of it, with his face speaking, was that of a gaping wound.

"Well, you needn't take *that* trouble. You see I'm such another."

"Such another as Phil——?"

He didn't blink. "I don't know for sure, but I guess I'm worse."

"Do you mean you're guilty——?"

"I mean I shall be wanted. Only I've stayed to take it."

Mark threw back his head, but only tightened his hands. He inexpressibly understood, and nothing in life had ever been so strange and dreadful to him as his thus helping himself by a longer and straighter stretch, as it were, to the monstrous sense of his friend's "education." It had been, in its immeasurable action, the education of business, of which the fruits were all around them. Yet prodigious was the interest, for prodigious truly—it seemed to loom before Mark—must have been the system. "To 'take' it?" he echoed; and then, though faltering a little, "To take what?"

He had scarce spoken when a long sharp sound shrilled in from the outer door, seeming of so high and peremptory a pitch that with the start it gave him his grasp of his host's shoulders relaxed an instant, though to the effect of no movement in *them* but what came from just a sensibly intenser vibration of the whole man. "For *that!*" said Newton Winch.

"Then you've known——?"

"I've expected. You've helped me to wait." And then as Mark gave an ironic wail: "You've tided me over. My condition has *wanted* somebody or something. Therefore, to complete this service, will you be so good as to open the door?"

Deep in the eyes Mark looked him, and still to the detection of no glimmer of the earlier man in the depths. The earlier man had been what he invidiously remem-

bered—yet would *he* had been the whole simpler story!
Then he moved his own eyes straight to the chair under
which the revolver lay and which was but a couple of
yards away. He felt his companion take this consciousness in, and it determined in them another long, mute
exchange. "What do you mean to do?"

"Nothing."

"On your honour?"

"*My* 'honour'?" his host returned with an accent that
he felt even as it sounded he should never forget.

It brought to his own face a crimson flush—he
dropped his guarding hands. Then as for a last look at
him: "You're wonderful!"

"We *are* wonderful," said Newton Winch, while,
simultaneously with the words, the pressed electric bell
again and for a longer time pierced the warm cigaretted
air.

Mark turned, threw up his arms, and it was only when
he had passed through the vestibule and laid his hand
on the door-knob that the horrible noise dropped. The
next moment he was face to face with two visitors, a
nondescript personage in a high hat and an astrakhan
collar and cuffs, and a great belted constable, a splendid
massive New York "officer" of the type he had had occasion to wonder at much again in the course of his walk,
the type so by itself—his wide observation quite suggested—among those of the peacemakers of the earth.
The pair stepped straight in—no word was said; but as
he closed the door behind them Mark heard the infallible crack of a discharged pistol and, so nearly with it
as to make all one violence, the sound of a great fall;
things the effect of which was to lift him, as it were,
with his company, across the threshold of the room in
a shorter time than that taken by this record of the fact.
But their rush availed little; Newton was stretched on

his back before the fire; he had held the weapon horribly to his temple, and his upturned face was disfigured.
The emissaries of the law, looking down at him, exhaled
simultaneously a gruff imprecation, and then while the
worthy in the high hat bent over the subject of their
visit the one in the helmet raised a severe pair of eyes
to Mark. "Don't you think, sir, you might have prevented it?"

Mark took a hundred things in, it seemed to him—
things of the scene, of the moment, and of all the strange
moments before; but one appearance more vividly even
than the others stared out at him. "I really think I must
practically have caused it."

1910

II

THREE NOUVELLES

The long tale or short novel—what James called the *nouvelle*—was a form of fiction to which he became increasingly addicted. No exact line of division can be drawn between his longer "short stories" and his *nouvelles*. He himself never specified the length of the latter, defining the type rather in terms of its fuller substance, treatment, detail, and imaginative economy. He called it "the loved *nouvelle* form," an opportunity to achieve for the "real art of representation" a "controlled and guarded acceptance, in fact a perfect economic mastery," in which "the general sense of the expansive, the explosive principle in one's material" may be "adroitly allowed to flush and colour and animate the disputed value, but with its other appetites and treacheries, its characteristic space-hunger and space-cunning, kept down." In practicing it he could devote his shrewdest faculties "to the only compactness that has a charm, to the only spareness that has a force, to the only simplicity that has a grace—those, in each order, that produce the *rich* effect." One critic, R. P. Blackmur, has said that the *nouvelle* became "perhaps James's favorite form . . . a small reflector capable of illuminating or mirroring a great deal of material. To the artist who practised in it the difficulties of its economy were a constant seduction and an exalted delight."

The longer tales of James which belong to the *nouvelle*

category will differ according to the definitions of different critics, but I judge that category to include, at one end, fairly concise examples like "The Author of Beltraffio," "The Pupil," "The Beast in the Jungle," and "The Bench of Desolation," which clearly surpass in scope and treatment his shorter tales, and, at the other, tales of virtual book length like *Daisy Miller*, "The Aspern Papers," *The Reverberator*, "The Turn of the Screw," and *In the Cage*. The three examples printed here are, in any event, among James's finest, and touch three of his radical subjects. In "The Pupil" (1891) he treats the theme of moral confusion or treachery in modern society through the piercing lens of a child's sensibility—a subject and method to which he returned in "The Turn of the Screw," *What Maisie Knew*, and *The Awkward Age*—and he handles it with a subtlety of psychological suggestion, in the compelling appeal that binds young Morgan to his tutor, that touches the secret spring of tragic emotion. "The Beast in the Jungle" (1903) is one of James's most celebrated stories. It has perhaps, and sometimes crudely, been overemphasized as a clue to his personal life and morality, but its drama of the fear of life that brings John Marcher to recognize his fate as that of "the man of his time, *the* man, to whom nothing on earth was to have happened," unquestionably gave James one of his masterpieces. In the New York Edition, as Mr. Leon Edel has noted, James grouped this tale with his stories of the quasi-supernatural, and thus, among the present fictional selections, it serves to touch the borders of that realm of the "ghostly" to which he contributed some of the most suggestive art of modern times. "The Bench of Desolation" (1909), the last tale but one that James published, is included here not only because I consider it another masterpiece—I agree with Edmund Wilson that it is "surely one of the most beautifully written and wonderfully developed short pieces in the whole range of James's work"—but because it has not been reprinted in collections of James's fiction in America since its first book publication forty years ago. It deals, moreover, not with the life of social privilege and civilized existences usually thought to be his special province but with the seamy world of poverty and hardship in which he is commonly considered inexpert but which— witness also *The Princess Casamassima* and *In The Cage*— he was sometimes able to treat with extraordinary insight and compassion.

"The Pupil" was first printed in *Longman's Magazine* in March and April 1891, and in book form in *The Lesson of the Master and Other Tales* in 1892. "The Beast in the Jungle" was first published in James's book of tales *The Better Sort* in 1903. The present texts of both these tales are taken from the New York Edition. "The Bench of Desolation" came too late to be included in that edition; it was first printed in *Putnam's Magazine*, October 1909 to January 1910, and was included in James's last book of fiction, *The Finer Grain*, in 1910. Again the reader is referred to the Bibliography in this book for other recommended titles among James's longer tales and *nouvelles*.

THE PUPIL

I

The poor young man hesitated and procrastinated: it cost him such an effort to broach the subject of terms, to speak of money to a person who spoke only of feelings and, as it were, of the aristocracy. Yet he was unwilling to take leave, treating his engagement as settled, without some more conventional glance in that direction than he could find an opening for in the manner of the large affable lady who sat there drawing a pair of soiled *gants de Suède* through a fat jewelled hand and, at once pressing and gliding, repeated over and over everything but the thing he would have liked to hear. He would have liked to hear the figure of his salary; but just as he was nervously about to sound that note the little boy came back—the little boy Mrs. Moreen had sent out of the room to fetch her fan. He came back without the fan, only with the casual observation that he couldn't find it. As he dropped this cynical confession he looked straight and hard at the candidate for the honour of taking his education in hand. This personage reflected somewhat grimly that the first thing he should have to teach his little charge would be to appear to address himself to his mother when he spoke to her—especially not to make her such an improper answer as that.

When Mrs. Moreen bethought herself of this pretext for getting rid of their companion Pemberton supposed it was precisely to approach the delicate subject of his remuneration. But it had been only to say some things about her son that it was better a boy of eleven shouldn't catch. They were extravagantly to his advantage save when she lowered her voice to sigh, tapping her left side familiarly, "And all overclouded by *this,* you know; all at the mercy of a weakness—!" Pemberton gathered that the weakness was in the region of the heart. He had known the poor child was not robust: this was the basis on which he had been invited to treat, through an English lady, an Oxford acquaintance, then at Nice, who happened to know both his needs and those of the amiable American family looking out for something really superior in the way of a resident tutor.

The young man's impression of his prospective pupil, who had come into the room as if to see for himself the moment Pemberton was admitted, was not quite the soft solicitation the visitor had taken for granted. Morgan Moreen was somehow sickly without being "delicate," and that he looked intelligent—it is true Pemberton would have enjoyed his being stupid—only added to

the suggestion that, as with his big mouth and big ears
he really couldn't be called pretty, he might too utterly
fail to please. Pemberton was modest, was even timid;
and the chance that his small scholar would prove cleverer than himself had quite figured, to his anxiety,
among the dangers of an untried experiment. He reflected, however, that these were risks one had to run
when one accepted a position, as it was called, in a private family; when as yet one's university honours had,
pecuniarily speaking, remained barren. At any rate when
Mrs. Moreen got up as to intimate that, since it was
understood he would enter upon his duties within the
week she would let him off now, he succeeded, in spite
of the presence of the child, in squeezing out a phrase
about the rate of payment. It was not the fault of the
conscious smile which seemed a reference to the lady's
expensive identity, it was not the fault of this demonstration, which had, in a sort, both vagueness and point, if
the allusion didn't sound rather vulgar. This was exactly
because she became still more gracious to reply: "Oh
I can assure you that all that will be quite regular."

Pemberton only wondered, while he took up his hat,
what "all that" was to amount to—people had such different ideas. Mrs. Moreen's words, however, seemed to
commit the family to a pledge definite enough to elicit
from the child a strange little comment in the shape of
the mocking foreign ejaculation "Oh la-la!"

Pemberton, in some confusion, glanced at him as he
walked slowly to the window with his back turned, his
hands in his pockets and the air in his elderly shoulders
of a boy who didn't play. The young man wondered
if he should be able to teach him to play, though his
mother had said it would never do and that this was
why school was impossible. Mrs. Moreen exhibited no
discomfiture; she only continued blandly: "Mr. Moreen

will be delighted to meet your wishes. As I told you, he has been called to London for a week. As soon as he comes back you shall have it out with him."

This was so frank and friendly that the young man could only reply, laughing as his hostess laughed: "Oh I don't imagine we shall have much of a battle."

"They'll give you anything you like," the boy remarked unexpectedly, returning from the window. "We don't mind what anything costs—we live awfully well."

"My darling, you're too quaint!" his mother exclaimed, putting out to caress him a practised but ineffectual hand. He slipped out of it, but looked with intelligent innocent eyes at Pemberton, who had already had time to notice that from one moment to the other his small satiric face seemed to change its time of life. At this moment it was infantine, yet it appeared also to be under the influence of curious intuitions and knowledges. Pemberton rather disliked precocity and was disappointed to find gleams of it in a disciple not yet in his teens. Nevertheless he divined on the spot that Morgan wouldn't prove a bore. He would prove on the contrary a source of agitation. This idea held the young man, in spite of a certain repulsion.

"You pompous little person! We're not extravagant!" Mrs. Moreen gaily protested, making another unsuccessful attempt to draw the boy to her side. "You must know what to expect," she went on to Pemberton.

"The less you expect the better!" her companion interposed. "But we *are* people of fashion."

"Only so far as *you* make us so!" Mrs. Moreen tenderly mocked. "Well then, on Friday—don't tell me you're superstitious—and mind you don't fail us. Then you'll see us all. I'm so sorry the girls are out. I guess you'll like the girls. And, you know, I've another son, quite different from this one."

"He tries to imitate me," Morgan said to their friend.

"He tries? Why he's twenty years old!" cried Mrs. Moreen.

"You're very witty," Pemberton remarked to the child —a proposition his mother echoed with enthusiasm, declaring Morgan's sallies to be the delight of the house.

The boy paid no heed to this; he only enquired abruptly of the visitor, who was surprised afterwards that he hadn't struck him as offensively forward: "Do you *want* very much to come?"

"Can you doubt it after such a description of what I shall hear?" Pemberton replied. Yet he didn't want to come at all; he was coming because he had to go somewhere, thanks to the collapse of his fortune at the end of a year abroad spent on the system of putting his scant patrimony into a single full wave of experience. He had had his full wave but couldn't pay the score at his inn. Moreover he had caught in the boy's eyes the glimpse of a far-off appeal.

"Well, I'll do the best I can for you," said Morgan; with which he turned away again. He passed out of one of the long windows; Pemberton saw him go and lean on the parapet of the terrace. He remained there while the young man took leave of his mother, who, on Pemberton's looking as if he expected a farewell from him, interposed with: "Leave him, leave him; he's so strange!" Pemberton supposed her to fear something he might say. "He's a genius—you'll love him," she added. "He's much the most interesting person in the family." And before he could invent some civility to oppose to this she wound up with: "But we're all good, you know!"

"He's a genius—you'll love him!" were words that recurred to our aspirant before the Friday, suggesting among many things that geniuses were not invariably loveable. However, it was all the better if there was an element that would make tutorship absorbing: he had perhaps taken too much for granted it would only disgust him. As he left the villa after his interview he looked up at the balcony and saw the child leaning over it. "We shall have great larks!" he called up.

Morgan hung fire a moment and then gaily returned: "By the time you come back I shall have thought of something witty!"

This made Pemberton say to himself "After all he's rather nice."

II

On the Friday he saw them all, as Mrs. Moreen had promised, for her husband had come back and the girls and the other son were at home. Mr. Moreen had a white moustache, a confiding manner and, in his buttonhole, the ribbon of a foreign order—bestowed, as Pemberton eventually learned, for services. For what services he never clearly ascertained: this was a point—one of a larger number—that Mr. Moreen's manner never confided. What it emphatically did confide was that he was even more a man of the world than you might first make out. Ulick, the firstborn, was in visible training for the same profession—under the disadvantage as yet, however, of a buttonhole but feebly floral and a moustache with no pretensions to type. The girls had hair and figures and manners and small fat feet, but had never been out alone. As for Mrs. Moreen, Pemberton saw on a nearer view that her elegance was intermittent and her parts didn't always match. Her husband, as she had promised, met with enthusiasm Pemberton's ideas in regard to a salary. The young man had endeavoured to keep these stammerings modest, and Mr. Moreen made it no secret that *he* found them wanting in "style." He further mentioned that he aspired to be intimate

with his children, to be their best friend, and that he
was always looking out for them. That was what he
went off for, to London and other places—to look out;
and this vigilance was the theory of life, as well as the
real occupation, of the whole family. They all looked
out, for they were very frank on the subject of its being
necessary. They desired it to be understood that they
were earnest people, and also that their fortune, though
quite adequate for earnest people, required the most
careful administration. Mr. Moreen, as the parent bird,
sought sustenance for the nest. Ulick invoked support
mainly at the club, where Pemberton guessed that it was
usually served on green cloth. The girls used to do up
their hair and their frocks themselves, and our young
man felt appealed to to be glad, in regard to Morgan's
education, that, though it must naturally be of the best,
it didn't cost too much. After a little he *was* glad, for-
getting at times his own needs in the interest inspired
by the child's character and culture and the pleasure of
making easy terms for him.

During the first weeks of their acquaintance Morgan
had been as puzzling as a page in an unknown language
—altogether different from the obvious little Anglo-
Saxons who had misrepresented childhood to Pemberton. Indeed the whole mystic volume in which the boy
had been amateurishly bound demanded some practice
in translation. Today, after a considerable interval, there
is something phantasmagoric, like a prismatic reflexion
or a serial novel, in Pemberton's memory of the queerness of the Moreens. If it were not for a few tangible
tokens—a lock of Morgan's hair cut by his own hand,
and the half-dozen letters received from him when they
were disjoined—the whole episode and the figures peo-
pling it would seem too inconsequent for anything but
dreamland. Their supreme quaintness was their success

—as it appeared to him for a while at the time; since he had never seen a family so brilliantly equipped for failure. Wasn't it success to have kept him so hatefully long? Wasn't it success to have drawn him in that first morning at déjeuner, the Friday he came—it was enough to *make* one superstitious—so that he utterly committed himself, and this not by calculation or on a signal, but from a happy instinct which made them, like a band of gipsies, work so neatly together? They amused him as much as if they had really been a band of gipsies. He was still young and had not seen much of the world —his English years had been properly arid; therefore the reversed conventions of the Moreens—for they had *their* desperate properties—struck him as topsy-turvy. He had encountered nothing like them at Oxford; still less had any such note been struck to his younger American ear during the four years at Yale in which he had richly supposed himself to be reacting against a Puritan strain. The reaction of the Moreens, at any rate, went ever so much further. He had thought himself very sharp that first day in hitting them all off in his mind with the "cosmopolite" label. Later it seemed feeble and colourless—confessedly helplessly provisional.

He yet when he first applied it felt a glow of joy—for an instructor he was still empirical—rise from the apprehension that living with them would really be to see life. Their sociable strangeness was an imitation of that— their chatter of tongues, their gaiety and good humour, their infinite dawdling (they were always getting themselves up, but it took for ever, and Pemberton had once found Mr. Moreen shaving in the drawing-room), their French, their Italian and, cropping up in the foreign fluencies, their cold tough slices of American. They lived on maccaroni and coffee—they had these articles prepared in perfection—but they knew recipes for a hundred other dishes. They overflowed with music and song, were always humming and catching each other up, and had a sort of professional acquaintance with Continental cities. They talked of "good places" as if they had been pickpockets or strolling players. They had at Nice a villa, a carriage, a piano and a banjo, and they went to official parties. They were a perfect calendar of the "days" of their friends, which Pemberton knew them, when they were indisposed, to get out of bed to go to, and which made the week larger than life when Mrs. Moreen talked of them with Paula and Amy. Their initiations gave their new inmate at first an almost dazzling sense of culture. Mrs. Moreen had translated something at some former period—an author whom it made Pemberton feel *borné* never to have heard of. They could imitate Venetian and sing Neapolitan, and when they wanted to say something very particular communicated with each other in an ingenious dialect of their own, an elastic spoken cipher which Pemberton at first took for some *patois* of one of their countries, but which he "caught on to" as he would not have grasped provincial development of Spanish or German.

"It's the family language—Ultramoreen," Morgan explained to him drolly enough; but the boy rarely condescended to use it himself, though he dealt in colloquial Latin as if he had been a little prelate.

Among all the "days" with which Mrs. Moreen's memory was taxed she managed to squeeze in one of her own, which her friends sometimes forgot. But the house drew a frequented air from the number of fine people who were freely named there and from several mysterious men with foreign titles and English clothes whom Morgan called the Princes and who, on sofas with the girls, talked French very loud—though sometimes with some oddity of accent—as if to show they were saying nothing improper. Pemberton wondered how the Princes could ever propose in that tone and so publicly: he took for granted cynically that this was what was desired of them. Then he recognised that even for the chance of such an advantage Mrs. Moreen would never allow Paula and Amy to receive alone. These young ladies were not at all timid, but it was just the safeguards that made them so candidly free. It was a houseful of Bohemians who wanted tremendously to be Philistines.

In one respect, however, certainly, they achieved no rigour—they were wonderfully amiable and ecstatic about Morgan. It was a genuine tenderness, an artless admiration, equally strong in each. They even praised his beauty, which was small, and were as afraid of him as if they felt him of finer clay. They spoke of him as a little angel and a prodigy—they touched on his want of health with long, vague faces. Pemberton feared at first an extravagance that might make him hate the boy, but before this happened he had become extravagant himself. Later, when he had grown rather to hate the others, it was a bribe to patience for him that they were at any rate nice about Morgan, going on tiptoe if they fancied he was showing symptoms, and even giving up somebody's "day" to procure him a pleasure. Mixed with this too was the oddest wish to make him independent, as if they had felt themselves not good enough for him. They passed him over to the new members of their circle very much as if wishing to force some charity of adoption on so free an agent and get rid of their own charge. They were delighted when they saw Morgan take so to his kind playfellow, and could think of no higher praise for the young man. It was strange how they contrived to reconcile the appearance, and indeed the essential fact, of adoring the child with their eagerness to wash their hands of him. Did they want to get rid of him before he should find them out? Pemberton was finding them out month by month. The boy's fond family, however this might be, turned their backs with exaggerated delicacy, as if to avoid the reproach of interfering. Seeing in time how little he had in common with them—it was by *them* he first observed it; they proclaimed it with complete humility—his companion was moved to speculate on the mysteries of transmission, the far jumps of heredity. Where his detachment from most of the things they represented had come from was more than an observer could say—it certainly had burrowed under two or three generations.

As for Pemberton's own estimate of his pupil, it was a good while before he got the point of view, so little had he been prepared for it by the smug young barbarians to whom the tradition of tutorship, as hitherto revealed to him, had been adjusted. Morgan was scrappy and surprising, deficient in many properties supposed common to the *genus* and abounding in others that were the portion only of the supernaturally clever. One day his friend made a great stride: it cleared up the question to perceive that Morgan *was* supernaturally clever and that, though the formula was temporarily meagre, this would be the only assumption on which one could successfully deal with him. He had the general quality of a child for whom life had not been simplified by school, a kind of homebred sensibility which might have been bad for himself but was charming for others, and a whole range of refinement and perception—little musical vibrations as taking as picked-up airs—begotten by wandering about Europe at the tail of his migratory tribe. This might not have been an education to recommend in advance, but its results with so special a subject were as appreciable as the marks on a piece of fine procelain.

There was at the same time in him a small strain of stoicism, doubtless the fruit of having had to begin early to bear pain, which counted for pluck and made it of less consequence that he might have been thought at school rather a polyglot little beast. Pemberton indeed quickly found himself rejoicing that school was out of the question: in any million of boys it was probably good for all but one, and Morgan was that millionth. It would have made him comparative and superior—it might have made him really require kicking. Pemberton would try to be school himself—a bigger seminary than five hundred grazing donkeys, so that, winning no prizes, the boy would remain unconscious and irresponsible and amusing—amusing, because, though life was already intense in his childish nature, freshness still made there a strong draught for jokes. It turned out that even in the still air of Morgan's various disabilities jokes flourished greatly. He was a pale lean acute undeveloped little cosmopolite, who liked intellectual gymnastics and who also, as regards the behaviour of mankind, had noticed more things than you might suppose, but who nevertheless had his proper playroom of superstitions, where he smashed a dozen toys a day.

III

At Nice once, toward evening, as the pair rested in the open air after a walk, and looked over the sea at the pink western lights, he said suddenly to his comrade: "Do you like it, you know—being with us all in this intimate way?"

"My dear fellow, why should I stay if I didn't?"

"How do I know you'll stay? I'm almost sure you won't, very long."

"I hope you don't mean to dismiss me," said Pemberton.

Morgan debated, looking at the sunset. "I think if I did right I ought to."

"Well, I know I'm supposed to instruct you in virtue; but in that case don't do right."

"You're very young—fortunately," Morgan went on, turning to him again.

"Oh yes, compared with you!"

"Therefore it won't matter so much if you do lose a lot of time."

"That's the way to look at it," said Pemberton accommodatingly.

They were silent a minute; after which the boy asked: "Do you like my father and my mother very much?"

"Dear me, yes. Charming people."

Morgan received this with another silence; then unexpectedly, familiarly, but at the same time affectionately, he remarked: "You're a jolly old humbug!"

For a particular reason the words made our young man change colour. The boy noticed in an instant that he had turned red, whereupon he turned red himself and pupil and master exchanged a longish glance in which there was a consciousness of many more things than are usually touched upon, even tacitly, in such a relation. It produced for Pemberton an embarrassment; it raised in a shadowy form a question—this was the first glimpse of it—destined to play a singular and, as he imagined, owing to the altogether peculiar conditions, an unprecedented part in his intercourse with his little companion. Later, when he found himself talking with the youngster in a way in which few youngsters could ever have been talked with, he thought of that clumsy moment on the bench at Nice as the dawn of an understanding that had broadened. What had added to the clumsiness then was that he thought it his duty to declare to Morgan that he might abuse him, Pemberton, as much as he liked, but must never abuse his parents. To this Morgan had the easy retort that he hadn't dreamed of abusing them; which appeared to be true: it put Pemberton in the wrong.

"Then why am I a humbug for saying *I* think them charming?" the young man asked, conscious of a certain rashness.

"Well—they're not your parents."

"They love you better than anything in the world—never forget that," said Pemberton.

"Is that why you like them so much?"

"They're very kind to me," Pemberton replied evasively.

"You *are* a humbug!" laughed Morgan, passing an arm into his tutor's. He leaned against him looking off at the sea again and swinging his long thin legs.

"Don't kick my shins," said Pemberton while he reflected "Hang it, I can't complain of them to the child!"

"There's another reason too," Morgan went on, keeping his legs still.

"Another reason for what?"

"Besides their not being your parents."

"I don't understand you," said Pemberton.

"Well, you will before long. All right!"

He did understand fully before long, but he made a fight even with himself before he confessed it. He thought it the oddest thing to have a struggle with the child about. He wondered he didn't hate the hope of the Moreens for bringing the struggle on. But by the time it began any such sentiment for that scion was closed to him. Morgan was a special case, and to know him was to accept him on his own odd terms. Pemberton had spent his aversion to special cases before arriving at knowledge. When at last he did arrive his quandary was great. Against every interest he had attached himself.

They would have to meet things together. Before they went home that evening at Nice the boy had said, clinging to his arm:

"Well, at any rate you'll hang on to the last."

"To the last?"

"Till you're fairly beaten."

"*You* ought to be fairly beaten!" cried the young man, drawing him closer.

IV

A year after he had come to live with them Mr. and Mrs. Moreen suddenly gave up the villa at Nice. Pemberton had got used to suddenness, having seen it practised on a considerable scale during two jerky little tours —one in Switzerland the first summer, and the other late in the winter, when they all ran down to Florence and then, at the end of ten days, liking it much less than they had intended, straggled back in mysterious depression. They had returned to Nice "for ever," as they said; but this didn't prevent their squeezing, one rainy muggy May night, into a second-class railway-carriage—you could never tell by which class they would travel— where Pemberton helped them to stow away a wonderful collection of bundles and bags. The explanation of this manœuvre was that they had determined to spend the summer "in some bracing place"; but in Paris they dropped into a small furnished apartment—a fourth floor in a third-rate avenue, where there was a smell on the staircase and the *portier* was hateful—and passed the next four months in blank indigence.

The better part of this baffled sojourn was for the preceptor and his pupil, who, visiting the Invalides and Notre Dame, the Conciergerie and all the museums, took a hundred remunerative rambles. They learned to know their Paris, which was useful, for they came back

another year for a longer stay, the general character
of which in Pemberton's memory to-day mixes pitiably
and confusedly with that of the first. He sees Morgan's
shabby knickerbockers—the everlasting pair that didn't
match his blouse and that as he grew longer could only
grow faded. He remembers the particular holes in his
three or four pair of coloured stockings.

Morgan was dear to his mother, but he never was
better dressed than was absolutely necessary—partly,
no doubt, by his own fault, for he was as indifferent to
his appearance as a German philosopher. "My dear fellow, you *are* coming to pieces," Pemberton would say
to him in sceptical remonstrance; to which the child
would reply, looking at him serenely up and down: "My
dear fellow, so are you! I don't want to cast you in the
shade." Pemberton could have no rejoinder for this—
the assertion so closely represented the fact. If however
the deficiencies of his own wardrobe were a chapter by
themselves he didn't like his little charge to look too
poor. Later he used to say "Well, if we're poor, why,
after all, shouldn't we look it?" and he consoled himself
with thinking there was something rather elderly and
gentlemanly in Morgan's disrepair—it differed from the
untidiness of the urchin who plays and spoils his things.
He could trace perfectly the degrees by which, in proportion as her little son confined himself to his tutor for
society, Mrs. Moreen shrewdly forbore to renew his
garments. She did nothing that didn't show, neglected
him because he escaped notice, and then, as he illustrated this clever policy, discouraged at home his public
appearances. Her position was logical enough—those
members of her family who did show had to be showy.

During this period and several others Pemberton was
quite aware of how he and his comrade might strike
people; wandering languidly through the Jardin des

Plantes as if they had nowhere to go, sitting on the winter days in the galleries of the Louvre, so splendidly ironical to the homeless, as if for the advantage of the *calorifère*. They joked about it sometimes: it was the sort of joke that was perfectly within the boy's compass. They figured themselves as part of the vast vague hand-to-mouth multitude of the enormous city and pretended they were proud of their position in it—it showed them "such a lot of life" and made them conscious of a democratic brotherhood. If Pemberton couldn't feel a sympathy in destitution with his small companion—for after all Morgan's fond parents would never have let him really suffer—the boy would at least feel it with him, so it came to the same thing. He used sometimes to wonder what people would think they were—to fancy they were looked askance at, as if it might be a suspected case of kidnapping. Morgan wouldn't be taken for a young patrician with a preceptor—he wasn't smart enough; though he might pass for his companion's sickly little brother. Now and then he had a five-franc piece, and except once, when they bought a couple of lovely neckties, one of which he made Pemberton accept, they laid it out scientifically in old books. This was sure to be a great day, always spent on the quays, in a rummage of the dusty boxes that garnish the parapets. Such occasions helped them to live, for their books ran low very soon after the beginning of their acquaintance. Pemberton had a good many in England, but he was obliged to write to a friend and ask him kindly to get some fellow to give him something for them.

If they had to relinquish that summer the advantage of the bracing climate the young man couldn't but suspect this failure of the cup when at their very lips to have been the effect of a rude jostle of his own. This had represented his first blow-out, as he called it, with his patrons; his first successful attempt—though there was little other success about it—to bring them to a consideration of his impossible position. As the ostensible eve of a costly journey the moment had struck him as favourable to an earnest protest, the presentation of an ultimatum. Ridiculous as it sounded, he had never yet been able to compass an uninterrupted private interview with the elder pair or with either of them singly. They were always flanked by their elder children, and poor Pemberton usually had his own little charge at his side. He was conscious of its being a house in which the surface of one's delicacy got rather smudged; nevertheless he had preserved the bloom of his scruple against announcing to Mr. and Mrs. Moreen with publicity that he shouldn't be able to go on longer without a little money. He was still simple enough to suppose Ulick and Paula and Amy might not know that since his arrival he had only had a hundred and forty francs; and he was magnanimous enough to wish not to compromise their parents in their eyes. Mr. Moreen now listened to him, as he listened to every one and to every thing, like a man of the world, and seemed to appeal to him—though not of course too grossly—to try and be a little more of one himself. Pemberton recognised in fact the importance of the character—from the advantage it gave Mr. Moreen. He was not even confused or embarrassed, whereas the young man in his service was more so than there was any reason for. Neither was he surprised—at least any more than a gentleman had to be who freely confessed himself a little shocked—though not perhaps strictly at Pemberton.

"We must go into this, mustn't we, dear?" he said to his wife. He assured his young friend that the matter should have his very best attention; and he melted into space as elusively as if, at the door, he were taking an inevitable but deprecatory precedence. When, the next moment, Pemberton found himself alone with Mrs. Moreen it was to hear her say "I see, I see"—stroking the roundness of her chin and looking as if she were only hesitating between a dozen easy remedies. If they didn't make their push Mr. Moreen could at least disappear for several days. During his absence his wife took up the subject again spontaneously, but her contribution to it was merely that she had thought all the while they were getting on so beautifully. Pemberton's reply to this revelation was that unless they immediately put down something on account he would leave them on the spot and for ever. He knew she would wonder how he would get away, and for a moment expected her to enquire. She didn't, for which he was almost grateful to her, so little was he in a position to tell.

"You won't, you *know* you won't—you're too interested," she said. "You *are* interested, you know you are, you dear kind man!" She laughed with almost condemnatory archness, as if it were a reproach—though she wouldn't insist; and flirted a soiled pocket-handkerchief at him.

Pemberton's mind was fully made up to take his step the following week. This would give him time to get an answer to a letter he had dispatched to England. If he did in the event nothing of the sort—that is if he stayed another year and then went away only for three months —it was not merely because before the answer to his letter came (most unsatisfactory when it did arrive) Mr. Moreen generously counted out to him, and again with the sacrifice to "form" of a marked man of the world, three hundred francs in elegant ringing gold. He was irritated to find that Mrs. Moreen was right, that he couldn't at the pinch bear to leave the child. This stood out clearer for the very reason that, the night

of his desperate appeal to his patrons, he had seen fully
for the first time where he was. Wasn't it another proof
of the success with which those patrons practised their
arts that they had managed to avert for so long the
illuminating flash? It descended on our friend with a
breadth of effect which perhaps would have struck
a spectator as comical, after he had returned to his little
servile room, which looked into a close court where
a bare dirty opposite wall took, with the sound of shrill
clatter, the reflexion of lighted back windows. He had
simply given himself away to a band of adventurers.
The idea, the word itself, wore a romantic horror for
him—he had always lived on such safe lines. Later it
assumed a more interesting, almost a soothing, sense:
it pointed a moral, and Pemberton could enjoy a moral.
The Moreens were adventurers not merely because they
didn't pay their debts, because they lived on society,
but because their whole view of life, dim and confused
and instinctive, like that of clever colour-blind animals,
was speculative and rapacious and mean. Oh they were
"respectable," and that only made them more *immondes!*
The young man's analysis, while he brooded, put it at
last very simply—they were adventurers because they
were toadies and snobs. That was the completest account of them—it was the law of their being. Even
when this truth became vivid to their ingenious inmate
he remained unconscious of how much his mind had
been prepared for it by the extraordinary little boy who
had now become such a complication in his life. Much
less could he then calculate on the information he was
still to owe the extraordinary little boy.

v

But it was during the ensuing time that the real problem
came up—the problem of how far it was excusable to

discuss the turpitude of parents with a child of twelve, of thirteen, of fourteen. Absolutely inexcusable and quite impossible it of course at first appeared; and indeed the question didn't press for some time after Pemberton had received his three hundred francs. They produced a temporary lull, a relief from the sharpest pressure. The young man frugally amended his wardrobe and even had a few francs in his pocket. He thought the Moreens looked at him as if he were almost too smart, as if they ought to take care not to spoil him. If Mr. Moreen hadn't been such a man of the world he would perhaps have spoken of the freedom of such neckties on the part of a subordinate. But Mr. Moreen was always enough a man of the world to let things pass— he had certainly shown that. It was singular how Pemberton guessed that Morgan, though saying nothing about it, knew something had happened. But three hundred francs, especially when one owed money, couldn't last for ever; and when the treasure was gone—the boy knew when it had failed—Morgan did break ground. The party had returned to Nice at the beginning of the winter, but not to the charming villa. They went to an hotel, where they stayed three months, and then moved to another establishment, explaining that they had left the first because, after waiting and waiting, they couldn't get the rooms they wanted. These apartments, the rooms they wanted, were generally very splendid; but fortunately they never *could* get them—fortunately, I mean, for Pemberton, who reflected always that if they had got them there would have been a still scanter educational fund. What Morgan said at last was said suddenly, irrelevantly, when the moment came, in the middle of a lesson, and consisted of the apparently unfeeling words: "You ought to *filer*, you know—you really ought."

Pemberton stared. He had learnt enough French slang from Morgan to know that to *filer* meant to cut sticks. "Ah my dear fellow, don't turn me off!"

Morgan pulled a Greek lexicon toward him—he used a Greek-German—to look out a word, instead of asking it of Pemberton. "You can't go on like this, you know."

"Like what, my boy?"

"You know they don't pay you up," said Morgan, blushing and turning his leaves.

"Don't pay me?" Pemberton stared again and feigned amazement. "What on earth put that into your head?"

"It has been there a long time," the boy replied rummaging his book.

Pemberton was silent, then he went on: "I say, what are you hunting for? They pay me beautifully."

"I'm hunting for the Greek for awful whopper," Morgan dropped.

"Find that rather for gross impertinence and disabuse your mind. What do I want of money?"

"Oh that's another question!"

Pemberton wavered—he was drawn in different ways. The severely correct thing would have been to tell the boy that such a matter was none of his business and bid him go on with his lines. But they were really too intimate for that; it was not the way he was in the habit of treating him; there had been no reason it should be. On the other hand Morgan had quite lighted on the truth—he really shouldn't be able to keep it up much longer; therefore why not let him know one's real motive for forsaking him? At the same time it wasn't decent to abuse to one's pupil the family of one's pupil; it was better to misrepresent than to do that. So in reply to his comrade's last exclamation he just declared, to dismiss the subject, that he had received several payments.

"I say—I say!" the boy ejaculated, laughing.

"That's all right," Pemberton insisted. "Give me your written rendering."

Morgan pushed a copybook across the table, and he began to read the page, but with something running in his head that made it no sense. Looking up after a minute or two he found the child's eyes fixed on him and felt in them something strange. Then Morgan said: "I'm not afraid of the stern reality."

"I haven't yet seen the thing you *are* afraid of—I'll do you that justice!"

This came out with a jump—it was perfectly true—and evidently gave Morgan pleasure. "I've thought of it a long time," he presently resumed.

"Well, don't think of it any more."

The boy appeared to comply, and they had a comfortable and even an amusing hour. They had a theory that they were very thorough, and yet they seemed always to be in the amusing part of lessons, the intervals between the dull dark tunnels, where there were waysides and jolly views. Yet the morning was brought to a violent end by Morgan's suddenly leaning his arms on the table, burying his head in them and bursting into tears: at which Pemberton was the more startled that, as it then came over him, it was the first time he had ever seen the boy cry and that the impression was consequently quite awful.

The next day, after much thought, he took a decision and, believing it to be just, immediately acted on it. He cornered Mr. and Mrs. Moreen again and let them know that if on the spot they didn't pay him all they owed him he wouldn't only leave their house but would tell Morgan exactly what had brought him to it.

"Oh you *haven't* told him?" cried Mrs. Moreen with a pacifying hand on her well-dressed bosom.

"Without warning you? For what do you take me?"
the young man returned.

Mr. and Mrs. Moreen looked at each other; he could
see that they appreciated, as tending to their security,
his superstition of delicacy, and yet that there was a certain alarm in their relief. "My dear fellow," Mr. Moreen
demanded, "what use *can* you have, leading the quiet
life we all do, for such a lot of money?"—a question to
which Pemberton made no answer, occupied as he was
in noting that what passed in the mind of his patrons
was something like: "Oh then, if we've felt that the
child, dear little angel, has judged us and how he regards us, and we haven't been betrayed, he must have
guessed—and in short it's *general!*" an inference that
rather stirred up Mr. and Mrs. Moreen, as Pemberton
had desired it should. At the same time, if he had supposed his threat would do something towards bringing
them round, he was disappointed to find them taking
for granted—how vulgar their perception *had* been!—
that he had already given them away. There was a mystic uneasiness in their parental breasts, and that had
been the inferior sense of it. None the less, however, his
threat did touch them; for if they had escaped it was
only to meet a new danger. Mr. Moreen appealed to
him, on every precedent, as a man of the world; but his
wife had recourse, for the first time since his domestica-
tion with them, to a fine *hauteur*, reminding him that
a devoted mother, with her child, had arts that pro-
tected her against gross misrepresentation.

"I should misrepresent you grossly if I accused you
of common honesty!" our friend replied; but as he closed
the door behind him sharply, thinking he had not done
himself much good, while Mr. Moreen lighted another
cigarette, he heard his hostess shout after him more
touchingly:

"Oh you do, you *do*, put the knife to one's throat!"

The next morning, very early, she came to his room. He recognised her knock, but had no hope she brought him money; as to which he was wrong, for she had fifty francs in her hand. She squeezed forward in her dressing-gown, and he received her in his own, between his bath-tub and his bed. He had been tolerably schooled by this time to the "foreign ways" of his hosts. Mrs. Moreen was ardent, and when she was ardent she didn't care what she did; so she now sat down on his bed, his clothes being on the chairs, and, in her preoccupation, forgot, as she glanced round, to be ashamed of giving him such a horrid room. What Mrs. Moreen's ardour now bore upon was the design of persuading him that in the first place she was very good-natured to bring him fifty francs, and that in the second, if he would only see it, he was really too absurd to expect to be *paid*. Wasn't he paid enough without perpetual money—wasn't he paid by the comfortable luxurious home he enjoyed with them all, without a care, an anxiety, a solitary want? Wasn't he sure of his position, and wasn't that everything to a young man like him, quite unknown, with singularly little to show, the ground of whose exorbitant pretensions it had never been easy to discover? Wasn't he paid above all by the sweet relation he had established with Morgan—quite ideal as from master to pupil—and by the simple privilege of knowing and living with so amazingly gifted a child; than whom really (and she meant literally what she said) there was no better company in Europe? Mrs. Moreen herself took to appealing to him as a man of the world; she said "Voyons, mon cher," and "My dear man, look here now"; and urged him to be reasonable, putting it before him that it was truly a chance for him. She spoke as if, according as he *should* be reasonable, he would prove himself worthy to be her son's tutor and of the extraordinary confidence they had placed in him.

After all, Pemberton reflected, it was only a difference of theory and the theory didn't matter much. They had hitherto gone on that of remunerated, as now they would go on that of gratuitous, service; but why should they have so many words about it? Mrs. Moreen at all events continued to be convincing; sitting there with her fifty francs she talked and reiterated as women reiterate, and bored and irritated him, while he leaned against the wall with his hands in the pockets of his wrapper, drawing it together round his legs and looking over the head of his visitor at the grey negations of his window. She wound up with saying: "You see I bring you a definite proposal."

"A definite proposal?"

"To make our relations regular, as it were—to put them on a comfortable footing."

"I see—it's a system," said Pemberton. "A kind of organised blackmail."

Mrs. Moreen bounded up, which was exactly what he wanted. "What do you mean by that?"

"You practise on one's fears—one's fears about the child if one should go away."

"And pray what would happen to him in that event?" she demanded with majesty.

"Why he'd be alone with *you*."

"And pray with whom *should* a child be but with those whom he loves most?"

"If you think that, why don't you dismiss me?"

"Do you pretend he loves you more than he loves *us?*" cried Mrs. Moreen.

"I think he ought to. I make sacrifices for him. Though I've heard of those *you* make I don't see them."

Mrs. Moreen stared a moment; then with emotion she

grasped her inmate's hand. "*Will* you make it—the sacrifice?"

He burst out laughing. "I'll see. I'll do what I can. I'll stay a little longer. Your calculation's just—I *do* hate intensely to give him up; I'm fond of him and he thoroughly interests me, in spite of the inconvenience I suffer. You know my situation perfectly. I haven't a penny in the world and, occupied as you see me with Morgan, am unable to earn money."

Mrs. Moreen tapped her undressed arm with her folded bank-note. "Can't you write articles? Can't you translate as *I* do?"

"I don't know about translating; it's wretchedly paid."

"I'm glad to earn what I can," said Mrs. Moreen with prodigious virtue.

"You ought to tell me who you do it for." Pemberton paused a moment, and she said nothing; so he added: "I've tried to turn off some little sketches, but the magazines won't have them—they're declined with thanks."

"You see then you're not such a phœnix," his visitor pointedly smiled—"to pretend to abilities you're sacrificing for our sake."

"I haven't time to do things properly," he ruefully went on. Then as it came over him that he was almost abjectly good-natured to give these explanations he added: "If I stay on longer it must be on one condition —that Morgan shall know distinctly on what footing I am."

Mrs. Moreen demurred. "Surely you don't want to show off to a child?"

"To show *you* off, do you mean?"

Again she cast about, but this time it was to produce a still finer flower. "And *you* talk of blackmail!"

"You can easily prevent it," said Pemberton.

"And *you* talk of practising on fears!" she bravely pushed on.

"Yes, there's no doubt I'm a great scoundrel."

His patroness met his eyes—it was clear she was in straits. Then she thrust out her money at him. "Mr. Moreen desired me to give you this on account."

"I'm much obliged to Mr. Moreen, but we *have* no account."

"You won't take it?"

"That leaves me more free," said Pemberton.

"To poison my darling's mind?" groaned Mrs. Moreen.

"Oh your darling's mind—!" the young man laughed.

She fixed him a moment, and he thought she was going to break out tormentedly, pleadingly: "For God's sake, tell me what *is* in it!" But she checked this impulse —another was stronger. She pocketed the money—the crudity of the alternative was comical—and swept out of the room with the desperate concession: "You may tell him any horror you like!"

VI

A couple of days after this, during which he had failed to profit by so free a permission, he had been for a quarter of an hour walking with his charge in silence when the boy became sociable again with the remark: "I'll tell you how I know it; I know it through Zénobie."

"Zénobie? Who in the world is *she?*"

"A nurse I used to have—ever so many years ago. A charming woman. I liked her awfully, and she liked me."

"There's no accounting for tastes. What is it you know through her?"

"Why what their idea is. She went away because they

didn't fork out. She did like me awfully, and she stayed two years. She told me all about it—that at last she could never get her wages. As soon as they saw how much she liked me they stopped giving her anything. They thought she'd stay for nothing—just *because,* don't you know?" And Morgan had a queer little conscious lucid look. "She did stay ever so long—as long as she could. She was only a poor girl. She used to send money to her mother. At last she couldn't afford it any longer, and went away in a fearful rage one night—I mean of course in a rage against *them.* She cried over me tremendously, she hugged me nearly to death. She told me all about it," the boy repeated. "She told me it was their idea. So I guessed, ever so long ago, that they have had the same idea with you."

"Zénobie was very sharp," said Pemberton. "And she made you so."

"Oh that wasn't Zénobie; that was nature. And experience!" Morgan laughed.

"Well, Zénobie was a part of your experience."

"Certainly I was a part of hers, poor dear!" the boy wisely sighed. "And I'm part of yours."

"A very important part. But I don't see how you know I've been treated like Zénobie."

"Do you take me for the biggest dunce you've known?" Morgan asked. "Haven't I been conscious of what we've been through together?"

"What we've been through?"

"Our privations—our dark days."

"Oh our days have been bright enough."

Morgan went on in silence for a moment. Then he said: "My dear chap, you're a hero!"

"Well, you're another!" Pemberton retorted.

"No I'm not, but I ain't a baby. I won't stand it any longer. You must get some occupation that pays. I'm

ashamed, I'm ashamed!" quavered the boy with a ring
of passion, like some high silver note from a small cathedral chorister, that deeply touched his friend.

"We ought to go off and live somewhere together,"
the young man said.

"I'll go like a shot if you'll take me."

"I'd get some work that would keep us both afloat,"
Pemberton continued.

"So would I. Why shouldn't *I* work? I ain't such a
beastly little muff as *that* comes to."

"The difficulty is that your parents wouldn't hear of
it. They'd never part with you; they worship the ground
you tread on. Don't you see the proof of it?" Pemberton
developed. "They don't dislike me; they wish me no
harm; they're very amiable people; but they're perfectly
ready to expose me to any awkwardness in life for your
sake."

The silence in which Morgan received his fond sophis-
try struck Pemberton somehow as expressive. After a
moment the child repeated: "You *are* a hero!" Then he
added: "They leave me with you altogether. You've all
the responsibility. They put me off on you from morning
till night. Why then should they object to my taking up
with you completely? I'd help you."

"They're not particularly keen about my being helped,
and they delight in thinking of you as *theirs*. They're
tremendously proud of you."

"I'm not proud of *them*. But you know that," Morgan
returned.

"Except for the little matter we speak of they're
charming people," said Pemberton, not taking up the
point made for his intelligence, but wondering greatly
at the boy's own, and especially at this fresh reminder
of something he had been conscious of from the first—
the strangest thing in his friend's large little composition,

a temper, a sensibility, even a private ideal, which made
him as privately disown the stuff his people were made of.
Morgan had in secret a small loftiness which made
him acute about betrayed meanness; as well as a critical
sense for the manners immediately surrounding him that
was quite without precedent in a juvenile nature, especially when one noted that it had not made this nature
"old-fashioned," as the word is of children—quaint or
wizened or offensive. It was as if he had been a little
gentleman and had paid the penalty by discovering that
he was the only such person in his family. This comparison didn't make him vain, but it could make him melancholy and a trifle austere. While Pemberton guessed at
these dim young things, shadows of shadows, he was
partly drawn on and partly checked, as for a scruple,
by the charm of attempting to sound the little cool shal-
lows that were so quickly growing deeper. When he
tried to figure to himself the morning twilight of childhood, so as to deal with it safely, he saw it was never
fixed, never arrested, that ignorance, at the instant he
touched it, was already flushing faintly into knowledge,
that there was nothing that at a given moment you could
say an intelligent child didn't know. It seemed to him
that he himself knew too much to imagine Morgan's
simplicity and too little to disembroil his tangle.

The boy paid no heed to his last remark; he only went
on: "I'd have spoken to them about their idea, as I call
it, long ago, if I hadn't been sure what they'd say."

"And what would they say?"

"Just what they said about what poor Zénobie told
me—that it was a horrid dreadful story, that they had
paid her every penny they owed her."

"Well, perhaps they had," said Pemberton.

"Perhaps they've paid you!"

"Let us pretend they have, and *n'en parlons plus.*"

"They accused her of lying and cheating"—Morgan stuck to historic truth. "That's why I don't want to speak to them."

"Lest they should accuse me too?" To this Morgan made no answer, and his companion, looking down at him—the boy turned away his eyes, which had filled —saw that he couldn't have trusted himself to utter. "You're right. Don't worry them," Pemberton pursued. "Except for that, they *are* charming people."

"Except for *their* lying and *their* cheating?"

"I say—I say!" cried Pemberton, imitating a little tone of the lad's which was itself an imitation.

"We must be frank, at the last; we *must* come to an understanding," said Morgan with the importance of the small boy who lets himself think he is arranging great affairs—almost playing at shipwreck or at Indians. "I know all about everything."

"I dare say your father has his reasons," Pemberton replied, but too vaguely, as he was aware.

"For lying and cheating?"

"For saving and managing and turning his means to the best account. He has plenty to do with his money. You're an expensive family."

"Yes, I'm very expensive," Morgan concurred in a manner that made his preceptor burst out laughing.

"He's saving for *you*," said Pemberton. "They think of you in everything they do."

"He might, while he's about it, save a little—" The boy paused, and his friend waited to hear what. Then Morgan brought out oddly: "A little reputation."

"Oh there's plenty of that. That's all right!"

"Enough of it for the people they know, no doubt. The people they know are awful."

"Do you mean the princes? We mustn't abuse the princes."

"Why not? They haven't married Paula—they haven't married Amy. They only clean out Ulick."

"You *do* know everything!" Pemberton declared.

"No I don't after all. I don't know what they live on, or how they live, or *why* they live! What have they got and how did they get it? Are they rich, are they poor, or have they a *modeste aisance*? Why are they always chiveying me about—living one year like ambassadors and the next like paupers? Who are they, anyway, and what are they? I've thought of all that—I've thought of a lot of things. They're so beastly worldly. That's what I hate most—oh I've *seen* it! All they care about is to make an appearance and to pass for something or other. What the dickens do they want to pass for? What *do* they, Mr. Pemberton?"

"You pause for a reply," said Pemberton, treating the question as a joke, yet wondering too and greatly struck with his mate's intense if imperfect vision. "I haven't the least idea."

"And what good does it do? Haven't I seen the way people treat them—the 'nice' people, the ones they want to know? They'll take anything from them—they'll lie down and be trampled on. The nice ones hate that—they just sicken them. You're the only really nice person we know."

"Are you sure? They don't lie down for me!"

"Well, you shan't lie down for them. You've got to go —that's what you've got to do," said Morgan.

"And what will become of you?"

"Oh I'm growing up. I shall get off before long. I'll see you later."

"You had better let me finish you," Pemberton urged, lending himself to the child's strange superiority.

Morgan stopped in their walk, looking up at him. He

had to look up much less than a couple of years before
—he had grown, in his loose leanness, so long and high.
"Finish me?" he echoed.

"There are such a lot of jolly things we can do together yet. I want to turn you out—I want you to do
me credit."

Morgan continued to look at him. "To give you credit
—do you mean?"

"My dear fellow, you're too clever to live."

"That's just what I'm afraid you think. No, no; it isn't
fair—I can't endure it. We'll separate next week. The
sooner it's over the sooner to sleep."

"If I hear of anything—any other chance—I promise
to go," Pemberton said.

Morgan consented to consider this. "But you'll be
honest," he demanded; "you won't pretend you haven't
heard?"

"I'm much more likely to pretend I have."

"But what can you hear of, this way, stuck in a hole
with us? You ought to be on the spot, to go to England
—you ought to go to America."

"One would think you were *my* tutor!" said Pemberton.

Morgan walked on and after a little had begun again:
"Well, now that you know I know and that we look
at the facts and keep nothing back—it's much more
comfortable, isn't it?"

"My dear boy, it's so amusing, so interesting, that it
will surely be quite impossible for me to forego such
hours as these."

This made Morgan stop once more. "You *do* keep
something back. Oh you're not straight—*I* am!"

"How am I not straight?"

"Oh you've got your idea!"

"My idea?"

"Why that I probably shan't make old—make older
—bones, and that you can stick it out till I'm removed."

"You *are* too clever to live!" Pemberton repeated.

"I call it a mean idea," Morgan pursued. "But I shall
punish you by the way I hang on."

"Look out or I'll poison you!" Pemberton laughed.

"I'm stronger and better every year. Haven't you
noticed that there hasn't been a doctor near me since
you came?"

"*I'm* your doctor," said the young man, taking his arm
and drawing him tenderly on again.

Morgan proceeded and after a few steps gave a sigh
of mingled weariness and relief. "Ah now that we look
at the facts it's all right!"

VII

They looked at the facts a good deal after this; and one
of the first consequences of their doing so was that Pemberton stuck it out, in his friend's parlance, for the purpose. Morgan made the facts so vivid and so droll, and
at the same time so bald and so ugly, that there was
fascination in talking them over with him, just as there
would have been heartlessness in leaving him alone with
them. Now that the pair had such perceptions in common it was useless for them to pretend they didn't judge
such people; but the very judgement and the exchange
of perceptions created another tie. Morgan had never
been so interesting as now that he himself was made
plainer by the sidelight of these confidences. What came
out in it most was the small fine passion of his pride.
He had plenty of that, Pemberton felt—so much that
one might perhaps wisely wish for it some early bruises.
He would have liked his people to have a spirit and
had waked up to the sense of their perpetually eating

humble-pie. His mother would consume any amount, and his father would consume even more than his mother. He had a theory that Ulick had wriggled out of an "affair" at Nice: there had once been a flurry at home, a regular panic, after which they all went to bed and took medicine, not to be accounted for on any other supposition. Morgan had a romantic imagination, fed by poetry and history, and he would have liked those who "bore his name"—as he used to say to Pemberton with the humour that made his queer delicacies manly—to carry themselves with an air. But their one idea was to get in with people who didn't want them and to take snubs as if they were honourable scars. Why people didn't want them more he didn't know—that was people's own affair; after all they weren't superficially repulsive, they were a hundred times cleverer than most of the dreary grandees, the "poor swells" they rushed about Europe to catch up with. "After all they *are* amusing—they are!" he used to pronounce with the wisdom of the ages. To which Pemberton always replied: "Amusing—the great Moreen troupe? Why they're altogether delightful; and if it weren't for the hitch that you and I (feeble performers!) make in the *ensemble* they'd carry everything before them."

What the boy couldn't get over was the fact that this particular blight seemed, in a tradition of self-respect, so undeserved and so arbitrary. No doubt people had a right to take the line they liked; but why should *his* people have liked the line of pushing and toadying and lying and cheating? What had their forefathers—all decent folk, so far as he knew—done to them, or what had *he* done to them? Who had poisoned their blood with the fifth-rate social ideal, the fixed idea of making smart acquaintances and getting into the *monde chic,* especially when it was foredoomed to failure and expo-

sure? They showed so what they were after; that was
what made the people they wanted not want *them*. And
never a wince for dignity, never a throb of shame at
looking each other in the face, never any independence
or resentment or disgust. If his father or his brother
would only knock some one down once or twice a year!
Clever as they were they never guessed the impression
they made. They were good-natured, yes—as good-
natured as Jews at the doors of clothing-shops! But was
that the model one wanted one's family to follow? Morgan had dim memories of an old grandfather, the maternal, in New York, whom he had been taken across the
ocean at the age of five to see: a gentleman with a high
neck-cloth and a good deal of pronunciation, who wore
a dress-coat in the morning, which made one wonder
what he wore in the evening, and had, or was supposed
to have, "property" and something to do with the Bible
Society. It couldn't have been but that *he* was a good
type. Pemberton himself remembered Mrs. Clancy, a
widowed sister of Mr. Moreen's, who was as irritating
as a moral tale and had paid a fortnight's visit to the family at Nice shortly after he came to live with them. She
was "pure and refined," as Amy said over the banjo, and
had the air of not knowing what they meant when they
talked, and of keeping something rather important back.
Pemberton judged that what she kept back was an approval of many of their ways; therefore it was to be
supposed that she too was of a good type, and that Mr.
and Mrs. Moreen and Ulick and Paula and Amy might
easily have been of a better one if they would.

But that they wouldn't was more and more perceptible from day to day. They continued to "chivey," as
Morgan called it, and in due time became aware of a
variety of reasons for proceeding to Venice. They mentioned a great many of them—they were always strik-

ingly frank and had the brightest friendly chatter, at the
late foreign breakfast in especial, before the ladies had
made up their faces, when they leaned their arms on
the table, had something to follow the *demi-tasse,* and,
in the heat of familiar discussion as to what they "really
ought" to do, fell inevitably into the languages in which
they could *tutoyer.* Even Pemberton liked them then; he
could endure even Ulick when he heard him give his little flat voice for the "sweet sea-city." That was what
made him have a sneaking kindness for them—that they
were so out of the workaday world and kept him so out
of it. The summer had waned when, with cries of ecstasy, they all passed out on the balcony that overhung
the Grand Canal. The sunsets then were splendid and
the Dorringtons had arrived. The Dorringtons were the
only reason they hadn't talked of at breakfast; but the
reasons they didn't talk of at breakfast always came out
in the end. The Dorringtons on the other hand came out
very little; or else when they did they stayed—as was
natural—for hours, during which periods Mrs. Moreen
and the girls sometimes called at their hotel (to see if
they had returned) as many as three times running. The
gondola was for the ladies, as in Venice too there were
"days," which Mrs. Moreen knew in their order an hour
after she arrived. She immediately took one herself, to
which the Dorringtons never came, though on a certain
occasion when Pemberton and his pupil were together
at Saint Mark's—where, taking the best walks they had
ever had and haunting a hundred churches, they spent
a great deal of time—they saw the old lord turn up with
Mr. Moreen and Ulick, who showed him the dim basilica
as if it belonged to them. Pemberton noted how much
less, among its curiosities, Lord Dorrington carried himself as a man of the world; wondering too whether, for
such services, his companions took a fee from him. The

autumn at any rate waned, the Dorringtons departed, and Lord Verschoyle, the eldest son, had proposed neither for Amy nor for Paula.

One sad November day, while the wind roared round the old palace and the rain lashed the lagoon, Pemberton, for exercise and even somewhat for warmth—the Moreens were horribly frugal about fires; it was a cause of suffering to their inmate—walked up and down the big bare *sala* with his pupil. The scagliola floor was cold, the high battered casements shook in the storm, and the stately decay of the place was unrelieved by a particle of furniture. Pemberton's spirits were low, and it came over him that the fortune of the Moreens was now even lower. A blast of desolation, a portent of disgrace and disaster, seemed to draw through the comfortless hall. Mr. Moreen and Ulick were in the Piazza, looking out for something, strolling drearily, in mackintoshes, under the arcades; but still, in spite of mackintoshes, unmistakeable men of the world. Paula and Amy were in bed—it might have been thought they were staying there to keep warm. Pemberton looked askance at the boy at his side, to see to what extent he was conscious of these dark omens. But Morgan, luckily for him, was now mainly conscious of growing taller and stronger and indeed of being in his fifteenth year. This fact was intensely interesting to him and the basis of a private theory—which, however, he had imparted to his tutor—that in a little while he should stand on his own feet. He considered that the situation would change—that in short he should be "finished," grown up, producible in the world of affairs and ready to prove himself of sterling ability. Sharply as he was capable at times of analysing, as he called it, his life, there were happy hours when he remained, as he also called it—and as the name, really, of their right ideal—"jolly" superficial; the proof of which was his fundamental assumption that he should presently go to Oxford, to Pemberton's college, and aided and abetted by Pemberton, do the most wonderful things. It depressed the young man to see how little in such a project he took account of ways and means: in other connexions he mostly kept to the measure. Pemberton tried to imagine the Moreens at Oxford and fortunately failed; yet unless they were to adopt it as a residence there would be no *modus vivendi* for Morgan. How could he live without an allowance, and where was the allowance to come from? He, Pemberton, might live on Morgan; but how could Morgan live on *him?* What was to become of him anyhow? Somehow the fact that he was a big boy now, with better prospects of health, made the question of his future more difficult. So long as he was markedly frail the great consideration he inspired seemed enough of an answer to it. But at the bottom of Pemberton's heart was the recognition of his probably being strong enough to live and not yet strong enough to struggle or to thrive. Morgan himself at any rate was in the first flush of the rosiest consciousness of adolescence, so that the beating of the tempest seemed to him after all but the voice of life and the challenge of fate. He had on his shabby little overcoat, with the collar up, but was enjoying his walk.

It was interrupted at last by the appearance of his mother at the end of the *sala*. She beckoned him to come to her, and while Pemberton saw him, complaisant, pass down the long vista and over the damp false marble, he wondered what was in the air. Mrs. Moreen said a word to the boy and made him go into the room she had quitted. Then, having closed the door after him, she directed her steps swiftly to Pemberton. There *was* something in the air, but his wildest flight of fancy wouldn't have suggested what it proved to be. She signified that she had made a pretext to get Morgan out of the way, and then she enquired—without hesitation —if the young man could favour her with the loan of three louis. While, before bursting into a laugh, he stared at her with surprise, she declared that she was awfully pressed for the money; she was desperate for it—it would save her life.

"Dear lady, *c'est trop fort!*" Pemberton laughed in the manner and with the borrowed grace of idiom that marked the best colloquial, the best anecdotic, moments of his friends themselves. "Where in the world do you suppose I should get three louis, *du train dont vous allez?*"

"I thought you worked—wrote things. Don't they pay you?"

"Not a penny."

"Are you such a fool as to work for nothing?"

"You ought surely to know that."

Mrs. Moreen stared, then she coloured a little. Pemberton saw she had quite forgotten the terms—if "terms" they could be called—that he had ended by accepting from herself; they had burdened her memory as little as her conscience. "Oh yes, I see what you mean —you've been very nice about that; but why drag it in so often?" She had been perfectly urbane with him ever since the rough scene of explanation in his room the morning he made her accept *his* "terms"—the necessity of his making his case known to Morgan. She had felt no resentment after seeing there was no danger Morgan would take the matter up with her. Indeed, attributing this immunity to the good taste of his influence with the boy, she had once said to Pemberton "My dear fellow, it's an immense comfort you're a gentleman." She repeated this in substance now. "Of course you're a gentleman—that's a bother the less!" Pemberton reminded her that he had not "dragged in" anything that wasn't already in as much as his foot was in his shoe; and she also repeated her prayer that, somewhere and somehow, he would find her sixty francs. He took the liberty of hinting that if he could find them it wouldn't be to lend them to *her*—as to which he consciously did himself injustice, knowing that if he had them he would certainly put them at her disposal. He accused himself, at bottom and not unveraciously, of a fantastic, a demoralised sympathy with her. If misery made strange bed-fellows it also made strange sympathies. It was moreover a part of the abasement of living with such people that one had to make vulgar retorts, quite out of one's own tradition of good manners. "Morgan, Morgan, to what pass have I come for you?" he groaned while Mrs. Moreen floated voluminously down the *sala* again to liberate the boy, wailing as she went that everything was too odious.

Before their young friend was liberated there came a thump at the door communicating with the staircase, followed by the apparition of a dripping youth who poked in his head. Pemberton recognised him as the bearer of a telegram and recognised the telegram as addressed to himself. Morgan came back as, after glancing at the signature—that of a relative in London—he was reading the words: "Found jolly job for you, engagement to coach opulent youth on own terms. Come at once." The answer happily was paid and the messenger waited. Morgan, who had drawn near, waited too and looked hard at Pemberton; and Pemberton, after a moment, having met his look, handed him the telegram. It was really by wise looks—they knew each other so well now —that, while the telegraph-boy, in his waterproof cape, made a great puddle on the floor, the thing was settled between them. Pemberton wrote the answer with a pen-

cil against the frescoed wall, and the messenger departed. When he had gone the young man explained
himself.

"I'll make a tremendous charge; I'll earn a lot of
money in a short time, and we'll live on it."

"Well, I hope the opulent youth will be a dismal
dunce—he probably will," Morgan parenthesised—
"and keep you a long time a-hammering of it in."

"Of course the longer he keeps me the more we shall
have for our old age."

"But suppose *they* don't pay you!" Morgan awfully
suggested.

"Oh there are not two such—!" But Pemberton pulled
up; he had been on the point of using too invidious a
term. Instead of this he said "Two such fatalities."

Morgan flushed—the tears came to his eyes. "*Dites
toujours* two such rascally crews!" Then in a different
tone he added: "Happy opulent youth!"

"Not if he's a dismal dunce."

"Oh they're happier then. But you can't have everything, can you?" the boy smiled.

Pemberton held him fast, hands on his shoulders—he
had never loved him so. "What will become of *you*,
what will you do?" He thought of Mrs. Moreen, desperate for sixty francs.

"I shall become an *homme fait*." And then as if he
recognised all the bearings of Pemberton's allusion: "I
shall get on with them better when you're not here."

"Ah don't say that—it sounds as if I set you against
them!"

"You do—the sight of you. It's all right; you know
what I mean. I shall be beautiful. I'll take their affairs
in hand; I'll marry my sisters."

"You'll marry yourself!" joked Pemberton; as high,

rather tense pleasantry would evidently be the right, or
the safest, tone for their separation.

It was, however, not purely in this strain that Morgan
suddenly asked: "But I say—how will you get to your
jolly job? You'll have to telegraph to the opulent youth
for money to come on."

Pemberton bethought himself. "They won't like that,
will they?"

"Oh look out for them!"

Then Pemberton brought out his remedy. "I'll go
to the American Consul; I'll borrow some money of
him—just for the few days, on the strength of the telegram."

Morgan was hilarious. "Show him the telegram—
then collar the money and stay!"

Pemberton entered into the joke sufficiently to reply
that for Morgan he was really capable of that; but the
boy, growing more serious, and to prove he hadn't
meant what he said, not only hurried him off to the Con-
sulate—since he was to start that evening, as he had
wired to his friend—but made sure of their affair by
going with him. They splashed through the tortuous
perforations and over the humpbacked bridges, and
they passed through the Piazza, where they saw Mr.
Moreen and Ulick go into a jeweller's shop. The Consul
proved accommodating—Pemberton said it wasn't the
letter, but Morgan's grand air—and on their way back
they went into Saint Mark's for a hushed ten minutes.
Later they took up and kept up the fun of it to the very
end; and it seemed to Pemberton a part of that fun
that Mrs. Moreen, who was very angry when he had
announced her his intention, should charge him, grotesquely and vulgarly and in reference to the loan she
had vainly endeavoured to effect, with bolting lest they

should "get something out" of him. On the other hand he had to do Mr. Moreen and Ulick the justice to recognise that when on coming in *they* heard the cruel news they took it like perfect men of the world.

VIII

When he got at work with the opulent youth, who was to be taken in hand for Balliol, he found himself unable to say if this aspirant had really such poor parts or if the appearance were only begotten of his own long association with an intensely living little mind. From Morgan he heard half a dozen times: the boy wrote charming young letters, a patchwork of tongues, with indulgent postscripts in the family Volapuk and, in little squares and rounds and crannies of the text, the drollest illustrations—letters that he was divided between the impulse to show his present charge as a vain, a wasted incentive, and the sense of something in them that publicity would profane. The opulent youth went up in due course and failed to pass; but it seemed to add to the presumption that brilliancy was not expected of him all at once that his parents, condoning the lapse, which they good-naturedly treated as little as possible as if it were Pemberton's, should have sounded the rally again, begged the young coach to renew the siege.

The young coach was now in a position to lend Mrs. Moreen three louis, and he sent her a post-office order even for a larger amount. In return for his favour he received a frantic scribbled line from her: "Implore you to come back instantly—Morgan dreadfully ill." They were on the rebound, once more in Paris—often as Pemberton had seen them depressed he had never seen them crushed—and communication was therefore rapid. He wrote to the boy to ascertain the state of his health, but awaited the answer in vain. He accordingly, after three days, took an abrupt leave of the opulent youth and, crossing the Channel, alighted at the small hotel, in the quarter of the Champs Élysées, of which Mrs. Moreen had given him the address. A deep if dumb dissatisfaction with this lady and her companions bore him company: they couldn't be vulgarly honest, but they could live at hotels, in velvety *entresols,* amid a smell of burnt pastilles, surrounded by the most expensive city in Europe. When he had left them in Venice it was with an irrepressible suspicion that something was going to happen; but the only thing that could have taken place was again their masterly retreat. "How is he? where is he?" he asked of Mrs. Moreen; but before she could speak these questions were answered by the pressure round his neck of a pair of arms, in shrunken sleeves, which still were perfectly capable of an effusive young foreign squeeze.

"Dreadfully ill—I don't see it!" the young man cried. And then to Morgan: "Why on earth didn't you relieve me? Why didn't you answer my letter?"

Mrs. Moreen declared that when she wrote he was very bad, and Pemberton learned at the same time from the boy that he had answered every letter he had received. This led to the clear inference that Pemberton's note had been kept from him so that the game to be practised should not be interfered with. Mrs. Moreen was prepared to see the fact exposed, as Pemberton saw the moment he faced her that she was prepared for a good many other things. She was prepared above all to maintain that she had acted from a sense of duty, that she was enchanted she had got him over, whatever they might say, and that it was useless of him to pretend he didn't know in all his bones that his place at such a time was with Morgan. He had taken the boy away from them and now had no right to abandon him. He had created for himself the gravest responsibilities and must at least abide by what he had done.

"Taken him away from you?" Pemberton exclaimed indignantly.

"Do it—do it for pity's sake; that's just what I want. I can't stand *this*—and such scenes. They're awful frauds—poor dears!" These words broke from Morgan, who had intermitted his embrace, in a key which made Pemberton turn quickly to him and see that he had suddenly seated himself, was breathing in great pain and was very pale.

"*Now* do you say he's not in a state, my precious pet?" shouted his mother, dropping on her knees before him with clasped hands, but touching him no more than if he had been a gilded idol. "It will pass—it's only for an instant; but don't say such dreadful things!"

"I'm all right—all right," Morgan panted to Pemberton, whom he sat looking up at with a strange smile, his hands resting on either side of the sofa.

"Now do you pretend I've been dishonest, that I've deceived?" Mrs. Moreen flashed at Pemberton as she got up.

"It isn't *he* says it, it's I!" the boy returned, apparently easier but sinking back against the wall; while his restored friend, who had sat down beside him, took his hand and bent over him.

"Darling child, one does what one can; there are so many things to consider," urged Mrs. Moreen. "It's his *place*—his only place. You see *you* think it is now."

"Take me away—take me away," Morgan went on, smiling to Pemberton with his white face.

"Where shall I take you, and how—oh *how*, my boy?" the young man stammered, thinking of the rude way in which his friends in London held that, for his convenience, with no assurance of prompt return, he had thrown them over; of the just resentment with which they would already have called in a successor, and of the scant help to finding fresh employment that resided for him in the grossness of his having failed to pass his pupil.

"Oh we'll settle that. You used to talk about it," said Morgan. "If we can only go all the rest's a detail."

"Talk about it as much as you like, but don't think you can attempt it. Mr. Moreen would never consent—it would be so *very* hand-to-mouth," Pemberton's hostess beautifully explained to him. Then to Morgan she made it clearer: "It would destroy our peace, it would break our hearts. Now that he's back it will be all the same again. You'll have your life, your work and your freedom, and we'll all be happy as we used to be. You'll bloom and grow perfectly well, and we won't have any more silly experiments, will we? They're too absurd. It's Mr. Pemberton's place—every one in his place. You in yours, your papa in his, me in mine—*n'est-ce pas, chéri?* We'll all forget how foolish we've been and have lovely times."

She continued to talk and to surge vaguely about the little draped stuffy salon while Pemberton sat with the boy, whose colour gradually came back; and she mixed up her reasons, hinting that there were going to be changes, that the other children might scatter (who knew?—Paula had her ideas) and that then it might be fancied how much the poor old parent-birds would want the little nestling. Morgan looked at Pemberton, who wouldn't let him move; and Pemberton knew exactly how he felt at hearing himself called a little nestling. He admitted that he had had one or two bad days, but he protested afresh against the wrong of his mother's having made them the ground of an appeal to poor Pemberton. Poor Pemberton could laugh now,

apart from the comicality of Mrs. Moreen's mustering
so much philosophy for her defence—she seemed to
shake it out of her agitated petticoats, which knocked
over the light gilt chairs—so little did their young companion, *marked,* unmistakeably marked at the best,
strike him as qualified to repudiate any advantage.

He himself was in for it at any rate. He should have
Morgan on his hands again indefinitely; though indeed
he saw the lad had a private theory to produce which
would be intended to smooth this down. He was obliged
to him for it in advance; but the suggested amend-
ment didn't keep his heart rather from sinking, any
more than it prevented him from accepting the prospect
on the spot, with some confidence moreover that he
should do even better if he could have a little supper.
Mrs. Moreen threw out more hints about the changes
that were to be looked for, but she was such a mixture
of smiles and shudders—she confessed she was very
nervous—that he couldn't tell if she were in high feather
or only in hysterics. If the family was really at last going to pieces why shouldn't she recognise the necessity
of pitching Morgan into some sort of lifeboat? This presumption was fostered by the fact that they were established in luxurious quarters in the capital of pleasure;
that was exactly where they naturally *would* be established in view of going to pieces. Moreover didn't she
mention that Mr. Moreen and the others were enjoying
themselves at the opera with Mr. Granger, and wasn't
that also precisely where one would look for them on
the eve of a smash? Pemberton gathered that Mr.
Granger was a rich vacant American—a big bill with a
flourishy heading and no items; so that one of Paula's
"ideas" was probably that this time she hadn't missed
fire—by which straight shot indeed she would have
shattered the general cohesion. And if the cohesion was

to crumble what would become of poor Pemberton? He
felt quite enough bound up with them to figure to his
alarm as a dislodged block in the edifice.

It was Morgan who eventually asked if no supper had
been ordered for him; sitting with him below, later, at
the dim delayed meal, in the presence of a great deal of
corded green plush, a plate of ornamental biscuit and an
aloofness marked on the part of the waiter. Mrs. Moreen
had explained that they had been obliged to secure a
room for the visitor out of the house; and Morgan's consolation—he offered it while Pemberton reflected on the
nastiness of luke-warm sauces—proved to be, largely,
that this circumstance would facilitate their escape. He
talked of their escape—recurring to it often afterwards
—as if they were making up a "boy's book" together.
But he likewise expressed his sense that there was something in the air, that the Moreens couldn't keep it up
much longer. In point of fact, as Pemberton was to see,
they kept it up for five or six months. All the while,
however, Morgan's contention was designed to cheer
him. Mr. Moreen and Ulick, whom he had met the day
after his return, accepted that return like perfect men
of the world. If Paula and Amy treated it even with less
formality an allowance was to be made for them, inasmuch as Mr. Granger hadn't come to the opera after all.
He had only placed his box at their service, with a bouquet for each of the party; there was even one apiece,
embittering the thought of his profusion, for Mr. Moreen
and Ulick. "They're all like that," was Morgan's comment; "at the very last, just when we think we've landed
them they're back in the deep sea!"

Morgan's comments in these days were more and
more free; they even included a large recognition of
the extraordinary tenderness with which he had been
treated while Pemberton was away. Oh yes, they

couldn't do enough to be nice to him, to show him they had him on their mind and make up for his loss. That was just what made the whole thing so sad and caused him to rejoice after all in Pemberton's return—he had to keep thinking of their affection less, had less sense of obligation. Pemberton laughed out at this last reason, and Morgan blushed and said "Well, dash it, you know what I mean." Pemberton knew perfectly what he meant; but there were a good many things that—dash it too!—it didn't make any clearer. This episode of his second sojourn in Paris stretched itself out wearily, with their resumed readings and wanderings and maunderings, their potterings on the quays, their hauntings of the museums, their occasional lingerings in the Palais Royal when the first sharp weather came on and there was a comfort in warm emanations, before Chevet's wonderful succulent window. Morgan wanted to hear all about the opulent youth—he took an immense interest in him. Some of the details of his opulence—Pemberton could spare him none of them—evidently fed the boy's appreciation of all his friend had given up to come back to him; but in addition to the greater reciprocity established by that heroism he had always his little brooding theory, in which there was a frivolous gaiety too, that their long probation was drawing to a close. Morgan's conviction that the Moreens couldn't go on much longer kept pace with the unexpended impetus with which, from month to month, they did go on. Three weeks after Pemberton had rejoined them they went on to another hotel, a dingier one than the first; but Morgan rejoiced that his tutor had at least still not sacrificed the advantage of a room outside. He clung to the romantic utility of this when the day, or rather the night, should arrive for their escape.

For the first time, in this complicated connexion, our

friend felt his collar gall him. It was, as he had said to
Mrs. Moreen in Venice, *trop fort*—everything was *trop
fort*. He could neither really throw off his blighting burden nor find in it the benefit of a pacified conscience or
of a rewarded affection. He had spent all the money ac-
cruing to him in England, and he saw his youth going
and that he was getting nothing back for it. It was all
very well of Morgan to count it for reparation that he
should now settle on him permanently—there was an
irritating flaw in such a view. He saw what the boy had
in his mind; the conception that as his friend had had
the generosity to come back he must show his gratitude by giving him his life. But the poor friend didn't
desire the gift—what could he do with Morgan's dreadful little life? Of course at the same time that Pemberton
was irritated he remembered the reason, which was very
honourable to Morgan and which dwelt simply in his
making one so forget that he was no more than a patched
urchin. If one dealt with him on a different basis one's
misadventures were one's own fault. So Pemberton
waited in a queer confusion of yearning and alarm for
the catastrophe which was held to hang over the house
of Moreen, of which he certainly at moments felt the
symptoms brush his cheek and as to which he wondered much in what form it would find its liveliest effect.

Perhaps it would take the form of sudden dispersal—
a frightened *sauve qui peut,* a scuttling into selfish corners. Certainly they were less elastic than of yore; they
were evidently looking for something they didn't find.
The Dorringtons hadn't re-appeared, the princes had
scattered; wasn't that the beginning of the end? Mrs.
Moreen had lost her reckoning of the famous "days";
her social calendar was blurred—it had turned its face
to the wall. Pemberton suspected that the great, the
cruel discomfiture had been the unspeakable behaviour

of Mr. Granger, who seemed not to know what he
wanted, or, what was much worse, what *they* wanted.
He kept sending flowers, as if to bestrew the path of his
retreat, which was never the path of a return. Flowers
were all very well, but—Pemberton could complete the
proposition. It was now positively conspicuous that in
the long run the Moreens were a social failure; so that
the young man was almost grateful the run had not been
short. Mr. Moreen indeed was still occasionally able to
get away on business and, what was more surprising,
was likewise able to get back. Ulick had no club, but
you couldn't have discovered it from his appearance,
which was as much as ever that of a person looking at
life from the window of such an institution; therefore
Pemberton was doubly surprised at an answer he once
heard him make his mother in the desperate tone of a
man familiar with the worst privations. Her question
Pemberton had not quite caught; it appeared to be an
appeal for a suggestion as to whom they might get to
take Amy. "Let the Devil take her!" Ulick snapped; so
that Pemberton could see that they had not only lost
their amiability but had ceased to believe in themselves.
He could also see that if Mrs. Moreen was trying to get
people to take her children she might be regarded as
closing the hatches for the storm. But Morgan would be
the last she would part with.

One winter afternoon—it was a Sunday—he and the
boy walked far together in the Bois de Boulogne. The
evening was so splendid, the cold lemon-coloured sunset so clear, the stream of carriages and pedestrians so
amusing and the fascination of Paris so great, that they
stayed out later than usual and became aware that they
should have to hurry home to arrive in time for dinner.
They hurried accordingly, arm-in-arm, good-humoured

and hungry, agreeing that there was nothing like Paris after all and that after everything too that had come and gone they were not yet sated with innocent pleasures. When they reached the hotel they found that, though scandalously late, they were in time for all the dinner they were likely to sit down to. Confusion reigned in the apartments of the Moreens—very shabby ones this time, but the best in the house—and before the interrupted service of the table, with objects displaced almost as if there had been a scuffle and a great wine-stain from an overturned bottle, Pemberton couldn't blink the fact that there had been a scene of the last proprietary firmness. The storm had come—they were all seeking refuge. The hatches were down, Paula and Amy were invisible—they had never tried the most casual art upon Pemberton, but he felt they had enough of an eye to him not to wish to meet him as young ladies whose frocks had been confiscated—and Ulick appeared to have jumped overboard. The host and his staff, in a word, had ceased to "go on" at the pace of their guests, and the air of embarrassed detention, thanks to a pile of gaping trunks in the passage, was strangely commingled with the air of indignant withdrawal.

When Morgan took all this in—and he took it in very quickly—he coloured to the roots of his hair. He had walked from his infancy among difficulties and dangers, but he had never seen a public exposure. Pemberton noticed in a second glance at him that the tears had rushed into his eyes and that they were tears of a new and untasted bitterness. He wondered an instant, for the boy's sake, whether he might successfully pretend not to understand. Not successfully, he felt, as Mr. and Mrs. Moreen, dinnerless by their extinguished hearth, rose before him in their little dishonoured salon, casting about with glassy eyes for the nearest port in such a storm. They were not prostrate but were horribly white, and Mrs. Moreen had evidently been crying. Pemberton quickly learned however that her grief was not for the loss of her dinner, much as she usually enjoyed it, but the fruit of a blow that struck even deeper, as she made all haste to explain. He would see for himself, so far as that went, how the great change had come, the dreadful bolt had fallen, and how they would now all have to turn themselves about. Therefore cruel as it was to them to part with their darling she must look to him to carry a little further the influence he had so fortunately acquired with the boy—to induce his young charge to follow him into some modest retreat. They depended on him—that was the fact—to take their delightful child temporarily under his protection: it would leave Mr. Moreen and herself so much more free to give the proper attention (too little, alas! had been given) to the readjustment of their affairs.

"We trust you—we feel we *can*," said Mrs. Moreen, slowly rubbing her plump white hands and looking with compunction hard at Morgan, whose chin, not to take liberties, her husband stroked with a tentative paternal forefinger.

"Oh yes—we feel that we *can*. We trust Mr. Pemberton fully, Morgan," Mr. Moreen pursued.

Pemberton wondered again if he might pretend not to understand; but everything good gave way to the intensity of Morgan's understanding. "Do you mean he may take me to live with him for ever and ever? May take me away, away, anywhere he likes?" cried the boy.

"For ever and ever? *Comme vous-y-allez!*" Mr. Moreen laughed indulgently. "For as long as Mr. Pemberton may be so good."

"We've struggled, we've suffered," his wife went on; "but you've made him so your own that we've already been through the worst of the sacrifice."

Morgan had turned away from his father—he stood looking at Pemberton with a light in his face. His sense of shame for their common humiliated state had dropped; the case had another side—the thing was to clutch at *that*. He had a moment of boyish joy, scarcely mitigated by the reflexion that with this unexpected consecration of his hope—too sudden and too violent; the turn taken was away from a *good* boy's book—the "escape" was left on their hands. The boyish joy was there an instant, and Pemberton was almost scared at the rush of gratitude and affection that broke through his first abasement. When he stammered "My dear fellow, what do you say to *that?*" how could one not say something enthusiastic? But there was more need for courage at something else that immediately followed and that made the lad sit down quickly on the nearest chair. He had turned quite livid and had raised his hand to his left side. They were all three looking at him, but Mrs. Moreen suddenly bounded forward. "Ah his darling little heart!" she broke out; and this time, on her knees before him and without respect for the idol, she caught him ardently in her arms. "You walked him too far, you hurried him too fast!" she hurled over her shoulder at Pemberton. Her son made no protest, and the next instant, still holding him, she sprang up with her face convulsed and with the terrified cry "Help, help! he's going, he's gone!" Pemberton saw with equal horror, by Morgan's own stricken face, that he was beyond their wildest recall. He pulled him half out of his mother's hands, and for a moment, while they held him together, they looked all their dismay into each other's eyes. "He couldn't stand it with his weak organ," said Pemberton—"the shock, the whole scene, the violent emotion."

"But I thought he *wanted* to go to you!" wailed Mrs. Moreen.

"I *told* you he didn't, my dear," her husband made answer. Mr. Moreen was trembling all over and was in his way as deeply affected as his wife. But after the very first he took his bereavement as a man of the world.

1891

THE BEAST IN THE JUNGLE

I

What determined the speech that startled him in the course of their encounter scarcely matters, being probably but some words spoken by himself quite without intention—spoken as they lingered and slowly moved together after their renewal of acquaintance. He had been conveyed by friends an hour or two before to the house at which she was staying; the party of visitors at the other house, of whom he was one, and thanks to whom it was his theory, as always, that he was lost in the crowd, had been invited over to luncheon. There had been after luncheon much dispersal, all in the interest of the original motive, a view of Weatherend itself and the fine things, intrinsic features, pictures, heirlooms, treasures of all the arts, that made the place almost famous; and the great rooms were so numerous that guests could wander at their will, hang back from the principal group and in cases where they took such matters with the last seriousness give themselves up to mysterious appreciations and measurements. There were persons to be observed, singly or in couples, bending toward objects in out-of-the-way corners with their hands on their knees and their heads nodding quite as with the emphasis of an excited sense of smell. When they were two they either mingled their sounds of ecstasy or melted into silences of even deeper import, so that there were aspects of the occasion that gave it for Marcher much the air of the "look round," previous to a sale highly advertised, that excites or quenches, as may be, the dream of acquisition. The dream of acquisition at Weatherend would have had to be wild indeed, and John Marcher found himself, among such suggestions, disconcerted almost equally by the presence of those who knew too much and by that of those who knew nothing. The great rooms caused so much poetry and history to press upon him that he needed some straying apart to feel in a proper relation with them, though this impulse was not, as happened, like the gloating of some of his companions, to be compared to the movements of a dog sniffing a cupboard. It had an issue promptly enough in a direction that was not to have been calculated.

It led, briefly, in the course of the October afternoon, to his closer meeting with May Bartram, whose face, a reminder, yet not quite a remembrance, as they sat much separated at a very long table, had begun merely by troubling him rather pleasantly. It affected him as the sequel of something of which he had lost the beginning. He knew it, and for the time quite welcomed it, as a continuation, but didn't know what it continued, which was an interest or an amusement the greater as he was also somehow aware—yet without a direct sign from her—that the young woman herself hadn't lost the thread. She hadn't lost it, but she wouldn't give it back

to him, he saw, without some putting forth of his hand
for it; and he not only saw that, but saw several things
more, things odd enough in the light of the fact at the
moment some accident of grouping brought them face
to face he was still merely fumbling with the idea that
any contact between them in the past would have had
no importance. If it had had no importance he scarcely
knew why his actual impression of her should so seem
to have so much; the answer to which, however, was
that in such a life as they all appeared to be leading for
the moment one could but take things as they came. He
was satisfied, without in the least being able to say why,
that this young lady might roughly have ranked in the
house as a poor relation; satisfied also that she was not
there on a brief visit, but was more or less a part of the
establishment—almost a working, a remunerated part.
Didn't she enjoy at periods a protection that she paid for
by helping, among other services, to show the place and
explain it, deal with the tiresome people, answer questions about the dates of the building, the styles of the
furniture, the authorship of the pictures, the favourite
haunts of the ghost? It wasn't that she looked as if you
could have given her shillings—it was impossible to
look less so. Yet when she finally drifted toward him,
distinctly handsome, though ever so much older—older
than when he had seen her before—it might have been
as an effect of her guessing that he had, within the
couple of hours, devoted more imagination to her than
to all the others put together, and had thereby penetrated to a kind of truth that the others were too stupid
for. She *was* there on harder terms than any one; she
was there as a consequence of things suffered, one way
and another, in the interval of years; and she remembered him very much as she was remembered—only a
good deal better.

By the time they at last thus came to speech they were alone in one of the rooms—remarkable for a fine portrait over the chimney-place—out of which their friends had passed, and the charm of it was that even before they had spoken they had practically arranged with each other to stay behind for talk. The charm, happily, was in other things too—partly in there being scarce a spot at Weatherend without something to stay behind for. It was in the way the autumn day looked into the high windows as it waned; the way the red light, breaking at the close from under a low sombre sky, reached out in a long shaft and played over old wainscots, old tapestry, old gold, old colour. It was most of all perhaps in the way she came to him as if, since she had been turned on to deal with the simpler sort, he might, should he choose to keep the whole thing down, just take her mild attention for a part of her general business. As soon as he heard her voice, however, the gap was filled up and the missing link supplied; the slight irony he divined in her attitude lost its advantage. He almost jumped at it to get there before her. "I met you years and years ago in Rome. I remember all about it." She confessed to disappointment—she had been so sure he didn't; and to prove how well he did he began to pour forth the particular recollections that popped up as he called for them. Her face and her voice, all at his service now, worked the miracle—the impression operating like the torch of a lamplighter who touches into flame, one by one, a long row of gas-jets. Marcher flattered himself the illumination was brilliant, yet he was really still more pleased on her showing him, with amusement, that in his haste to make everything right he had got most things rather wrong. It hadn't been at Rome—it had been at Naples; and it hadn't been eight years before—it had been more nearly ten. She hadn't been, either, with her uncle and aunt, but with her mother and her brother; in addition to which it was not with the Pembles *he* had been, but with the Boyers, coming down in their company from Rome—a point on which she insisted, a little to his confusion, and as to which she had her evidence in hand. The Boyers she had known, but didn't know the Pembles, though she had heard of them, and it was the people he was with who had made them acquainted. The incident of the thunderstorm that had raged round them with such violence as to drive them for refuge into an excavation—this incident had not occurred at the Palace of the Cæsars, but at Pompeii, on an occasion when they had been present there at an important find.

He accepted her amendments, he enjoyed her corrections, though the moral of them was, she pointed out, that he *really* didn't remember the least thing about her; and he only felt it as a drawback that when all was made strictly historic there didn't appear much of anything left. They lingered together still, she neglecting her office—for from the moment he was so clever she had no proper right to him—and both neglecting the house, just waiting as to see if a memory or two more wouldn't again breathe on them. It hadn't taken them many minutes, after all, to put down on the table, like the cards of a pack, those that constituted their respective hands; only what came out was that the pack was unfortunately not perfect—that the past, invoked, invited, encouraged, could give them, naturally, no more than it had. It had made them anciently meet—her at twenty, him at twenty-five; but nothing was so strange, they seemed to say to each other, as that, while so occupied, it hadn't done a little more for them. They looked at each other as with the feeling of an occasion missed; the present would have been so much better if

the other, in the far distance, in the foreign land, hadn't
been so stupidly meagre. There weren't apparently, all
counted, more than a dozen little old things that had
succeeded in coming to pass between them; trivialities
of youth, simplicities of freshness, stupidities of ignorance, small possible germs, but too deeply buried—too
deeply (didn't it seem?) to sprout after so many years.
Marcher could only feel he ought to have rendered her
some service—saved her from a capsized boat in the Bay
or at least recovered her dressing-bag, filched from her
cab in the streets of Naples by a lazzarone with a sti-
letto. Or it would have been nice if he could have been
taken with fever all alone at his hotel, and she could
have come to look after him, to write to his people, to
drive him out in convalescence. *Then* they would be in
possession of the something or other that their actual
show seemed to lack. It yet somehow presented itself,
this show, as too good to be spoiled; so that they were
reduced for a few minutes more to wondering a little
helplessly why—since they seemed to know a certain
number of the same people—their reunion had been so
long averted. They didn't use that name for it, but their
delay from minute to minute to join the others was a
kind of confession that they didn't quite want it to be
a failure. Their attempted supposition of reasons for
their not having met but showed how little they knew
of each other. There came in fact a moment when
Marcher felt a positive pang. It was vain to pretend she
was an old friend, for all the communities were wanting,
in spite of which it was as an old friend that he saw
she would have suited him. He had new ones enough—
was surrounded with them for instance on the stage of
the other house; as a new one he probably wouldn't
have so much as noticed her. He would have liked to
invent something, get her to make believe with him that

some passage of a romantic or critical kind *had* originally
occurred. He was really almost reaching out in imagination—as against time—for something that would do, and
saying to himself that if it didn't come this sketch of a
fresh start would show for quite awkwardly bungled.
They would separate, and now for no second or no third
chance. They would have tried and not succeeded.
Then it was, just at the turn, as he afterwards made it
out to himself, that, everything else failing, she herself
decided to take up the case and, as it were, save the situation. He felt as soon as she spoke that she had been
consciously keeping back what she said and hoping to
get on without it; a scruple in her that immensely
touched him when, by the end of three or four minutes
more, he was able to measure it. What she brought out,
at any rate, quite cleared the air and supplied the link
—the link it was so odd he should frivolously have managed to lose.

"You know you told me something I've never forgotten and that again and again has made me think of
you since; it was that tremendously hot day when we
went to Sorrento, across the bay, for the breeze. What I
allude to was what you said to me, on the way back,
as we sat under the awning of the boat enjoying the
cool. Have you forgotten?"

He had forgotten and was even more surprised than
ashamed. But the great thing was that he saw in this
no vulgar reminder of any "sweet" speech. The vanity
of women had long memories, but she was making no
claim on him of a compliment or a mistake. With another woman, a totally different one, he might have
feared the recall possibly even of some imbecile "offer."
So, in having to say that he had indeed forgotten, he
was conscious rather of a loss than of a gain; he already
saw an interest in the matter of her mention. "I try to

think—but I give it up. Yet I remember the Sorrento day."

"I'm not very sure you do," May Bartram after a moment said; "and I'm not very sure I ought to want you to. It's dreadful to bring a person back at any time to what he was ten years before. If you've lived away from it," she smiled, "so much the better."

"Ah if *you* haven't why should I?" he asked.

"Lived away, you mean, from what I myself was?"

"From what *I* was. I was of course an ass," Marcher went on; "but I would rather know from you just the sort of ass I was than—from the moment you have something in your mind—not know anything."

Still, however, she hesitated. "But if you've completely ceased to be that sort—?"

"Why I can then all the more bear to know. Besides, perhaps I haven't."

"Perhaps. Yet if you haven't," she added, "I should suppose you'd remember. Not indeed that *I* in the least connect with my impression the invidious name you use. If I had only thought you foolish," she explained, "the thing I speak of wouldn't so have remained with me. It was about yourself." She waited as if it might come to him; but as, only meeting her eyes in wonder, he gave no sign, she burnt her ships. "Has it ever happened?"

Then it was that, while he continued to stare, a light broke for him and the blood slowly came to his face, which began to burn with recognition. "Do you mean I told you—?" But he faltered, lest what came to him shouldn't be right, lest he should only give himself away.

"It was something about yourself that it was natural one shouldn't forget—that is if one remembered you at all. That's why I ask you," she smiled, "if the thing you then spoke of has ever come to pass?"

Oh then he saw, but he was lost in wonder and found himself embarrassed. This, he also saw, made her sorry for him, as if her allusion had been a mistake. It took him but a moment, however, to feel it hadn't been, much as it had been a surprise. After the first little shock of it her knowledge on the contrary began, even if rather strangely, to taste sweet to him. She was the only other person in the world then who would have it, and she had had it all these years, while the fact of his having so breathed his secret had unaccountably faded from him. No wonder they couldn't have met as if nothing had happened. "I judge," he finally said, "that I know what you mean. Only I had strangely enough lost any sense of having taken you so far into my confidence."

"Is it because you've taken so many others as well?"

"I've taken nobody. Not a creature since then."

"So that I'm the only person who knows?"

"The only person in the world."

"Well," she quickly replied, "I myself have never spoken. I've never, never repeated of you what you told me." She looked at him so that he perfectly believed her. Their eyes met over it in such a way that he was without a doubt. "And I never will."

She spoke with an earnestness that, as if almost excessive, put him at ease about her possible derision. Somehow the whole question was a new luxury to him—that is from the moment she was in possession. If she didn't take the sarcastic view she clearly took the sympathetic, and that was what he had had, in all the long time, from no one whomsoever. What he felt was that he couldn't at present have begun to tell her, and yet could profit perhaps exquisitely by the accident of having done so of old. "Please don't then. We're just right as it is."

"Oh I am," she laughed, "if you are!" To which she added: "Then you do still feel in the same way?"

It was impossible he shouldn't take to himself that she was really interested, though it all kept coming as perfect surprise. He had thought of himself so long as abominably alone, and lo he wasn't alone a bit. He hadn't been, it appeared, for an hour—since those moments on the Sorrento boat. It was *she* who had been, he seemed to see as he looked at her—she who had been made so by the graceless fact of his lapse of fidelity. To tell her what he had told her—what had it been but to ask something of her? something that she had given, in her charity, without his having, by a remembrance, by a return of the spirit, failing another encounter, so much as thanked her. What he had asked of her had been simply at first not to laugh at him. She had beautifully not done so for ten years, and she was not doing so now. So he had endless gratitude to make up. Only for that he must see just how he had figured to her. "What, exactly, was the account I gave—?"

"Of the way you did feel? Well, it was very simple. You said you had had from your earliest time, as the deepest thing within you, the sense of being kept for something rare and strange, possibly prodigious and terrible, that was sooner or later to happen to you, that you had in your bones the foreboding and the conviction of, and that would perhaps overwhelm you."

"Do you call that very simple?" John Marcher asked.

She thought a moment. "It was perhaps because I seemed, as you spoke, to understand it."

"You do understand it?" he eagerly asked.

Again she kept her kind eyes on him. "You still have the belief?"

"Oh!" he exclaimed helplessly. There was too much to say.

"Whatever it's to be," she clearly made out, "it hasn't yet come."

He shook his head in complete surrender now. "It hasn't yet come. Only, you know, it isn't anything I'm to *do*, to achieve in the world, to be distinguished or admired for. I'm not such an ass as *that*. It would be much better, no doubt, if I were."

"It's to be something you're merely to suffer?"

"Well, say to wait for—to have to meet, to face, to see suddenly break out in my life; possibly destroying all further consciousness, possibly annihilating me; possibly, on the other hand, only altering everything, striking at the root of all my world and leaving me to the consequences, however they shape themselves."

She took this in, but the light in her eyes continued for him not to be that of mockery. "Isn't what you describe perhaps but the expectation—or at any rate the sense of danger, familiar to so many people—of falling in love?"

John Marcher wondered. "Did you ask me that before?"

"No—I wasn't so free-and-easy then. But it's what strikes me now."

"Of course," he said after a moment, "it strikes you. Of course it strikes *me*. Of course what's in store for me may be no more than that. The only thing is," he went on, "that I think if it had been that I should by this time know."

"Do you mean because you've *been* in love?" And then as he but looked at her in silence: "You've been in love, and it hasn't meant such a cataclysm, hasn't proved the great affair?"

"Here I am, you see. It hasn't been overwhelming."

"Then it hasn't been love," said May Bartram.

"Well, I at least thought it was. I took it for that— I've taken it till now. It was agreeable, it was delightful,

it was miserable," he explained. "But it wasn't strange.
It wasn't what *my* affair's to be."

"You want something all to yourself—something that
nobody else knows or *has* known?"

"It isn't a question of what I 'want'—God knows I
don't want anything. It's only a question of the apprehension that haunts me—that I live with day by day."

He said this so lucidly and consistently that he could
see it further impose itself. If she hadn't been interested
before she'd have been interested now. "Is it a sense
of coming violence?"

Evidently now too again he liked to talk of it. "I don't
think of it as—when it does come—necessarily violent.
I only think of it as natural and as of course above all
unmistakeable. I think of it simply as *the* thing. The
thing will of itself appear natural."

"Then how will it appear strange?"

Marcher bethought himself. "It won't—to *me*."

"To whom then?"

"Well," he replied, smiling at last, "say to you."

"Oh then I'm to be present?"

"Why you *are* present—since you know."

"I see." She turned it over. "But I mean at the catastrophe."

At this, for a minute, their lightness gave way to their
gravity; it was as if the long look they exchanged held
them together. "It will only depend on yourself—if
you'll watch with me."

"Are you afraid?" she asked.

"Don't leave me *now*," he went on.

"Are you afraid?" she repeated.

"Do you think me simply out of my mind?" he pursued instead of answering. "Do I merely strike you as
a harmless lunatic?"

"No," said May Bartram. "I understand you. I believe you."

"You mean you feel how my obsession—poor old thing!—may correspond to some possible reality?"

"To some possible reality."

"Then you *will* watch with me?"

She hesitated, then for the third time put her question. "Are you afraid?"

"Did I tell you I was—at Naples?"

"No, you said nothing about it."

"Then I don't know. And I should *like* to know," said John Marcher. "You'll tell me yourself whether you think so. If you'll watch with me you'll see."

"Very good then." They had been moving by this time across the room, and at the door, before passing out, they paused as for the full wind-up of their understanding. "I'll watch with you," said May Bartram.

II

The fact that she "knew"—knew and yet neither chaffed him nor betrayed him—had in a short time begun to constitute between them a goodly bond, which became more marked when, within the year that followed their afternoon at Weatherend, the opportunities for meeting multiplied. The event that thus promoted these occasions was the death of the ancient lady her great-aunt, under whose wing, since losing her mother, she had to such an extent found shelter, and who, though but the widowed mother of the new successor to the property, had succeeded—thanks to a high tone and a high temper—in not forfeiting the supreme position at the great house. The deposition of this personage arrived but with her death, which, followed by many changes, made in particular a difference for the young woman in whom Marcher's expert attention had recognised from the first a dependent with a pride that might ache though it didn't bristle. Nothing for a long time had made him easier than the thought that the aching must have been much soothed by Miss Bartram's now finding herself able to set up a small home in London. She had acquired property, to an amount that made that luxury just possible, under her aunt's extremely complicated will, and when the whole matter began to be straightened out, which indeed took time, she let him know that the happy issue was at last in view. He had seen her again before that day, both because she had more than once accompanied the ancient lady to town and because he had paid another visit to the friends who so conveniently made of Weatherend one of the charms of their own hospitality. These friends had taken him back there; he had achieved there again with Miss Bartram some quiet detachment; and he had in London succeeded in persuading her to more than one brief absence from her aunt. They went together, on these latter occasions, to the National Gallery and the South Kensington Museum, where, among vivid reminders, they talked of Italy at large—not now attempting to recover, as at first, the taste of their youth and their ignorance. That recovery, the first day at Weatherend, had served its purpose well, had given them quite enough; so that they were, to Marcher's sense, no longer hovering about the headwaters of their stream, but had felt their boat pushed sharply off and down the current.

They were literally afloat together; for our gentleman this was marked, quite as marked as that the fortunate cause of it was just the buried treasure of her knowledge. He had with his own hands dug up this little hoard, brought to light—that is to within reach of the dim day constituted by their discretions and privacies—the object of value the hiding-place of which he had, after putting it into the ground himself, so strangely, so long forgotten. The rare luck of his having again just stumbled on the spot made him indifferent to any other question; he would doubtless have devoted more time to the odd accident of his lapse of memory if he hadn't been moved to devote so much to the sweetness, the comfort, as he felt, for the future, that this accident itself had helped to keep fresh. It had never entered into his plan that any one should "know," and mainly for the reason that it wasn't in him to tell any one. That would have been impossible, for nothing but the amusement of a cold world would have waited on it. Since, however, a mysterious fate had opened his mouth betimes, in spite of him, he would count that a compensation and profit by it to the utmost. That the right person *should* know tempered the asperity of his secret more even than his shyness had permitted him to imagine; and May Bartram was clearly right, because—well, because there she was. Her knowledge simply settled it; he would have been sure enough by this time had she been wrong. There was that in his situation, no doubt, that disposed him too much to see her as a mere confidant, taking all her light for him from the fact—the fact only—of her interest in his predicament; from her mercy, sympathy, seriousness, her consent not to regard him as the funniest of the funny. Aware, in fine, that her price for him was just in her giving him this constant sense of his being admirably spared, he was careful to remember that she had also a life of her own, with things that might happen to *her,* things that in friendship one should likewise take account of. Something fairly remarkable came to pass with him, for that matter, in this connexion—something represented by a certain passage of his consciousness, in the suddenest way, from one extreme to the other.

He had thought himself, so long as nobody knew, the most disinterested person in the world, carrying his concentrated burden, his perpetual suspense, ever so quietly, holding his tongue about it, giving others no glimpse of it nor of its effect upon his life, asking of them no allowance and only making on his side all those that were asked. He hadn't disturbed people with the queerness of their having to know a haunted man, though he had had moments of rather special temptation on hearing them say they were forsooth "unsettled." If they were as unsettled as he was—he who had never been settled for an hour in his life—they would know what it meant. Yet it wasn't, all the same, for him to make them, and he listened to them civilly enough. This was why he had such good—though possibly such rather colourless—manners; this was why, above all, he could regard himself, in a greedy world, as decently—as in fact perhaps even a little sublimely—unselfish. Our point is accordingly that he valued this character quite sufficiently to measure his present danger of letting it lapse, against which he promised himself to be much on his guard. He was quite ready, none the less, to be selfish just a little, since surely no more charming occasion for it had come to him. "Just a little," in a word, was just as much as Miss Bartram, taking one day with another, would let him. He never would be in the least coercive, and would keep well before him the lines on which consideration for her—the very highest—ought to proceed. He would thoroughly establish the heads under which her affairs, her requirements, her peculiarities—he went so far as to give them the latitude of that name—would come into their intercourse. All this naturally was a sign of how much he took the intercourse itself for granted. There was nothing more to be done about *that*. It simply existed; had sprung into being with her first penetrating

question to him in the autumn light there at Weatherend. The real form it should have taken on the basis that
stood out large was the form of their marrying. But the
devil in this was that the very basis itself put marrying
out of the question. His conviction, his apprehension,
his obsession, in short, wasn't a privilege he could invite
a woman to share; and that consequence of it was precisely what was the matter with him. Something or other
lay in wait for him, amid the twists and the turns of the
months and the years, like a crouching beast in the jungle. It signified little whether the crouching beast were
destined to slay him or to be slain. The definite point
was the inevitable spring of the creature; and the definite lesson from that was that a man of feeling didn't
cause himself to be accompanied by a lady on a tiger-
hunt. Such was the image under which he had ended
by figuring his life.

They had at first, none the less, in the scattered hours
spent together, made no allusion to that view of it;
which was a sign he was handsomely alert to give that
he didn't expect, that he in fact didn't care, always to
be talking about it. Such a feature in one's outlook was
really like a hump on one's back. The difference it made
every minute of the day existed quite independently
of discussion. One discussed of course *like* a hunchback,
for there was always, if nothing else, the hunchback
face. That remained, and she was watching him; but
people watched best, as a general thing, in silence, so
that such would be predominantly the manner of their
vigil. Yet he didn't want, at the same time, to be tense
and solemn; tense and solemn was what he imagined he
too much showed for with other people. The thing to be,
with the one person who knew, was easy and natural—
to make the reference rather than be seeming to avoid
it, to avoid it rather than be seeming to make it, and

to keep it, in any case, familiar, facetious even, rather than pedantic and portentous. Some such consideration as the latter was doubtless in his mind for instance when he wrote pleasantly to Miss Bartram that perhaps the great thing he had so long felt as in the lap of the gods was no more than this circumstance, which touched him so nearly, of her acquiring a house in London. It was the first allusion they had yet again made, needing any other hitherto so little; but when she replied, after having given him the news, that she was by no means satisfied with such a trifle as the climax to so special a suspense, she almost set him wondering if she hadn't even a larger conception of singularity for him than he had for himself. He was at all events destined to become aware little by little, as time went by, that she was all the while looking at his life, judging it, measuring it, in the light of the thing she knew, which grew to be at last, with the consecration of the years, never mentioned between them save as "the real truth" about him. That had always been his own form of reference to it, but she adopted the form so quietly that, looking back at the end of a period, he knew there was no moment at which it was traceable that she had, as he might say, got inside his idea, or exchanged the attitude of beautifully indulging for that of still more beautifully believing him.

It was always open to him to accuse her of seeing him but as the most harmless of maniacs, and this, in the long run—since it covered so much ground—was his easiest description of their friendship. He had a screw loose for her, but she liked him in spite of it and was practically, against the rest of the world, his kind wise keeper, unremunerated but fairly amused and, in the absence of other near ties, not disreputably occupied. The rest of the world of course thought him queer, but she, she only, knew how, and above all why, queer;

which was precisely what enabled her to dispose the concealing veil in the right folds. She took his gaiety from him—since it had to pass with them for gaiety— as she took everything else; but she certainly so far justified by her unerring touch his finer sense of the degree to which he had ended by convincing her. *She* at least never spoke of the secret of his life except as "the real truth about you," and she had in fact a wonderful way of making it seem, as such, the secret of her own life too. That was in fine how he so constantly felt her as allowing for him; he couldn't on the whole call it anything else. He allowed himself, but she, exactly, allowed still more; partly because, better placed for a sight of the matter, she traced his unhappy perversion through reaches of its course into which he could scarce follow it. He knew how he felt, but, besides knowing that, she knew how he *looked* as well; he knew each of the things of importance he was insidiously kept from doing, but she could add up the amount they made, understand how much, with a lighter weight on his spirit, he might have done, and thereby established how, clever as he was, he fell short. Above all she was in the secret of the difference between the forms he went through—those of his little office under Government, those of caring for his modest patrimony, for his library, for his garden in the country, for the people in London whose invitations he accepted and repaid—and the detachment that reigned beneath them and that made of all behaviour, all that could in the least be called behaviour, a long act of dissimulation. What it had come to was that he wore a mask painted with the social simper, out of the eyeholes of which there looked eyes of an expression not in the least matching the other features. This the stupid world, even after years, had never more than half-discovered. It was only May Bartram who had, and she

achieved, by an art indescribable, the feat of at once—
or perhaps it was only alternately—meeting the eyes
from in front and mingling her own vision, as from over
his shoulder, with their peep through the apertures.

So while they grew older together she did watch with
him, and so she let this association give shape and colour
to her own existence. Beneath *her* forms as well detachment had learned to sit, and behaviour had become for
her, in the social sense, a false account of herself. There
was but one account of her that would have been true
all the while and that she could give straight to nobody,
least of all to John Marcher. Her whole attitude was a
virtual statement, but the perception of that only seemed
called to take its place for him as one of the many things
necessarily crowded out of his consciousness. If she had
moreover, like himself, to make sacrifices to their real
truth, it was to be granted that her compensation might
have affected her as more prompt and more natural.
They had long periods, in this London time, during
which, when they were together, a stranger might have
listened to them without in the least pricking up his
ears; on the other hand the real truth was equally liable
at any moment to rise to the surface, and the auditor
would then have wondered indeed what they were talking about. They had from an early hour made up their
mind that society was, luckily, unintelligent, and the
margin allowed them by this had fairly become one of
their commonplaces. Yet there were still moments when
the situation turned almost fresh—usually under the
effect of some expression drawn from herself. Her expressions doubtless repeated themselves, but her intervals were generous. "What saves us, you know, is that
we answer so completely to so usual an appearance: that
of the man and woman whose friendship has become
such a daily habit—or almost—as to be at last indispen-

sable." That for instance was a remark she had frequently enough had occasion to make, though she had given it at different times different developments. What we are especially concerned with is the turn it happened to take from her one afternoon when he had come to see her in honour of her birthday. This anniversary had fallen on a Sunday, at a season of thick fog and general outward gloom; but he had brought her his customary offering, having known her now long enough to have established a hundred small traditions. It was one of his proofs to himself, the present he made her on her birthday, that he hadn't sunk into real selfishness. It was mostly nothing more than a small trinket, but it was always fine of its kind, and he was regularly careful to pay for it more than he thought he could afford. "Our habit saves you at least, don't you see? because it makes you, after all, for the vulgar, indistinguishable from other men. What's the most inveterate mark of men in general? Why the capacity to spend endless time with dull women—to spend it I won't say without being bored, but without minding that they are, without being driven off at a tangent by it; which comes to the same thing. I'm your dull woman, a part of the daily bread for which you pray at church. That covers your tracks more than anything."

"And what covers yours?" asked Marcher, whom his dull woman could mostly to this extent amuse. "I see of course what you mean by your saving me, in this way and that, so far as other people are concerned—I've seen it all along. Only what is it that saves *you*? I often think, you know, of that."

She looked as if she sometimes thought of that too, but rather in a different way. "Where other people, you mean, are concerned?"

"Well, you're really so in with me, you know—as a

sort of result of my being so in with yourself. I mean of my having such an immense regard for you, being so tremendously mindful of all you've done for me. I sometimes ask myself if it's quite fair. Fair I mean to have so involved and—since one may say it—interested you. I almost feel as if you hadn't really had time to do anything else."

"Anything else but be interested?" she asked. "Ah what else does one ever want to be? If I've been 'watching' with you, as we long ago agreed I was to do, watching's always in itself an absorption."

"Oh certainly," John Marcher said, "if you hadn't had your curiosity—! Only doesn't it sometimes come to you as time goes on that your curiosity isn't being particularly repaid?"

May Bartram had a pause. "Do you ask that, by any chance, because you feel at all that yours isn't? I mean because you have to wait so long."

Oh he understood what she meant! "For the thing to happen that never does happen? For the beast to jump out? No, I'm just where I was about it. It isn't a matter as to which I can *choose*, I can decide for a change. It isn't one as to which there *can* be a change. It's in the lap of the gods. One's in the hands of one's law—there one is. As to the form the law will take, the way it will operate, that's its own affair."

"Yes," Miss Bartram replied; "of course one's fate's coming, of course it *has* come in its own form and its own way, all the while. Only, you know, the form and the way in your case were to have been—well, something so exceptional and, as one may say, so particularly *your* own."

Something in this made him look at her with suspicion. "You say 'were to *have* been,' as if in your heart you had begun to doubt."

"Oh!" she vaguely protested.

"As if you believed," he went on, "that nothing will now take place."

She shook her head slowly but rather inscrutably. "You're far from my thought."

He continued to look at her. "What then is the matter with you?"

"Well," she said after another wait, "the matter with me is simply that I'm more sure than ever my curiosity, as you call it, will be but too well repaid."

They were frankly grave now; he had got up from his seat, had turned once more about the little drawing-room to which, year after year, he brought his inevitable topic; in which he had, as he might have said, tasted their intimate community with every sauce, where every object was as familiar to him as the things of his own house and the very carpets were worn with his fitful walk very much as the desks in old counting-houses are worn by the elbows of generations of clerks. The generations of his nervous moods had been at work there, and the place was the written history of his whole middle life. Under the impression of what his friend had just said he knew himself, for some reason, more aware of these things; which made him, after a moment, stop again before her. "Is it possibly that you've grown afraid?"

"Afraid?" He thought, as she repeated the word, that his question had made her, a little, change colour; so that, lest he should have touched on a truth, he explained very kindly: "You remember that that was what you asked *me* long ago—that first day at Weatherend."

"Oh yes, and you told me you didn't know—that I was to see for myself. We've said little about it since, even in so long a time."

"Precisely," Marcher interposed—"quite as if it were too delicate a matter for us to make free with. Quite as if we might find, on pressure, that I *am* afraid. For then," he said, "we shouldn't, should we? quite know what to do."

She had for the time no answer to this question. "There have been days when I thought you were. Only, of course," she added, "there have been days when we have thought almost anything."

"Everything. Oh!" Marcher softly groaned as with a gasp, half-spent, at the face, more uncovered just then than it had been for a long while, of the imagination always with them. It had always had its incalculable moments of glaring out, quite as with the very eyes of the very Beast, and, used as he was to them, they could still draw from him the tribute of a sigh that rose from the depths of his being. All they had thought, first and last, rolled over him; the past seemed to have been reduced to mere barren speculation. This in fact was what the place had just struck him as so full of—the simplification of everything but the state of suspense. That remained only by seeming to hang in the void surrounding it. Even his original fear, if fear it had been, had lost itself in the desert. "I judge, however," he continued, "that you see I'm not afraid now."

"What I see, as I make it out, is that you've achieved something almost unprecedented in the way of getting used to danger. Living with it so long and so closely you've lost your sense of it; you know it's there, but you're indifferent, and you cease even, as of old, to have to whistle in the dark. Considering what the danger is," May Bartram wound up, "I'm bound to say I don't think your attitude could well be surpassed."

John Marcher faintly smiled. "It's heroic?"

"Certainly—call it that."

It was what he would have liked indeed to call it.
"I *am* then a man of courage?"

"That's what you were to show me."

He still, however, wondered. "But doesn't the man
of courage know what he's afraid of—or *not* afraid of?
I don't know *that,* you see. I don't focus it. I can't name
it. I only know I'm exposed."

"Yes, but exposed—how shall I say?—so directly.
So intimately. That's surely enough."

"Enough to make you feel then—as what we may call
the end and the upshot of our watch—that I'm not
afraid?"

"You're not afraid. But it isn't," she said, "the end
of our watch. That is it isn't the end of yours. You've
everything still to see."

"Then why haven't *you?*" he asked. He had had, all
along, to-day, the sense of her keeping something back,
and he still had it. As this was his first impression of that
it quite made a date. The case was the more marked as
she didn't at first answer; which in turn made him go on.
"You know something I don't." Then his voice, for that
of a man of courage, trembled a little. "You know what's
to happen." Her silence, with the face she showed, was
almost a confession—it made him sure. "You know, and
you're afraid to tell me. It's so bad that you're afraid I'll
find out."

All this might be true, for she did look as if, unexpectedly to her, he had crossed some mystic line that she had
secretly drawn round her. Yet she might, after all, not
have worried; and the real climax was that he himself,
at all events, needn't. "You'll never find out."

III

It was all to have made, none the less, as I have said,
a date; which came out in the fact that again and again,

even after long intervals, other things that passed between them wore in relation to this hour but the character of recalls and results. Its immediate effect had been
indeed rather to lighten insistence—almost to provoke
a reaction; as if their topic had dropped by its own
weight and as if moreover, for that matter, Marcher had
been visited by one of his occasional warnings against
egotism. He had kept up, he felt, and very decently on
the whole, his consciousness of the importance of not
being selfish, and it was true that he had never sinned in
that direction without promptly enough trying to press
the scales the other way. He often repaired his fault,
the season permitting, by inviting his friend to accompany him to the opera; and it not infrequently thus
happened that, to show he didn't wish her to have but
one sort of food for her mind, he was the cause of her
appearing there with him a dozen nights in the month.
It even happened that, seeing her home at such times,
he occasionally went in with her to finish, as he called it,
the evening, and, the better to make his point, sat down
to the frugal but always careful little supper that
awaited his pleasure. His point was made, he thought,
by his not eternally insisting with her on himself; made
for instance, at such hours, when it befell that, her piano
at hand and each of them familiar with it, they went
over passages of the opera together. It chanced to be
on one of these occasions, however, that he reminded
her of her not having answered a certain question he had
put to her during the talk that had taken place between
them on her last birthday. "What is it that saves *you*?"
—saved her, he meant, from that appearance of variation from the usual human type. If he had practically
escaped remark, as she pretended, by doing, in the most
important particular, what most men do—find the answer to life in patching up an alliance of a sort with a

woman no better than himself—how had she escaped it, and how could the alliance, such as it was, since they must suppose it had been more or less noticed, have failed to make her rather positively talked about?

"I never said," May Bartram replied, "that it hadn't made me a good deal talked about."

"Ah well then you're not 'saved.'"

"It hasn't been a question for me. If you've had your woman I've had," she said, "my man."

"And you mean that makes you all right?"

Oh it was always as if there were so much to say! "I don't know why it shouldn't make me—humanly, which is what we're speaking of—as right as it makes you."

"I see," Marcher returned. "'Humanly,' no doubt, as showing that you're living for something. Not, that is, just for me and my secret."

May Bartram smiled. "I don't pretend it exactly shows that I'm not living for you. It's my intimacy with you that's in question."

He laughed as he saw what she meant. "Yes, but since, as you say, I'm only, so far as people make out, ordinary, you're—aren't you?—no more than ordinary either. You help me to pass for a man like another. So if I *am*, as I understand you, you're not compromised. Is that it?"

She had another of her waits, but she spoke clearly enough. "That's it. It's all that concerns me—to help you to pass for a man like another."

He was careful to acknowledge the remark handsomely. "How kind, how beautiful, you are to me! How shall I ever repay you?"

She had her last grave pause, as if there might be a choice of ways. But she chose. "By going on as you are."

It was into this going on as he was that they relapsed,

and really for so long a time that the day inevitably came for a further sounding of their depths. These depths, constantly bridged over by a structure firm enough in spite of its lightness and of its occasional oscillation in the somewhat vertiginous air, invited on occasion, in the interest of their nerves, a dropping of the plummet and a measurement of the abyss. A difference had been made moreover, once for all, by the fact that she had all the while not appeared to feel the need of rebutting his charge of an idea within her that she didn't dare to express—a charge uttered just before one of the fullest of their later discussions ended. It had come up for him then that she "knew" something and that what she knew was bad—too bad to tell him. When he had spoken of it as visibly so bad that she was afraid he might find it out, her reply had left the matter too equivocal to be let alone and yet, for Marcher's special sensibility, almost too formidable again to touch. He circled about it at a distance that alternately narrowed and widened and that still wasn't much affected by the consciousness in him that there was nothing she could "know," after all, any better than he did. She had no source of knowledge he hadn't equally—except of course that she might have finer nerves. That was what women had where they were interested; they made out things, where people were concerned, that the people often couldn't have made out for themselves. Their nerves, their sensibility, their imagination, were conductors and revealers, and the beauty of May Bartram was in particular that she had given herself so to his case. He felt in these days what, oddly enough, he had never felt before, the growth of a dread of losing her by some catastrophe— some catastrophe that yet wouldn't at all be *the* catastrophe: partly because she had almost of a sudden begun to strike him as more useful to him than ever yet, and partly by reason of an appearance of uncertainty in her health, coincident and equally new. It was characteristic of the inner detachment he had hitherto so successfully cultivated and to which our whole account of him is a reference, it was characteristic that his complications, such as they were, had never yet seemed so as at this crisis to thicken about him, even to the point of making him ask himself if he were, by any chance, of a truth, within sight or sound, within touch or reach, within the immediate jurisdiction, of the thing that waited.

When the day came, as come it had to, that his friend confessed to him her fear of a deep disorder in her blood, he felt somehow the shadow of a change and the chill of a shock. He immediately began to imagine aggravations and disasters, and above all to think of her peril as the direct menace for himself of personal privation. This indeed gave him one of those partial recoveries of equanimity that were agreeable to him—it showed him that what was still first in his mind was the loss she herself might suffer. "What if she should have to die before knowing, before seeing—?" It would have been brutal, in the early stages of her trouble, to put that question to her; but it had immediately sounded for him to his own concern, and the possibility was what most made him sorry for her. If she did "know," moreover, in the sense of her having had some—what should he think?—mystical irresistible light, this would make the matter not better, but worse, inasmuch as her original adoption of his own curiosity had quite become the basis of her life. She had been living to see what would *be* to be seen, and it would quite lacerate her to have to give up before the accomplishment of the vision. These reflexions, as I say, quickened his generosity; yet. make them as he might, he saw himself, with the lapse of the period, more and more disconcerted. It lapsed for him with a strange steady sweep, and the oddest oddity was that it gave him, independently of the threat of much inconvenience, almost the only positive surprise his career, if career it could be called, had yet offered him. She kept the house as she had never done; he had to go to her to see her—she could meet him nowhere now, though there was scarce a corner of their loved old London in which she hadn't in the past, at one time or another, done so; and he found her always seated by her fire in the deep old-fashioned chair she was less and less able to leave. He had been struck one day, after an absence exceeding his usual measure, with her suddenly looking much older to him than he had ever thought of her being; then he recognised that the suddenness was all on his side—he had just simply and suddenly noticed. She looked older because inevitably, after so many years, she *was* old, or almost; which was of course true in still greater measure of her companion. If she was old, or almost, John Marcher assuredly was, and yet it was her showing of the lesson, not his own, that brought the truth home to him. His surprises began here; when once they had begun they multiplied; they came rather with a rush: it was as if, in the oddest way in the world, they had all been kept back, sown in a thick cluster, for the late afternoon of life, the time at which for people in general the unexpected has died out.

One of them was that he should have caught himself —for he *had* so done—*really* wondering if the great accident would take form now as nothing more than his being condemned to see this charming woman, this admirable friend, pass away from him. He had never so unreservedly qualified her as while confronted in thought with such a possibility; in spite of which there was small doubt for him that as an answer to his long riddle the mere effacement of even so fine a feature of his situation would be an abject anticlimax. It would represent, as connected with his past attitude, a drop of dignity under the shadow of which his existence could only become the most grotesque of failures. He had been far from holding it a failure—long as he had waited for the appearance that was to make it a success. He had waited for quite another thing, not for such a thing as that. The breath of his good faith came short, however, as he recognised how long he had waited, or how long at least his companion had. That she, at all events, might be recorded as having waited in vain—this affected him sharply, and all the more because of his at first having done little more than amuse himself with the idea. It grew more grave as the gravity of her condition grew, and the state of mind it produced in him, which he himself ended by watching as if it had been some definite disfigurement of his outer person, may pass for another of his surprises. This conjoined itself still with another, the really stupefying consciousness of a question that he would have allowed to shape itself had he dared. What did everything mean—what, that is, did *she* mean, she and her vain waiting and her probable death and the soundless admonition of it all—unless that, at this time of day, it was simply, it was overwhelmingly too late? He had never at any stage of his queer consciousness admitted the whisper of such a correction; he had never till within these last few months been so false to his conviction as not to hold that what was to come to him had time, whether *he* struck himself as having it or not. That at last, at last, he certainly hadn't it, to speak of, or had it but in the scantiest measure—such, soon enough, as things went with him, became the inference with which his old obsession had to reckon:

and this it was not helped to do by the more and more confirmed appearance that the great vagueness casting the long shadow in which he had lived had, to attest itself, almost no margin left. Since it was in Time that he was to have met his fate, so it was in Time that his fate was to have acted; and as he waked up to the sense of no longer being young, which was exactly the sense of being stale, just as that, in turn, was the sense of being weak, he waked up to another matter beside. It all hung together; they were subject, he and the great vagueness, to an equal and indivisible law. When the possibilities themselves had accordingly turned stale, when the secret of the gods had grown faint, had perhaps even quite evaporated, that, and that only, was failure. It wouldn't have been failure to be bankrupt, dishonoured, pilloried, hanged; it was failure not to be anything. And so, in the dark valley into which his path had taken its unlooked-for twist, he wondered not a little as he groped. He didn't care what awful crash might overtake him, with what ignominy or what monstrosity he might yet be associated—since he wasn't after all too utterly old to suffer—if it would only be decently proportionate to the posture he had kept, all his life, in the threatened presence of it. He had but one desire left— that he shouldn't have been "sold."

IV

Then it was that, one afternoon, while the spring of the year was young and new she met all in her own way his frankest betrayal of these alarms. He had gone in late to see her, but evening hadn't settled and she was presented to him in that long fresh light of waning April days which affects us often with a sadness sharper than the greyest hours of autumn. The week had been warm, the spring was supposed to have begun early, and May

Bartram sat, for the first time in the year, without a fire; a fact that, to Marcher's sense, gave the scene of which she formed part a smooth and ultimate look, an air of knowing, in its immaculate order and cold meaningless cheer, that it would never see a fire again. Her own aspect—he could scarce have said why—intensified this note. Almost as white as wax, with the marks and signs in her face as numerous and as fine as if they had been etched by a needle, with soft white draperies relieved by a faded green scarf on the delicate tone of which the years had further refined, she was the picture of a serene and exquisite but impenetrable sphinx, whose head, or indeed all whose person, might have been powdered with silver. She was a sphinx, yet with her white petals and green fronds she might have been a lily too—only an artificial lily, wonderfully imitated and constantly kept, without dust or stain, though not exempt from a slight droop and a complexity of faint creases, under some clear glass bell. The perfection of household care, of high polish and finish, always reigned in her rooms, but they now looked most as if everything had been wound up, tucked in, put away, so that she might sit with folded hands and with nothing more to do. She was "out of it," to Marcher's vision; her work was over; she communicated with him as across some gulf or from some island of rest that she had already reached, and it made him feel strangely abandoned. Was it—or rather wasn't it—that if for so long she had been watching with him the answer to their question must have swum into her ken and taken on its name, so that her occupation was verily gone? He had as much as charged her with this in saying to her, many months before, that she even then knew something she was keeping from him. It was a point he had never since ventured to press, vaguely fearing as he did that it might become a difference, perhaps a disagreement, between them. He had in this later time turned nervous, which was what he in all the other years had never been; and the oddity was that his nervousness should have waited till he had begun to doubt, should have held off so long as he was sure. There was something, it seemed to him, that the wrong word would bring down on his head, something that would so at least ease off his tension. But he wanted not to speak the wrong word; that would make everything ugly. He wanted the knowledge he lacked to drop on him, if drop it could, by its own august weight. If she was to forsake him it was surely for her to take leave. This was why he didn't directly ask her again what she knew; but it was also why, approaching the matter from another side, he said to her in the course of his visit: "What do you regard as the very worst that at this time of day *can* happen to me?"

He had asked her that in the past often enough; they had, with the odd irregular rhythm of their intensities and avoidances, exchanged ideas about it and then had seen the ideas washed away by cool intervals, washed like figures traced in sea-sand. It had ever been the mark of their talk that the oldest allusions in it required but a little dismissal and reaction to come out again, sounding for the hour as new. She could thus at present meet his enquiry quite freshly and patiently. "Oh yes, I've repeatedly thought, only it always seemed to me of old that I couldn't quite make up my mind. I thought of dreadful things, between which it was difficult to choose; and so must you have done."

"Rather! I feel now as if I had scarce done anything else. I appear to myself to have spent my life in thinking of nothing *but* dreadful things. A great many of them I've at different times named to you, but there were others I couldn't name."

"They were too, too dreadful?"

"Too, too dreadful—some of them."

She looked at him a minute, and there came to him as he met it an inconsequent sense that her eyes, when one got their full clearness, were still as beautiful as they had been in youth, only beautiful with a strange cold light—a light that somehow was a part of the effect, if it wasn't rather a part of the cause, of the pale hard sweetness of the season and the hour. "And yet," she said at last, "there are horrors we've mentioned."

It deepened the strangeness to see her, as such a figure in such a picture, talk of "horrors," but she was to do in a few minutes something stranger yet—though even of this he was to take the full measure but afterwards—and the note of it already trembled. It was, for the matter of that, one of the signs that her eyes were having again the high flicker of their prime. He had to admit, however, what she said. "Oh yes, there were times when we did go far." He caught himself in the act of speaking as if it all were over. Well, he wished it were; and the consummation depended for him clearly more and more on his friend.

But she had now a soft smile. "Oh far—!"

It was oddly ironic. "Do you mean you're prepared to go further?"

She was frail and ancient and charming as she continued to look at him, yet it was rather as if she had lost the thread. "Do you consider that we went far?"

"Why I thought it the point you were just making—that we *had* looked most things in the face."

"Including each other?" She still smiled. "But you're quite right. We've had together great imaginations, often great fears; but some of them have been unspoken."

"Then the worst—we haven't faced that. I *could* face it, I believe, if I knew what you think it. I feel," he ex-

plained, "as if I had lost my power to conceive such
things." And he wondered if he looked as blank as he
sounded. "It's spent."

"Then why do you assume," she asked, "that mine
isn't?"

"Because you've given me signs to the contrary. It
isn't a question for you of conceiving, imagining, comparing. It isn't a question now of choosing." At last he
came out with it. "You know something I don't. You've
shown me that before."

These last words had affected her, he made out in
a moment, exceedingly, and she spoke with firmness.
"I've shown you, my dear, nothing."

He shook his head. "You can't hide it."

"Oh, oh!" May Bartram sounded over what she
couldn't hide. It was almost a smothered groan.

"You admitted it months ago, when I spoke of it to
you as of something you were afraid I should find out.
Your answer was that I couldn't, that I wouldn't, and
I don't pretend I have. But you had something therefore
in mind, and I now see how it must have been, how it
still is, the possibility that, of all possibilities, has settled
itself for you as the worst. This," he went on, "is why
I appeal to you. I'm only afraid of ignorance today—I'm
not afraid of knowledge." And then as for a while she
said nothing: "What makes me sure is that I see in your
face and feel here, in this air and amid these appearances, that you're out of it. You've done. You've had
your experience. You leave me to my fate."

Well, she listened, motionless and white in her chair,
as on a decision to be made, so that her manner was
fairly an avowal, though still, with a small fine inner stiffness, an imperfect surrender. "It *would* be the worst,"
she finally let herself say. "I mean the thing I've never
said."

It hushed him a moment. "More monstrous than all the monstrosities we've named?"

"More monstrous. Isn't that what you sufficiently express," she asked, "in calling it the worst?"

Marcher thought. "Assuredly—if you mean, as I do, something that includes all the loss and all the shame that are thinkable."

"It would if it *should* happen," said May Bartram. "What we're speaking of, remember, is only my idea."

"It's your belief," Marcher returned. "That's enough for me. I feel your beliefs are right. Therefore if, having this one, you give me no more light on it, you abandon me."

"No, no!" she repeated. "I'm with you—don't you see?—still." And as to make it more vivid to him she rose from her chair—a movement she seldom risked in these days—and showed herself, all draped and all soft, in her fairness and slimness. "I haven't forsaken you."

It was really, in its effort against weakness, a generous assurance, and had the success of the impulse not, happily, been great, it would have touched him to pain more than to pleasure. But the cold charm in her eyes had spread, as she hovered before him, to all the rest of her person, so that it was for the minute almost a recovery of youth. He couldn't pity her for that; he could only take her as she showed—as capable even yet of helping him. It was as if, at the same time, her light might at any instant go out; wherefore he must make the most of it. There passed before him with intensity the three or four things he wanted most to know; but the question that came of itself to his lips really covered the others. "Then tell me if I shall consciously suffer."

She promptly shook her head. "Never!"

It confirmed the authority he imputed to her, and it

produced on him an extraordinary effect. "Well, what's better than that? Do you call that the worst?"

"You think nothing is better?" she asked.

She seemed to mean something so special that he again sharply wondered, though still with the dawn of a prospect of relief. "Why not, if one doesn't *know?*" After which, as their eyes, over his question, met in a silence, the dawn deepened and something to his purpose came prodigiously out of her very face. His own, as he took it in, suddenly flushed to the forehead, and he gasped with the force of a perception to which, on the instant, everything fitted. The sound of his gasp filled the air; then he became articulate. "I see—if I don't suffer!"

In her own look, however, was doubt. "You see what?"

"Why what you mean—what you've always meant."

She again shook her head. "What I mean isn't what I've always meant. It's different."

"It's something new?"

She hung back from it a little. "Something new. It's not what you think. I see what you think."

His divination drew breath then; only her correction might be wrong. "It isn't that I *am* a blockhead?" he asked between faintness and grimness. "It isn't that it's all a mistake?"

"A mistake?" she pityingly echoed. *That* possibility, for her, he saw, would be monstrous; and if she guaranteed him the immunity from pain it would accordingly not be what she had in mind. "Oh no," she declared; "it's nothing of that sort. You've been right."

Yet he couldn't help asking himself if she weren't, thus pressed, speaking but to save him. It seemed to him he should be most in a hole if his history should prove all a platitude. "Are you telling me the truth, so

that I shan't have been a bigger idiot than I can bear
to know? I *haven't* lived with a vain imagination, in the
most besotted illusion? I haven't waited but to see the
door shut in my face?"

She shook her head again. "However the case stands
that isn't the truth. Whatever the reality, it *is* a reality.
The door isn't shut. The door's open," said May Bartram.

"Then something's to come?"

She waited once again, always with her cold sweet
eyes on him. "It's never too late." She had, with her
gliding step, diminished the distance between them,
and she stood nearer to him, close to him, a minute, as if
still charged with the unspoken. Her movement might
have been for some finer emphasis of what she was at
once hesitating and deciding to say. He had been standing by the chimney-piece, fireless and sparely adorned,
a small perfect old French clock and two morsels of rosy
Dresden constituting all its furniture; and her hand
grasped the shelf while she kept him waiting, grasped
it a little as for support and encouragement. She only
kept him waiting, however; that is he only waited. It
had become suddenly, from her movement and attitude,
beautiful and vivid to him that she had something more
to give him; her wasted face delicately shone with it—
it glittered almost as with the white lustre of silver in
her expression. She was right, incontestably, for what
he saw in her face was the truth, and strangely, without
consequence, while their talk of it as dreadful was still
in the air, she appeared to present it as inordinately soft.
This, prompting bewilderment, made him but gape the
more gratefully for her revelation, so that they continued
for some minutes silent, her face shining at him, her
contact imponderably pressing, and his stare all kind but
all expectant. The end, none the less, was that what he

had expected failed to come to him. Something else took place instead, which seemed to consist at first in the mere closing of her eyes. She gave way at the same instant to a slow fine shudder, and though he remained staring—though he stared in fact but the harder—turned off and regained her chair. It was the end of what she had been intending, but it left him thinking only of that.

"Well, you don't say—?"

She had touched in her passage a bell near the chimney and had sunk back strangely pale. "I'm afraid I'm too ill."

"Too ill to tell me?" It sprang up sharp to him, and almost to his lips, the fear she might die without giving him light. He checked himself in time from so expressing his question, but she answered as if she had heard the words.

"Don't you know—now?"

" 'Now'—?" She had spoken as if some difference had been made within the moment. But her maid, quickly obedient to her bell, was already with them. "I know nothing." And he was afterwards to say to himself that he must have spoken with odious impatience, such an impatience as to show that, supremely disconcerted, he washed his hands of the whole question.

"Oh!" said May Bartram.

"Are you in pain?" he asked as the woman went to her.

"No," said May Bartram.

Her maid, who had put an arm round her as if to take her to her room, fixed on him eyes that appealingly contradicted her; in spite of which, however, he showed once more his mystification. "What then has happened?"

She was once more, with her companion's help, on her feet, and, feeling withdrawal imposed on him, he had blankly found his hat and gloves and had reached the door. Yet he waited for her answer. "What *was* to," she said.

V

He came back the next day, but she was then unable to see him, and as it was literally the first time this had occurred in the long stretch of their acquaintance he turned away, defeated and sore, almost angry—or feeling at least that such a break in their custom was really the beginning of the end—and wandered alone with his thoughts, especially with the one he was least able to keep down. She was dying and he would lose her; she was dying and his life would end. He stopped in the Park, into which he had passed, and stared before him at his recurrent doubt. Away from her the doubt pressed again; in her presence he had believed her, but as he felt his forlornness he threw himself into the explanation that, nearest at hand, had most of a miserable warmth for him and least of a cold torment. She had deceived him to save him—to put him off with something in which he should be able to rest. What could the thing that was to happen to him be, after all, but just this thing that had begun to happen? Her dying, her death, his consequent solitude—*that* was what he had figured as the Beast in the Jungle, that was what had been in the lap of the gods. He had had her word for it as he left her—what else on earth could she have meant? It wasn't a thing of a monstrous order; not a fate rare and distinguished; not a stroke of fortune that overwhelmed and immortalised; it had only the stamp of the common doom. But poor Marcher at this hour judged the common doom sufficient. It would serve his turn, and even as the consummation of infinite waiting he would bend his pride to accept it. He sat down on a bench in the twilight. He hadn't been a fool. Something had *been,* as she had said, to come. Before he rose indeed it had quite struck him that the final fact really matched with the long avenue through which he had had to reach it. As sharing his suspense and as giving herself all, giving her life, to bring it to an end, she had come with him every step of the way. He had lived by her aid, and to leave her behind would be cruelly, damnably to miss her. What could be more overwhelming than that?

Well, he was to know within the week, for though she kept him a while at bay, left him restless and wretched during a series of days on each of which he asked about her only again to have to turn away, she ended his trial by receiving him where she had always received him. Yet she had been brought out at some hazard into the presence of so many of the things that were, consciously, vainly, half their past, and there was scant service left in the gentleness of her mere desire, all too visible, to check his obsession and wind up his long trouble. That was clearly what she wanted, the one thing more for her own peace while she could still put out her hand. He was so affected by her state that, once seated by her chair, he was moved to let everything go; it was she herself therefore who brought him back, took up again, before she dismissed him, her last word of the other time. She showed how she wished to leave their business in order. "I'm not sure you understood. You've nothing to wait for more. It *has* come."

Oh how he looked at her! "Really?"

"Really."

"The thing that, as you said, *was* to?"

"The thing that we began in our youth to watch for." Face to face with her once more he believed her; it was a claim to which he had so abjectly little to oppose. "You mean that it has come as a positive definite occurrence, with a name and a date?"

"Positive. Definite. I don't know about the 'name,' but oh with a date!"

He found himself again too helplessly at sea. "But come in the night—come and passed me by?"

May Bartram had her strange faint smile. "Oh no, it hasn't passed you by!"

"But if I haven't been aware of it and it hasn't touched me—?"

"Ah your not being aware of it"—and she seemed to hesitate an instant to deal with this—"your not being aware of it is the strangeness *in* the strangeness. It's the wonder *of* the wonder." She spoke as with the softness almost of a sick child, yet now at last, at the end of all, with the perfect straightness of a sibyl. She visibly knew that she knew, and the effect on him was of something co-ordinate, in its high character, with the law that had ruled him. It was the true voice of the law; so on her lips would the law itself have sounded. "It *has* touched you," she went on. "It has done its office. It has made you all its own."

"So utterly without my knowing it?"

"So utterly without your knowing it." His hand, as he leaned to her, was on the arm of her chair, and, dimly smiling always now, she placed her own on it. "It's enough if *I* know it."

"Oh!" he confusedly breathed, as she herself of late so often had done.

"What I long ago said is true. You'll never know now, and I think you ought to be content. You've *had* it," said May Bartram.

"But had what?"

"Why what was to have marked you out. The proof

of your law. It has acted. I'm too glad," she then bravely added, "to have been able to see what it's *not*."

He continued to attach his eyes to her, and with the sense that it was all beyond him, and that *she* was too, he would still have sharply challenged her hadn't he so felt it an abuse of her weakness to do more than take devoutly what she gave him, take it hushed as to a revelation. If he did speak, it was out of the foreknowledge of his loneliness to come. "If you're glad of what it's 'not' it might then have been worse?"

She turned her eyes away, she looked straight before her; with which after a moment: "Well, you know our fears."

He wondered. "It's something then we never feared?"

On this slowly she turned to him. "Did we ever dream, with all our dreams, that we should sit and talk of it thus?"

He tried for a little to make out that they had; but it was as if their dreams, numberless enough, were in solution in some thick cold mist through which thought lost itself. "It might have been that we couldn't talk?"

"Well"—she did her best for him—"not from this side. This, you see," she said, "is the *other* side."

"I think," poor Marcher returned, "that all sides are the same to me." Then, however, as she gently shook her head in correction: "We mightn't, as it were, have got across—?"

"To where we are—no. We're *here*"—she made her weak emphasis.

"And much good does it do us!" was her friend's frank comment.

"It does us the good it can. It does us the good that *it* isn't here. It's past. It's behind," said May Bartram. "Before—" but her voice dropped.

He had got up, not to tire her, but it was hard to

combat his yearning. She after all told him nothing but that his light had failed—which he knew well enough without her. "Before—?" he blankly echoed.

"Before, you see, it was always to *come*. That kept it present."

"Oh I don't care what comes now! Besides," Marcher added, "it seems to me I liked it better present, as you say, than I can like it absent with *your* absence."

"Oh mine!"—and her pale hands made light of it.

"With the absence of everything." He had a dreadful sense of standing there before her for—so far as anything but this proved, this bottomless drop was concerned—the last time of their life. It rested on him with a weight he felt he could scarce bear, and this weight it apparently was that still pressed out what remained in him of speakable protest. "I believe you; but I can't begin to pretend I understand. *Nothing*, for me, is past; nothing *will* pass till I pass myself, which I pray my stars may be as soon as possible. Say, however," he added, "that I've eaten my cake, as you contend, to the last crumb—how can the thing I've never felt at all be the thing I was marked out to feel?"

She met him perhaps less directly, but she met him unperturbed. "You take your 'feelings' for granted. You were to suffer your fate. That was not necessarily to know it."

"How in the world—when what is such knowledge but suffering?"

She looked up at him a while in silence. "No—you don't understand."

"I suffer," said John Marcher.

"Don't, dont!"

"How can I help at least *that?*"

"*Don't!*" May Bartram repeated.

She spoke it in a tone so special, in spite of her weak-

ness, that he stared an instant—stared as if some light,
hitherto hidden, had shimmered across his vision. Darkness again closed over it, but the gleam had already become for him an idea. "Because I haven't the right—?"

"Don't *know*—when you needn't," she mercifully
urged. "You needn't—for we shouldn't."

"Shouldn't?" If he could but know what she meant!

"No—it's too much."

"Too much?" he still asked but, with a mystification
that was the next moment of a sudden to give way. Her
words, if they meant something, affected him in this
light—the light also of her wasted face—as meaning
all, and the sense of what knowledge had been for herself came over him with a rush which broke through
into a question. "Is it of that then you're dying?"

She but watched him, gravely at first, as to see, with
this, where he was, and she might have seen something
or feared something that moved her sympathy. "I would
live for you still—if I could." Her eyes closed for a little,
as if, withdrawn into herself, she were for a last time
trying. "But I can't!" she said as she raised them again
to take leave of him.

She couldn't indeed, as but too promptly and sharply
appeared, and he had no vision of her after this that
was anything but darkness and doom. They had parted
for ever in that strange talk; access to her chamber of
pain, rigidly guarded, was almost wholly forbidden him;
he was feeling now moreover, in the face of doctors,
nurses, the two or three relatives attracted doubtless by
the presumption of what she had to "leave," how few
were the rights, as they were called in such cases, that
he had to put forward, and how odd it might even
seem that their intimacy shouldn't have given him more
of them. The stupidest fourth cousin had more, even
though she had been nothing in such a person's life

She had been a feature of features in *his*, for what else
was it to have been so indispensable? Strange beyond
saying were the ways of existence, baffling for him the
anomaly of his lack, as he felt it to be, of producible
claim. A woman might have been, as it were, everything
to him, and it might yet present him in no connexion
that any one seemed held to recognise. If this was the
case in these closing weeks it was the case more sharply
on the occasion of the last offices rendered, in the great
grey London cemetery, to what had been mortal, to
what had been precious, in his friend. The concourse at
her grave was not numerous, but he saw himself treated
as scarce more nearly concerned with it than if there
had been a thousand others. He was in short from this
moment face to face with the fact that he was to profit
extraordinarily little by the interest May Bartram had
taken in him. He couldn't quite have said what he expected, but he hadn't surely expected this approach to a
double privation. Not only had her interest failed him,
but he seemed to feel himself unattended—and for a
reason he couldn't seize—by the distinction, the dignity,
the propriety, if nothing else, of the man markedly bereaved. It was as if in the view of society he had not
been markedly bereaved, as if there still failed some
sign or proof of it, and as if none the less his character
could never be affirmed nor the deficiency ever made
up. There were moments as the weeks went by when he
would have liked, by some almost aggressive act, to take
his stand on the intimacy of his loss, in order that it
might be questioned and his retort, to the relief of his
spirit, so recorded; but the moments of an irritation more
helpless followed fast on these, the moments during
which, turning things over with a good conscience but
with a bare horizon, he found himself wondering if he
oughtn't to have begun, so to speak, further back.

He found himself wondering indeed at many things, and this last speculation had others to keep it company. What could he have done, after all, in her lifetime, without giving them both, as it were, away? He couldn't have made known she was watching him, for that would have published the superstition of the Beast. This was what closed his mouth now—now that the Jungle had been threshed to vacancy and that the Beast had stolen away. It sounded too foolish and too flat; the difference for him in this particular, the extinction in his life of the element of suspense, was such as in fact to surprise him. He could scarce have said what the effect resembled; the abrupt cessation, the positive prohibition, of music perhaps, more than anything else, in some place all adjusted and all accustomed to sonority and to attention. If he could at any rate have conceived lifting the veil from his image at some moment of the past (what had he done, after all, if not lift it to *her*?) so to do this to-day, to talk to people at large of the Jungle cleared and confide to them that he now felt it as safe, would have been not only to see them listen as to a goodwife's tale, but really to hear himself tell one. What it presently came to in truth was that poor Marcher waded through his beaten grass, where no life stirred, where no breath sounded, where no evil eye seemed to gleam from a possible lair, very much as if vaguely looking for the Beast, and still more as if acutely missing it. He walked about in an existence that had grown strangely more spacious, and, stopping fitfully in places where the undergrowth of life struck him as closer, asked himself yearningly, wondered secretly and sorely, if it would have lurked here or there. It would have at all events *sprung;* what was at least complete was his belief in the truth itself of the assurance given him. The change from his old sense to his new was absolute and final: what was to happen *had* so absolutely and finally happened that he was as little able to know a fear for his future as to know a hope; so absent in short was any question of anything still to come. He was to live entirely with the other question, that of his unidentified past, that of his having to see his fortune impenetrably muffled and masked.

The torment of this vision became then his occupation; he couldn't perhaps have consented to live but for the possibility of guessing. She had told him, his friend, not to guess; she had forbidden him, so far as he might, to know, and she had even in a sort denied the power in him to learn: which were so many things, precisely, to deprive him of rest. It wasn't that he wanted, he argued for fairness, that anything past and done should repeat itself; it was only that he shouldn't, as an anticlimax, have been taken sleeping so sound as not to be able to win back by an effort of thought the lost stuff of consciousness. He declared to himself at moments that he would either win it back or have done with consciousness for ever; he made this idea his one motive in fine, made it so much his passion that none other, to compare with it, seemed ever to have touched him. The lost stuff of consciousness became thus for him as a strayed or stolen child to an unappeasable father; he hunted it up and down very much as if he were knocking at doors and enquiring of the police. This was the spirit in which, inevitably, he set himself to travel; he started on a journey that was to be as long as he could make it; it danced before him that, as the other side of the globe couldn't possibly have less to say to him, it might, by a possibility of suggestion, have more. Before he quitted London, however, he made a pilgrimage to May Bartram's grave, took his way to it through the endless avenues of the grim suburban metropolis, sought it out in the wilderness of tombs, and, though he had come but for the renewal of the act of farewell, found himself, when he had at last stood by it, beguiled into long intensities. He stood for an hour, powerless to turn away and yet powerless to penetrate the darkness of death; fixing with his eyes her inscribed name and date, beating his forehead against the fact of the secret they kept, drawing his breath, while he waited, as if some sense would in pity of him rise from the stones. He kneeled on the stones, however, in vain; they kept what they concealed; and if the face of the tomb did become a face for him it was because her two names became a pair of eyes that didn't know him. He gave them a last long look, but no palest light broke.

VI

He stayed away, after this, for a year; he visited the depths of Asia, spending himself on scenes of romantic interest, of superlative sanctity; but what was present to him everywhere was that for a man who had known what *he* had known the world was vulgar and vain. The state of mind in which he had lived for so many years shone out to him, in reflexion, as a light that coloured and refined, a light beside which the glow of the East was garish and cheap and thin. The terrible truth was that he had lost—with everything else—a distinction as well; the things he saw couldn't help being common when he had become common to look at them. He was simply now one of them himself—he was in the dust, without a peg for the sense of difference; and there were hours when, before the temples of gods and the sepulchres of kings, his spirit turned for nobleness of association to the barely discriminated slab in the London suburb. That had become for him, and more intensely with time and distance, his one witness of a past glory. It was all that was left to him for proof or pride,

yet the past glories of Pharaohs were nothing to him as
he thought of it. Small wonder then that he came back
to it on the morrow of his return. He was drawn there
this time as irresistibly as the other, yet with a confidence, almost, that was doubtless the effect of the
many months that had elapsed. He had lived, in spite
of himself, into his change of feeling, and in wandering
over the earth had wandered, as might be said, from the
circumference to the centre of his desert. He had settled
to his safety and accepted perforce his extinction; figuring to himself, with some colour, in the likeness of certain little old men he remembered to have seen, of
whom, all meagre and wizened as they might look, it
was related that they had in their time fought twenty
duels or been loved by ten princesses. They indeed had
been wondrous for others while he was but wondrous
for himself; which, however, was exactly the cause of
his haste to renew the wonder by getting back, as he
might put it, into his own presence. That had quickened
his steps and checked his delay. If his visit was prompt
it was because he had been separated so long from the
part of himself that alone he now valued.

It's accordingly not false to say that he reached his
goal with a certain elation and stood there again with a
certain assurance. The creature beneath the sod *knew*
of his rare experience, so that, strangely now, the place
had lost for him its mere blankness of expression. It met
him in mildness—not, as before, in mockery; it wore
for him the air of conscious greeting that we find, after
absence, in things that have closely belonged to us and
which seem to confess of themselves to the connexion.
The plot of ground, the graven tablet, the tended flowers affected him so as belonging to him that he resembled for the hour a contented landlord reviewing a
piece of property. Whatever had happened—well, had

happened. He had not come back this time with the
vanity of that question, his former worrying "What,
what?" now practically so spent. Yet he would none
the less never again so cut himself off from the spot; he
would come back to it every month, for if he did nothing else by its aid he at least held up his head. It thus
grew for him, in the oddest way, a positive resource;
he carried out his idea of periodical returns, which took
their place at last among the most inveterate of his habits. What it all amounted to, oddly enough, was that in
his finally so simplified world this garden of death gave
him the few square feet of earth on which he could still
most live. It was as if, being nothing anywhere else for
any one, nothing even for himself, he were just everything here, and if not for a crowd of witnesses or indeed for any witness but John Marcher, then by clear
right of the register that he could scan like an open
page. The open page was the tomb of his friend, and
there were the facts of the past, there the truth of his
life, there the backward reaches in which he could lose
himself. He did this from time to time with such effect
that he seemed to wander through the old years with
his hand in the arm of a companion who was, in the most
extraordinary manner, his other, his younger self; and to
wander, which was more extraordinary yet, round and
round a third presence—not wandering she, but stationary, still, whose eyes, turning with his revolution, never
ceased to follow him, and whose seat was his point, so
to speak, of orientation. Thus in short he settled to live
—feeding all on the sense that he once *had* lived, and
dependent on it not alone for a support but for an identity.

It sufficed him in its way for months and the year
elapsed; it would doubtless even have carried him further but for an accident, superficially slight, which

moved him, quite in another direction, with a force beyond any of his impressions of Egypt or of India. It was
a thing of the merest chance—the turn, as he afterwards
felt, of a hair, though he was indeed to live to believe
that if light hadn't come to him in this particular fashion
it would still have come in another. He was to live to
believe this, I say, though he was not to live, I may not
less definitely mention, to do much else. We allow him at
any rate the benefit of the conviction, struggling up for
him at the end, that, whatever might have happened or
not happened, he would have come round of himself to
the light. The incident of an autumn day had put the
match to the train laid from of old by his misery. With
the light before him he knew that even of late his ache
had only been smothered. It was strangely drugged, but
it throbbed; at the touch it began to bleed. And the
touch, in the event, was the face of a fellow mortal.
This face, one grey afternoon when the leaves were thick
in the alleys, looked into Marcher's own, at the cemetery, with an expression like the cut of a blade. He felt
it, that is, so deep down that he winced at the steady
thrust. The person who so mutely assaulted him was
a figure he had noticed, on reaching his own goal,
absorbed by a grave a short distance away, a grave apparently fresh, so that the emotion of the visitor would
probably match it for frankness. This fact alone forbade
further attention, though during the time he stayed he
remained vaguely conscious of his neighbour, a middle-
aged man apparently, in mourning, whose bowed back,
among the clustered monuments and mortuary yews,
was constantly presented. Marcher's theory that these
were elements in contact with which he himself revived,
had suffered, on this occasion, it may be granted, a
marked, an excessive check. The autumn day was dire
for him as none had recently been, and he rested with

a heaviness he had not yet known on the low stone table that bore May Bartram's name. He rested without power to move, as if some spring in him, some spell vouchsafed, had suddenly been broken for ever. If he could have done that moment as he wanted he would simply have stretched himself on the slab that was ready to take him, treating it as a place prepared to receive his last sleep. What in all the wide world had he now to keep awake for? He stared before him with the question, and it was then that, as one of the cemetery walks passed near him, he caught the shock of the face.

His neighbour at the other grave had withdrawn, as he himself, with force enough in him, would have done by now, and was advancing along the path on his way to one of the gates. This brought him close, and his pace was slow, so that—and all the more as there was a kind of hunger in his look—the two men were for a minute directly confronted. Marcher knew him at once for one of the deeply stricken—a perception so sharp that nothing else in the picture comparatively lived, neither his dress, his age, nor his presumable character and class; nothing lived but the deep ravage of the features he showed. He *showed* them—that was the point; he was moved, as he passed, by some impulse that was either a signal for sympathy or, more possibly, a challenge to an opposed sorrow. He might already have been aware of our friend, might at some previous hour have noticed in him the smooth habit of the scene, with which the state of his own senses so scantly consorted, and might thereby have been stirred as by an overt discord. What Marcher was at all events conscious of was in the first place that the image of scarred passion presented to him was conscious too—of something that profaned the air; and in the second that, roused, startled, shocked, he was yet the next moment looking after it, as it went, with envy. The most extraordinary thing that had happened to him—though he had given that name to other matters as well—took place, after his immediate vague stare, as a consequence of this impression. The stranger passed, but the raw glare of his grief remained, making our friend wonder in pity what wrong, what wound it expressed, what injury not to be healed. What had the man *had,* to make him by the loss of it so bleed and yet live?

Something—and this reached him with a pang—that *he,* John Marcher, hadn't; the proof of which was precisely John Marcher's arid end. No passion had ever touched him, for this was what passion meant; he had survived and maundered and pined, but where had been *his* deep ravage? The extraordinary thing we speak of was the sudden rush of the result of this question. The sight that had just met his eyes named to him, as in letters of quick flame, something he had utterly, insanely missed, and what he had missed made these things a train of fire, made them mark themselves in an anguish of inward throbs. He had seen *outside* of his life, not learned it within, the way a woman was mourned when she had been loved for herself: such was the force of his conviction of the meaning of the stranger's face, which still flared for him as a smoky torch. It hadn't come to him, the knowledge, on the wings of experience; it had brushed him, jostled him, upset him, with the disrespect of chance, the insolence of accident. Now that the illumination had begun, however, it blazed to the zenith, and what he presently stood there gazing at was the sounded void of his life. He gazed, he drew breath, in pain; he turned in his dismay, and, turning, he had before him in sharper incision than ever the open page of his story. The name on the table smote him as the passage of his neighbour had done, and what it said

to him, full in the face, was that *she* was what he had
missed. This was the awful thought, the answer to all
the past, the vision at the dread clearness of which he
grew as cold as the stone beneath him. Everything fell
together, confessed, explained, overwhelmed; leaving
him most of all stupefied at the blindness he had cherished. The fate he had been marked for he had met
with a vengeance—he had emptied the cup to the lees;
he had been the man of his time, *the* man, to whom
nothing on earth was to have happened. That was the
rare stroke—that was his visitation. So he saw it, as we
say, in pale horror, while the pieces fitted and fitted. So
she had seen it while he didn't, and so she served at
this hour to drive the truth home. It was the truth, vivid
and monstrous, that all the while he had waited the
wait was itself his portion. This the companion of his
vigil had at a given moment made out, and she had then
offered him the chance to baffle his doom. One's doom,
however, was never baffled, and on the day she told
him his own had come down she had seen him but stupidly stare at the escape she offered him.

The escape would have been to love her; then, *then*
he would have lived. *She* had lived—who could say
now with what passion?—since she had loved him for
himself; whereas he had never thought of her (ah how
it hugely glared at him!) but in the chill of his egotism
and the light of her use. Her spoken words came back
to him—the chain stretched and stretched. The Beast
had lurked indeed, and the Beast, at its hour, had sprung;
it had sprung in that twilight of the cold April when,
pale, ill, wasted, but all beautiful, and perhaps even
then recoverable, she had risen from her chair to stand
before him and let him imaginably guess. It had sprung
as he didn't guess; it had sprung as she hopelessly
turned from him, and the mark, by the time he left her,

had fallen where it *was* to fall. He had justified his fear and achieved his fate; he had failed, with the last exactitude, of all he was to fail of; and a moan now rose to his lips as he remembered she had prayed he mightn't know. This horror of waking—*this* was knowledge, knowledge under the breath of which the very tears in his eyes seemed to freeze. Through them, none the less, he tried to fix it and hold it; he kept it there before him so that he might feel the pain. That at least, belated and bitter, had something of the taste of life. But the bitterness suddenly sickened him, and it was as if, horribly, he saw, in the truth, in the cruelty of his image, what had been appointed and done. He saw the Jungle of his life and saw the lurking Beast; then, while he looked, perceived it, as by a stir of the air, rise, huge and hideous, for the leap that was to settle him. His eyes darkened—it was close; and, instinctively turning, in his hallucination, to avoid it, he flung himself, face down, on the tomb.

1903

*

THE BENCH OF DESOLATION

I

She had practically, he believed, conveyed the intimation, the horrid, brutal, vulgar menace, in the course of their last dreadful conversation, when, for whatever was left him of pluck or confidence—confidence in what he would fain have called a little more aggressively the strength of his position—he had judged best not to take it up. But this time there was no question of not understanding, or of pretending he didn't; the ugly, the awful words, ruthlessly formed by her lips, were like the fingers of a hand that she might have thrust into her pocket for extraction of the monstrous object that would serve best for—what should he call it?—a gage of battle.

"If I haven't a very different answer from you within the next three days I shall put the matter into the hands of my solicitor, whom it may interest you to know I've already seen. I shall bring an action for 'breach' against you, Herbert Dodd, as sure as my name's Kate Cookham."

There it was, straight and strong—yet he felt he could say for himself, when once it had come, or even, already just as it was coming, that it turned on, as if she had moved an electric switch, the very brightest light of his own very reasons. There *she* was, in all the grossness of her native indelicacy, in all her essential excess of will and destitution of scruple; and it was the woman capable of that ignoble threat who, his sharper sense of her quality having become so quite deterrent, was now making for him a crime of it that he shouldn't wish to tie himself to her for life. The vivid, lurid thing was the reality, all unmistakable, of her purpose; she had thought her case well out; had measured its odious, specious presentability; had taken, he might be sure, the very best advice obtainable at Properley, where there was always a first-rate promptitude of everything fourth-rate; it was disgustingly certain, in short, that she'd proceed. She was sharp and adroit, moreover—distinctly in certain ways a masterhand; how otherwise, with her so limited mere attractiveness, should she have entangled him? He couldn't shut eyes to the very probable truth that if she should try it she'd pull it off. She *knew* she would—precisely; and her assurance was thus the very proof of her cruelty. That she had pretended she loved him was comparatively nothing; other women had pretended it, and other women too had really done it; but that she had pretended he could possibly have been right and safe and blest in loving *her*, a creature of the kind who could sniff that squalor of the lawcourt, of claimed damages and brazen lies and published kisses, of love-letters read amid obscene guffaws, as a positive tonic to resentment, as a high incentive to her course— this was what put him so beautifully in the right. It was what might signify in a woman all through, he had said to himself, the mere imagination of such machinery. Truly what a devilish conception and what an appalling nature!

But there was no doubt, luckily, either, that he *could* plant his feet the firmer for his now intensified sense of these things. He was to live, it appeared, abominably worried, he was to live consciously rueful, he was to live perhaps even what a scoffing world would call abjectly exposed; but at least he was to live saved. In spite of his clutch of which steadying truth, however, and in spite of his declaring to her, with many other angry protests and pleas, that the line of conduct she announced was worthy of a vindictive barmaid, a lurking fear in him, too deep to counsel mere defiance, made him appear to keep open a little, till he could somehow turn round again, the door of a possible composition. He had scoffed at her claim, at a threat, at her thinking she could hustle and bully him—"Such a way, my eye, to call back to life a dead love!"—yet his instinct was ever, prudentially but helplessly, for gaining time, even if time only more woefully to quake; and gained it now by not absolutely giving for his ultimatum that he wouldn't think of coming round. He didn't in the smallest degree mean to come round, but it was characteristic of him that he

could for three or four days breathe a little easier by
having left her under the impression that he perhaps
might. At the same time he couldn't have said—what
had conduced to bring out, in retort, her own last word,
the word on which they had parted—"Do you mean to
say you yourself would now be *willing* to marry and live
with a man of whom you could feel, the thing done,
that he'd be all the while thinking of you in the light of
a hideous coercion?" "Never you mind about my willingness," Kate had answered; "you've known what that
has been for the last six months. Leave that to me, my
willingness—I'll take care of it all right; and just see
what conclusion you can come to about your own."

He was to remember afterward how he had wondered
whether, turned upon her in silence while her odious
lucidity reigned unchecked, his face had shown her
anything like the quantity of hate he felt. Probably not
at all; no man's face *could* express that immense amount;
especially the fair, refined, intellectual, gentleman-like
face which had had—and by her own more than once
repeated avowal—so much to do with the enormous
fancy she had originally taken to him. "Which—frankly
now—would you personally *rather* I should do," he had
at any rate asked her with an intention of supreme irony:
"just sordidly marry you on top of this, or leave you the
pleasure of your lovely appearance in court and of your
so assured (since that's how you feel it) big haul of
damages? Shan't you be awfully disappointed, in fact,
if I don't let you get something better out of me than a
poor plain ten-shilling gold ring and the rest of the blas-
phemous rubbish, as we should make it between us,
pronounced at the altar? I take it of course," he had
swaggered on, "that your pretension wouldn't be for a
moment that I should—after the act of profanity—take
up my life with you."

"It's just as much my dream as ever it was, Herbert Dodd, to take up mine with *you!* Remember for me that I can do with it, my dear, that my idea is for even as much as that of you!" she had cried; "remember that for me, Herbert Dodd; remember, remember!"

It was on this she had left him frankly under a mortal chill. There might have been a last ring of an appeal or a show of persistent and perverse tenderness in it, however preposterous any such matter; but in point of fact her large, clean, plain brown face—so much too big for her head, he now more than ever felt it to be, just as her head was so much too big for her body, and just as her hats had an irritating way of appearing to decline choice and conformity in respect to *any* of her dimensions—presented itself with about as much expression as his own shop-window when the broad, blank, sallow blind was down. He was fond of his shop-window with some good show on; he had a fancy for a good show and was master of twenty different schemes of taking arrangements for the old books and prints, "high class rarities" his modest catalogue called them, in which he dealt and which his maternal uncle, David Geddes, had, as he liked to say, "handed down" to him. His widowed mother had screwed the whole thing, the stock and the connexion and the rather bad little house in the rather bad little street, out of the ancient worthy, shortly before his death, in the name of the youngest and most interesting, the "delicate" one and the literary of her five scattered and struggling children. He could enjoy his happiest collocation and contrast and effects, his harmonies and varieties of tones and faded leather and cloth, his sought colour notes and the high clearnesses, here and there, of his white and beautifully figured price labels, which pleased him enough in themselves almost to console him for not oftener having to break, on a customer's insistence, into the balanced composition. But the dropped expanse of time-soiled canvas, the thing of Sundays and holidays, with just his name, "Herbert Dodd, Successor," painted on below his uncle's antique style, the feeble pen-like flourishes already quite archaic—this ugly vacant mask which might so easily be taken for the mask of failure, somehow always gave him a chill.

That had been just the sort of chill—the analogy was complete—of Kate Cookham's last look. He supposed people doing an awfully good and sure and steady business in whatever line could see a whole front turned to vacancy that way, and merely think of the hours off represented by it. Only for this—nervously to bear it, in other words, and Herbert Dodd, quite with the literary temperament himself, was capable of that amount of play of fancy, or even of morbid analysis—you had to be on some footing, you had to feel some confidence, pretty different to his own up till now. He had never *not* enjoyed passing his show on the other side of the street and taking it in thence with a casual obliquity; but he had never held optical commerce with the drawn blind for a moment longer than he could help. It *always* looked horribly final and as if it never would come up again. Big and bare, with his name staring at him from the middle, it thus offered in its grimness a term of comparison for Miss Cookham's ominous visage. She never wore pretty, dotty, transparent veils, as Nan Drury did, and the words "Herbert Dodd"—save that she had sounded them at him there two or three times more like a Meg Merrilies or the bold bad woman in one of the melodramas of high life given during the fine season in the pavilion at the end of the Properley Pier— were dreadfully, were permanently seated on her lips. *She* was grim, no mistake.

That evening, alone in the back room above the shop,
he saw so little that he could do that, consciously demoralized for the hour, he gave way to tears about it.
Her taking a stand so incredibly "low," that was what
he couldn't get over. The particular bitterness of his cup
was having let himself in for a struggle on such terms—
the use, on her side, of the vulgarest process known to
the law: the vulgarest, the vulgarest, he kept repeating
that, clinging to the help rendered him by his imputation
to his terrorist of the vice he sincerely believed he had
ever, among difficulties (for oh, he recognized the difficulties!), sought to keep most alien to him. He knew
what he was, in a dismal down-trodden sphere enough
—the lean young proprietor of an old business that had
itself rather shrivelled with age than ever grown fat,
the purchase and the sale of second-hand books and
prints, with the back-street of a long-fronted south coast
watering-place (Old Town by good luck) for the dusky
field of his life. But he had gone in for all the education
he could get—his educated customers would often hang
about for more talk by the half-hour at a time, he actually feeling himself, and almost with a scruple hold them
there; which meant that he had had (he couldn't be
blind to that) natural taste and had lovingly cultivated
and formed it. Thus from as far back as he could remember, there had been things all round him that he had
suffered from when other people didn't; and he had kept
most of his suffering to himself—which had taught him,
in a manner, *how* to suffer, and how almost to like to.

So, at any rate, he had never let go his sense of certain differences, he had done everything he could to
keep it up—whereby everything that was vulgar was
on the wrong side of his line. He had believed, for a
series of strange, oppressed months, that Kate Cookham's manners and tone were on the right side; she had

been governess—for young children—in two very good private families, and now had classes in literature and history for bigger girls who were sometimes brought in by their mammas; in fact, coming in one day to look over his collection of students' manuals, and drawing it out, as so many did, for the evident sake of his conversation, she had appealed to him that very first time by her apparently pronounced intellectual side—goodness knew she didn't even then by the physical!—which she had artfully kept in view till she had entangled him past undoing. And it had all been but the cheapest of traps—when he came to take the pieces apart a bit—laid over a brazen avidity. What he now collapsed for, none the less—what he sank down on a chair at a table and nursed his weak, scared sobs in his resting arms for—was the fact that, whatever the trap, it held him as with the grip of sharp, murderous steel. There he was; there he was; alone in the brown summer dusk—brown through *his* windows—he cried and he cried. He shouldn't get out without losing a limb. The only question was which of his limbs it should be.

Before he went out, later on—for he at last felt the need to—he could, however, but seek to remove from his face and his betraying eyes, over his washstand, the traces of his want of fortitude. He brushed himself up; with which, catching his stricken image a bit spectrally in an old dim toilet-glass, he knew again, in a flash, the glow of righteous resentment. Who should be assured against coarse usage if a man of his really elegant, perhaps in fact a trifle over-refined or "effete" appearance, his absolutely gentlemanlike type, couldn't be? He never went so far as to rate himself, with exaggeration, a gentleman; but he would have maintained against all comers, with perfect candour and as claiming a high advantage, that he was, in spite of that liability to blub-

ber, "like" one; which he *was* no doubt, for that matter,
at several points. Like what lady then, who could ever
possibly have been taken for one, was Kate Cookham,
and therefore how could one have anything of the intimate and private order—out with her fairly and on the
plane, the only possible one, of common equality? He
might find himself crippled for life; he believed verily,
the more he thought, that that was what was before him.
But he ended by seeing this doom in the almost redeeming light of the fact that it would all have been
because he was, comparatively, too aristocratic. Yes, a
man in his station couldn't afford to carry that so far—it
must sooner or later, in one way or the other, spell ruin.
Never mind—it was the only thing he could be. Of
course he should exquisitely suffer—but when hadn't
he exquisitely suffered? How was he going to get
through life by *any* arrangement without that? No wonder any woman such as Kate Cookham had been so keen
to annex so rare a value. The right thing would have
been that the highest price should be paid for it—by
such a different sort of logic from this nightmare of *his*
having to pay.

II

Which was the way, of course, he talked to Nan Drury
—as he had felt the immediate wild need to; for he
should perhaps be able to bear it all somehow or other
with *her;*—while they sat together when time and freedom served, on one of the very last, the far westward
benches of the interminable sea-front. It wasn't every
one who walked so far, especially at that flat season—
the only ghost of a bustle now, save for the gregarious,
the obstreperous haunters of the fluttering, far-shining
Pier, being reserved for the sunny Parade of mid-winter. It wasn't every one who cared for the sunsets

(which you got awfully well from there, and which were a particularly strong point of the lower, the more "sympathetic" as Herbert Dodd liked to call it, Properley horizon) as he had always intensely cared, and as he had found Nan Drury care; to say nothing of his having also observed how little they directly spoke to Miss Cookham. He had taught this oppressive companion to notice them a bit, as he had taught her plenty of other things, but that was a different matter; for the reason that the "Land's End" (stretching a point if it carried off that name) had been, and had had to be by their lack of more sequestered resorts and conveniences, the scene of so much of what he styled their wooing time —or, to put it more properly, of the time during which she had made the straightest and most unabashed love to *him:* just as it could henceforth but render possible, under an equal rigour, that he should enjoy these periods of consolation from beautiful, gentle, tender-souled Nan, to whom he was now at last, after the wonderful way they had helped each other to behave, going to make love, absolutely unreserved and abandoned, absolutely reckless and romantic love, a refuge from poisonous reality, as hard as ever he might.

The league-long, paved, lighted, garden-plotted, seated and refuged Marina renounced its more or less celebrated attractions to break off short here; and an inward curve of the kindly westward shore almost made a wide-armed bay, with all the ugliness between town and country, and the further casual fringe of the coast, turning, as the day waned, to rich afternoon blooms of grey and brown and distant—it might fairly have been beautiful Hampshire—blue. Here it was that all the blighted summer, with Nan—from the dreadful May-day on—he gave himself up to the reaction of intimacy with the *kind* of woman, at least, that he liked; even if of everything else that might make life possible he was to be, by what he could make out, for ever starved. Here it was that—as well as whatever other scraps of occasions they could manage—Nan began to take off and fold up and put away in her pocket her pretty, dotty, becoming veil; as under the logic of his having so tremendously ceased, in the shake of his dark storm-gust, to be engaged to another woman. Her removal of that trusted obstacle to a trusted friend's assuring himself whether the peachlike bloom of her finer facial curves bore the test of much further inquiry into their cool sweetness as might reinforce a mere baffled gaze—her momentous, complete surrender of so much of her charm, let us say, both marked the change in the situation of the pair and established the record of their perfect observance of every propriety for so long as before. They afterward, in fact could have dated it, their full clutch of their freedom and the bliss of their having so little henceforth to consider save their impotence, their poverty, their ruin; dated it from the hour of his recital to her of the—at the first blush—quite appalling upshot of his second and conclusive "scene of violence" with the mistress of his fortune, when the dire terms of his release had had to be formally, and oh! so abjectly, acceded to. She "compromised," the cruel brute, for Four Hundred Pounds down—for not a farthing less would she stay her strength from the "proceedings." No jury in the land but would give her six on the nail ("Oh, she knew quite where she was, thank you!"), and he might feel lucky to get off with a whole skin. This was the sum, then, for which she had grovellingly compounded—under an agreement sealed by a supreme exchange of remarks.

" 'Where in the name of lifelong ruin are you to *find* Four Hundred?' " Miss Cookham had mockingly re-

peated after him while he gasped as from the grip on
his collar. "That's *your* look-out and I should have
thought you'd have made sure you knew before you
decided on your base perfidy." And then she mouthed
and minced with ever so false a gentility, her consistent,
her sickening conclusion. "Of course—I may mention
again—if you too distinctly object to the trouble of
looking, you know where to find *me.*"

"I had rather starve to death than ever go within
a mile of you!" Herbert described himself as having
sweetly answered; and that was accordingly where *they*
devotedly but desperately were—he and she, penniless
Nan Drury. Her father, of Drury & Dean, was like so far
too many of the other of the anxious characters who
peered through the dull window glass of dusty offices
at Properley, an Estate and House Agent, Surveyor,
Valuer and Auctioneer; she was the prettiest of six, with
two brothers, neither of them the least use, but, thanks
to the manner in which their main natural protector
appeared to languish under the accumulation of his
attributes, they couldn't be said very particularly or
positively to live. Their continued collective existence
was a good deal of a miracle even to themselves though
they had fallen into the way of not unnecessarily, or too
nervously, exchanging remarks upon it, and had even
in a sort, from year to year, got used to it. Nan's brooding pinkness when he talked to her, her so very parted
lips, considering her pretty teeth, her so very parted
eyelids, considering her pretty eyes, all of which might
have been those of some waxen image of uncritical faith
cooled the heat of his helplessness very much as if he
were laying his head on a tense silk pillow. She had, it
was true, forms of speech, familiar watchwords, that
affected him as small scratchy perforations of the smooth
surface from within; but his pleasure in her and need

of her were independent of such things and really almost altogether determined by the fact of the happy, even if all so lonely, forms and instincts in her which claimed kinship with his own. With her natural elegance stamped on her as by a die, with her dim and disinherited individual refinement of grace, which would have made any one wonder who she was anywhere—hat and veil and feather-boa and smart umbrella-knob and all—with her regular God-given distinction of type, in fine, she couldn't abide vulgarity much more than he could.

Therefore it didn't seem to him, under his stress, to matter particularly, for instance, if she *would* keep on referring so many things to the time, as she called it, when she came into his life—his own great insistence and contention being that she hadn't in the least entered there until his mind was wholly made up to eliminate his other friend. What that methodical fury was so fierce to bring home to him was the falsity to herself involved in the later acquaintance; whereas just his precious right to hold up his head to everything—before himself at least—sprang from the fact that she couldn't make dates fit anyhow. He hadn't so much as heard of his true beauty's existence (she had come back a few weeks before from her two years with her terrible trying deceased aunt at Swindon, previous to which absence she had been an unnoticeable chit) till days and days, ever so many, upon his honour, after he had struck for freedom by his first great backing-out letter—the precious document, the treat for a British jury, in which, by itself, Miss Cookham's firm instructed her to recognize the prospect of a fortune. The way the ruffians had been "her" ruffians—it appeared as if she had posted them behind her from the first of her beginning her game!— and the way "instructions" bounced out, with it, at a touch, larger than life, as if she had arrived with her pocket full of them! The date of the letter, taken with its other connexions, and the date of *her* first give-away for himself, his seeing her get out of the Brighton train with Bill Frankle that day he had gone to make the row at the Station parcels' office about the miscarriage of the box from Wales—those were the facts it sufficed him to point to, as he had pointed to them for Nan Drury's benefit, goodness knew, often and often enough. If he didn't seek occasion to do so for anyone else's—in open court as they said—that was his own affair, or at least his and Nan's.

It little mattered, meanwhile, if on their bench of desolation all that summer—and, it may be added, for summers and summers, to say nothing of winters, there and elsewhere, to come—she did give way to her artless habit of not contradicting him enough, which led to her often trailing up and down before him, too complacently, the untimely shreds and patches of his own glooms and desperations. "Well, I'm glad I *am* in your life, terrible as it is, however and whenever I did come in!" and *"Of course* you'd rather have starved—and it seems pretty well as if we shall, doesn't it?—than have bought her off by a false, abhorrent love, wouldn't you?" and "It isn't as if she hadn't made up to you the way she did before you had so much as looked at her, is it? or as if you hadn't shown her what you felt her really to be before you had so much as looked at *me,* is it either?" and "Yes, how on earth, pawning the shoes on your feet, you're going to raise another shilling—*that's* what you want to know, poor darling, don't you?"

III

His creditor, at the hour it suited her, transferred her base of operations to town, to which impenetrable scene she had also herself retired; and his raising of the first

Two Hundred, during five exasperating and miserable months, and then of another Seventy piece-meal, bleed-ingly, after long delays and under the epistolary whip-lash cracked by the London solicitor in his wretched ear even to an effect of the very report of Miss Cookham's tongue—these melancholy efforts formed a scramble up an arduous steep where steps were planted and missed, and bared knees were excoriated, and clutches at wayside tufts succeeded and failed, on a system to which poor Nan could have intelligently entered only if she had been somehow less ladylike. She kept putting into his mouth the sick quaver of where he should find the always inextinguishable rest, long after he had in silent rage fallen away from any further payment at all —at first, he had but too blackly felt, for himself, to the still quite possible non-exclusion of some penetrating ray of "exposure." He didn't care a tuppenny damn now, and in point of fact, after he had by hook and by crook succeeded in being able to unload to the tune of Two-Hundred-and-Seventy, and then simply returned the newest reminder of his outstanding obligation unopened, this later belated but real sign of fight, the first he had risked, remarkably caused nothing at all to happen; nothing at least but his being moved to quite tragically rueful wonder as to whether exactly some such demon-stration mightn't have served his turn at an earlier stage.

He could by this time at any rate measure his ruin— with three fantastic mortgages on his house, his shop, his stock, and a burden of interest to carry under which his business simply stretched itself inanimate, without strength for a protesting kick, without breath for an appealing groan. Customers lingering for further enjoy-ment of the tasteful remarks he had cultivated the un-obtrusive art of throwing in, would at this crisis have found plenty to repay them, might his wit have strayed a little more wildly still, towards a circuitous egotistical outbreak, from the immediate question of the merits of this and that author or of the condition of this and that volume. He had come to be conscious through it all of strangely glaring at people when they tried to haggle—and not, as formerly, with the glare of derisive comment on their over-done humour, but with that of fairly idiot-ized surrender; as if they were much mistaken in sup-posing, for the sake of conversation, that he might take himself for saveable by the difference between seven-pence and ninepence. He watched every thing impossi-ble and deplorable happen, as in an endless prolongation of his nightmare; watched himself proceed that is, with the finest, richest incoherence to the due preparation of his catastrophe. Everything came to seem *equally* part of this—in complete defiance of proportion; even his final command of detachment, on the bench of deso-lation (where each successive fact of his dire case regu-larly cut itself out black, yet of senseless silhouette, against the red west), in respect to poor Nan's flat in-felicities, which for the most part kept no pace with the years or with change, but only shook like hard peas in a child's rattle, the same peas always of course, so long as the rattle didn't split open with usage or from some-body's act of irritation. They represented, or they had long done so, her contribution to the more superficial of the two branches of intimacy—the intellectual alter-native, the one that didn't merely consist in her prepar-ing herself for his putting his arm round her waist.

There were to have been moments, nevertheless, all the first couple of years, when she did touch in him, though to his actively dissimulating it a more or less sensitive nerve—moments as they were too, to do her justice, when she treated him not to his own wisdom, or even folly, served up cold, but to a certain small bitter fruit of her personal, her unnatural, plucking. "I wonder that since *she* took legal advice so freely, to come down on you, you didn't take it yourself, a little, before being so sure you stood no chance. Perhaps *your* people would have been sure of something quite different—*perhaps,* I only say, you know." She "only" said it, but she said it, none the less, in the early time, about once a fortnight. In the later, and especially after their marriage, it had a way of coming up again to the exclusion, as it seemed to him, of almost everything else; in fact, during the most dismal years, the three of the loss of their two children, the long stretch of sordid embarrassment ending in her death, he was afterwards to think of her as having generally said it several times a day. He was then also to remember that his answer, before she had learnt to discount it, had been inveterately at hand: "What would any solicitor have done or wanted to do but drag me into the hideous public arena"—he had always so put it—"that it has been at any rate my pride and my honour, the one rag of self-respect covering my nakedness, to have loathed and avoided from every point of view?"

That had disposed of it so long as he cared, and by that time he had ceased to care for anything it had also lost itself in the rest of the vain babble of home. After his wife's death, during his year of mortal solitude, it woke again as an echo of far-off things—far-off, very far-off—because he felt then not ten but twenty years older. That was by reason simply of the dead weight with which his load of debt had settled—the persistence of his misery dragging itself out. With all that had come and gone the bench of desolation was still there, just as the immortal flush of the westward sky kept hanging its indestructible curtain. He had never got away—everything had left him, but he himself had been able to turn his back on nothing—and now, his day's labour before a dirty desk at the Gas Works ended, he more often than not, almost any season at temperate Properley serving his turn, took his slow, straight way to the Land's End and, collapsing there to rest, sat often for an hour at a time staring before him. He might in these sessions, with his eyes on the grey-green sea, have been counting again and still recounting the beads, almost all worn smooth, of his rosary of pain—which had for the fingers of memory and the recurrences of wonder the same felt break of the smaller ones by the larger that would have aided a pious mumble in some dusky altar-chapel.

If it has been said of him that when once full submersion, as from far back, had visibly begun to await him, he watched himself, in a cold lucidity, *do* punctually and necessarily each of the deplorable things that were inconsistent with his keeping afloat, so at present again he might have been held agaze just by the presented grotesqueness of that vigil. Such ghosts of dead seasons were all he *had* now to watch—such a recaptured sense, for instance, as that of the dismal unavailing awareness that had attended his act of marriage. He had let submersion final and absolute become the signal for it—a mere minor determinant having been the more or less contemporaneously unfavourable effect on the business of Drury & Dean of the sudden disappearance of Mr. Dean with the single small tin box into which the certificate of the firm's credit had been found to be compressible. That had been his only form—or had at any rate seemed his only one. He couldn't not have married, no doubt, just as he couldn't not have suffered the last degree of humiliation and almost of want, or just as his wife and children couldn't not have died of the little he was able, under dire reiterated pinches, to do for them; but it *was* "rum," for final solitary brooding, that he hadn't appeared to see his way definitely to undertake the support of a family till the last scrap of his little low-browed, high-toned business and the last figment of "property" in the old tiled and timbered shell that housed it had been sacrificed to creditors mustering six rows deep.

Of course what had counted too in the odd order was that, even at the end of the two or three years he had "allowed" her, Kate Cookham, gorged with his unholy tribute, had become the subject of no successful siege on the part either of Bill Frankle or, by what he could make out, of anyone else. She had judged decent—he could do her that justice—to take herself personally out of his world, as he called it, for good and all, as soon as he had begun regularly to bleed; and, to whatever lucrative practice she might be devoting her great talents in London or elsewhere, he felt his conscious curiosity about her as cold, with time, as the passion of vain protest that she had originally left him to. He could recall but two direct echoes of her in all the bitter years —both communicated by Bill Frankle, disappointed and exposed and at last quite remarkably ingenuous sneak, who had also, from far back, taken to roaming the world, but who, during a period, used fitfully and ruefully to reappear. Herbert Dodd had quickly seen, at their first meeting—every one meets every one sooner or later at Properley, if meeting it could always be called, either in the glare or the gloom of the explodedly attractive Embankment—that no silver stream of which he himself had been the remoter source could have played over the career of this all but repudiated acquaintance. That hadn't fitted with his first, his quite primitive raw vision of the probabilities, and he had further been puzzled when, much later on, it had come to him in a roundabout way that Miss Cookham was supposed to be, or to have been, among them for a few days "on the quiet," and that Frankle, who had seen her and who claimed to know more about it than he said, was cited as authority for the fact. But he hadn't himself at this juncture seen Frankle; he had only wondered, and a degree of mystification had even remained.

That memory referred itself to the dark days of old Drury's smash, the few weeks between his partner's dastardly flight and Herbert's own comment on it in the form of his standing up with Nan for the nuptial benediction of the Vicar of St. Bernard's on a very cold, bleak December morning and amid a circle of seven or eight long-faced, red-nosed, and altogether dowdy persons. Poor Nan herself had come to affect him as scarce other than red-nosed and dowdy by that time, but this only added, in his then, and indeed to his lasting view, to his general and his particular morbid bravery. He had cultivated ignorance, there were small inward immaterial luxuries he could scrappily cherish even among other, and the harshest, destitutions; and one of them was represented by this easy refusal of his mind to render to certain passages of his experience, to various ugly images, names, associations, the homage of continued attention. That served him, that helped him; but what happened when, a dozen dismal years having worn themselves away, he sat single and scraped bare again, as if his long wave of misfortune had washed him far beyond everything and then conspicuously retreated, was that, thus stranded by tidal action, deposited in the lonely hollow of his fate, he felt even sustaining pride turn to nought and heard no challenge from it when old mystifications, stealing forth in the dusk of the day's work done, scratched at the door of speculation and hung about, through the idle hours, for irritated notice.

The evenings of his squalid clerkship were all leisure now, but there was nothing at all near home, on the other hand, for his imagination, numb and stiff from its long chill, to begin to play with. Voices from far off would quaver to him therefore in the stillness; where he knew for the most recurrent, little by little, the faint wail of his wife. He had become deaf to it in life, but at present, after so great an interval, he listened again, listened and listened, and seemed to hear it sound as by the pressure of some weak broken spring. It phrased for his ear her perpetual question, the one she had come to at the last as under the obsession of a discovered and resented wrong, a wrong withal that had its source much more in his own action than anywhere else. "That you didn't make *sure* she could have done anything, that you didn't make sure and that you were too afraid!"— this commemoration had ended by playing such a part of Nan's finally quite contracted consciousness as to exclude everything else.

At the time, somehow, he had made his terms with it; he had then more urgent questions to meet than that of the poor creature's taste in worrying pain; but actually it struck him—not the question, but the fact itself of the taste—as the one thing left over from all that had come and gone. So it was; nothing remained to him in the world, on the bench of desolation, but the option of taking up that echo—together with an abundance of free time for doing so. That he hadn't made sure of what might or what mightn't have been done to him, that he had been too afraid—had the proposition a possible bearing on his present apprehension of things? To reply indeed he would have had to be able to say what his present apprehension of things, left to itself, amounted to; an uninspiring effort indeed he judged it, sunk to so poor a pitch was his material of thought—though it might at last have been the feat he sought to perform as he stared at the grey-green sea.

IV

It was seldom he was disturbed in any form of sequestered speculation, or that at his times of predilection,
especially that of the long autumn blankness between
the season of trippers and the season of Bath-chairs,
there were westward stragglers enough to jar upon his
settled sense of priority. For himself his seat, the term of
his walk, was consecrated; it had figured to him for
years as the last (though there were others, not immediately near it, and differently disposed, that might
have aspired to the title); so that he could invidiously
distinguish as he approached, make out from a distance
any accident of occupation, and never draw nearer
while that unpleasantness lasted. What he disliked was
to compromise on his tradition, whether for a man, a
woman, or a connoodling couple; it was to idiots of this
last composition he most objected, he having sat there,
in the past, alone, having sat there interminably with
Nan, having sat there with—well, with other women
when women, at hours of ease, could still care or count
for him, but having never shared the place with any
shuffling or snuffling strangers.

It was a world of fidgets and starts, however, the
world of his present dreariness; he alone possessed in
it, he seemed to make out, of the secret of the dignity
of sitting still with one's fate; so that if he took a turn
about or rested briefly elsewhere even foolish philan-
derers—though this would never have been his and
Nan's way—ended soon by some adjournment as visibly
pointless as their sprawl. Then, their backs turned, he
would drop down on it, the bench of desolation—which
was what he, and he only, made it, by sad adoption;
where, for that matter, moreover, once he had settled
at his end, it was marked that nobody else came to sit.

He saw people, along the Marina, take this liberty with other resting presences; but his own struck them perhaps in general as either of too grim or just of too dingy a vicinage. He might have affected the fellow-lounger as a man evil, unsociable, possibly engaged in working out the idea of crime; or otherwise more probably—for on the whole he surely looked harmless—devoted to the worship of some absolutely unpractical remorse.

On a certain October Saturday he had got off as usual, early; but the afternoon light, his pilgrimage drawing to its aim, could still show him, at long range, the rare case of an established usurper. His impulse was then, as by custom, to deviate a little and wait, all the more that the occupant of the bench was a lady, and that ladies, when alone, were—at that austere end of the varied frontal stretch—markedly discontinuous; but he kept on at sight of this person's rising, while he was still fifty yards off, and proceeding, her back turned, to the edge of the broad terrace, the outer line of which followed the interspaced succession of seats and was guarded by an iron rail from the abruptly lower level of the beach. Here she stood before the sea, while our friend on his side, recognizing no reason to the contrary, sank into the place she had quitted. There were other benches, eastward and off by the course of the drive, for vague ladies. The lady indeed thrust upon Herbert's vision might have struck an observer either as not quite vague or as vague with a perverse intensity suggesting design.

Not that our own observer at once thought of these things; he only took in, and with no great interest, that the obtruded presence was a "real" lady; that she was dressed—he noticed such matters—with a certain elegance of propriety or intention of harmony; and that she remained perfectly still for a good many minutes;

so many, in fact, that he presently ceased to heed her, and that as she wasn't straight before him, but as far to the left as was consistent with his missing her profile, he had turned himself to one of his sunsets again (though it wasn't quite one of his best) and let it hold him for a time that enabled her to alter her attitude and present a fuller view. Without other movement, but her back now to the sea and her face to the odd person who had appropriated her corner, she had taken a sustained look at him before he was aware she had stirred. On that apprehension, however, he became also promptly aware of her direct, her applied observation. As his sense of this quickly increased he wondered who she was and what she wanted—what, as it were, was the matter with her; it suggested to him the next thing, that she had, under some strange idea, actually been waiting for him. Any idea about him to-day on the part of any one could only be strange.

Yes, she stood there with the ample width of the Marina between them, but turned to him, for all the world, as to show frankly that she was concerned with him. And she *was*—oh, yes—a real lady: a middle-aged person, of good appearance and of the best condition, in quiet but "handsome" black, save for very fresh white kid gloves, and with a pretty, dotty, becoming veil, predominantly white, adjusted to her countenance; which through it somehow, even to his imperfect sight, showed strong fine black brows and what he would have called on the spot character. But she was pale; her black brows were the blacker behind the flattering tissue; she still kept a hand, for support, on the terrace-rail, while the other, at the end of an extended arm that had an effect of rigidity, clearly pressed hard on the knob of a small and shining umbrella, the lower extremity of whose stick was equally, was sustainingly, firm on the

walk. So this mature, qualified, important person stood
and looked at the limp undistinguished—oh, his values
of aspect now!—shabby man on the bench.

It was extraordinary, but the fact of her interest, by
immensely surprising, by immediately agitating him,
blinded him at first to her identity and, for the space of
his long stare, diverted him from it; with which even
then, when recognition did break, the sense of the
shock, striking inward, simply consumed itself in gaping
stillness. He sat there motionless and weak, fairly faint
with surprise, and there was no instant, in all the succession of so many, at which Kate Cookham could have
caught the special sign of his intelligence. Yet that she
did catch something he saw—for he saw her steady herself, by her two supported hands, to meet it; while, after
she had done so, a very wonderful thing happened, of
which he could scarce, later on, have made a clear statement, though he was to think it over again and again.
She moved toward him, she reached him, she stood
there, she sat down near him, he merely passive and
wonderstruck, unresentfully "impressed," gaping and
taking it in—and all as with an open allowance on the
part of each, so that they positively and quite intimately
met in it, of the impertinence for their case, this case
that brought them again, after horrible years, face to
face, of the vanity, the profanity, the impossibility, of
anything between them but silence.

Nearer to him, beside him at a considerable interval
(oh, she was immensely considerate!) she presented him,
in the sharp terms of her transformed state—but thus
the more amply, formally, ceremoniously—with the
reasons that would serve him best for not having precipitately known her. She was simply another and a
totally different person, and the exhibition of it to which
she had proceeded with this solemn anxiety was all,

obviously, for his benefit—once he had, as he appeared
to be doing, provisionally accepted her approach. He
had remembered her as inclined to the massive and
disowned by the graceful; but this was a spare, fine,
worn, almost wasted lady—who had repaired waste, it
was true, however, with something he could only appreciate as a rich accumulation of manner. She was
strangely older, so far as that went—marked by experience and as if many things had happened to her; her
face had suffered, to its improvement, contraction and
concentration; and if he had granted, of old and from
the first, that her eyes were remarkable, had they yet
ever had for him this sombre glow? Withal something
said she had flourished—he felt it, wincing at it, as that;
she had had a life, a career, a history, something that
her present waiting air and nervous consciousness
couldn't prevent his noting there as a deeply latent assurance. She had flourished, she had flourished—though
to learn it after this fashion was somehow at the same
time not to feel she flaunted it. It wasn't thus execration that she revived in him; she made in fact, exhibi-
tively, as he could only have put it, the matter of long
ago irrelevant, and these extraordinary minutes of their
reconstituted relation—how many? how few?—addressed themselves altogether to new possibilities.

Still it after a little awoke in him as with the throb of
a touched nerve that his own very attitude was supplying a connection; he knew presently that he wouldn't
have had her go, *couldn't* have made a sign to her for
it—which was what she had been uncertain of—without speaking to him; and that therefore he was, as at
the other, the hideous time, passive to whatever she
might do. She was even yet, she was always, in possession of him; she had known how and where to find
him and had appointed that he should see her, and,

though he had never dreamed it was again to happen to
him, he was meeting it already as if it might have been
the only thing that the least humanly *could*. Yes, he
had come back there to flop, by long custom, upon the
bench of desolation *as* the man in the whole place,
precisely, to whom nothing worth more than tuppence
could happen; whereupon in the grey desert of his consciousness, the very earth had suddenly opened and
flamed. With this, further, it came over him that he
hadn't been prepared and that his wretched appearance
must show it. He wasn't fit to receive a visit—any visit;
a flush for his felt misery, in the light of her opulence,
broke out in his lean cheeks. But if he coloured he sat
as he was—she should at least, as a visitor, be satisfied.
His eyes only, at last, turned from her and resumed a
little their gaze at the sea. That however didn't relieve
him, and he perpetrated in the course of another moment the odd desperate gesture of raising both his hands
to his face and letting them, while he pressed it to them,
cover and guard it. It was as he held them there that she
at last spoke.

"I'll go away if you wish me to." And then she waited
a moment. "I mean now, now that you've seen I'm here.
I wanted you to know it, and I thought of writing—I
was afraid of our meeting accidentally. Then I was
afraid that if I wrote you might refuse. So I thought of
this way—as I knew you must come out here." She
went on with pauses, giving him a chance to make a
sign. "I've waited several days. But I'll do what you
wish. Only I should like in that case to come back."
Again she stopped; but strange was it to him that he
wouldn't have made her break off. She held him in
boundless wonder. "I came down—I mean I came from
town—on purpose. I'm staying on still, and I've a great
patience and will give you time. Only may I say it's

important? Now that I do see you," she brought out in the same way, "I see how inevitable it was—I mean that I should have wanted to come. But you must feel about it as you can," she wound up—"till you get used to the idea."

She spoke so for accommodation, for discretion, for some ulterior view already expressed in her manner, that, after taking well in, from behind his hands, that this was her very voice—oh, lady-like!—heard, and heard in deprecation of displeasure, after long years again, he uncovered his face and freshly met her eyes. More than ever he couldn't have known her. Less and less remained of the figure all the facts of which had long ago so hardened for him. She was a handsome, grave, authoritative, but refined and, as it were, physically rearranged person—she, the outrageous vulgarity of whose prime assault had kept him shuddering so long as a shudder was in him. That atrocity in her was what everything had been built on, all strangely, it was slipping from him; so that, after the oddest fashion conceivable, when he felt he mustn't let her go, it was as if he were putting out a hand to *save* the past, the hideous, real, unalterable past, exactly as she had been the cause of its being and the cause of his undergoing it. He should have been too awfully "sold" if he wasn't going to have been right about her.

"I don't mind," he heard himself at last say. Not to mind had seemed for the instant the length he was prepared to go; but he was afterward aware of how soon he must have added; "You've come on purpose to see me?" He was on the point of putting to her further: "What then do you want of me?" But he would keep —yes, in time—from appearing to show he cared. If he showed he cared, where then would be his revenge? So he was already, within five minutes, thinking his revenge uncomfortably over instead of just comfortably knowing it. What came to him, at any rate, as they actually fell to talk, was that, with such precautions, considerations, reduplications of consciousness, almost avowed feelings of her way on her own part, and light fingerings of his chords of sensibility, she was understanding, she *had* understood, more things than all the years, up to this strange eventide, had given him an inkling of. They talked, they went on—he hadn't let her retreat, to whatever it committed him and however abjectly it did so; yet keeping off and off, dealing with such surface facts as involved ancient acquaintance but kept abominations at bay. The recognition, the attestation that she *had* come down for him, that there would be reasons, that she had even hovered and watched, assured herself a little of his habits (which she managed to speak of as if, on their present ampler development, they were much to be deferred to), held them long enough to make vivid how, listen as stiffly or as serenely as he might, she sat there in fear, just as she had so stood there at first, and that her fear had really to do with her calculation of some sort of chance with him. What chance could it possibly be? Whatever it might have done, on this prodigious showing, with Kate Cookham, it made the present witness to the state of his fortunes simply exquisite: he ground his teeth secretly together as he saw he should have to take *that.* For what did it mean but that she would have liked to pity him if she could have done it with safety? Ah, however, he must give her no measure of safety!

By the time he had remarked, with that idea, that she probably saw few changes about them there that weren't for the worse—the place was going down, down and down, so fast that goodness knew where it would stop—and had also mentioned that in spite of

this he himself remained faithful, with all its faults
loving it still; by the time he had after that fashion,
superficially indulged her, adding a few further light
and just sufficiently dry reflexions on local matters, the
disappearance of landmarks and important persons, the
frequency of gales, the low policy of the Town Council
in playing down to cheap excursionists: by the time
he had so acquitted himself, and she had observed,
of her own motion, that she was staying at the Royal,
which he knew for the time-honoured, the conservative
and exclusive hotel, he had made out for himself at least,
the amazing fact that he had been landed by his troubles, at the end of time, in a "social relation," of all
things in the world, and how of that luxury he was now
having unprecedented experience. He had but once in
his life had his nose in the Royal, on the occasion of
his himself delivering a parcel during some hiatus in his
succession of impossible small boys and meeting in the
hall the lady who had bought of him, in the morning,
a set of Crabbe; largely, he flattered himself, under the
armful persuasion of his acute remarks on that author,
gracefully associated by him, in the colloquy, he remembered, with a glance at Charles Lamb as well, and who
went off, in a day or two, without settling, though he
received her cheque from London three or four months
later.

That hadn't been a social relation; and truly, deep
within his appeal to himself to be remarkable, to be
imperturbable and impenetrable, to be in fact quite incomparable now, throbbed the intense vision of his
drawing out and draining dry the sensation he had begun to taste. He would do it, moreover—that would be
the refinement of his art—not only without the betraying
anxiety of a single question, but just even by seeing her
flounder (since she must, in a vagueness deeply discon-

certing to her) as to her real effect on him. She was
distinctly floundering by the time he had brought her—
it had taken ten minutes—down to a consciousness of
absurd and twaddling topics, to the reported and precarious state, for instance, of the syndicate running the
Bijou Theatre at the Pierhead—all as an admonition that
she might want him to know why she was thus waiting
on him, might want it for all she was worth, before he
had ceased to be so remarkable as not to ask her. He
didn't—and this assuredly was wondrous enough—
want to do anything worse to her than let her flounder;
but he was willing to do that so long as it mightn't prevent his seeing at least where *he* was. He seemed still
to see where he was even to the minute that followed
her final break-off, clearly intended to be resolute, from
make-believe talk.

"I wonder if I might prevail on you to come to tea
with me to-morrow at five."

He didn't so much as answer it—though he could
scarcely believe his ears. To-morrow was Sunday, and
the proposal referred, clearly, to the custom of "five-
o'clock tea," known to him only by the contemporary
novel of manners and the catchy advertisements of table
linen. He had never in his life been present at any such
luxurious rite, but he was offering practical indifference
to it as a false mark of his sense that his social relation
had already risen to his chin. "I gave up my very modest, but rather interesting little old book business, perhaps you know, ever so long ago."

She floundered so that she could say nothing—meet
that with no possible word; all the less too that his tone,
casual and colourless, wholly defied any apprehension
of it as a reverse. Silence only came; but after a moment
she returned to her effort. "If you *can* come I shall be at
home. To see you otherwise than thus was, in fact,

what, as I tell you, I came down for. But I leave it," she returned, "to your feeling."

He had at this, it struck him, an inspiration; which he required, however, a minute or two to decide to carry out; a minute or two during which the shake of his foot over his knee became an intensity of fidget. "Of course I know I still owe you a large sum of money. If it's about *that* you wish to see me," he went on, "I may as well tell you just here that I shall be able to meet my full obligation in the future as little as I've met it in the past. I can never," said Herbert Dodd, "pay up that balance."

He had looked at her while he spoke, but on finishing looked off at the sea again and continued to agitate his foot. He knew now what he had done, and why; and the sense of her fixed dark eyes on him during his speech and after didn't alter his small contentment. Yet even when she still said nothing he didn't turn round; he simply kept his corner as if *that* were his point made, should it even be the last word between them. It might have been, for that matter, from the way in which she presently rose, gathering herself, her fine umbrella and her very smart reticule, in the construction of which shining gilt much figured, well together, and, after standing another instant, moved across to the rail of the terrace as she had done before and remained, as before, with her back to him, though this time, it well might be, under a different fear. A quarter of an hour ago she hadn't tried him, and had had that anxiety; now that she had tried him it wasn't easier—but she was thinking what she still could do. He left her to think—nothing, in fact, more interesting than the way she might decide had ever happened to him; but it was a part of this also that as she turned round and came nearer again he didn't rise, he gave her no help. If she got any, at least, from his looking up at her only, meeting her fixed eyes

once more in silence, that was her own affair. "You
must think," she said—"you must take all your time,
but I shall be at home." She left it to him thus—she
insisted, with her idea, on leaving him somewhere too.
And on her side as well she showed an art—which re-
sulted, after another instant, in his having to rise to his
feet. He flushed afresh as he did it—it exposed him so
shabbily the more; and now if she took him in, with
each of his seedy items, from head to foot, he didn't and
couldn't and wouldn't know it, attaching his eyes hard
and straight to something quite away from them.

It stuck in his throat to say he'd come, but she had so
curious a way with her that he still less could say he
wouldn't, and in a moment had taken refuge in something that was neither. "Are you married?"—he put it to
her with that plainness, though it had seemed before
he said it to do more for him than while she waited before replying.

"No, I'm not married," she said; and then had another wait that might have amounted to a question of
what this had to do with it.

He surely couldn't have told her; so that he had recourse, a little poorly as he felt, but to an "Oh!" that
still left them opposed. He turned away for it—that
is for the poorness, which, lingering in the air, had almost a vulgar platitude; and when he presently again
wheeled about she had fallen off as for quitting him,
only with a pause, once more, for a last look. It was all
a bit awkward, but he had another happy thought,
which consisted in his silently raising his hat as for a
sign of dignified dismissal. He had cultivated of old, for
the occasions of life, the right, the discriminated bow,
and now, out of the grey limbo of the time when he
could care for such things, this flicker of propriety leaped
and worked. She might, for that matter, herself have

liked it; since, receding further, only with her white face toward him, she paid it the homage of submission. He remained dignified, and she almost humbly went.

v

Nothing in the world, on the Sunday afternoon, could have prevented him from going; he was not after all destitute of three or four such articles of clothing as, if they wouldn't particularly grace the occasion, wouldn't positively dishonour it. That deficiency might have kept him away, but no voice of the spirit, no consideration of pride. It sweetened his impatience, in fact—for he fairly felt it a long time to wait—that his pride would really most find its account in his acceptance of these conciliatory steps. From the moment he could put it in that way—that he couldn't refuse to hear what she might have, so very elaborately, to say for herself—he ought certainly to be at his ease; in illustration of which he whistled odd snatches to himself as he hung about on that cloud-dappled autumn Sunday, a mild private minstrelsy that his lips hadn't known since when? The interval of the twenty-four hours, made longer by a night of many more revivals than oblivions, had, in fact, dragged not a little; in spite of which, however, our extremely brushed-up and trimmed and polished friend knew an unprecedented flutter as he was ushered, at the Royal Hotel, into Miss Cookham's sitting-room. Yes, it was an adventure, and he had never had an adventure in his life; the term, for him, was essentially a term of high appreciation—such as disqualified for that figure, under due criticism, every single passage of his past career.

What struck him at the moment as qualifying in the highest degree this actual passage was the fact that at no great distance from his hostess in the luxurious room, as he apprehended it, in which the close of day had begun to hang a few shadows, sat a gentleman who rose as she rose, and whose name she at once mentioned to him. He had for Herbert Dodd all the air of a swell, the gentleman—rather red-faced and bald-headed, but moustachioed, waistcoated, necktied to the highest pitch, with an effect of chains and rings, of shining teeth in a glassily monocular smile; a wondrous apparition to have been asked to "meet" him, as in contemporary fiction, or for him to have been asked to meet. "Captain Roper, Mr. Herbert Dodd"—their entertainer introduced them, yes; but with a sequel immediately afterwards more disconcerting apparently to Captain Roper himself even than to her second and more breathless visitor; a "Well then, good-bye till the next time," with a hand thrust straight out, which allowed the personage so addressed no alternative but to lay aside his teacup, even though Herbert saw there was a good deal left in it, and glare about him for his hat. Miss Cookham had had her tea-tray on a small table before her, she had served Captain Roper while waiting for Mr. Dodd; but she simply dismissed him now, with a high sweet unmistakable decision, a knowledge of what she was about, as our hero would have called it, which enlarged at a stroke the latter's view of the number of different things and sorts of things, in the sphere of manners and ways of those living at their ease, that a social relation would put before one. Captain Roper would have liked to remain, would have liked more tea, but Kate signified in this direct fashion that she had had enough of him. Herbert had seen things, in his walk of life—rough things, plenty; but never things smoothed with that especial smoothness, carried out as it were by the fine form of Captain Roper's own retreat, which included even a bright convulsed leave-taking cognisance of the plain, vague individual, of no lustre at all and with the very low-class guard of an old silver watch buttoned away under an ill-made coat, to whom he was sacrificed.

It came to Herbert as he left the place a shade less remarkable—though there was still wonder enough and to spare—that he had been even publicly and designedly sacrificed; exactly so that, as the door closed behind him, Kate Cookham, standing there to wait for it, could seem to say, across the room, to the friend of her youth, only by the expression of her fine eyes: "There—see what I do for you!" "For" him—that was the extraordinary thing, and not less so that he was already, within three minutes, after this fashion, taking it in as by the intensity of a new light; a light that was one somehow with this rich inner air of the plush-draped and much-mirrored hotel, where the firelight and the approach of evening confirmed together the privacy, and the loose curtains at the wide window were parted for a command of his old lifelong Parade—the field of life so familiar to him from below and in the wind and the wet, but which he had never in all the long years hung over at this vantage.

"He's an acquaintance, but a bore," his hostess explained in respect to Captain Roper. "He turned up yesterday, but I didn't invite him, and I had said to him before you came in that I was expecting a gentleman with whom I should wish to be alone. I go quite straight at my idea that way, as a rule; but you know," she now strikingly went on, "how straight I go. And he had had," she added, "his tea."

Dodd had been looking all round—had taken in, with the rest, the brightness, the distinguished elegance, as he supposed it, of the tea-service with which she was dealing and the variously-tinted appeal of certain sa-

voury edibles on plates. "Oh, but he *hadn't* had his tea!"
he heard himself the next moment earnestly reply;
which speech had at once betrayed, he was then quickly
aware, the candour of his interest, the unsophisticated
state that had survived so many troubles. If he were so
interested how could he be proud, and if he was proud
how could he be so interested?

He had made her at any rate laugh outright, and
was further conscious, for this, both that it was the first
time of that since their new meeting, and that it didn't
affect him as harsh. It affected him, however, as free, for
she replied at once, still smiling and as a part of it:
"Oh! I think we shall get on!"

This told him he had made some difference for her,
shown her the way, or something like it, that she hadn't
been sure of yesterday; which, moreover, wasn't what
he had intended—he had come armed for showing her
nothing; so that after she had gone on, with the same
grin of gaiety, "You must at any rate comfortably have
yours," there was but one answer for him to make.

His eyes played again over the tea things—they
seemed strangely to help him; but he didn't sit down.
"I've come, as you see—but I've come, please, to understand; and if you require to be alone with me, and if I
break bread with you, it seems to me I should first know
exactly where I am and to what you suppose I so commit myself." He had thought it out and over and over,
particularly the turn about breaking bread; though perhaps he didn't give it, in her presence—this was impossible, her presence altered so many things—quite
the full sound or the weight he had planned.

But it had none the less come to his aid—it had made
her perfectly grave. "You commit yourself to nothing.
You're perfectly free. It's only I who commit myself."

On which, while she stood there as if all handsomely and deferentially waiting for him to consider and decide, he would have been naturally moved to ask her what she committed herself then *to*—so moved, that is, if he hadn't, before saying it, thought more sharply still of something better. "Oh, that's another thing."

"Yes, that's another thing," Kate Cookham returned. To which she added, "So *now* won't you sit down?" He sank with deliberation into the seat from which Captain Roper had risen; she went back to her own, and while she did so spoke again. "I'm *not* free. At least," she said over her tea tray, "I'm free only for this."

Everything was there before them and around them, everything massive and shining, so that he had instinctively fallen back in his chair as for the wondering, the resigned acceptance of it; where her last words stirred in him a sense of odd depreciation. Only for "that"? "That" was everything, at this moment, to his long inanition, and the effect, as if she had suddenly and perversely mocked him, was to press the string of a protest. "Isn't 'this' then riches?"

"Riches?" she smiled over, handing him his cup—for she had triumphed in having struck from him a question.

"I mean haven't you a lot of money." He didn't care now that it was out; his cup was in his hand, and what was that but proved interest? He had succumbed to the social relation.

"Yes, I've money. Of course you wonder—but I've wanted you to wonder. It was to make you take that in that I came. So now you know," she said, leaning back where she faced him, but in a straighter chair and with her arms closely folded, after a fashion characteristic of her, as for some control of her nerves.

"You came to show you've money?"

"That's one of the things. Not a lot—not even very much. But enough," said Kate Cookham.

"Enough? I should think so!" he again couldn't help a bit crudely exhaling.

"Enough for what I wanted. I don't always live like this—not at all. But I came to the best hotel on purpose. I wanted to show you I could. Now," she asked, "do you understand?"

"Understand?" He only gaped.

She threw up her loosed arms, which dropped again beside her. "I did it *for* you!—I did it *for* you!"

"'For' me——?"

"What I did—what I did here of old."

He stared, trying to see it. "When you made me pay you?"

"The Two Hundred and Seventy, all I could get from you, as you reminded me yesterday, so that I had to give up the rest. It was my idea," she went on—"it was my idea."

"To bleed me quite to death?" Oh, his ice was broken now!

"To make you raise money—since you could, you *could*. You did, you did—so what better proof?"

His hands fell from what he had touched; he could only stare—her own manner for it was different now too. "I did. I did indeed—!" And the woeful weak simplicity of it, which seemed somehow all that was left him, fell even on his own ear.

"Well then, here it is—it isn't lost!" she returned with a graver face.

"'Here' it is," he gasped, "my poor agonised old money—my blood?"

"Oh, it's *my* blood too, you must know now!" She held up her head as not before—as for her right to speak of the thing to-day most precious to her. "I took it, but this—my being here this way—is what I've made of it! That was the idea I had!"

Her "ideas," as things to boast of, staggered him. "To have everything in the world, like this, at my wretched expense?"

She had folded her arms back again—grasping each elbow she sat firm; she knew he could see, and had known well from the first, what she had wanted to say, difficult, monstrous though it might be. "No more than my own—but to do something with your money that you'd never do yourself."

"Myself, myself?" he wonderingly wailed. "Do you know—or don't you?—what my life has been?"

She waited, and for an instant, though the light in the room had failed a little more and would soon be mainly that of the flashing lamps on the windy Parade, he caught from her dark eye a silver gleam of impatience. "You've suffered and you've worked—which, God knows, is what I've done! *Of course* you've suffered," she said—"you inevitably had to! We have to," she went on, "to do or to be or to get anything."

"And pray what have I done or been or got?" Herbert Dodd found it almost desolately natural to demand.

It made her cover him again as with all she was thinking of. "Can you imagine nothing, or can't you conceive——?" And then as her challenge struck deeper in, deeper down than it had yet reached and with the effect of a rush of the blood to his face, "It was *for* you, it was *for* you!" she again broke out—"and for what or for whom else could it have been?"

He saw things to a tune now that made him answer straight: "I thought at one time it might have been for Bill Frankle."

"Yes, that was the way you treated me," Miss Cookham as plainly replied.

But he let this pass; his thought had already got away
from it. "What good then—it's having been from me—
has that ever done me?"

"Doesn't it do you any good *now?*" his friend returned. To which she added, with another dim play
of her tormented brightness, before he could speak:
"But if you won't even have your tea——!"

He had in fact touched nothing, and if he could have
explained, would have pleaded very veraciously that his
appetite, keen when he came in, had somehow suddenly failed. It was beyond eating or drinking, what she
seemed to want him to take from her. So if he looked before him, over the array, it was to say, very grave and
graceless: "Am I to understand that you offer to repay
me?"

"I offer to repay you with interest, Herbert Dodd"
—and the emphasis of the great word was wonderful.

It held him in his place a minute, and held his eyes
upon her; after which, agitated too sharply to sit·still,
he pushed back his chair and stood up. It was as if mere
distress or dismay at first worked in him, and was in
fact a wave of deep and irresistible emotion which
made him, on his feet, sway as in a great trouble and
then, to correct it, throw himself stiffly toward the window, where he stood and looked out unseeing. The road,
the wide terrace beyond, the seats, the eternal sea beyond that, the lighted lamps now flaring in the October
night wind, with the few dispersed people abroad at the
tea hour; these things, meeting and melting into the
firelit hospitality at his elbow—or was it that portentous amenity that melted into *them?*—seemed to form
round him and to put before him, all together, the
strangest of circles and the newest of experiences, in

which the unforgettable and the unimaginable were confoundingly mixed. "Oh, oh, oh!"—he could almost howl for it.

And then, while a thick blur for some moments mantled everything, he knew she had got up, that she stood watching him, allowing for everything, again all "cleverly" patient with him, and he heard her speak again as with studied quietness and clearness. "I wanted to take care of you—it was what I first wanted—and what you first consented to. I'd have done it, oh, I'd have done it, I'd have loved you and helped you and guarded you, and you'd have had no trouble, no bad blighting ruin, in all your easy, yes, just your quiet jolly and comfortable life. I showed you and proved to you this—I brought it home to you, as I fondly fancied, and it made me briefly happy. You swore you cared for me, you wrote it and made me believe it—you pledged me your honour and your faith. Then you turned and changed suddenly, from one day to another; everything altered, you broke your vows, you as good as told me you only wanted it off. You faced me with dislike, and in fact tried not to face me at all; you behaved as if you hated me—you had seen a girl, of great beauty, I admit, who made me a fright and bore."

This brought them straight round. "No, Kate Cookham."

"Yes, Herbert Dodd." She but shook her head, calmly and nobly, in the now gathered dusk, and her memories and her cause and her character—or was it only her arch-subtlety, her line and her "idea"?—gave her an extraordinarily large assurance.

She had touched, however, the treasure of his own case—his terrible own case that began to live again at once by the force of her talking of hers, and which could always all cluster about his great asseveration. "No, no,

never, never; I had never seen her then and didn't
dream of her; so that when you yourself began to be
harsh and sharp with me, and to seem to want to quarrel, I could have but one idea—which was an appearance you didn't in the least, as I saw it then, account
for or disprove."

"An appearance——?" Kate desired, as with high as-
tonishment, to know which one.

"How *shouldn't* I have supposed you really to care
for Bill Frankle—as, thoroughly believing the motive
of your claim for my money to be its help to your marrying him, since you couldn't marry me. I was only
surprised when, time passing, I made out that that
hadn't happened; and perhaps," he added the next
instant, with something of a conscious lapse from the
finer style, "hadn't been the question."

She had listened to this only staring, and she was silent after he had said it, so silent for some instants that
while he considered her something seemed to fail him,
much as if he had thrown out his foot for a step and not
found the place to rest it. He jerked round to the window again, and then she answered, but without passion,
unless it was that of her weariness for something stupid
and forgiven in him, "Oh, the blind the pitiful folly!"
—to which, as it might perfectly have applied to her
own behaviour, he returned nothing. She had, moreover, at once gone on. "Put it then that there wasn't
much to do—between your finding that you loathed
me for another woman, or discovering only, when it
came to the point, that you loathed me quite enough
for myself."

Which, offered him in that immensely effective fashion, he recognized that he must just unprotestingly and
not so very awkardly—not so *very!*—take from her;
since, whatever he had thus come to her for, it wasn't to

perjure himself with any pretence that, "another woman" or no other woman, he hadn't for years and years, abhorred her. Now he was taking tea with her —or rather, literally, seemed not to be; but this made no difference, and he let her express it as she would while he distinguished a man he knew, Charley Coote, outside on the Parade, under favour of the empty hour and one of the flaring lamps, making up to a young woman with whom (it struck out grotesquely in his manner) he had never before conversed. Dodd's own position was that of acquiescing in this recall of what had so bitterly been—but he hadn't come back to her, of himself, to stir up, to recall or to recriminate, and for *her* it could be the very lesson of her whole present act that if she touched everything. Soon enough she was indeed, and all overwhelmingly, touching everything—with a hand of which the boldness grew.

"But I didn't let *that,* even, make a difference in what I wanted—which was all," she said, "and had only and passionately been, to take care of you. I had *no* money whatever—nothing then of my own, not a penny to come by anyhow: so it wasn't with mine I could do it. But I could do it with yours," she amazingly wound up —"if I could once get yours out of you."

He faced straight about again—his eyebrows higher than they had ever been in his life. "Mine? What penny of it was mine? What scrap beyond a bare mean little living had I ever pretended to have?"

She held herself still a minute, visibly with force; only her eyes consciously attached to the seat of a chair the back of which her hands, making it tilt toward her a little, grasped as for support. "You pretended to have enough to marry me—and that was all I afterwards claimed of you when you wouldn't." He was on the point of retorting that he had absolutely pretended to nothing—least of all to the primary desire that such a way of putting it fastened on him: he was on the point for ten seconds of giving her full in the face: "I never *had* any such dream until you yourself—infatuated with me as, frankly, you on the whole appeared to be—got round me and muddled me up and made me behave as if in a way that went against the evidence of my senses." But he was to feel as quickly that, whatever the ugly, the spent, the irrecoverable truth, he might better have bitten his tongue off: there beat on him there this strange and other, this so prodigiously different beautiful and dreadful truth that no far remembrance and no abiding ache of his own could wholly falsify, and that was indeed all out with her next words. "That—*using* it for you and using you yourself for your own future—was my motive. I've led my life, which has been an affair, I assure you; and, as I've told you without your quite seeming to understand, I've brought everything fivefold back to you."

The perspiration broke out on his forehead. "Everything's mine?" he quavered as for the piercing pain of it.

"Everything!" said Kate Cookham.

So it told him how she had loved him—but with the tremendous effect at once of its only glaring out at him from the whole thing that it was verily she, a thousand times over, who, in the exposure of his youth and his vanity, had, on the bench of desolation, the scene of yesterday's own renewal, left for him no forward step to take. It hung there for him tragically vivid again, the hour she had first found him sequestered and accessible after making his acquaintance at his shop. And from this, by a succession of links that fairly clicked to his ear as with their perfect fitting, the fate and the pain and the payment of others stood together in a great grim order. Everything there then was *his*—to make him ask what had been Nan's, poor Nan's of the constant question of whether he need have collapsed. She was before him, she was between them, his little dead dissatisfied wife; across all whose final woe and whose lowly grave he was to reach out, it appeared, to take gifts. He saw them too, the gifts; saw them—she bristled with them—in his actual companion's brave and sincere and authoritative figure, her strangest of demonstrations. But the other appearance was intenser, as if their ghost had waved wild arms; so that half a minute hadn't passed before the one thing that remained of Nan, and that yet thus became a quite mighty and momentous poor thing, was sitting on his lips as for its sole opportunity.

"Can you give me your word of honour that I mightn't, under decent advice, have defied you?"

It made her turn very white; but now that she had said what she *had* said she could still hold up her head. "Certainly you might have defied me, Herbert Dodd."

"They would have told me you had no legal case?"

Well, if she was pale she was bold. "You talk of decent advice——!" She broke off, there was too much to say, and all needless. What she said instead was: "They would have told you I had nothing."

"I didn't so much as ask," her sad visitor remarked.

"Of course you didn't so much as ask."

"I couldn't be so outrageously vulgar," he went on.

"*I* could, by God's help!" said Kate Cookham.

"Thank you." He had found at his command a tone that made him feel more gentlemanlike than he had ever felt in his life or should doubtless ever feel again. It might have been enough—but somehow as they stood there with this immense clearance between them it wasn't. The clearance was like a sudden gap or great

bleak opening through which there blew upon them a
deadly chill. Too many things had fallen away, too many
new rolled up and over him, and they made something
within shake him to his base. It upset the full vessel, and
though she kept her eyes on him he let that consequence
come, bursting into tears, weakly crying there before
her even as he had cried to himself in the hour of his
youth when she had made him groundlessly fear. She
turned away then—*that* she couldn't watch, and had
presently flung herself on the sofa and, all responsively
wailing, buried her own face on the cushioned arm. So
for a minute their smothered sobs only filled the room.
But he made out, through this disorder, where he had
put down his hat; his stick and his new tan-coloured
gloves—they had cost two-and-thruppence and would
have represented sacrifices—were on the chair beside
it. He picked these articles up and all silently and softly
—gasping, that is, but quite on tiptoe—reached the door
and let himself out.

VI

Off there on the bench of desolation a week later she
made a more particular statement, which it had taken
the remarkably tense interval to render possible. After
leaving her at the hotel that last Sunday he had gone
forth in his reaggravated trouble and walked straight
before him, in the teeth of the west wind, close to the
iron rails of the stretched Marina and with his tell-tale
face turned from persons occasionally met and toward
the surging sea. At the Land's End, even in the confirmed
darkness and the perhaps imminent big blow, his immemorial nook, small shelter as it yielded, had again
received him; and it was in the course of this heedless
session, no doubt, where the agitated air had nothing to
add to the commotion within him, that he began to look

his extraordinary fortune a bit straighter in the face and
see it confess itself at once a fairy-tale and a nightmare.
That, visibly, confoundingly, she was still attached to
him (attached in fact was a mild word!) and that the
unquestionable proof of it was in this offered pecuniary
salve, of the thickest composition, for his wounds
and sores and shames—these things were the fantastic
fable, the tale of money in handfuls, that he seemed to
have only to stand there and swallow and digest and
feel himself full-fed by; but the whole of the rest was
nightmare, and most of all nightmare his having thus to
thank one through whom Nan and his little girls had
known torture.

He didn't care for himself now, and this unextin-
guished and apparently inextinguishable charm by
which he had held her was a fact incredibly romantic;
but he gazed with a longer face than he had ever had
for anything in the world at this potential acceptance of
a great bouncing benefit from the person he intimately,
if even in a manner indirectly, associated with the conditions to which his lovely wife and his little girls (who
would have been lovely too) had pitifully succumbed.
He had accepted the social relation—which meant he
had taken even that on trial—without knowing what it
so dazzlingly masked; for a social relation it had become with a vengeance when it drove him about the
place as now at his hours of freedom (and he actually
and recklessly took, all demoralized and unstrung and
unfit either for work or anything else, other liberties
that would get him into trouble) under this queer torment of irreconcilable things, of bewildered consciousness of tenderness and patience and cruelty, of great
evident mystifying facts that were as little to be questioned as to be conceived or explained, and that were
yet least, withal, to be lost sight of.

On that Sunday night he had wandered wild, inco-
herently ranging and throbbing, but this became the law
of the next days as well, since he lacked more than ever
all other resort or refuge and had nowhere to carry, to
deposit, or contractedly let loose and lock up, as it were,
his swollen consciousness, which fairly split in twain the
raw shell of his sordid little boarding-place. The arch of
the sky and the spread of sea and shore alone gave him
space; he could roam with himself anywhere, in short,
far or near—he could only never take himself back.
That certitude—that this was impossible to him even
should she wait there among her plushes and bronzes
ten years—was the thing he kept closest clutch of; it did
wonders of what he would call his self-respect. Exactly
as he had left her so he would stand off—even though
at moments when he pulled up sharp somewhere to
put himself an intensest question his heart almost stood
still. The days of the week went by, and as he had left
her she stayed; to the extent, that is, of his having
neither sight nor sound of her, and of the failure of
every sign. It took nerve, he said, not to return to her,
even for curiosity—since how, after all, in the name of
wonder, had she invested the fruits of her extortion to
such advantage, there being no chapter of all the ob-
scurity of the years to beat that for queerness? But he
dropped, tired to death, on benches, half a dozen times
an evening—exactly on purpose to recognize that the
nerve required was just the nerve he had.

As the days without a token from her multiplied he
came in as well for hours—and these indeed mainly on
the bench of desolation—of sitting stiff and stark in presence of the probability that he had lost everything for
ever. When he passed the Royal he never turned an
eyelash, and when he met Captain Roper on the Front,
three days after having been introduced to him, he "cut

him dead"—another privileged consequence of a social
relation—rather than seem to himself to make the re-
motest approach to the question of whether Miss Cookham had left Properley. He had cut people in the
days of his life before, just as he had come to being
himself cut—since there had been no time for him
wholly without one or other face of that necessity—
but had never affected such a severance as of this rare
connexion which helped to give him thus the measure of
his really precious sincerity. If he had lost what had
hovered before him he had lost it, his only tribute to
which proposition was to grind his teeth with one of
those "scrunches," as he would have said, of which the
violence fairly reached his ear. It wouldn't make him
lift a finger, and in fact if Kate had simply taken herself
off on the Tuesday or the Wednesday she would have
been reabsorbed again into the darkness from which
she had emerged—and no lifting of fingers, the unspeakable chapter closed, would ever more avail. That
at any rate was the kind of man he still was—even after
all that had come and gone, and even if for a few dazed
hours certain things had seemed pleasant. The dazed
hours had passed, the surge of the old bitterness had
dished him (shouldn't he have been shamed if he
hadn't?) and he might sit there as before, as always,
with nothing at all on earth to look to. He had therefore
wrongfully believed himself to be degraded; and the
last word about him would be that he *couldn't* then, it
appeared, sink to vulgarity as he had tried to let his
miseries make him.

And yet on the next Sunday morning, face to face
with him again at the Land's End, what she very soon
came to was: "As if I believed you didn't *know* by what
cord you hold me!" Absolutely, too, and just that morning in fact, above all, he wouldn't, he quite couldn't

have taken his solemn oath that he hadn't a sneaking
remnant, as he might have put it to himself—a remnant
of faith in tremendous things still to come of their interview. The day was sunny and breezy, the sea of a
cold purple; he wouldn't go to church as he mostly went
of most Sunday mornings, that being in its way too a social relation—and not least when two-and-thruppenny
tan-coloured gloves were new; which indeed he had the
art of keeping them for ages. Yet he would dress himself
as he scarce mustered resources for even to figure on
the fringe of Society, local and transient, at St. Bernard's,
and in this trim he took his way westward; occupied
largely, as he went, it might have seemed to any person
pursuing the same course and happening to observe him,
in a fascinated study of the motions of his shadow, the
more or less grotesque shape projected, in front of him
and mostly a bit to the right, over the blanched asphalt
of the Parade and dangling and dancing at such a rate,
shooting out and then contracting, that, viewed in themselves, its eccentricities might have formed the basis of
an interesting challenge: "Find the state of mind, guess
the nature of the agitation, possessing the person so
remarkably represented!" Herbert Dodd, for that matter,
might have been himself attempting to make by the
sun's sharp aid some approach to his immediate horo-
scope.

It had at any rate been thus put before him that the
dandling and dancing of his image occasionally gave
way to perfect immobility, when he stopped and kept
his eyes on it. "Suppose she should come, suppose
she *should!*" it is revealed at least to ourselves that he
had at these moments audibly breathed—breathed with
the intensity of an arrest between hope and fear. It had
glimmered upon him from early, with the look of the
day, that, given all else that could happen, this would

be rather, as he put it, in her line; and the possibility
lived for him, as he proceeded, to the tune of a suspense
almost sickening. It was, from one small stage of his
pilgrimage to another, the "For ever, never!" of the
sentimental case the playmates of his youth used to pretend to settle by plucking the petals of a daisy. But it
came to his truly turning faint—so "queer" he felt—
when, at the gained point of the long stretch from which
he could always tell, he arrived within positive sight of
his immemorial goal. His seat was taken and she was
keeping it for him—it could only be *she* there in possession; whereby it shone out for Herbert Dodd that if he
hadn't been quite sure of her recurrence she had at least
been quite sure of his. *That* pulled him up to some purpose, where recognition began for them—or to the effect,
in other words, of his pausing to judge if he could bear,
for the sharpest note of their intercourse, this inveterate
demonstration of her making him do what she liked.
What settled the question for him then—and just while
they avowedly watched each other, over the long interval, before closing, as if, on either side, for the major
advantage—what settled it was this very fact that what
she liked she liked so terribly. If it were simply to "use"
him, as she had said the last time, and no matter to the
profit of which of them she called it, one might let it go
for that; since it could make her wait over, day after day,
in that fashion, and with such a spending of money, on
the hazard of their meeting again. How could she be the
least sure he would ever again consent to it after the
proved action on him, a week ago, of her last monstrous
honesty? It was indeed positively as if he were now himself putting this influence—and for their common edification—to the supreme, to the finest test. He had a sublime, an ideal flight, which lasted about a minute. "Suppose, now that I see her there and what she has taken so

characteristically for granted, suppose I just show her
that she *hasn't* only confidently to wait or whistle for
me, and that the length of my leash is greater than she
measures, and that everything's impossible always?—
show it by turning my back on her now and walking
straight away. She won't be able not to understand
that!"

Nothing had passed, across their distance, but the
mute apprehension of each on the part of each; the
whole expanse, at the church hour, was void of other
life (he had scarce met a creature on his way from end
to end) and the sun-seasoned gusts kept brushing the
air and all the larger prospect clean. It was through this
beautiful lucidity that he watched her watch him, as it
were—watch him for what he would do. Neither moved
at this high tension; Kate Cookham, her face fixed on
him, only waited with a stiff appearance of leaving
him, not for dignity but—to an effect of even deeper perversity—for kindness, free to choose. It yet somehow
affected him at present, this attitude, as a gauge of her
knowing too—knowing, that is, that he wasn't really free,
that this was the thinnest of vain parades, the poorest of
hollow heroics, that his need, his solitude, his suffered
wrong, his exhausted rancour, his foredoomed submission to any shown interest, all hung together too heavy
on him to let the weak wings of his pride do more than
vaguely tremble. They couldn't, they didn't carry him a
single beat further away; according to which he stood
rooted, neither retreating nor advancing, but presently
correcting his own share of their bleak exchange by
looking off at the sea. Deeply conscious of the awkwardness this posture gave him, he yet clung to it as the last
shred of his honour, to the clear argument that it was
one thing for him to have felt beneath all others, the previous days, that she was to be counted on, but quite a

different for her to have felt that *he* was. His checked approach arriving thus at no term, could in these odd conditions have established that he wasn't only if Kate Cookham had, as either of them might have said, taken it so—if she had given up the game at last by rising, by walking away and adding to the distance between them, and he had then definitely let her vanish into space. It became a fact that when she did finally rise— though after how long our record scarce takes on itself to say—it was not to confirm their separation but to put an end to it; and this by slowly approaching him till she had come within earshot. He had wondered, once aware of it in spite of his averted face, what she would say and on what note, as it were, she would break their week's silence; so that he had to recognize anew, her voice reaching him, that remarkable quality in her which again and again came up for him as her art.

"There are twelve hundred and sixty pounds, to be definite, but I have it all down for you—and you've only to draw."

They lost themselves, these words, rare and exquisite, in the wide bright genial medium and the Sunday stillness, but even while that occurred and he was gaping for it, she was herself there, in her battered ladylike truth, to answer for them, to represent them, and, if a further grace than their simple syllabled beauty were conceivable, almost embarrassingly to cause them to materialize. Yes, she let her smart and tight little reticule hang as if it bulged, beneath its clasp, with the whole portentous sum, and he felt himself glare again at this vividest of her attested claims. She might have been ready, on the spot, to open the store to the plunge of his hand, or, with the situation otherwise conceived, to impose on his pauperized state an acceptance of alms on a scale unprecedented in the annals of street charity.

Nothing so much counted for him, however, neither grave numeral nor elegant fraction, as the short, rich, rounded word that the breeze had picked up as it dropped and seemed now to blow about between them. "To draw—to draw?" Yes, he gaped at it as if it had no sense; the fact being that even while he did so he was reading into her use of the term more romance than any word in the language had ever had for him. He, Herbert Dodd, was to live to "draw," like people, scarce hampered by the conditions of earth, whom he had remotely and circuitously heard about, and in fact when he walked back with her to where she had been sitting it was very much, for his strained nerves, as if the very bench of desolation itself were to be the scene of that exploit and he mightn't really live till he reached it.

When they had sat down together she did press the spring of her reticule, extracting from it, not a handful of gold nor a packet of crisp notes, but an oblong sealed letter, which she had thus waited on him, she remarked, on purpose to deliver, and which would certify, with sundry particulars, to the credit she had opened for him at a London bank. He took it from her without looking at it, and held it, in the same manner, conspicuous and unassimilated, for most of the rest of the immediate time, appearing embarrassed with it, nervously twisting and flapping it, yet thus publicly retaining it even while aware, beneath everything, of the strange, the quite dreadful, wouldn't it be? engagement that such inaction practically stood for. He could accept money to that amount, yes—but not for nothing in return. For what then in return? He kept asking himself for what, while she said other things and made above all, in her high, shrewd, successful way, the point that, no, he needn't pretend that his conviction of her continued personal interest in him wouldn't have tided him

over any question besetting him since their separation.
She put it to him that the deep instinct of where he
should at last find her must confidently have worked for
him, since she confessed to her instinct of where she
should find *him;* which meant—oh, it came home to
him as he fingered his sealed treasure!—neither more
nor less than that she had now created between them
an equality of experience. He wasn't to have done all
the suffering, *she* was to have "been through" things he
couldn't even guess at; and, since he was bargaining
away his right ever again to allude to the unforgettable,
so much there was of it, what her tacit proposition came
to was that they were "square" and might start afresh.

He didn't take up her charge, as his so compromised
"pride" yet in a manner prompted him, that he had
enjoyed all the week all those elements of ease about
her; the most he achieved for that was to declare, with
an ingenuity contributing to float him no small distance further, that of course he had turned up at their
old place of tryst, which had been, through the years,
the haunt of his solitude and the goal of his walk any
Sunday morning that seemed too beautiful for church;
but that he hadn't in the least built on her presence
there—since that supposition gave him, she would
understand, wouldn't she? the air, disagreeable to him,
of having come in search of her. Her quest of himself,
once he had been seated there, would have been
another matter—but in short, "Of course after all you
did come to me, just now, didn't you?" He felt himself,
too, lamely and gracelessly grin, as for the final kick of
his honour, in confirmation of the record that he had
then yielded but to her humility. Her humility became
for him at this hour and to this tune, on the bench of
desolation, a quantity more prodigious and even more
mysterious than that other guaranteed quantity the

finger-tips of his left hand could feel the tap of by the
action of his right; though what was in especial extraordinary was the manner in which she could keep making
him such allowances and yet meet him again, at some
turn, as with her residuum for her clever self so great.

"Come to you, Herbert Dodd?" she imperturbably
echoed. "I've been coming to you for the last ten years!"

There had been for him just before his sixty supreme
seconds of intensest aspiration—a minute of his keeping
his certificate poised for a sharp thrust back at her, the
thrust of the wild freedom of his saying: "No, no, I
can't give them up; I can't simply sink them deep down
in my soul for ever, with no cross in all my future to
mark *that* burial; so that if this is what our arrangement means I must decline to have anything to do with
it." The words none the less hadn't come, and when she
had herself, a couple of minutes later, spoken those
others, the blood rose to his face as if, given his stiffness
and her extravagance, he had just indeed saved himself.

Everything in fact stopped, even his fidget with his
paper; she imposed a hush, she imposed at any rate the
conscious decent form of one, and he couldn't afterward
have told how long, at this juncture, he must have sat
simply gazing before him. It was so long, at any rate,
that Kate herself got up—and quite indeed, presently,
as if her own forms were now at an end. He had returned
her nothing—so what was she waiting for? She had been
on the two other occasions momentarily at a loss, but
never so much so, no doubt, as was thus testified to by
her leaving the bench and moving over once more to
the rail of the terrace. She could carry it off, in a manner, with her resources, that she was waiting with so
little to wait for; she could face him again, after looking off at the sea, as if this slightly stiff delay, not wholly
exempt from awkwardness, had been but a fine scruple

of her courtesy. She had gathered herself in; after giving him time to appeal she could take it that he had decided and that nothing was left for her to do. "Well then," she clearly launched at him across the broad walk—"well then, good-bye."

She had come nearer with it, as if he might rise for some show of express separation; but he only leaned back motionless, his eyes on her now—he kept her a moment before him. "Do you mean that we don't—that we don't——?" But he broke down.

"Do I 'mean'——?" She remained as for questions he might ask, but it was well-nigh as if there played through her dotty veil an irrepressible irony for that particular one. "I've meant, for long years, I think, all I am capable of meaning. I've meant so much that I can't mean more. So there it is."

"But if you go," he appealed—and with a sense as a final flatness, however he arranged it, for his own attitude—"but if you go shan't I see you again?"

She waited a little and it was strangely for him now as if—though at last so much more gorged with her tribute than she had ever been with his—something still depended on her. "Do you *like* to see me?" she very simply asked.

At this he did get up; that was easier than to say—at least with responsive simplicity; and again for a little he looked hard and in silence at his letter; which, at last, however, raising his eyes to her own for the act, while he masked their conscious ruefulness, to his utmost, in some air of assurance, he slipped into the inner pocket of his coat, letting it settle there securely. "You're too wonderful." But he frowned at her with it as never in his life. "Where does it all come from?"

"The wonder of poor me?" Kate Cookham said. "It comes from *you.*"

He shook his head slowly—feeling, with his letter there against his heart, such a new agility, almost such a new range of interest. "I mean so *much* money—so extraordinary much."

Well, she held him a while blank. "Does it seem to you extraordinarily much—twelve-hundred-and-sixty? Because you know," she added, "it's all."

"It's enough!" he returned with a slight thoughtful droop of his head to the right and his eyes attached to the far horizon as through a shade of shyness for what he was saying. He felt all her own lingering nearness somehow on his cheek.

"It's enough? Thank you then!" she rather oddly went on.

He shifted a little his posture. "It was more than a hundred a year—for you to get together."

"Yes," she assented, "that was what year by year I tried for."

"But you could live all the while and have that——!" Yes, he was at liberty, as he hadn't been, quite pleasantly to marvel. All his wonderments in life had been hitherto unanswered—and didn't the change mean that here again was the social relation?

"Ah, I didn't live as you saw me the other day."

"Yes," he answered—and didn't he the next instant feel he must fairly have smiled with it?—"the other day you *were* going it!"

"For once in my life," said Kate Cookham. "I've left the hotel," she after a moment added.

"Ah, you're in—a—lodgings?" he found himself inquiring as for positive sociability.

She had apparently a slight shade of hesitation, but in an instant it was all right; as what he showed he wanted to know she seemed mostly to give him. "Yes—but far of course from here. Up on the hill." To which, after another instant, "At The Mount, Castle Terrace," she subjoined.

"Oh, I *know* The Mount. And Castle Terrace is awfully sunny and nice."

"Awfully sunny and nice," Kate Cookham took from him.

"So that if it isn't," he pursued, "like the Royal, why you're at least comfortable."

"I shall be comfortable anywhere now," she replied with a certain dryness.

It was astonishing, however, what had become of his own. "Because I've accepted——?"

"Call it that!" she dimly smiled.

"I hope then at any rate," he returned, "you can now thoroughly rest." He spoke as for a cheerful conclusion and moved again also to smile, though with a poor grimace, no doubt; since what he seemed most clearly to feel was that since he "accepted" he mustn't, for his last note, have accepted in sulkiness or gloom. With that, at the same time, he couldn't but know, in all his fibres, that with such a still-watching face as the dotty veil didn't disguise for him there was no possible concluding, at least on his part. On hers, on hers it was—as he had so often for a week had reflectively to pronounce things —another affair. Ah, somehow, both formidably and helpfully, her face concluded—yet in a sense so strangely enshrouded in things she didn't tell him. What *must* she, what mustn't she, have done? What she had said—she had really told him nothing—was no account of her life; in the midst of which conflict of opposed recognitions, at any rate, it was as if, for all he could do, he himself now considerably floundered. "But I can't think—I can't think——!"

"You can't think I can have made so much money in the time and been honest?"

"Oh, you've been *honest!*" Herbert Dodd distinctly allowed.

It moved her stillness to a gesture—which, however, she had as promptly checked; and she went on the next instant as for further generosity to his failure of thought. "Everything was possible, under my stress, with my hatred."

"Your hatred——?" For she had paused as if it were after all too difficult.

"Of what I should for so long have been doing to you."

With this, for all his failures, a greater light than any yet shone upon him. "It made you think of ways——?"

"It made me think of everything. It made me work," said Kate Cookham. She added, however, the next moment: "But that's my story."

"And I mayn't hear it?"

"No—because I mayn't hear yours."

"Oh, mine——!" he said with the strangest, saddest yet after all most resigned sense of surrender of it; which he tried to make sound as if he couldn't have told it, for its splendour of misery, even if he would.

It seemed to move in her a little, exactly, that sense of the invidious. "Ah, mine too, I assure you——!"

He rallied at once to the interest. "Oh, we *can* talk then?"

"Never," she most oddly replied. "Never," said Kate Cookham.

They remained so, face to face; the effect of which for him was that he had after a little understood why. That was fundamental. "Well, I see."

Thus confronted they stayed; and then, as he saw with a contentment that came up from deeper still, it was indeed she who, with her worn fine face, would conclude. "But I can take care of you."

"You *have!*" he said as with nothing left of him but a beautiful appreciative candour.

"Oh, but you'll want it now in a way——!" she responsibly answered.

He waited a moment, dropping again on the seat. So, while she still stood, he looked up at her; with the sense somehow that there were too many things and that they were all together, terribly, irresistibly, doubtless blessedly, in her eyes and her whole person; which thus affected him for the moment as more than he could bear. He leaned forward, dropping his elbows to his knees and pressing his head on his hands. So he stayed, saying nothing; only, with the sense of her own sustained, renewed and wonderful action, knowing that an arm had passed round him and that he was held. She was beside him on the bench of desolation.

1909

III

CRITICISM

*

EDITOR'S NOTE

James began his public career as a critic. His first published work was a review of Nassau W. Senior's *Essays on Fiction* in *The North American Review* of October 1864, when he was twenty-one. His reviews and critical articles appeared in increasing numbers during the next decade in *The Nation, The North American, The Atlantic Monthly,* and *The Independent.* In 1878 he put out his first book of critical studies, *French Poets and Novelists.* His work as critic became part of his literary profession; it appeared regularly in American and English periodicals over a space of fifty years, and reached a kind of climax in the critical prefaces he wrote for his own fiction in the New York Edition of 1907-1909. His last contribution to a magazine in his lifetime was an article he wrote for *The Nation* of July 8, 1915, commemorating its founding fifty years earlier and his own share in it. He is, among writers of fiction in English, the pre-eminent case of the critic as novelist and the novelist as critic.

The present selections cover this career from 1865 to 1915. The earliest examples I include are two reviews James wrote for *The Nation* in 1865: one of Whitman's *Drum Taps* in the issue of November 16, the other of Dickens' *Our Mutual Friend* in the issue of December 21. I include them not because they present the full critical case on either Whitman or Dickens, or even James's own full dealings with these two writers, but because they show two of the formidable forces in the literature of his early lifetime with which he had to break in order to decide his own purpose and aims in art. Whitman represented for him the expansive democratic emotion and visionary gusto in American poetry which he saw as directly opposed to his own critical temperament. Dickens stood for the capacious methods and popular sentiment in Victorian fiction from which James was convinced the novel must be rescued if it was to fulfill its destiny as a form of art and moral intelligence. Dickens was, of course, one of the authors James had most greedily devoured in childhood; and years later, when he came to write his memoirs, he remembered how much the England he first encountered was the England Dickens had made real to him. Whitman came to be treated with greater sympathy in later years: his *Calamus* was discussed with considerable indulgence when James wrote about it in an "American Letter" for the London journal *Literature* of April 16, 1898; and Mrs. Wharton, in her memoir, *A Backward Glance* (1934), tells how James read Whitman's poems aloud at Lenox in 1905 "in a mood of subdued ecstasy" that made the two "divergent intelligences" seem to "walk together like gods." (The occasion ended, however, with James flinging up his hands and crying out "with the old stammer and twinkle: 'Oh, yes, a great genius; undoubtedly a very great genius! Only one cannot help deploring his too-extensive acquaintance with the foreign languages.'") I believe, none the less, that the two reviews of 1865, for all their youthful severity, are documents of radical importance in James's intellectual history, and that they also show brilliantly his critical acumen at the age of twenty-two.

"The Art of Fiction," which heads these selections, is James's most famous essay in criticism and the keystone of his arch. It was written as a rejoinder to Walter Besant's lecture on behalf of popular and realistic standards in fiction delivered at the Royal Institution on April 25, 1884. James's riposte appeared in *Longman's Magazine* for September 1884, and in book form in a volume titled *The Art of Fiction* in Boston in 1885, where it was included along with Besant's essay. (Robert Louis Stevenson in turn contributed a demurrer on both Besant and James—"A Humble Remonstrance"—to *Longman's* for December 1884.) In 1888 James included the essay in his *Partial Portraits,* from which the present text is taken. The letter which I have titled "The Great Form" was sent to a summer school at Deerfield, Mass., in the summer of 1889, and repeats, this time specifically for an American audience, the central doctrine of "The Art of Fiction." The essay "Criticism" first appeared as "The Science of Criticism" in *The New Review* (London) for May 1891, and was included under its present title in James's book *Essays in London and Elsewhere* in 1893.

The four passages on Hawthorne, Turgenev (James spelled the name *Turgénieff*), Balzac, and Flaubert show James dealing with four great modern masters who strongly influenced his own conception and practice of his art and on all of whom he wrote numerous times. The discussion of *The Scarlet Letter* is taken from Chapter V of the book on *Hawthorne* (1879). The essay on Turgenev was written for the *Library of the World's Best Literature,* edited by Charles Dudley Warner (1897); here the reader should also consult the essays on Turgenev in *French Poets and Novelists* (1878) and in *Partial Portraits* (1888). The passage on Balzac is from one of James's later essays on the French master who attracted him most powerfully; it comes from a critical introduction he wrote for Balzac's novel *Deux Jeunes Mariées* when it appeared in London as *Two Young Brides* in 1902, and was included in his *Notes on Novelists* in 1914. The account of Flaubert's *Madame Bovary* is taken from an introduction James wrote for an English edition of the novel in 1902, and it was also included in *Notes on Novelists* in 1914.

The circumstances of the letters James wrote in 1915 to H. G. Wells, one of the younger novelists who had aroused his liveliest admiration but from whose standards and practice in fiction he was later to find himself estranged, are explained in the note I have prefixed to them. They show

James in a last rally of defense on behalf of his art and purposes in fiction, and are taken from *The Letters of Henry James* as edited by Percy Lubbock (1920).

THE ART OF FICTION

I should not have affixed so comprehensive a title to these few remarks, necessarily wanting in any completeness upon a subject the full consideration of which would carry us far, did I not seem to discover a pretext for my temerity in the interesting pamphlet lately published under this name by Mr. Walter Besant. Mr. Besant's lecture at the Royal Institution—the original form of his pamphlet—appears to indicate that many persons are interested in the art of fiction, and are not indifferent to such remarks, as those who practise it may attempt to make about it. I am therefore anxious not to lose the benefit of this favourable association, and to edge in a few words under cover of the attention which Mr. Besant is sure to have excited. There is something very encouraging in his having put into form certain of his ideas on the mystery of story-telling.

It is a proof of life and curiosity—curiosity on the part of the brotherhood of novelists as well as on the part of their readers. Only a short time ago it might have been supposed that the English novel was not what the French call *discutable*. It had no air of having a theory, a conviction, a consciousness of itself behind it—of being the expression of an artistic faith, the result of choice and comparison. I do not say it was necessarily the worse for that: it would take much more courage than

I possess to intimate that the form of the novel as Dickens and Thackeray (for instance) saw it had any taint of incompleteness. It was, however, *naïf* (if I may help myself out with another French word); and evidently if it be destined to suffer in any way for having lost its *naïveté* it has now an idea of making sure of the corresponding advantages. During the period I have alluded to there was a comfortable, good-humoured feeling abroad that a novel is a novel, as a pudding is a pudding, and that our only business with it could be to swallow it. But within a year or two, for some reason or other, there have been signs of returning animation— the era of discussion would appear to have been to a certain extent opened. Art lives upon discussion, upon experiment, upon curiosity, upon variety of attempt, upon the exchange of views and the comparison of standpoints; and there is a presumption that those times when no one has anything particular to say about it, and has no reason to give for practice or preference, though they may be times of honour, are not times of development—are times, possibly even, a little of dulness. The successful application of any art is a delightful spectacle, but the theory too is interesting; and though there is a great deal of the latter without the former I suspect there has never been a genuine success that has not had a latent core of conviction. Discussion, suggestion, formulation, these things are fertilizing when they are frank and sincere. Mr. Besant has set an excellent example in saying what he thinks, for his part, about the way in which fiction should be written, as well as about the way in which it should be published; for his view of the "art," carried on into an appendix, covers that too. Other labourers in the same field will doubtless take up the argument, they will give it the light of their experience, and the effect will surely be to make our interest in the novel a little more what it had for some time threatened to fail to be—a serious, active, inquiring interest, under protection of which this delightful study may, in moments of confidence, venture to say a little more what it thinks of itself.

It must take itself seriously for the public to take it so. The old superstition about fiction being "wicked" has doubtless died out in England; but the spirit of it lingers in a certain oblique regard directed toward any story which does not more or less admit that it is only a joke. Even the most jocular novel feels in some degree the weight of the proscription that was formerly directed against literary levity: the jocularity does not always succeed in passing for orthodoxy. It is still expected, though perhaps people are ashamed to say it, that a production which is after all only a "make-believe" (for what else is a "story"?) shall be in some degree apologetic—shall renounce the pretension of attempting really to represent life. This, of course, any sensible, wide-awake story declines to do, for it quickly perceives that the tolerance granted to it on such a condition is only an attempt to stifle it disguised in the form of generosity. The old evangelical hostility to the novel, which was as explicit as it was narrow, and which regarded it as little less favourable to our immortal part than a stage-play, was in reality far less insulting. The only reason for the existence of a novel is that it does attempt to represent life. When it relinquishes this attempt, the same attempt that we see on the canvas of the painter, it will have arrived at a very strange pass. It is not expected of the picture that it will make itself humble in order to be forgiven; and the analogy between the art of the painter and the art of the novelist is, so far as I am able to see, complete. Their inspiration is the same, their process (allowing for the different quality of the vehicle) is the same, their success is the same. They may learn from each other, they may explain and sustain each other. Their cause is the same, and the honour of one is the honour of another. The Mahometans think a picture an unholy thing, but it is a long time since any Christian did, and it is therefore the more odd that in the Christian mind the traces (dissimulated though they may be) of a suspicion of the sister art should linger to this day. The only effectual way to lay it to rest is to emphasize the analogy to which I just alluded—to insist on the fact that as the picture is reality, so the novel is history. That is the only general description (which does it justice) that we may give of the novel. But history also is allowed to represent life; it is not, any more than painting, expected to apologize. The subject-matter of fiction is stored up likewise in documents and records, and if it will not give itself away, as they say in California, it must speak with assurance, with the tone of the historian. Certain accomplished novelists have a habit of giving themselves away which must often bring tears to the eyes of people who take their fiction seriously. I was lately struck, in reading over many pages of Anthony Trollope, with his want of discretion in this particular. In a digression, a parenthesis or an aside, he concedes to the reader that he and this trusting friend are only "making believe." He admits that the events he narrates have not really happened, and that he can give his narrative any turn the reader may like best. Such a betrayal of a sacred office seems to me, I confess, a terrible crime; it is what I mean by the attitude of apology, and it shocks me every whit as much in Trollope as it would have shocked me in Gibbon or Macaulay. It implies that the novelist is less occupied in looking for the truth (the truth, of course I mean, that he assumes, the premises that we must grant him,

whatever they may be) than the historian, and in doing
so it deprives him at a stroke of all his standing-room.
To represent and illustrate the past, the actions of men,
is the task of either writer, and the only difference that
I can see is, in proportion as he succeeds, to the honour
of the novelist, consisting as it does in his having more
difficult in collecting his evidence, which is so far from
being purely literary. It seems to me to give him a great
character, the fact that he has at once so much in common with the philosopher and the painter; this double
analogy is a magnificent heritage.

It is of all this evidently that Mr. Besant is full when
he insists upon the fact that fiction is one of the *fine* arts,
deserving in its turn of all the honours and emoluments
that have hitherto been reserved for the successful profession of music, poetry, painting, architecture. It is
impossible to insist too much on so important a truth,
and the place that Mr. Besant demands for the work of
the novelist may be represented, a trifle less abstractly,
by saying that he demands not only that it shall be
reputed artistic, but that it shall be reputed very artistic
indeed. It is excellent that he should have struck this
note, for his doing so indicates that there was need of it,
that his proposition may be to many people a novelty.
One rubs one's eyes at the thought; but the rest of Mr.
Besant's essay confirms the revelation. I suspect in truth
that it would be possible to confirm it still further, and
that one would not be far wrong in saying that in addition to the people to whom it has never occurred that
a novel ought to be artistic, there are a great many
others who, if this principle were urged upon them,
would be filled with an indefinable mistrust. They would
find it difficult to explain their repugnance, but it would
operate strongly to put them on their guard. "Art," in
our Protestant communities, where so many things have

got so strangely twisted about, is supposed in certain circles to have some vaguely injurious effect upon those who make it an important consideration, who let it weigh in the balance. It is assumed to be opposed in some mysterious manner to morality, to amusement, to instruction. When it is embodied in the work of the painter (the sculptor is another affair!) you know what it is: it stands there before you, in the honesty of pink and green and a gilt frame; you can see the worst of it at a glance, and you can be on your guard. But when it is introduced into literature it becomes more insidious —there is danger of its hurting you before you know it. Literature should be either instructive or amusing, and there is in many minds an impression that these artistic preoccupations, the search for form, contribute to neither end, interfere indeed with both. They are too frivolous to be edifying, and too serious to be diverting; and they are moreover priggish and paradoxical and superfluous. That, I think, represents the manner in which the latent thought of many people who read novels as an exercise in skipping would explain itself if it were to become articulate. They would argue, of course, that a novel ought to be "good," but they would interpret this term in a fashion of their own, which indeed would vary considerably from one critic to another. One would say that being good means representing virtuous and aspiring characters, placed in prominent positions; another would say that it depends on a "happy ending," on a distribution at the last of prizes, pensions, husbands, wives, babies, millions, appended paragraphs, and cheerful remarks. Another still would say that it means being full of incident and movement, so that we shall wish to jump ahead, to see who was the mysterious stranger, and if the stolen will was ever found, and shall not be distracted from this pleasure by any tiresome analysis or "description." But they would all agree that the "artistic" idea would spoil some of their fun. One would hold it accountable for all the description, another would see it revealed in the absence of sympathy. Its hostility to a happy ending would be evident, and it might even in some cases render any ending at all impossible. The "ending" of a novel is, for many persons, like that of a good dinner, a course of dessert and ices, and the artist in fiction is regarded as a sort of meddlesome doctor who forbids agreeable aftertastes. It is therefore true that this conception of Mr. Besant's of the novel as a superior form encounters not only a negative but a positive indifference. It matters little that as a work of art it should really be as little or as much of its essence to supply happy endings, sympathetic characters, and an objective tone, as if it were a work of mechanics: the association of ideas, however incongruous, might easily be too much for it if an eloquent voice were not sometimes raised to call attention to the fact that it is at once as free and as serious a branch of literature as any other.

Certainly this might sometimes be doubted in presence of the enormous number of works of fiction that appeal to the credulity of our generation, for it might easily seem that there could be no great character in a commodity so quickly and easily produced. It must be admitted that good novels are much compromised by bad ones, and that the field at large suffers discredit from overcrowding. I think, however, that this injury is only superficial, and that the superabundance of written fiction proves nothing against the principle itself. It has been vulgarized, like all other kinds of literature, like everything else to-day, and it has proved more than some kinds accessible to vulgarization. But there is as much difference as there ever was between a good novel and a bad one: the bad is swept with all the daubed canvases and spoiled marble into some unvisited limbo, or infinite rubbish-yard beneath the back-windows of the world, and the good subsists and emits its light and stimulates our desire for perfection. As I shall take the liberty of making but a single criticism of Mr. Besant, whose tone is so full of the love of his art, I may as well have done with it at once. He seems to me to mistake in attempting to say so definitely beforehand what sort of an affair the good novel will be. To indicate the danger of such an error as that has been the purpose of these few pages; to suggest that certain traditions on the subject, applied *a priori,* have already had much to answer for, and that the good health of an art which undertakes so immediately to reproduce life must demand that it be perfectly free. It lives upon exercise, and the very meaning of exercise is freedom. The only obligation to which in advance we may hold a novel, without incurring the accusation of being arbitrary, is that it be interesting. That general responsibility rests upon it, but it is the only one I can think of. The ways in which it is at liberty to accomplish this result (of interesting us) strike me as innumerable, and such as can only suffer from being marked out or fenced in by prescription. They are as various as the temperament of man, and they are successful in proportion as they reveal a particular mind, different from others. A novel is in its broadest definition a personal, a direct impression of life: that, to begin with, constitutes its value, which is greater or less according to the intensity of the impression. But there will be no intensity at all, and therefore no value, unless there is freedom to feel and say. The tracing of a line to be followed, of a tone to be taken, of a form to be filled out, is a limitation of that freedom and a suppression of the very thing that we are most curious about. The form, it seems to me, is to be appreciated after the fact: then the author's choice has been made, his standard has been indicated; then we can follow lines and directions and compare tones and resemblances. Then in a word we can enjoy one of the most charming of pleasures, we can estimate quality, we can apply the test of execution. The execution belongs to the author alone; it is what is most personal to him, and we measure him by that. The advantage, the luxury, as well as the torment and responsibility of the novelist, is that there is no limit to what he may attempt as an executant—no limit to his possible experiments, efforts, discoveries, successes. Here it is especially that he works, step by step, like his brother of the brush, of whom we may always say that he has painted his picture in a manner best known to himself. His manner is his secret, not necessarily a jealous one. He cannot disclose it as a general thing if he would; he would be at a loss to teach it to others. I say this with a due recollection of having insisted on the community of method of the artist who paints a picture and the artist who writes a novel. The painter *is* able to teach the rudiments of his practice, and it is possible, from the study of good work (granted the aptitude), both to learn how to paint and to learn how to write. Yet it remains true, without injury to the *rapprochement,* that the literary artist would be obliged to say to his pupil much more than the other, "Ah, well, you must do it as you can!" It is a question of degree, a matter of delicacy. If there are exact sciences, there are also exact arts, and the grammar of painting is so much more definite that it makes the difference.

I ought to add, however, that if Mr. Besant says at the beginning of his essay that the "laws of fiction may be laid down and taught with as much precision and exactness as the laws of harmony, perspective, and proportion," he mitigates what might appear to be an extravagance by applying his remark to "general" laws, and by expressing most of these rules in a manner with which it would certainly be unaccommodating to disagree. That the novelist must write from his experience, that his "characters must be real and such as might be met with in actual life"; that "a young lady brought up in a quiet country village should avoid descriptions of garrison life," and "a writer whose friends and personal experiences belong to the lower middle-class should carefully avoid introducing his characters into society"; that one should enter one's notes in a common-place book; that one's figures should be clear in outline; that making them clear by some trick of speech or of carriage is a bad method, and "describing them at length" is a worse one; that English Fiction should have a "conscious moral purpose"; that "it is almost impossible to estimate too highly the value of careful workmanship —that is, of style"; that "the most important point of all is the story," that "the story is everything": these are principles with most of which it is surely impossible not to sympathize. That remark about the lower middle-class writer and his knowing his place is perhaps rather chilling; but for the rest I should find it difficult to dissent from any one of these recommendations. At the same time, I should find it difficult positively to assent to them, with the exception, perhaps, of the injunction as to entering one's notes in a common-place book. They scarcely seem to me to have the quality that Mr. Besant attributes to the rules of the novelist—the "precision and exactness" of "the laws of harmony, perspective, and proportion." They are suggestive, they are even inspiring, but they are not exact, though they are doubtless as much so as the case admits of: which is a proof of that liberty of interpretation for which I just contended.

For the value of these different injunctions—so beautiful and so vague—is wholly in the meaning one attaches to them. The characters, the situation, which strike one as real will be those that touch and interest one most, but the measure of reality is very difficult to fix. The reality of Don Quixote or of Mr. Micawber is a very delicate shade; it is a reality so coloured by the author's vision that, vivid as it may be, one would hesitate to propose it as a model: one would expose one's self to some very embarrassing questions on the part of a pupil. It goes without saying that you will not write a good novel unless you possess the sense of reality; but it will be difficult to give you a recipe for calling that sense into being. Humanity is immense, and reality has a myriad forms; the most one can affirm is that some of the flowers of fiction have the odour of it, and others have not; as for telling you in advance how your nosegay should be composed, that is another affair. It is equally excellent and inconclusive to say that one must write from experience; to our supposititious aspirant such a declaration might savour of mockery. What kind of experience is intended, and where does it begin and end? Experience is never limited, and it is never complete; it is an immense sensibility, a kind of huge spider-web of the finest silken threads suspended in the chamber of consciousness, and catching every air-borne particle in its tissue. It is the very atmosphere of the mind; and when the mind is imaginative—much more when it happens to be that of a man of genius—it takes to itself the faintest hints of life, it converts the very pulses of the air into revelations. The young lady living in a village has only to be a damsel upon whom nothing is lost to make it quite unfair (as it seems to me) to declare to her that she shall have nothing to say about the military. Greater miracles have been seen than that,

imagination assisting, she should speak the truth about
some of these gentlemen. I remember an English novelist, a woman of genius, telling me that she was much
commended for the impression she had managed to give
in one of her tales of the nature and way of life of the
French Protestant youth. She had been asked where she
learned so much about this recondite being, she had
been congratulated on her peculiar opportunities. These
opportunities consisted in her having once, in Paris, as
she ascended a staircase, passed an open door where,
in the household of a *pasteur,* some of the young Prot-
estants were seated at table round a finished meal. The
glimpse made a picture; it lasted only a moment, but
that moment was experience. She had got her direct
personal impression, and she turned out her type. She
knew what youth was, and what Protestantism; she also
had the advantage of having seen what it was to be
French, so that she converted these ideas into a concrete
image and produced a reality. Above all, however, she
was blessed with the faculty which when you give it
an inch takes an ell, and which for the artist is a much
greater source of strength than any accident of residence
or of place in the social scale. The power to guess the
unseen from the seen, to trace the implication of things,
to judge the whole piece by the pattern, the condition of
feeling life in general so completely that you are well on
your way to knowing any particular corner of it—this
cluster of gifts may almost be said to constitute experience, and they occur in country and in town, and
in the most differing stages of education. If experience
consists of impressions, it may be said that impressions
are experience, just as (have we not seen it?) they are
the very air we breathe. Therefore, if I should certainly
say to a novice, "Write from experience and experience
only," I should feel that this was rather a tantalizing

monition if I were not careful immediately to add, "Try to be one of the people on whom nothing is lost!"

I am far from intending by this to minimize the importance of exactness—of truth of detail. One can speak best from one's own taste, and I may therefore venture to say that the air of reality (solidity of specification) seems to me to be the supreme virtue of a novel—the merit on which all its other merits (including that conscious moral purpose of which Mr. Besant speaks) helplessly and submissively depend. If it be not there they are all as nothing, and if these be there, they owe their effect to the success with which the author has produced the illusion of life. The cultivation of this success, the study of this exquisite process, form, to my taste, the beginning and the end of the art of the novelist. They are his inspiration, his despair, his reward, his torment, his delight. It is here in very truth that he competes with life; it is here that he competes with his brother the painter in *his* attempt to render the look of things, the look that conveys their meaning, to catch the colour, the relief, the expression, the surface, the substance of the human spectacle. It is in regard to this that Mr. Besant is well inspired when he bids him take notes. He cannot possibly take too many, he cannot possibly take enough. All life solicits him, and to "render" the simplest surface, to produce the most momentary illusion, is a very complicated business. His case would be easier, and the rule would be more exact, if Mr. Besant had been able to tell him what notes to take. But this, I fear, he can never learn in any manual; it is the business of his life. He has to take a great many in order to select a few, he has to work them up as he can, and even the guides and philosophers who might have most to say to him must leave him alone when it comes to the application of precepts, as we leave the painter in communion with his palette. That his characters "must be clear in outline," as Mr. Besant says—he feels that down to his boots; but how he shall make them so is a secret between his good angel and himself. It would be absurdly simple if he could be taught that a great deal of "description" would make them so, or that on the contrary the absence of description and the cultivation of dialogue, or the absence of dialogue and the multiplication of "incident," would rescue him from his difficulties. Nothing, for instance, is more possible than that he be of a turn of mind for which this odd, literal opposition of description and dialogue, incident and description, has little meaning and light. People often talk of these things as if they had a kind of internecine distinctness, instead of melting into each other at every breath, and being intimately associated parts of one general effort of expression. I cannot imagine composition existing in a series of blocks, nor conceive, in any novel worth discussing at all, of a passage of description that is not in its intention narrative, a passage of dialogue that is not in its intention descriptive, a touch of truth of any sort that does not partake of the nature of incident, or an incident that derives its interest from any other source than the general and only source of the success of a work of art—that of being illustrative. A novel is a living thing, all one and continuous, like any other organism, and in proportion as it lives will it be found, I think, that in each of the parts there is something of each of the other parts. The critic who over the close texture of a finished work shall pretend to trace a geography of items will mark some frontiers as artificial, I fear, as any that have been known to history. There is an old-fashioned distinction between the novel of character and the novel of incident which must have cost many a smile to the intending fabulist who was keen about his work. It appears to me as little to the point as the equally celebrated distinction between the novel and the romance—to answer as little to any reality. There are bad novels and good novels, as there are bad pictures and good pictures; but that is the only distinction in which I see any meaning, and I can as little imagine speaking of a novel of character as I can imagine speaking of a picture of character. When one says picture one says of character, when one says novel one says of incident, and the terms may be transposed at will. What is character but the determination of incident? What is incident but the illustration of character? What is either a picture or a novel that is *not* of character? What else do we seek in it and find in it? It is an incident for a woman to stand up with her hand resting on a table and look out at you in a certain way; or if it be not an incident I think it will be hard to say what it is. At the same time it is an expression of character. If you say you don't see it (character in *that—allons donc!*), this is exactly what the artist who has reasons of his own for thinking he *does* see it undertakes to show you. When a young man makes up his mind that he has not faith enough after all to enter the church as he intended, that is an incident, though you may not hurry to the end of the chapter to see whether perhaps he doesn't change once more. I do not say that these are extraordinary or startling incidents. I do not pretend to estimate the degree of interest proceeding from them, for this will depend upon the skill of the painter. It sounds almost puerile to say that some incidents are intrinsically much more important than others, and I need not take this precaution after having professed my sympathy for the major ones in remarking that the only classification of the novel that I can understand is into that which has life and that which has it not.

The novel and the romance, the novel of incident and that of character—these clumsy separations appear to me to have been made by critics and readers for their own convenience, and to help them out of some of their occasional queer predicaments, but to have little reality or interest for the producer, from whose point of view it is of course that we are attempting to consider the art of fiction. The case is the same with another shadowy category which Mr. Besant apparently is disposed to set up—that of the "modern English novel"; unless indeed it be that in this matter he has fallen into an accidental confusion of standpoints. It is not quite clear whether he intends the remarks in which he alludes to it to be didactic or historical. It is as difficult to suppose a person intending to write a modern English as to suppose him writing an ancient English novel: that is a label which begs the question. One writes the novel, one paints the picture, of one's language and of one's time, and calling it modern English will not, alas! make the difficult task any easier. No more, unfortunately, will calling this or that work of one's fellow-artist a romance—unless it be, of course, simply for the pleasantness of the thing, as for instance when Hawthorne gave this heading to his story of *Blithedale*. The French, who have brought the theory of fiction to remarkable completeness, have but one name for the novel, and have not attempted smaller things in it, that I can see, for that. I can think of no obligation to which the "romancer" would not be held equally with the novelist; the standard of execution is equally high for each. Of course it is of execution that we are talking—that being the only point of a novel that is open to contention. This is perhaps too often lost sight of, only to produce interminable confusions and cross-purposes. We must grant the artist his subject, his idea, his *donnée*: our criticism is applied only to what he

makes of it. Naturally I do not mean that we are bound
to like it or find it interesting: in case we do not our
course is perfectly simple—to let it alone. We may believe that of a certain idea even the most sincere novelist
can make nothing at all, and the event may perfectly
justify our belief; but the failure will have been a failure
to execute, and it is in the execution that the fatal weakness is recorded. If we pretend to respect the artist at
all, we must allow him his freedom of choice, in the face,
in particular cases, of innumerable presumptions that
the choice will not fructify. Art derives a considerable
part of its beneficial exercise from flying in the face of
presumptions, and some of the most interesting experiments of which it is capable are hidden in the bosom of
common things. Gustave Flaubert has written a story
about the devotion of a servant-girl to a parrot, and the
production, highly-finished as it is, cannot on the whole
be called a success. We are perfectly free to find it flat,
but I think it might have been interesting; and I, for my
part, am extremely glad he should have written it; it is
a contribution to our knowledge of what can be done—
or what cannot. Ivan Turgénieff has written a tale about
a deaf and dumb serf and a lap-dog, and the thing is
touching, loving, a little masterpiece. He struck the note
of life where Gustave Flaubert missed it—he flew in the
face of a presumption and achieved a victory.

Nothing, of course, will ever take the place of the
good old fashion of "liking" a work of art or not liking it:
the most improved criticism will not abolish that primitive, that ultimate test. I mention this to guard myself
from the accusation of intimating that the idea, the subject, of a novel or a picture, does not matter. It matters,
to my sense, in the highest degree, and if I might put
up a prayer it would be that artists should select none
but the richest. Some, as I have already hastened to

admit, are much more remunerative than others, and it would be a world happily arranged in which persons intending to treat them should be exempt from confusions and mistakes. This fortunate condition will arrive only, I fear, on the same day that critics become purged from error. Meanwhile, I repeat, we do not judge the artist with fairness unless we say to him,

"Oh, I grant you your starting-point, because if I did not I should seem to prescribe to you, and heaven forbid I should take that responsibility. If I pretend to tell you what you must not take, you will call upon me to tell you then what you must take; in which case I shall be prettily caught. Moreover, it isn't till I have accepted your data that I can begin to measure you. I have the standard, the pitch; I have no right to tamper with your flute and then criticize your music. Of course I may not care for your idea at all; I may think it silly, or stale, or unclean; in which case I wash my hands of you altogether. I may content myself with believing that you will not have succeeded in being interesting, but I shall, of course, not attempt to demonstrate it, and you will be as indifferent to me as I am to you. I needn't remind you that there are all sorts of tastes: who can know it better? Some people, for excellent reasons, don't like to read about carpenters; others, for reasons even better, don't like to read about courtesans. Many object to Americans. Others (I believe they are mainly editors and publishers) won't look at Italians. Some readers don't like quiet subjects; others don't like bustling ones. Some enjoy a complete illusion, others the consciousness of large concessions. They choose their novels accordingly, and if they don't care about your idea they won't, *a fortiori,* care about your treatment."

So that it comes back very quickly, as I have said, to the liking: in spite of M. Zola, who reasons less powerfully than he represents, and who will not reconcile himself to this absoluteness of taste, thinking that there are certain things that people ought to like, and that they can be made to like. I am quite at a loss to imagine anything (at any rate in this matter of fiction) that people *ought* to like or to dislike. Selection will be sure to take care of itself, for it has a constant motive behind it. That motive is simply experience. As people feel life, so they will feel the art that is most closely related to it. This closeness of relation is what we should never forget in talking of the effort of the novel. Many people speak of it as a factitious, artificial form, a product of ingenuity, the business of which is to alter and arrange the things that surround us, to translate them into conventional, traditional moulds. This, however, is a view of the matter which carries us but a very short way, condemns the art to an eternal repetition of a few familiar *clichés*, cuts short its development, and leads us straight up to a dead wall. Catching the very note and trick, the strange irregular rhythm of life, that is the attempt whose strenuous force keeps Fiction upon her feet. In proportion as in what she offers us we see life *without* rearrangement do we feel that we are touching the truth; in proportion as we see it *with* rearrangement do we feel that we are being put off with a substitute, a compromise and convention. It is not uncommon to hear an extraordinary assurance of remark in regard to this matter of rearranging, which is often spoken of as if it were the last word of art. Mr. Besant seems to me in danger of falling into the great error with his rather unguarded talk about "selection." Art is essentially selection, but it is a selection whose main care is to be

typical, to be inclusive. For many people art means rose-
coloured window-panes, and selection means picking
a bouquet for Mrs. Grundy. They will tell you glibly
that artistic considerations have nothing to do with the
disagreeable, with the ugly; they will rattle off shallow
commonplaces about the province of art and the limits
of art till you are moved to some wonder in return as to
the province and the limits of ignorance. It appears to
me that no one can ever have made a seriously artistic
attempt without becoming conscious of an immense
increase—a kind of revelation—of freedom. One perceives in that case—by the light of a heavenly ray—
that the province of art is all life, all feeling, all observation, all vision. As Mr. Besant so justly intimates, it is
all experience. That is a sufficient answer to those who
maintain that it must not touch the sad things of life, who
stick into its divine unconscious bosom little prohibitory
inscriptions on the end of sticks, such as we see in public
gardens—"It is forbidden to walk on the grass; it is forbidden to touch the flowers; it is not allowed to introduce dogs or to remain after dark; it is requested to keep
to the right." The young aspirant in the line of fiction
whom we continue to imagine will do nothing without
taste, for in that case his freedom would be of little use
to him; but the first advantage of his taste will be to
reveal to him the absurdity of the little sticks and tickets.
If he have taste, I must add, of course he will have ingenuity, and my disrespectful reference to that quality
just now was not meant to imply that it is useless in fiction. But it is only a secondary aid; the first is a capacity
for receiving straight impressions.

Mr. Besant has some remarks on the question of "the
story" which I shall not attempt to criticize, though they
seem to me to contain a singular ambiguity, because
I do not think I understand them. I cannot see what is

meant by talking as if there were a part of a novel which is the story and part of it which for mystical reasons is not—unless indeed the distinction be made in a sense in which it is difficult to suppose that any one should attempt to convey anything. "The story," if it represents anything, represents the subject, the idea, the *donnée* of the novel; and there is surely no "school"—Mr. Besant speaks of a school—which urges that a novel should be all treatment and no subject. There must assuredly be something to treat; every school is intimately conscious of that. This sense of the story being the idea, the starting-point, of the novel, is the only one that I see in which it can be spoken of as something different from its organic whole; and since in proportion as the work is successful the idea permeates and penetrates it, informs and animates it, so that every word and every punctuation-point contribute directly to the expression, in that proportion do we lose our sense of the story being a blade which may be drawn more or less out of its sheath. The story and the novel, the idea and the form, are the needle and thread, and I never heard of a guild of tailors who recommended the use of the thread without the needle, or the needle without the thread. Mr. Besant is not the only critic who may be observed to have spoken as if there were certain things in life which constitute stories, and certain others which do not. I find the same odd implication in an entertaining article in the *Pall Mall Gazette*, devoted, as it happens, to Mr. Besant's lecture. "The story is the thing!" says this graceful writer, as if with a tone of opposition to some other idea. I should think it was, as every painter who, as the time for "sending in" his picture looms in the distance, finds himself still in quest of a subject—as every belated artist not fixed about his theme will heartily agree. There are some subjects which speak to us and others

which do not, but he would be a clever man who should
undertake to give a rule—an *index expurgatorius*—by
which the story and the no-story should be known apart.
It is impossible (to me at least) to imagine any such
rule which shall not be altogether arbitrary. The writer
in the *Pall Mall* opposes the delightful (as I suppose)
novel of *Margot la Balafrée* to certain tales in which
"Bostonian nymphs" appear to have "rejected English
dukes for psychological reasons." I am not acquainted
with the romance just designated, and can scarcely forgive the *Pall Mall* critic for not mentioning the name
of the author, but the title appears to refer to a lady
who may have received a scar in some heroic adventure.
I am inconsolable at not being acquainted with this episode, but am utterly at a loss to see why it is a story
when the rejection (or acceptance) of a duke is not,
and why a reason, psychological or other, is not a subject when a cicatrix is. They are all particles of the multitudinous life with which the novel deals, and surely
no dogma which pretends to make it lawful to touch
the one and unlawful to touch the other will stand for
a moment on its feet. It is the special picture that must
stand or fall, according as it seem to possess truth or to
lack it. Mr. Besant does not, to my sense, light up the
subject by intimating that a story must, under penalty
of not being a story, consist of "adventures." Why of
adventures more than of green spectacles? He mentions
a category of impossible things, and among them he
places "fiction without adventure." Why without adventure, more than without matrimony, or celibacy, or
parturition, or cholera, or hydropathy, or Jansenism?
This seems to me to bring the novel back to the hapless
little *rôle* of being an artificial, ingenious thing—bring
it down from its large, free character of an immense and
exquisite correspondence with life. And what *is* adven-

ture, when it comes to that, and by what sign is the listening pupil to recognize it? It is an adventure—an immense one—for me to write this little article; and for a Bostonian nymph to reject an English duke is an adventure only less stirring, I should say, than for an English duke to be rejected by a Bostonian nymph. I see dramas within dramas in that, and innumerable points of view. A psychological reason is, to my imagination, an object adorably pictorial; to catch the tint of its complexion—I feel as if that idea might inspire one to Titianesque efforts. There are few things more exciting to me, in short, than a psychological reason, and yet, I protest, the novel seems to me the most magnificent form of art. I have just been reading, at the same time, the delightful story of *Treasure Island*, by Mr. Robert Louis Stevenson and, in a manner less consecutive, the last tale from M. Edmond de Goncourt, which is entitled *Chérie*. One of these works treats of murders, mysteries, islands of dreadful renown, hair-breadth escapes, miraculous coincidences and buried doubloons. The other treats of a little French girl who lived in a fine house in Paris, and died of wounded sensibility because no one would marry her. I call *Treasure Island* delightful, because it appears to me to have succeeded wonderfully in what it attempts; and I venture to bestow no epithet upon *Chérie*, which strikes me as having failed deplorably in what it attempts—that is in tracing the development of the moral consciousness of a child. But one of these productions strikes me as exactly as much of a novel as the other, and as having a "story" quite as much. The moral consciousness of a child is as much a part of life as the islands of the Spanish Main, and the one sort of geography seems to me to have those "surprises" of which Mr. Besant speaks quite as much as the other. For myself (since it comes back in the last resort, as I say, to the preference of the individual), the picture of the child's experience has the advantage that I can at successive steps (an immense luxury, near to the "sensual pleasure" of which Mr. Besant's critic in the *Pall Mall* speaks) say Yes or No, as it may be, to what the artist puts before me. I have been a child in fact, but I have been on a quest for a buried treasure only in supposition, and it is a simple accident that with M. de Goncourt I should have for the most part to say No. With George Eliot, when she painted that country with a far other intelligence, I always said Yes.

The most interesting part of Mr. Besant's lecture is unfortunately the briefest passage—his very cursory allusion to the "conscious moral purpose" of the novel. Here again it is not very clear whether he be recording a fact or laying down a principle; it is a great pity that in the latter case he should not have developed his idea. This branch of the subject is of immense importance, and Mr. Besant's few words point to considerations of the widest reach, not to be lightly disposed of. He will have treated the art of fiction but superficially who is not prepared to go every inch of the way that these considerations will carry him. It is for this reason that at the beginning of these remarks I was careful to notify the reader that my reflections on so large a theme have no pretension to be exhaustive. Like Mr. Besant, I have left the question of the morality of the novel till the last, and at the last I find I have used up my space. It is a question surrounded with difficulties, as witness the very first that meets us, in the form of a definite question, on the threshold. Vagueness, in such a discussion, is fatal, and what is the meaning of your morality and your conscious moral purpose? Will you not define your terms and explain how (a novel being a picture) a picture can be either moral or immoral? You

wish to paint a moral picture or carve a moral statue:
will you not tell us how you would set about it? We
are discussing the Art of Fiction; questions of art are
questions (in the widest sense) of execution; questions
of morality are quite another affair, and will you not let
us see how it is that you find it so easy to mix them up?
These things are so clear to Mr. Besant that he has
deduced from them a law which he sees embodied in
English Fiction, and which is "a truly admirable thing
and a great cause for congratulation." It is a great cause
for congratulation indeed when such thorny problems
become as smooth as silk. I may add that in so far as
Mr. Besant perceives that in point of fact English Fiction has addressed itself preponderantly to these delicate
questions he will appear to many people to have made
a vain discovery. They will have been positively struck,
on the contrary, with the moral timidity of the usual
English novelist; with his (or with her) aversion to face
the difficulties with which on every side the treatment of
reality bristles. He is apt to be extremely shy (whereas
the picture that Mr. Besant draws is a picture of boldness), and the sign of his work, for the most part, is a
cautious silence on certain subjects. In the English novel
(by which of course I mean the American as well),
more than in any other, there is a traditional difference
between that which people know and that which they
agree to admit that they know, that which they see and
that which they speak of, that which they feel to be a
part of life and that which they allow to enter into literature. There is the great difference, in short, between
what they talk of in conversation and what they talk of
in print. The essence of moral energy is to survey the
whole field, and I should directly reverse Mr. Besant's
remark and say not that the English novel has a purpose, but that it has a diffidence. To what degree a pur-

pose in a work of art is a source of corruption I shall not attempt to inquire; the one that seems to me least dangerous is the purpose of making a perfect work. As for our novel, I may say lastly on this score that as we find it in England to-day it strikes me as addressed in a large degree to "young people," and that this in itself constitutes a presumption that it will be rather shy. There are certain things which it is generally agreed not to discuss, not even to mention, before young people. That is very well, but the absence of discussion is not a symptom of the moral passion. The purpose of the English novel—"a truly admirable thing, and a great cause for congratulation"—strikes me therefore as rather negative.

There is one point at which the moral sense and the artistic sense lie very near together; that is in the light of the very obvious truth that the deepest quality of a work of art will always be the quality of the mind of the producer. In proportion as that intelligence is fine will the novel, the picture, the statue partake of the substance of beauty and truth. To be constituted of such elements is, to my vision, to have purpose enough. No good novel will ever proceed from a superficial mind; that seems to me an axiom which, for the artist in fiction, will cover all needful moral ground: if the youthful aspirant take it to heart it will illuminate for him many of the mysteries of "purpose." There are many other useful things that might be said to him, but I have come to the end of my article, and can only touch them as I pass. The critic in the *Pall Mall Gazette*, whom I have already quoted, draws attention to the danger, in speaking of the art of fiction, of generalizing. The danger that he has in mind is rather, I imagine, that of particularizing, for there are some comprehensive remarks which, in addition to those embodied in Mr. Besant's suggestive lecture, might without fear of misleading him be addressed to the ingenuous student. I should remind him first of the magnificence of the form that is open to him, which offers to sight so few restrictions and such innumerable opportunities. The other arts, in comparison, appear confined and hampered; the various conditions under which they are exercised are so rigid and definite. But the only condition that I can think of attaching to the composition of the novel is, as I have already said, that it be sincere. This freedom is a splendid privilege, and the first lesson of the young novelist is to learn to be worthy of it.

"Enjoy it as it deserves [I should say to him]; take possession of it, explore it to its utmost extent, publish it, rejoice in it. All life belongs to you, and do not listen either to those who would shut you up into corners of it and tell you that it is only here and there that art inhabits, or to those who would persuade you that this heavenly messenger wings her way outside of life altogether, breathing a superfine air, and turning away her head from the truth of things. There is no impression of life, no manner of seeing it and feeling it, to which the plan of the novelist may not offer a place; you have only to remember that talents so dissimilar as those of Alexandre Dumas and Jane Austen, Charles Dickens and Gustave Flaubert have worked in this field with equal glory. Do not think too much about optimism and pessimism; try and catch the colour of life itself. In France to-day we see a prodigious effort (that of Émile Zola, to whose solid and serious work no explorer of the capacity of the novel can allude without respect), we see an extraordinary effort vitiated by a spirit of pessimism on a narrow basis. M. Zola is magnificent, but he strikes an English reader as ignorant; he has an air of working

in the dark; if he had as much light as energy, his results would be of the highest value. As for the aberra-
tions of a shallow optimism, the ground (of English fiction especially) is strewn with their brittle particles as
with broken glass. If you must indulge in conclusions,
let them have the taste of a wide knowledge. Remember
that your first duty is to be as complete as possible—
to make as perfect a work. Be generous and delicate
and pursue the prize."

1884. From Partial Portraits (1888).

"THE GREAT FORM"

[In the summer of 1889 there was held at Deerfield, Massachusetts, a summer school on "The Novel," to which Henry
James, then in England, was invited to contribute. The appeal
of the school's organizers told him that it was their object to discuss and resist "the materialism of our present
tendencies" in this form of literature. Henry James, unable
to attend the sessions, participated by letter; his message
was then published in full in the *New York Tribune* of
Sunday, August 4, 1889, and summarized in briefer form
in *The Critic* (New York) of August 17, 1889. This letter
was rediscovered by Mr. Leon Edel and published by him
in the *Times Literary Supplement* (London) of July 29,
1939, with a note in which he remarks that the letter "is
interesting, for it is a reiteration, in concise form, of the
views set forth by James in his famous essay 'The Art of
Fiction,' while being at the same time probably the most
concrete advice he ever vouchsafed his countrymen on
novel-writing." *Editor's note*.]

I am afraid I can do little more than thank you for your courteous invitation to be present at the sittings of your delightfully sounding school of romance, which ought to inherit happiness and honour from such a name. I am so very far away from you that I am afraid I can't participate very intelligently in your discussions, but I can only give them the furtherance of a dimly discriminating sympathy. I am not sure that I apprehend very well your apparent premise "the materialism of our present tendencies," and I suspect that this would require some clearing up before I should be able (if even then) to contribute any suggestive or helpful word. To tell the truth, I can't help thinking that we already talk too much about the novel, about and around it, in proportion to the quantity of it having any importance that we produce. What I should say to the nymphs and swains who propose to converse about it under the great trees at Deerfield is: "Oh, do something from your point of view; an ounce of example is worth a ton of generalities; do something with the great art and the great form; do something with life. Any point of view is interesting that is a direct impression of life. You each have an impression coloured by your individual conditions; make that into a picture, a picture framed by your own personal wisdom, your glimpse of the American world. The field is vast for freedom, for study, for observation, for satire, for truth." I don't think I really do know what you mean by "materializing tendencies" any more than I should by "spiritualizing" or "etherealizing." There are no tendencies worth anything but to see the actual or the imaginative, which is just as visible, and to paint it. I have only two little words for the matter remotely approaching to rule or doctrine; one is life and the other freedom. Tell the ladies and gentlemen, the ingenious inquirers, to consider life directly and closely, and not to be put off with mean and puerile falsities, and be conscientious about it. It is infinitely large, various and comprehensive. Every sort of mind will find what it looks for in it, whereby the novel becomes truly multifarious and illustrative. That is what I mean by liberty; give it its head and let it range. If it is in a bad way, and the English novel is, I think, nothing but absolute freedom can refresh it and restore its self-respect. Hence these raw brevities and please convey to your companions, my dear sir, the cordial good wishes of yours and theirs,

Henry James

1889

CRITICISM

If literary criticism may be said to flourish among us at all, it certainly flourishes immensely, for it flows through the periodical press like a river that has burst its dikes. The quantity of it is prodigious, and it is a commodity of which, however the demand may be estimated, the supply will be sure to be in any supposable extremity the last thing to fail us. What strikes the observer above all, in such an affluence, is the unexpected proportion the discourse uttered bears to the objects discoursed of —the paucity of examples, of illustrations and productions, and the deluge of doctrine suspended in the void; the profusion of talk and the contraction of experiment, of what one may call literary conduct. This, indeed, ceases to be an anomaly as soon as we look at the con-

ditions of contemporary journalism. Then we see that
these conditions have engendered the practice of "reviewing"—a practice that in general has nothing in
common with the art of criticism. Periodical literature
is a huge, open mouth which has to be fed—a vessel of
immense capacity which has to be filled. It is like a regular train which starts at an advertised hour, but which is
free to start only if every seat be occupied. The seats
are many, the train is ponderously long, and hence the
manufacture of dummies for the seasons when there are
not passengers enough. A stuffed mannikin is thrust into
the empty seat, where it makes a creditable figure till
the end of the journey. It looks sufficiently like a pas-
senger, and you know it is not one only when you perceive that it neither says anything nor gets out. The
guard attends to it when the train is shunted, blows the
cinders from its wooden face and gives a different crook
to its elbow, so that it may serve for another run. In this
way, in a well-conducted periodical, the blocks of *rem-
plissage* are the dummies of criticism—the recurrent,
regulated breakers in the tide of talk. They have a reason
for being, and the situation is simpler when we perceive
it. It helps to explain the disproportion I just mentioned, as well, in many a case, as the quality of the particular discourse. It helps us to understand that the "organs of public opinion" must be no less copious than
punctual, that publicity must maintain its high standard, that ladies and gentlemen may turn an honest penny
by the free expenditure of ink. It gives us a glimpse of
the high figure presumably reached by all the honest pen-
nies accumulated in the cause, and throws us quite into
a glow over the march of civilization and the way we
have organized our conveniences. From this point of
view it might indeed go far towards making us enthusiastic about our age. What is more calculated to inspire us

with a just complacency than the sight of a new and
flourishing industry, a fine economy of production? The
great business of reviewing has, in its roaring routine,
many of the signs of blooming health, many of the features which beguile one into rendering an involuntary
homage to successful enterprise.

Yet it is not to be denied that certain captious persons
are to be met who are not carried away by the spectacle,
who look at it much askance, who see but dimly whither
it tends, and who find no aid to vision even in the great
light (about itself, its spirit, and its purposes, among
other things) that it might have been expected to diffuse. "Is there any such great light at all?" we may imagine the most restless of the sceptics to inquire, "and
isn't the effect rather one of a certain kind of pretentious
and unprofitable gloom?" The vulgarity, the crudity, the
stupidity which this cherished combination of the
offhand review and of our wonderful system of publicity
have put into circulation on so vast a scale may be represented, in such a mood, as an unprecedented invention
for darkening counsel. The bewildered spirit may ask
itself, without speedy answer, What is the function in
the life of man of such a periodicity of platitude and irrelevance? Such a spirit will wonder how the life of
man survives it, and, above all, what is much more important, how literature resists it; whether, indeed, literature does resist it and is not speedily going down beneath it. The signs of this catastrophe will not in the case
we suppose be found too subtle to be pointed out—the
failure of distinction, the failure of style, the failure of
knowledge, the failure of thought. The case is therefore
one for recognizing with dismay that we are paying a
tremendous price for the diffusion of penmanship and
opportunity; that the multiplication of endowments
for chatter may be as fatal as an infectious disease; that

literature lives essentially, in the sacred depths of its being, upon example, upon perfection wrought; that, like other sensitive organisms, it is highly susceptible of demoralization, and that nothing is better calculated than irresponsible pedagogy to make it close its ears and lips. To be puerile and untutored about it is to deprive it of air and light, and the consequence of its keeping bad company is that it loses all heart. We may, of course, continue to talk about it long after it has bored itself to death, and there is every appearance that this is mainly the way in which our descendants will hear of it. They will, however, acquiesce in its extinction.

This, I am aware, is a dismal conviction, and I do not pretend to state the case gaily. The most I can say is that there are times and places in which it strikes one as less desperate than at others. One of the places is Paris, and one of the times is some comfortable occasion of being there. The custom of rough-and-ready reviewing is, among the French, much less rooted than with us, and the dignity of criticism is, to my perception, in consequence much higher. The art is felt to be one of the most difficult, the most delicate, the most occasional; and the material on which it is exercised is subject to selection, to restriction. That is, whether or no the French are always right as to what they do notice, they strike me as infallible as to what they don't. They publish hundreds of books which are never noticed at all, and yet they are much neater bookmakers than we. It is recognized that such volumes have nothing to say to the critical sense, that they do not belong to literature, and that the possession of the critical sense is exactly what makes it impossible to read them and dreary to discuss them—places them, as a part of critical experience, out of the question. The critical sense, in France, *ne se dérange pas,* as the phrase is, for so little.

No one would deny, on the other hand, that when it does set itself in motion it goes further than with us. It handles the subject in general with finer finger-tips. The bluntness of ours, as tactile implements addressed to an exquisite process, is still sometimes surprising, even after frequent exhibition. We blunder in and out of the affair as if it were a railway station—the easiest and most public of the arts. It is in reality the most complicated and the most particular. The critical sense is so far from frequent that it is absolutely rare, and the possession of the cluster of qualities that minister to it is one of the highest distinctions. It is a gift inestimably precious and beautiful; therefore, so far from thinking that it passes overmuch from hand to hand, one knows that one has only to stand by the counter an hour to see that business is done with baser coin. We have too many small schoolmasters; yet not only do I not question in literature the high utility of criticism, but I should be tempted to say that the part it plays may be the supremely beneficent one when it proceeds from deep sources, from the efficient combination of experience and perception. In this light one sees the critic as the real helper of the artist, a torch-bearing outrider, the interpreter, the brother. The more the tune is noted and the direction observed the more we shall enjoy the convenience of a critical literature. When one thinks of the outfit required for free work in this spirit, one is ready to pay almost any homage to the intelligence that has put it on; and when one considers the noble figure completely equipped—armed *cap-à-pie* in curiosity and sympathy—one falls in love with the apparition. It certainly represents the knight who has knelt through his long vigil and who has the piety of his office. For there is something sacrificial in his function, inasmuch as he offers himself as a general touchstone. To lend himself,

to project himself and steep himself, to feel and feel till
he understands, and to understand so well that he can
say, to have perception at the pitch of passion and expression as embracing as the air, to be infinitely curious
and incorrigibly patient, and yet plastic and inflammable
and determinable, stooping to conquer and serving to
direct—these are fine chances for an active mind,
chances to add the idea of independent beauty to the
conception of success. Just in proportion as he is sentient and restless, just in proportion as he reacts and
reciprocates and penetrates, is the critic a valuable
instrument; for in literature assuredly criticism *is* the
critic, just as art is the artist; it being assuredly the artist
who invented art and the critic who invented criticism,
and not the other way round.

And it is with the kinds of criticism exactly as it is
with the kinds of art—the best kind, the only kind
worth speaking of, is the kind that springs from the liveliest experience. There are a hundred labels and tickets,
in all this matter, that have been pasted on from the outside and appear to exist for the convenience of pass-
ers-by; but the critic who lives *in* the house, ranging
through its innumerable chambers, knows nothing about
the bills on the front. He only knows that the more impressions he has the more he is able to record, and that
the more he is saturated, poor fellow, the more he can
give out. His life, at this rate, is heroic, for it is immensely vicarious. He has to understand for others, to
answer for them; he is always under arms. He knows
that the whole honour of the matter, for him, besides
the success in his own eyes, depends upon his being
indefatigably supple, and that is a formidable order. Let
me not speak, however, as if his work were a conscious
grind, for the sense of effort is easily lost in the enthusiasm of curiosity. Any vocation has its hours of intensity

that is so closely connected with life. That of the critic, in literature, is connected doubly, for he deals with life at second-hand as well as at first; that is, he deals with the experience of others, which he resolves into his own, and not of those invented and selected others with whom the novelist makes comfortable terms, but with the uncompromising swarm of authors, the clamorous children of history. He has to make them as vivid and as free as the novelist makes *his* puppets, and yet he has, as the phrase is, to take them as they come. We must be easy with him if the picture, even when the aim has really been to penetrate, is sometimes confused, for there are baffling and there are thankless subjects; and we make everything up to him by the peculiar purity of our esteem when the portrait is really, like the happy portraits of the other art, a text preserved by translation.

1891. From *Essays in London and Elsewhere* (1893).

MR. WALT WHITMAN

It has been a melancholy task to read this book;[1] and it is a still more melancholy one to write about it. Perhaps since the day of Mr. Tupper's *Philosophy* there has been no more difficult reading of the poetic sort. It exhibits the effort of an essentially prosaic mind to lift itself, by a prolonged muscular strain, into poetry. Like hundreds of other good patriots, during the last four years, Mr. Walt Whitman has imagined that a cer-

[1] *Drum-Taps,* by Walt Whitman (1865).

tain amount of violent sympathy with the great deeds and sufferings of our soldiers, and of admiration for our national energy, together with a ready command of picturesque language, are sufficient inspiration for a poet. If this were the case, we had been a nation of poets. The constant developments of the war moved us continually to strong feeling and to strong expression of it. But in those cases in which these expressions were written out and printed with all due regard to prosody, they failed to make poetry, as any one may see by consulting now in cold blood the back volumes of the *Rebellion Record.*

Of course the city of Manhattan, as Mr. Whitman delights to call it, when regiments poured through it in the first months of the war, and its own sole god, to borrow the words of a real poet, ceased for a while to be the millionaire, was a noble spectacle, and a poetical statement to this effect is possible. *Of course* the tumult of a battle is grand, the results of a battle tragic, and the untimely deaths of young men a theme for elegies. But he is not a poet who merely reiterates these plain facts *ore rotundo.* He only sings them worthily who views them from a height. Every tragic event collects about it a number of persons who delight to dwell upon its superficial points—of minds which are bullied by the *accidents* of the affair. The temper of such minds seems to us to be the reverse of the poetic temper; for the poet, although he incidentally masters, grasps, and uses the superficial traits of his theme, is really a poet only in so far as he extracts its latent meaning and holds it up to common eyes. And yet from such minds most of our war-verses have come, and Mr. Whitman's utterances, much as the assertion may surprise his friends, are in this respect no exception to general fashion. They are an exception, however, in that they openly pretend to be something better; and this it is that makes them melancholy reading.

Mr. Whitman is very fond of blowing his own trumpet, and he has made very explicit claims for his books. "Shut not your doors," he exclaims at the outset—

Shut not your doors to me, proud libraries,
For that which was lacking among you all, yet needed most,
    I bring;
A book I have made for your dear sake, O soldiers,
And for you, O soul of man, and you, love of comrades;
The words of my book nothing, the life of it everything;
A book separate, not link'd with the rest, nor felt by the
    intellect;
But you will feel every word, O Libertad! arm'd Libertad!
It shall pass by the intellect to swim the sea, the air,
    With joy with you, O soul of man.

These are great pretensions, but it seems to us that the following are even greater:

From Paumanok starting, I fly like a bird,
Around and around to soar, to sing the idea of all;
To the north betaking myself, to sing there arctic songs,
To Kanada, 'till I absorb Kanada in myself—to Michigan
    then,
To Wisconsin, Iowa, Minnesota, to sing their songs (they
    are inimitable);
Then to Ohio and Indiana, to sing theirs—to Missouri and
    Kansas and Arkansas to sing theirs,
To Tennessee and Kentucky—to the Carolinas and Georgia,
    to sing theirs,
To Texas, and so along up toward California, to roam
    accepted everywhere;
To sing first (to the tap of the war-drum, if need be)
The idea of all—of the western world, one and inseparable,
And then the song of each member of these States.

Mr. Whitman's primary purpose is to celebrate the greatness of our armies; his secondary purpose is to celebrate the greatness of the city of New York. He pursues these objects through a hundred pages of matter which remind us irresistibly of the story of the college professor who, on a venturesome youth bringing him a theme done in blank verse, reminded him that it was not customary in writing prose to begin each line with a capital. The frequent capitals are the only marks of verse in Mr. Whitman's writings. There is, fortunately, but one attempt at rhyme. We say fortunately, for if the inequality of Mr. Whitman's lines were self-registering, as it would be in the case of an anticipated syllable at their close, the effect would be painful in the extreme. As the case stands, each line stands off by itself, in resolute independence of its companions, without a visible goal.

But if Mr. Whitman does not write verse, he does not write ordinary prose. The reader has seen that liberty is "libertad." In like manner, comrade is "camerado"; Americans are "Americanos"; a pavement is a "trottoir," and Mr. Whitman himself is a "chansonnier." If there is one thing that Mr. Whitman is not, it is this, for Béranger was a *chansonnier*. To appreciate the force of our conjunction, the reader should compare his military lyrics with Mr. Whitman's declamations. Our author's novelty, however, is not in his words, but in the form of his writing. As we have said, it begins for all the world like verse and turns out to be arrant prose. It is more like Mr. Tupper's proverbs than anything we have met.

But what if, in form, it *is* prose? it may be asked. Very good poetry has come out of prose before this. To this we would reply that it must first have gone into it. Prose, in order to be good poetry, must first be good prose. As a general principle, we know of no circumstance more likely to impugn a writer's earnestness than the adoption of an anomalous style. He must have something very original to say if none of the old vehicles will carry his thoughts. Of course he *may* be surprisingly original. Still, presumption is against him. If on examination the matter of his discourse proves very valuable, it justifies, or at any rate excuses, his literary innovation.

But if, on the other hand, it is of a common quality, with nothing new about it but its manners, the public will judge the writer harshly. The most that can be said of Mr. Whitman's vaticinations is, that, cast in a fluent and familiar manner, the average substance of them might escape unchallenged. But we have seen that Mr. Whitman prides himself especially on the substance— the life—of his poetry. It may be rough, it may be grim, it may be clumsy—such we take to be the author's argument—but it is sincere, it is sublime, it appeals to the soul of man, it is the voice of a people. He tells us, in the lines quoted, that the words of his book are nothing. To our perception they are everything, and very little at that.

A great deal of verse that is nothing but words has, during the war, been sympathetically sighed over and cut out of newspaper corners, because it has possessed a certain simple melody. But Mr. Whitman's verse, we are confident, would have failed even of this triumph, for the simple reason that no triumph, however small, is won but through the exercise of art, and that this volume is an offence against art. It is not enough to be grim and rough and careless; common sense is also necessary, for it is by common sense that we are judged. There exists in even the commonest minds, in literary matters, a certain precise instinct of conservatism, which is very shrewd in detecting wanton eccentricities.

To this instinct Mr. Whitman's attitude seems monstrous. It is monstrous because it pretends to persuade the soul while it slights the intellect; because it pretends to gratify the feelings while it outrages the taste. The point is that it does this *on theory*, wilfully, consciously, arrogantly. It is the little nursery game of "open your mouth and shut your eyes." Our hearts are often touched through a compromise with the artistic sense, but never in direct violation of it. Mr. Whitman sits down at the outset and counts out the intelligence. This were indeed a wise precaution on his part if the intelligence were only submissive! But when she is deliberately insulted, she takes her revenge by simply standing erect and open-eyed. This is assuredly the best she can do. And if she could find a voice she would probably address Mr. Whitman as follows:—

"You came to woo my sister, the human soul. Instead of giving me a kick as you approach, you should either greet me courteously, or, at least, steal in unobserved. But now you have me on your hands. Your chances are poor. What the human heart desires above all is sincerity, and you do not appear to me sincere. For a lover you talk entirely too much about yourself. In one place you threaten to absorb Kanada. In another you call upon the city of New York to incarnate you, as you have incarnated it. In another you inform us that neither youth pertains to you nor 'delicatesse,' that you are awkward in the parlour, that you do not dance, and that you have neither bearing, beauty, knowledge, nor fortune. In another place, by an allusion to your 'little songs,' you seem to identify yourself with the third person of the Trinity.

"For a poet who claims to sing 'the idea of all,' this is tolerably egotistical. We look in vain, however, through your book for a single idea. We find nothing but flashy imitations of ideas. We find a medley of extravagances

and commonplaces. We find art, measure, grace, sense
sneered at on every page, and nothing positive given us
in their stead. To be positive one must have something
to say; to be positive requires reason, labour, and art;
and art requires, above all things, a suppression of one's
self, a subordination of one's self to an idea. This will
never do for you, whose plan is to adapt the scheme
of the universe to your own limitations. You cannot en-
tertain and exhibit ideas; but, as we have seen, you are
prepared to incarnate them. It is for this reason, doubtless, that when once you have planted yourself squarely
before the public, and in view of the great service you
have done to the ideal, have become, as you say, 'accepted everywhere,' you can afford to deal exclusively
in words. What would be bald nonsense and dreary platitudes in any one else becomes sublimity in you.

"But all this is a mistake. To become adopted as a
national poet, it is not enough to discard everything in
particular and to accept everything in general, to amass
crudity upon crudity, to discharge the undigested contents of your blotting-book into the lap of the public.
You must respect the public which you address; for it
has taste, if you have not. It delights in the grand, the
heroic, and the masculine; but it delights to see these
conceptions cast into worthy form. It is indifferent to
brute sublimity. It will never do for you to thrust your
hands into your pockets and cry out that, as the research
of form is an intolerable bore, the shortest and most
economical way for the public to embrace its idols—for
the nation to realize its genius—is in your own person.

"This democratic, liberty-loving, American populace,
this stern and war-tried people, is a great civiliser. It is
devoted to refinement. If it has sustained a monstrous
war, and practised human nature's best in so many ways
for the last five years, it is not to put up with spurious

poetry afterwards. To sing aright our battles and our glories it is not enough to have served in a hospital (however praiseworthy the task in itself), to be aggressively careless, inelegant, and ignorant, and to be constantly preoccupied with yourself. It is not enough to be rude, lugubrious, and grim. You must also be serious. You must forget yourself in your ideas. Your personal qualities—the vigour of your temperament, the manly independence of your nature, the tenderness of your heart—these facts are impertinent. You must be *possessed,* and you must thrive to possess your possession. If in your striving you break into divine eloquence, then you are a poet. If the idea which possesses you is the idea of your country's greatness, then you are a national poet; and not otherwise."

1865. Here reprinted from Views and Reviews by
Henry James, edited by LeRoy Phillips (1908).

✳

THE LIMITATIONS OF DICKENS

Our Mutual Friend is, to our perception, the poorest of Mr. Dickens's works. And it is poor with the poverty not of momentary embarrassment, but of permanent exhaustion. It is wanting in inspiration. For the last ten years it has seemed to us that Mr. Dickens has been unmistakeably forcing himself. *Bleak House* was forced; *Little Dorrit* was laboured; the present work is dug out as with a spade and pickaxe.

Of course—to anticipate the usual argument—who but Dickens could have written it? Who, indeed? Who else would have established a lady in business in a novel on the admirably solid basis of her always putting on gloves and tying a handkerchief around her head in moments of grief, and of her habitually addressing her family with "Peace! hold!" It is needless to say that Mrs. Reginald Wilfer is first and last the occasion of considerable true humour. When, after conducting her daughter to Mrs. Boffin's carriage, in sight of all the envious neighbours, she is described as enjoying her triumph during the next quarter of an hour by airing herself on the doorstep "in a kind of splendidly serene trance," we laugh with as uncritical a laugh as could be desired of us. We pay the same tribute to her assertions, as she narrates the glories of the society she enjoyed at her father's table, that she has known as many as three copper-plate engravers exchanging the most exquisite sallies and retorts there at one time. But when to these we have added a dozen more happy examples of the humour which was exhaled from every line of Mr. Dickens's earlier writings, we shall have closed the list of the merits of the work before us.

To say that the conduct of the story, with all its complications, betrays a long-practised hand, is to pay no compliment worthy the author. If this were, indeed, a compliment, we should be inclined to carry it further, and congratulate him on his success in what we should call the manufacture of fiction; for in so doing we should express a feeling that has attended us throughout the book. Seldom, we reflected, had we read a book so intensely *written*, so little seen, known, or felt.

In all Mr. Dickens's works the fantastic has been his great resource; and while his fancy was lively and vigorous it accomplished great things. But the fantastic, when the fancy is dead, is a very poor business. The movement of Mr. Dickens's fancy in Mr. Wilfer and Mr. Boffin and Lady Tippins, and the Lammles and Miss Wren, and even in Eugene Wrayburn, is, to our mind, a movement lifeless, forced, mechanical. It is the letter of his old humour without the spirit. It is hardly too much to say that every character here put before us is a mere bundle of eccentricities, animated by no principle of nature whatever.

In former days there reigned in Mr. Dickens's extravagances a comparative consistency; they were exaggerated statements of types that really existed. We had, perhaps, never known a Newman Noggs, nor a Pecksniff, nor a Micawber; but we had known persons of whom these figures were but the strictly logical consummation. But among the grotesque creatures who occupy the pages before us, there is not one whom we can refer to as an existing type. In all Mr. Dickens's stories, indeed, the reader has been called upon, and has willingly consented, to accept a certain number of figures or creatures of pure fancy, for this was the author's poetry. He was, moreover, always repaid for his concession by a peculiar beauty or power in these exceptional characters. But he is now expected to make the same concession, with a very inadequate reward.

What do we get in return for accepting Miss Jenny Wren as a possible person? This young lady is the type of a certain class of characters of which Mr. Dickens has made a specialty, and with which he has been accustomed to draw alternate smiles and tears, according as he pressed one spring or another. But this is very cheap merriment and very cheap pathos. Miss Jenny Wren is a poor little dwarf, afflicted, as she constantly reiterates, with a "bad back" and "queer legs," who makes doll's dresses, and is for ever pricking at those with whom she converses in the air, with her needle, and assuring them that she knows their "tricks and their manners." Like all Mr. Dickens's pathetic characters, she is a little monster; she is deformed, unhealthy, unnatural; she belongs to the troop of hunchbacks, imbeciles, and precocious children who have carried on the sentimental business in all Mr. Dickens's novels; the little Nells, the Smikes, the Paul Dombeys.

Mr. Dickens goes as far out of the way for his wicked people as he does for his good ones. Rogue Riderhood, indeed, in the present story, is villainous with a sufficiently natural villainy; he belongs to that quarter of society in which the author is most at his ease. But was there ever such wickedness as that of the Lammles and Mr. Fledgeby? Not that people have not been as mischievous as they; but was any one ever mischievous in that singular fashion? Did a couple of elegant swindlers ever take such particular pains to be aggressively inhuman?—for we can find no other word for the gratuitous distortions to which they are subjected. The word *humanity* strikes us as strangely discordant, in the midst of these pages; for, let us boldly declare it, there is no humanity here.

Humanity is nearer home than the Boffins, and the Lammles, and the Wilfers, and the Veneerings. It is in what men have in common with each other, and not what they have in distinction. The people just named have nothing in common with each other, except the fact that they have nothing in common with mankind at large. What a world were this world if the world of *Our Mutual Friend* were an honest reflection of it! But a community of eccentrics is impossible. Rules alone are consistent with each other; exceptions are inconsistent. Society is maintained by natural sense and natural feeling. We cannot conceive a society in which these principles are not in some manner represented. Where in these pages are the depositaries of that intelligence without which the movement of life would cease? Who represents nature?

Accepting half of Mr. Dickens's persons as intentionally grotesque, where are those exemplars of sound humanity who should afford us the proper measure of their companions' variations? We ought not, in justice to the author, to seek them among his weaker—that is, his mere conventional—characters; in John Harmon, Lizzie Hexam, or Mortimer Lightwood; but we assuredly cannot find them among his stronger—that is, his artificial creations.

Suppose we take Eugene Wrayburn and Bradley Headstone. They occupy a half-way position between the habitual probable of nature and the habitual impossible of Mr. Dickens. A large portion of the story rests upon the enmity borne by Headstone to Wrayburn, both being in love with the same woman. Wrayburn is a gentleman, and Headstone is one of the people. Wrayburn is well-bred, careless, elegant, sceptical, and idle: Headstone is a high-tempered, hard-working, ambitious young schoolmaster. There lay in the opposition of these two characters a very good story. But the prime requisite was that they should *be* characters: Mr. Dickens, according to his usual plan, has made them simply figures, and between them the story that was to be, the story that should have been, has evaporated. Wrayburn lounges about with his hands in his pockets, smoking a cigar, and talking nonsense. Headstone strides about, clenching his fists and biting his lips and grasping his stick.

There is one scene in which Wrayburn chaffs the schoolmaster with easy insolence, while the latter writhes impotently under his well-bred sarcasm. This scene is very clever, but it is very insufficient. If the majority of

readers were not so very timid in the use of words we
should call it vulgar. By this we do not mean to indicate
the conventional impropriety of two gentlemen exchanging lively personalities; we mean to emphasise the essentially small character of these personalities. In other
words, the moment, dramatically, is great, while the
author's conception is weak. The friction of two *men*,
of two characters, of two passions, produces stronger
sparks than Wrayburn's boyish repartees and Headstone's melodramatic commonplaces.

Such scenes as this are useful in fixing the limits of
Mr. Dickens's insight. Insight is, perhaps, too strong a
word; for we are convinced that it is one of the chief
conditions of his genius not to see beneath the surface of
things. If we might hazard a definition of his literary
character, we should, accordingly, call him the greatest
of superficial novelists. We are aware that this definition
confines him to an inferior rank in the department of
letters which he adorns; but we accept this consequence
of our proposition. It were, in our opinion, an offence
against humanity to place Mr. Dickens among the greatest novelists. For, to repeat what we have already intimated, he has created nothing but figure. He has added
nothing to our understanding of human character. He
is master of but two alternatives: he reconciles us to
what is commonplace, and he reconciles us to what is
odd. The value of the former service is questionable; and
the manner in which Mr. Dickens performs it sometimes
conveys a certain impression of charlatanism. The value
of the latter service is incontestable, and here Mr. Dickens is an honest, an admirable artist.

But what is the condition of the truly great novelist?
For him there are no alternatives, for him there are no
oddities, for him there is nothing outside of humanity.
He cannot shirk it; it imposes itself upon him. For

him alone, therefore, there is a true and a false; for him alone, it is possible to be right, because it is possible to be wrong. Mr. Dickens is a great observer and a great humourist, but he is nothing of a philosopher.

Some people may hereupon say, so much the better; we say, so much the worse. For a novelist very soon has need of a little philosophy. In treating of Micawber, and Boffin, and Pickwick, *et hoc genus omne*, he can, indeed, dispense with it, for this—we say it with all deference—is not serious writing. But when he comes to tell the story of a passion, a story like that of Headstone and Wrayburn, he becomes a moralist as well as an artist. He must know *man* as well as *men*, and to know man is to be a philosopher.

The writer who knows men alone, if he have Mr. Dickens's humour and fancy, will give us figures and pictures for which we cannot be too grateful, for he will enlarge our knowledge of the world. But when he introduces men and women whose interest is preconceived to lie not in the poverty, the weakness, the drollery of their natures, but in their complete and unconscious subjection to ordinary and healthy human emotions, all his humour, all his fancy, will avail him nothing if, out of the fullness of his sympathy, he is unable to prosecute those generalisations in which alone consists the real greatness of a work of art.

This may sound like very subtle talk about a very simple matter. It is rather very simple talk about a very subtle matter. A story based upon those elementary passions in which alone we seek the true and final manifestation of character must be told in a spirit of intellectual superiority to those passions. That is, the author must understand what he is talking about. The perusal of a story so told is one of the most elevating experiences within the reach of the human mind. The

perusal of a story which is not so told is infinitely depressing and unprofitable.

1865. From Views and Reviews (1908).

*

HAWTHORNE: *THE SCARLET LETTER*

His publisher, Mr. Fields, in a volume entitled *Yester-
days with Authors,* has related the circumstances in
which Hawthorne's masterpiece came into the world.
"In the winter of 1849, after he had been ejected from
the Custom-house, I went down to Salem to see him
and inquire after his health, for we heard he had been
suffering from illness. He was then living in a modest
wooden house. . . . I found him alone in a chamber
over the sitting-room of the dwelling, and as the day
was cold he was hovering near a stove. We fell into
talk about his future prospects, and he was, as I feared
I should find him, in a very desponding mood." His
visitor urged him to bethink himself of publishing something, and Hawthorne replied by calling his attention to
the small popularity his published productions had yet
acquired, and declaring he had done nothing and had
no spirit for doing anything. The narrator of the incident
urged upon him the necessity of a more hopeful view of
his situation, and proceeded to take leave. He had not
reached the street, however, when Hawthorne hurried
to overtake him, and, placing a roll of MS. in his hand,
bade him take it to Boston, read it, and pronounce upon
it. "It is either very good or very bad," said the author;

"I don't know which." "On my way back to Boston,"
says Mr. Fields, "I read the germ of *The Scarlet Letter;*
before I slept that night I wrote him a note all aglow
with admiration of the marvellous story he had put into
my hands, and told him that I would come again to
Salem the next day and arrange for its publication. I
went on in such an amazing state of excitement, when
we met again in the little house, that he would not believe I was really in earnest. He seemed to think I was
beside myself, and laughed sadly at my enthusiasm."
Hawthorne, however, went on with the book and finished it, but it appeared only a year later. His biographer
quotes a passage from a letter which he wrote in February, 1850, to his friend Horatio Bridge. "I finished my
book only yesterday; one end being in the press at
Boston, while the other was in my head here at Salem,
so that, as you see, my story is at least fourteen miles
long. . . . My book, the publisher tells me, will not be
out before April. He speaks of it in tremendous terms
of approbation; so does Mrs. Hawthorne, to whom I
read the conclusion last night. It broke her heart, and
sent her to bed with a grievous headache—which I
look upon as a triumphant success. Judging from the
effect upon her and the publisher, I may calculate on
what bowlers call a ten-strike. But I don't make any
such calculation." And Mr. Lathrop calls attention, in
regard to this passage, to an allusion in the *English
Note-Books* (September 14, 1855). "Speaking of Thackeray, I cannot but wonder at his coolness in respect
to his own pathos, and compare it to my emotions
when I read the last scene of *The Scarlet Letter* to my
wife, just after writing it—tried to read it rather, for
my voice swelled and heaved as if I were tossed up and
down on an ocean as it subsides after a storm. But I
was in a very nervous state then, having gone through

a great diversity of emotion while writing it, for many months."

The work has the tone of the circumstances in which it was produced. If Hawthorne was in a sombre mood, and if his future was painfully vague, *The Scarlet Letter* contains little enough of gaiety or of hopefulness. It is densely dark, with a single spot of vivid colour in it; and it will probably long remain the most consistently gloomy of English novels of the first order. But I just now called it the author's masterpiece, and I imagine it will continue to be, for other generations than ours, his most substantial title to fame. The subject had probably lain a long time in his mind, as his subjects were apt to do; so that he appears completely to possess it, to know it and feel it. It is simpler and more complete than his other novels; it achieves more perfectly what it attempts, and it has about it that charm, very hard to express, which we find in an artist's work the first time he has touched his highest mark—a sort of straightness and naturalness of execution, an unconsciousness of his public, and freshness of interest in his theme. It was a great success, and he immediately found himself famous. The writer of these lines, who was a child at the time, remembers dimly the sensation the book produced, and the little shudder with which people alluded to it, as if a peculiar horror were mixed with its attractions. He was too young to read it himself, but its title, upon which he fixed his eyes as the book lay upon the table, had a mysterious charm. He had a vague belief, indeed, that the "letter" in question was one of the documents that come by the post, and it was a source of perpetual wonderment to him that it should be of such an unaccustomed hue. Of course it was difficult to explain to a child the significance of poor Hester Prynne's blood-coloured A. But the mystery was at last partly dispelled by his being taken to see a collection of pictures (the annual exhibition of the National Academy), where he encountered a representation of a pale, handsome woman, in a quaint black dress and a white coif, holding between her knees an elfish-looking little girl, fantastically dressed, and crowned with flowers. Embroidered on the woman's breast was a great crimson *A*, over which the child's fingers, as she glanced strangely out of the picture, were maliciously playing. I was told that this was Hester Prynne and little Pearl, and that when I grew older I might read their interesting history. But the picture remained vividly imprinted on my mind; I had been vaguely frightened and made uneasy by it; and when, years afterwards, I first read the novel, I seemed to myself to have read it before, and to be familiar with its two strange heroines. I mention this incident simply as an indication of the degree to which the success of *The Scarlet Letter* had made the book what is called an actuality. Hawthorne himself was very modest about it; he wrote to his publisher, when there was a question of his undertaking another novel, that what had given the history of Hester Prynne its "vogue" was simply the introductory chapter. In fact, the publication of *The Scarlet Letter* was in the United States a literary event of the first importance. The book was the finest piece of imaginative writing yet put forth in the country. There was a consciousness of this in the welcome that was given it—a satisfaction in the idea of America having produced a novel that belonged to literature, and to the forefront of it. Something might at last be sent to Europe as exquisite in quality as anything that had been received, and the best of it was that the thing was absolutely American; it belonged to the soil, to the air; it came out of the very heart of New England.

It is beautiful, admirable, extraordinary; it has in the highest degree that merit which I have spoken of as the mark of Hawthorne's best things—an indefinable purity and lightness of conception, a quality which in a work of art affects one in the same way as the absence of grossness does in a human being. His fancy, as I just now said, had evidently brooded over the subject for a long time; the situation to be represented had disclosed itself to him in all its phases. When I say in all its phases, the sentence demands modification; for it is to be remembered that if Hawthorne laid his hand upon the well-worn theme, upon the familiar combination of the wife, the lover, and the husband, it was after all but to one period of the history of these three persons that he attached himself. The situation is the situation after the woman's fault has been committed, and the current of expiation and repentance has set in. In spite of the relation between Hester Prynne and Arthur Dimmesdale, no story of love was surely ever less of a "love story." To Hawthorne's imagination the fact that these two persons had loved each other too well was of an interest comparatively vulgar; what appealed to him was the idea of their moral situation in the long years that were to follow. The story, indeed, is in a secondary degree that of Hester Prynne; she becomes, really, after the first scene, an accessory figure; it is not upon her the *dénoûment* depends. It is upon her guilty lover that the author projects most frequently the cold, thin rays of his fitfully-moving lantern, which makes here and there a little luminous circle, on the edge of which hovers the livid and sinister figure of the injured and retributive husband. The story goes on, for the most part, between the lover and the husband—the tormented young Puritan minister, who carries the secret of his own lapse from pastoral purity locked up beneath an exterior that commends itself to the reverence of his flock, while he sees the softer partner of his guilt standing in the full glare of exposure and humbling herself to the misery of atonement—between this more wretched and pitiable culprit, to whom dishonour would come as a comfort and the pillory as a relief, and the older, keener, wiser man, who, to obtain satisfaction for the wrong he has suffered, devises the infernally ingenious plan of conjoining himself with his wronger, living with him, living upon him, and while he pretends to minister to his hidden ailment and to sympathise with his pain, revels in his unsuspected knowledge of these things and stimulates them by malignant arts. The attitude of Roger Chillingworth, and the means he takes to compensate himself—these are the highly original elements in the situation that Hawthorne so ingeniously treats. None of his works are so impregnated with that after-sense of the old Puritan consciousness of life to which allusion has so often been made. If, as M. Montégut says, the qualities of his ancestors *filtered* down through generations into his composition, *The Scarlet Letter* was, as it were, the vessel that gathered up the last of the precious drops. And I say this not because the story happens to be of so-called historical cast, to be told of the early days of Massachusetts and of people in steeple-crowned hats and sad-coloured garments. The historical colouring is rather weak than otherwise; there is little elaboration of detail, of the modern realism of research; and the author has made no great point of causing his figures to speak the English of their period. Nevertheless, the book is full of the moral presence of the race that invented Hester's penance—diluted and complicated with other things, but still perfectly recognisable. Puritanism, in a word, is there, not only objectively, as

Hawthorne tried to place it there, but subjectively as well. Not, I mean, in his judgment of his characters, in any harshness of prejudice, or in the obtrusion of a moral lesson; but in the very quality of his own vision, in the tone of the picture, in a certain coldness and exclusiveness of treatment.

The faults of the book are, to my sense, a want of reality and an abuse of the fanciful element—of a certain superficial symbolism. The people strike me not as characters, but as representatives, very picturesquely arranged, of a single state of mind; and the interest of the story lies, not in them, but in the situation, which is insistently kept before us, with little progression, though with a great deal, as I have said, of a certain stable variation; and to which they, out of their reality, contribute little that helps it to live and move. I was made to feel this want of reality, this over-ingenuity, of *The Scarlet Letter*, by chancing not long since upon a novel which was read fifty years ago much more than to-day, but which is still worth reading—the story of *Adam Blair*, by John Gibson Lockhart. This interesting and powerful little tale has a great deal of analogy with Hawthorne's novel—quite enough, at least, to suggest a comparison between them; and the comparison is a very interesting one to make, for it speedily leads us to larger considerations than simple resemblances and divergences of plot.

Adam Blair, like Arthur Dimmesdale, is a Calvinistic minister who becomes the lover of a married woman, is overwhelmed with remorse at his misdeed, and makes a public confession of it; then expiates it by resigning his pastoral office and becoming a humble tiller of the soil, as his father had been. The two stories are of about the same length, and each is the masterpiece (putting aside of course, as far as Lockhart is concerned,

the *Life of Scott*) of the author. They deal alike with
the manners of a rigidly theological society, and even
in certain details they correspond. In each of them, between the guilty pair, there is a charming little girl;
though I hasten to say that Sarah Blair (who is not the
daughter of the heroine, but the legitimate offspring of
the hero, a widower) is far from being as brilliant and
graceful an apparition as the admirable little Pearl of
The Scarlet Letter. The main difference between the
two tales is the fact that in the American story the husband plays an all-important part, and in the Scottish
plays almost none at all. *Adam Blair* is the history of
the passion, and *The Scarlet Letter* the history of its
sequel; but nevertheless, if one has read the two books
at a short interval, it is impossible to avoid confronting
them. I confess that a large portion of the interest of
Adam Blair, to my mind, when once I had perceived
that it would repeat in a great measure the situation of
The Scarlet Letter, lay in noting its difference of tone.
It threw into relief the passionless quality of Hawthorne's novel, its element of cold and ingenious fantasy, its elaborate imaginative delicacy. These things
do not precisely constitute a weakness in *The Scarlet
Letter;* indeed, in a certain way they constitute a great
strength; but the absence of a certain something warm
and straightforward, a trifle more grossly human and
vulgarly natural, which one finds in *Adam Blair,* will
always make Hawthorne's tale less touching to a large
number of even very intelligent readers, than a love-
story told with the robust, synthetic pathos which served
Lockhart so well. His novel is not of the first rank (I
should call it an excellent second-rate one), but it
borrows a charm from the fact that his vigorous, but
not strongly imaginative, mind was impregnated with
the reality of his subject. He did not always succeed in

rendering this reality; the expression is sometimes awkward and poor. But the reader feels that his vision was clear, and his feeling about the matter very strong and rich. Hawthorne's imagination, on the other hand, plays with his theme so incessantly, leads it such a dance through the moon-lighted air of his intellect, that the thing cools off, as it were, hardens and stiffens, and, producing effects much more exquisite, leaves the reader with a sense of having handled a splendid piece of silversmith's work. Lockhart, by means much more vulgar, produces at moments a greater illusion, and satisfies our inevitable desire for something, in the people in whom it is sought to interest us, that shall be of the same pitch and the same continuity with ourselves. Above all, it is interesting to see how the same subject appears to two men of a thoroughly different cast of mind and of a different race. Lockhart was struck with the warmth of the subject that offered itself to him, and Hawthorne with its coldness; the one with its glow, its sentimental interest—the other with its shadow, its moral interest. Lockhart's story is as decent, as severely draped, as *The Scarlet Letter;* but the author has a more vivid sense than appears to have imposed itself upon Hawthorne, of some of the incidents of the situation he describes; his tempted man and tempting woman are more actual and personal; his heroine in especial, though not in the least a delicate or a subtle conception, has a sort of credible, visible, palpable property, a vulgar roundness and relief, which are lacking to the dim and chastened image of Hester Prynne. But I am going too far; I am comparing simplicity with subtlety, the usual with the refined. Each man wrote as his turn of mind impelled him, but each expressed something more than himself. Lockhart was a dense, substantial Briton, with a taste for the concrete, and Hawthorne was a thin New Englander, with a miasmatic conscience.

In *The Scarlet Letter* there is a great deal of symbolism; there is, I think, too much. It is overdone at times, and becomes mechanical; it ceases to be impressive, and grazes triviality. The idea of the mystic *A* which the young minister finds imprinted upon his breast and eating into his flesh, in sympathy with the embroidered badge that Hester is condemned to wear, appears to me to be a case in point. This suggestion should, I think, have been just made and dropped; to insist upon it and return to it, is to exaggerate the weak side of the subject. Hawthorne returns to it constantly, plays with it, and seems charmed by it; until at last the reader feels tempted to declare that his enjoyment of it is puerile. In the admirable scene, so superbly conceived and beautifully executed, in which Mr. Dimmesdale, in the stillness of the night, in the middle of the sleeping town, feels impelled to go and stand upon the scaffold where his mistress had formerly enacted her dreadful penance, and then, seeing Hester pass along the street, from watching at a sick-bed, with little Pearl at her side, calls them both to come and stand there beside him— in this masterly episode the effect is almost spoiled by the introduction of one of these superficial conceits. What leads up to it is very fine—so fine that I cannot do better than quote it as a specimen of one of the striking pages of the book.

But before Mr. Dimmesdale had done speaking, a light gleamed far and wide over all the muffled sky. It was doubtless caused by one of those meteors which the night-watcher may so often observe burning out to waste in the vacant regions of the atmosphere. So powerful was its radiance that it thoroughly illuminated the dense medium of cloud, betwixt the sky and earth. The great vault brightened, like the dome of an immense lamp. It showed the familiar scene of the street with the distinctness of mid-day, but also with the awfulness that is always imparted to familiar objects by an unaccustomed light. The wooden houses, with their jutting stories and quaint gable-peaks; the door-steps and thresholds, with the early grass springing up about them; the garden-plots, black with freshly-turned earth; the wheel-track, little worn, and, even in the market-place, margined with green on either side;—all were visible, but with a singularity of aspect that seemed to give another moral interpretation to the things of this world than they had ever borne before. And there stood the minister, with his hand over his heart; and Hester Prynne, with the embroidered letter glimmering on her bosom; and little Pearl, herself a symbol, and the connecting-link between these two. They stood in the noon of that strange and solemn splendour, as if it were the light that is to reveal all secrets, and the daybreak that shall unite all that belong to one another.

That is imaginative, impressive, poetic; but when, almost immediately afterwards, the author goes on to say that "the minister looking upward to the zenith, beheld there the appearance of an immense letter—the letter A—marked out in lines of dull red light," we feel that he goes too far and is in danger of crossing the line that separates the sublime from its intimate neighbour. We are tempted to say that this is not moral tragedy, but physical comedy. In the same way, too much is made of the intimation that Hester's badge had a scorching property, and that if one touched it one would immediately withdraw one's hand. Hawthorne is perpetually looking for images which shall place themselves in picturesque correspondence with the spiritual facts with which he is concerned, and of course the search is of the very essence of poetry. But in such a process discretion is everything, and when the image becomes importunate it is in danger of seeming to stand for nothing more serious than itself. When Hester meets the minister by appointment in the forest, and sits talking with him while little Pearl wanders away and plays by the edge of the brook, the child is represented as at last making her way over to the other side of the woodland stream, and disporting herself there in a manner which makes her mother feel herself "in some indistinct and tantalising manner, estranged from Pearl; as if the child, in her lonely ramble through the forest, had strayed out of the sphere in which she and her mother dwelt together, and was now vainly seeking to return to it." And Hawthorne devotes a chapter to this idea of the child's having, by putting the brook between Hester and herself, established a kind of spiritual gulf, on the verge of which her little fantastic person innocently mocks at her mother's sense of bereavement. This conception belongs, one would say, quite to the lighter order of a story-teller's devices, and the reader hardly goes with Hawthorne in the large development he gives to it. He hardly goes with him either, I think, in his extreme predilection for a small number of vague ideas which are represented by such terms as "sphere" and "sympathies." Hawthorne makes too liberal a use of these two substantives; it is the solitary defect of his style; and it counts as a defect partly because the words in question are a sort of specialty with certain writers immeasurably inferior to himself.

I had not meant, however, to expatiate upon his defects, which are of the slenderest and most venial kind. *The Scarlet Letter* has the beauty and harmony of all original and complete conceptions, and its weaker spots, whatever they are, are not of its essence; they are mere light flaws and inequalities of surface. One can often return to it; it supports familiarity and has the inexhaustible charm and mystery of great works of art. It is admirably written. Hawthorne afterwards polished his style to a still higher degree, but in his later productions—it is almost always the case in a writer's later productions—there is a touch of mannerism. In *The Scarlet Letter* there is a high degree of polish, and at the same time a charming freshness; his phrase is less conscious of itself. His biographer very justly calls attention to the fact that his style was excellent from the beginning; that he appeared to have passed through no phase of learning how to write, but was in possession of his means from the first of his handling a pen. His early tales, perhaps, were not of a character to subject his faculty of expression to a very severe test, but a man who had not Hawthorne's natural sense of language would certainly have contrived to write them less well. This natural sense of language—this turn for saying things lightly and yet touchingly, picturesquely yet simply, and for infusing a gently colloquial tone into matter of the most unfamiliar import, he had evidently cultivated with great assiduity. I have spoken of the anomalous character of his Note-Books—of his going to such pains often to make a record of incidents which either were not worth remembering or could be easily remembered without its aid. But it helps us to understand the Note-Books if we regard them as a literary exercise. They were compositions, as school-boys say, in which the subject was only the pretext, and the main point was to write a certain amount of excellent English. Hawthorne must at least have written a great many of these things for practice, and he must often have said to himself that it was better practice to write about trifles, because it was a greater tax upon one's skill to make them interesting. And his theory was just, for he has almost always made his trifles interesting. In his novels his art of saying things well is very positively tested, for here he treats of those matters among which it is very easy for a blundering writer to go wrong—the subtleties and mysteries of life, the moral and spiritual maze. In such a passage as one I have marked for quotation from *The Scarlet Letter*, there is the stamp of the genius of style.

Hester Prynne, gazing steadfastly at the clergyman, felt a dreary influence come over her, but wherefore or whence she knew not, unless that he seemed so remote from her own sphere and utterly beyond her reach. One glance of recognition she had imagined must needs pass between them. She thought of the dim forest with its little dell of solitude, and love, and anguish, and the mossy tree-trunk, where, sitting hand in hand, they had mingled their sad and passionate talk with the melancholy murmur of the brook. How deeply had they known each other then! And was this the man? She hardly knew him now! He, moving proudly past, enveloped as it were in the rich music, with the procession of majestic and venerable fathers; he, so un-attainable in his worldly position, and still more so in that far vista in his unsympathising thoughts, through which she now beheld him! Her spirit sank with the idea that all must have been a delusion, and that vividly as she had dreamed it, there could be no real bond betwixt the clergy-man and herself. And thus much of woman there was in Hester, that she could scarcely forgive him—least of all now, when the heavy footstep of their approaching fate might be heard, nearer, nearer, nearer!—for being able to withdraw himself so completely from their mutual world, while she groped darkly, and stretched forth her cold hands, and found him not!

From Chapter V of *Hawthorne* (1879).

*

IVAN TURGÉNIEFF

(1818-1883)

There is perhaps no novelist of alien race who more naturally than Ivan Turgénieff inherits a niche in a Library for English readers; and this not because of any advance or concession that in his peculiar artistic independence he ever made, or could dream of making, such readers, but because it was one of the effects of his peculiar genius to give him, even in his lifetime, a special place in the regard of foreign publics. His position is in this respect singular; for it is his Russian savor that as much as anything has helped generally to domesticate him.

Born in 1818, at Orel in the heart of Russia, and dying in 1883, at Bougival near Paris, he had spent in Germany and France the latter half of his life; and had incurred in his own country in some degree the reprobation that is apt to attach to the absent—the penalty they pay for such extension or such beguilement as they may have happened to find over the border. He belonged to the class of large rural proprietors of land and of serfs; and with his ample patrimony, offered one of the few examples of literary labor achieved in high independence of the question of gain—a character that he shares with his illustrious contemporary Tolstoy, who is of a type in other respects so different. It may give us an idea of his primary situation to imagine some large Virginian or Carolinian slaveholder, during the first half of the century, inclining to "Northern" views; and becoming (though not predominantly under pressure of these, but rather by the operation of an exquisite genius) the great American novelist—one of the great novelists of the world. Born under a social and political order sternly repressive, all Turgénieff's deep instincts, all his moral passion, placed him on the liberal side; with the consequence that early in life, after a period spent at a German university, he found himself, through the accident of a trifling public utterance, under such suspicion in high places as to be sentenced to a term of tempered exile—confinement to his own estate. It was partly under these circumstances perhaps that he gathered material for the work from the appearance of which his reputation dates—*A Sportsman's Sketches,* published in two volumes in 1852. This admirable collection of impressions of homely country life, as the old state of servitude had made it, is often spoken of as having borne to the great decree of Alexander II the relation borne by Mrs. Beecher Stowe's famous novel to the emancipation of the Southern slaves. Incontestably, at any rate, Turgénieff's rustic studies sounded, like *Uncle Tom's Cabin,* a particular hour: with the difference, however, of not having at the time produced an agitation—of having rather presented the case with an art too insidious for instant recognition, an art that stirred the depths more than the surface.

The author was designated promptly enough, at any rate, for such influence as might best be exercised at a distance: he travelled, he lived abroad; early in the sixties he was settled in Germany; he acquired property at Baden-Baden, and spent there the last years of the prosperous period—in the history of the place—of which the Franco-Prussian War was to mark the violent term. He cast in his lot after that event mainly with the victims of the lost cause; setting up a fresh home in Paris—near which city he had, on the Seine, a charming alternate residence—and passing in it, and in the country, save for brief revisitations, the remainder of his days. His friendships, his attachments, in the world of art and of letters, were numerous and distinguished; he never married; he produced, as the years went on, without precipitation or frequency; and these were the years during which his reputation gradually established itself as, according to the phrase, European—a phrase denoting in this case, perhaps, a public more alert in the United States even than elsewhere.

Tolstoy, his junior by ten years, had meanwhile come to fruition; though, as in fact happened, it was not till after Turgénieff's death that the greater fame of *War and Peace* and of *Anna Karénina* began to be blown about the world. One of the last acts of the elder writer, performed on his death-bed, was to address to the other (from whom for a considerable term he had been estranged by circumstances needless to reproduce) an appeal to return to the exercise of the genius that Tolstoy had already so lamentably, so monstrously forsworn. "I am on my death-bed; there is no possibility of my recovery. I write you expressly to tell you how happy I have been to be your contemporary, and to utter my last, my urgent prayer. Come back, my friend, to your literary labors. That gift came to you from the source from which all comes to us. Ah, how happy I should be could I think you would listen to my entreaty! My friend, great writer of our Russian land, respond to it, obey it!" These words, among the most touching surely ever addressed by one great spirit to another, throw an indirect light—perhaps I may even say a direct one—upon the nature and quality of Turgénieff's artistic temperament; so much so that I regret being without opportunity, in this place, to gather such aid for a portrait of him as might be supplied by following out the unlikeness between the pair. It would be too easy to say that Tolstoy was, from the Russian point of view, for home consumption, and Turgénieff for foreign: *War and Peace* has probably had more readers in Europe and America than *A House of Gentlefolk* or *On the Eve* or *Smoke*—a circumstance less detrimental than it may appear to my claim of our having, in the Western world, supremely adopted the author of the latter works. Turgénieff is in a peculiar degree what I may call the novelists' novelist—an artistic influence extraordinarily valuable and ineradicably established. The perusal of Tolstoy —a wonderful mass of life—is an immense event, a kind of splendid accident, for each of us: his name represents nevertheless no such eternal spell of method, no such quiet irresistibility of presentation, as shines, close to us and lighting our possible steps, in that of his precursor. Tolstoy is a reflector as vast as a natural lake; a monster harnessed to his great subject—all human life!—as an elephant might be harnessed, for purposes of traction, not to a carriage, but to a coach-house. His own case is prodigious, but his example for others dire: disciples not elephantine he can only mislead and betray.

One by one, for thirty years, with a firm, deliberate hand, with intervals and patiences and waits, Turgénieff pricked in his sharp outlines. His great external mark is probably his concision: an ideal he never threw over— it shines most perhaps even when he is least brief— and that he often applied with a rare felicity. He has masterpieces of a few pages; his perfect things are sometimes his least prolonged. He abounds in short tales, episodes clipped as by the scissors of Atropos; but for a direct translation of the whole we have still to wait—depending meanwhile upon the French and German versions, which have been, instead of the original text (thanks to the paucity among us of readers of Russian), the source of several published in English. For the novels and *A Sportsman's Sketches* we depend upon the nine volumes (1897) of Mrs. Garnett. We touch here upon the remarkable side, to our vision, of the writer's fortune —the anomaly of his having constrained to intimacy even those who are shut out from the enjoyment of his medium, for whom that question is positively prevented from existing. Putting aside extrinsic intimations, it is impossible to read him without the conviction of his being, in the vividness of his own tongue, of the strong type of those made to bring home to us the happy truth of the unity, in a generous talent, of material and form —of their being inevitable faces of the same medal; the type of those, in a word, whose example deals death to the perpetual clumsy assumption that subject and style are—æsthetically speaking, or in the living work— different and separable things. We are conscious, reading him in a language not his own, of not being reached by his personal tone, his individual accent.

It is a testimony therefore to the intensity of his presence, that so much of his particular charm does reach us; that the mask turned to us has, even without his expression, still so much beauty. It is the beauty (since we must try to formulate) of the finest presentation of the familiar. His vision is of the world of character and feeling, the world of the relations life throws up at every hour and on every spot; he deals little, on the whole, in the miracles of chance—the hours and spots over the edge of time and space; his air is that of the great central region of passion and motive, of the usual, the inevitable, the intimate—the intimate for weal or woe. No theme that he ever chooses but strikes us as full; yet with all have we the sense that their animation comes from within, and is not pinned to their backs like the pricking objects used of old in the horse-races of the Roman carnival, to make the animals run. Without a patch of "plot" to draw blood, the story he mainly tells us, the situation he mainly gives, runs as if for dear life. His first book was practically full evidence of what, if we have to specify, is finest in him—the effect, for the commonest truth, of an exquisite envelope of poetry. In this medium of feeling—full, as it were, of all the echoes and shocks of the universal danger and need—everything in him goes on; the sense of fate and folly and pity and wonder and beauty. The tenderness, the humor, the variety of *A Sportsman's Sketches* revealed on the spot an observer with a rare imagination. These faculties had attached themselves, together, to small things and to great: to the misery, the simplicity, the piety, the patience, of the unemancipated peasant; to all the natural wonderful life of earth and air and winter and summer and field and forest; to queer apparitions of country neighbors, of strange local eccentrics; to old-world practices and superstitions; to secrets gathered and types disinterred and impressions absorbed in the long, close contacts with man and nature involved in the passionate pursuit of game. Magnificent in stature and original vigor, Turgénieff, with his love of the chase, or rather perhaps of the inspiration he found in it, would have been the model of the mighty hunter, had not such an image been a little at variance with his natural mildness, the softness that often accompanies the sense of an extraordinary reach of limb and play of muscle. He was in person the model rather of the strong man at rest: massive and towering, with the voice of innocence and the smile almost of childhood. What seemed still more of a contradiction to so much of him, however, was that his work was all delicacy and fancy, penetration and compression.

If I add, in their order of succession, *Rudin, Fathers*

and Children, Spring Floods, and *Virgin Soil,* to the
three novels I have (also in their relation of time) named
above, I shall have indicated the larger blocks of the
compact monument, with a base resting deep and inter-
stices well filled, into which that work disposes itself.
The list of his minor productions is too long to draw out:
I can only mention, as a few of the most striking—
"A Correspondence," "The Wayside Inn," "The Briga-
dier," "The Dog," "The Jew," "Visions," "Mumu,"
"Three Meetings," "A First Love," "The Forsaken,"
"Assia," "The Journal of a Superfluous Man," "The
Story of Lieutenant Yergunov," "A King Lear of the
Steppe." The first place among his novels would be
difficult to assign: general opinion probably hesitates
between *A House of Gentlefolk* and *Fathers and Children.* My own predilection is great for the exquisite *On
the Eve;* though I admit that in such a company it
draws no supremacy from being exquisite. What is less
contestable is that *Virgin Soil*—published shortly before
his death, and the longest of his fictions—has, although
full of beauty, a minor perfection.

Character, character expressed and exposed, is in all
these things what we inveterately find. Turgénieff's
sense of it was the great light that artistically guided
him; the simplest account of him is to say that the mere
play of it constitutes in every case his sufficient drama.
No one has had a closer vision, or a hand at once more
ironic and more tender, for the individual figure. He sees
it with its minutest signs and tricks—all its heredity
of idiosyncrasies, all its particulars of weakness and
strength, of ugliness and beauty, of oddity and charm;
and yet it is of his essence that he sees it in the general
flood of life, steeped in its relations and contacts, struggling or submerged, a hurried particle in the stream.
This gives him, with his quiet method, his extraordinary

breadth; dissociates his rare power to particularize from dryness or hardness, from any peril of caricature. He understands so much that we almost wonder he can express anything; and his expression is indeed wholly in absolute projection, in illustration, in giving of everything the unexplained and irresponsible specimen. He is of a spirit so human that we almost wonder at his control of his matter; of a pity so deep and so general that we almost wonder at his curiosity. The element of poetry in him is constant, and yet reality stares through it without the loss of a wrinkle. No one has more of that sign of the born novelist which resides in a respect unconditioned for the freedom and vitality, the absoluteness when summoned, of the creatures he invokes; or is more superior to the strange and second-rate policy of explaining or presenting them by reprobation or apology—of taking the short cuts and anticipating the emotions and judgments about them that should be left, at the best, to the perhaps not most intelligent reader. And yet his system, as it may summarily be called, of the mere particularized report, has a lucidity beyond the virtue of the cruder moralist.

If character, as I say, is what he gives us at every turn, I should speedily add that he offers it not in the least as a synonym, in our Western sense, of resolution and prosperity. It wears the form of the almost helpless detachment of the short-sighted individual soul; and the perfection of his exhibition of it is in truth too often but the intensity of what, for success, it just does not produce. What works in him most is the question of the will; and the most constant induction he suggests, bears upon the sad figure that principle seems mainly to make among his countrymen. He had seen—he suggests to us —its collapse in a thousand quarters; and the most general tragedy, to his view, is that of its desperate adventures and disasters, its inevitable abdication and defeat. But if the men, for the most part, let it go, it takes refuge in the other sex; many of the representatives of which, in his pages, are supremely strong—in wonderful addition, in various cases, to being otherwise admirable. This is true of such a number—the younger women, the girls, the "heroines" in especial—that they form in themselves, on the ground of moral beauty, of the finest distinction of soul, one of the most striking groups the modern novel has given us. They are heroines to the letter, and of a heroism obscure and undecorated: it is almost they alone who have the energy to determine and to act. Elena, Lisa, Tatyana, Gemma, Marianna—we can write their names and call up their images, but I lack space to take them in turn. It is by a succession of the finest and tenderest touches that they live; and this, in all Turgénieff's work, is the process by which he persuades and succeeds.

It was his own view of his main danger that he sacrificed too much to detail; was wanting in composition, in the gift that conduces to unity of impression. But no novelist is closer and more cumulative; in none does distinction spring from a quality of truth more independent of everything but the subject, but the idea itself. This idea, this subject, moreover—a spark kindled by the innermost friction of things—is always as interesting as an unopened telegram. The genial freedom—with its exquisite delicacy—of his approach to this "innermost" world, the world of our finer consciousness, has in short a side that I can only describe and commemorate as nobly disinterested; a side that makes too many of his rivals appear to hold us in comparison by violent means, and introduce us in comparison to vulgar things.

1897

*

HONORÉ DE BALZAC

Stronger than ever, even than under the spell of first
acquaintance and of the early time, is the sense—thanks
to a renewal of intimacy and, I am tempted to say, of
loyalty—that Balzac stands signally apart, that he is
the first and foremost member of his craft, and that
above all the Balzac-lover is in no position till he has
cleared the ground by saying so. The Balzac-lover alone,
for that matter, is worthy to have his word on so happy
an occasion as this[1] about the author of *La Comédie
Humaine,* and it is indeed not easy to see how the
amount of attention so inevitably induced could at the
worst have failed to find itself turning to an act of homage. I have been deeply affected, to be frank, by the
mere refreshment of memory, which has brought in its
train moreover consequences critical and sentimental
too numerous to figure here in their completeness. The
authors and the books that have, as we say, done something for us, become part of the answer to our curiosity
when our curiosity had the freshness of youth, these
particular agents exist for us, with the lapse of time,
as the substance itself of knowledge: they have been
intellectually so swallowed, digested and assimilated
that we take their general use and suggestion for

[1] The appearance of a translation of the *Deux Jeunes
Mariées* in A Century of French Romance. [This essay by
James on Balzac originally appeared as a critical introduction
to Balzac's novel *Deux Jeunes Mariées* when it appeared in
this series as *The Two Young Brides* in London in 1902.
Editor's note.]

granted, cease to be aware of them because they have passed out of sight. But they have passed out of sight simply by having passed into our lives. They have become a part of our personal history, a part of ourselves, very often, so far as we may have succeeded in best expressing ourselves. Endless, however, are the uses of great persons and great things, and it may easily happen in these cases that the connection, even as an "excitement"—the form mainly of the connections of youth— is never really broken. We have largely been living on our benefactor—which is the highest acknowledgment one can make; only, thanks to a blest law that operates in the long run to rekindle excitement, we are accessible to the sense of having neglected him. Even when we may not constantly have read him over the neglect is quite an illusion, but the illusion perhaps prepares us for the finest emotion we are to have owed to the acquaintance. Without having abandoned or denied our author we yet come expressly back to him, and if not quite in tatters and in penitence like the Prodigal Son, with something at all events of the tenderness with which we revert to the parental threshold and hearthstone, if not, more fortunately, to the parental presence. The beauty of this adventure, that of seeing the dust blown off a relation that had been put away as on a shelf, almost out of reach, at the back of one's mind, consists in finding the precious object not only fresh and intact, but with its firm lacquer still further figured, gilded and enriched. It is all overscored with traces and impressions —vivid, definite, almost as valuable as itself—of the recognitions and agitations it originally produced in us. Our old—that is our young—feelings are very nearly what page after page most gives us. The case has become a case of authority *plus* association. If Balzac in himself is indubitably wanting in the sufficiently common felicity we know as charm, it is this association that may on occasion contribute the grace.

The impression then, confirmed and brightened, is of the mass and weight of the figure and of the extent of ground it occupies; a tract on which we might all of us together quite pitch our little tents, open our little booths, deal in our little wares, and not materially either diminish the area or impede the circulation of the occupant. I seem to see him in such an image moving about as Gulliver among the pigmies, and not less good-natured than Gulliver for the exercise of any function, without exception, that can illustrate his larger life. The first and the last word about the author of *Les Contes Drolatiques* is that of all novelists he is the most serious —by which I am far from meaning that in the human comedy as he shows it the comic is an absent quantity. His sense of the comic was on the scale of his extraordinary senses in general, though his expression of it suffers perhaps exceptionally from that odd want of elbow-room —the penalty somehow of his close-packed, pressed-down contents—which reminds us of some designedly beautiful thing but half-disengaged from the clay or the marble. It is the scheme and the scope that are supreme in him, applying this moreover not to mere great intention, but to the concrete form, the proved case, in which we possess them. We most of us aspire to achieve at the best but a patch here and there, to pluck a sprig or a single branch, to break ground in a corner of the great garden of life. Balzac's plan was simply to do everything that could be done. He proposed to himself to "turn over" the great garden from north to south and from east to west; a task—immense, heroic, to this day immeasurable—that he bequeathed us the partial performance of, a prodigious ragged clod, in the twenty monstrous years representing his productive career, years of concentration and sacrifice the vision of which still makes us ache. He had indeed a striking good fortune, the only one he was to enjoy as an harassed and exasperated worker: the great garden of life presented itself to him absolutely and exactly in the guise of the great garden of France, a subject vast and comprehensive enough, yet with definite edges and corners. This identity of his universal with his local and national vision is the particular thing we should doubtless call his greatest strength were we preparing agreeably to speak of it also as his visible weakness. Of Balzac's weaknesses, however, it takes some assurance to talk; there is always plenty of time for them; they are the last signs we know him by—such things truly as in other painters of manners often come under the head of mere exuberance of energy. So little in short do they earn the invidious name even when we feel them as defects.

What he did above all was to read the universe, as hard and as loud as he could, *into* the France of his time; his own eyes regarding his work as at once the drama of man and a mirror of the mass of social phenomena the most rounded and registered, most organized and administered, and thereby most exposed to systematic observation and portrayal, that the world had seen. There are happily other interesting societies, but these are for schemes of such an order comparatively loose and incoherent, with more extent and perhaps more variety, but with less of the great enclosed and exhibited quality, less neatness and sharpness of arrangement, fewer categories, subdivisions, juxtapositions. Balzac's France was both inspiring enough for an immense prose epic and reducible enough for a report or a chart. To allow his achievement all its dignity we should doubtless say also treatable enough for a history, since it was as a patient historian, a Benedictine of the actual, the living painter of his living time, that he regarded himself and handled his material. All painters of manners and fashions, if we will, are historians, even when they least don the uniform: Fielding, Dickens, Thackeray, George Eliot, Hawthorne among ourselves. But the great difference between the great Frenchman and the eminent others is that, with an imagination of the highest power, an unequalled intensity of vision, he saw his subject in the light of science as well, in the light of the bearing of all its parts on each other, and under pressure of a passion for exactitude, an appetite, the appetite of an ogre, for *all* the kinds of facts. We find I think in the union here suggested something like the truth about his genius, the nearest approach to a final account of him. Of imagination on one side all compact, he was on the other an insatiable reporter of the immediate, the material, the current combination, and perpetually moved by the historian's impulse to fix, preserve and explain them. One asks one's self as one reads him what concern the poet has with so much arithmetic and so much criticism, so many statistics and documents, what concern the critic and the economist have with so many passions, characters and adventures. The contradiction is always before us; it springs from the inordinate scale of the author's two faces; it explains more than anything else his eccentricities and difficulties. It accounts for his want of grace, his want of the lightness associated with an amusing literary form, his bristling surface, his closeness of texture, so rough with richness, yet so productive of the effect we have in mind when we speak of not being able to see the wood for the trees.

A thorough-paced votary, for that matter, can easily afford to declare at once that this confounding duality of character does more things still, or does at least the most important of all—introduces us without mercy

(mercy for ourselves I mean) to the oddest truth we could have dreamed of meeting in such a connection. It was certainly *a priori* not to be expected we should feel it of him, but our hero is after all not in his magnificence totally an artist: which would be the strangest thing possible, one must hasten to add, were not the smallness of the practical difference so made even stranger. His endowment and his effect are each so great that the anomaly makes at the most a difference only by adding to his interest for the critic. The critic worth his salt is indiscreetly curious and wants ever to know how and why—whereby Balzac is thus a still rarer case for him, suggesting that exceptional curiosity may have exceptional rewards. The question of what makes the artist on a great scale is interesting enough; but we feel it in Balzac's company to be nothing to the question of what on an equal scale frustrates him. The scattered pieces, the *disjecta membra* of the character are here so numerous and so splendid that they prove misleading; we pile them together, and the heap assuredly is monumental; it forms an overtopping figure. The genius this figure stands for, none the less, is really such a lesson to the artist as perfection itself would be powerless to give; it carries him so much further into the special mystery. Where it carries him, at the same time, I must not in this scant space attempt to say—which would be a loss of the fine thread of my argument. I stick to our point in putting it, more concisely, that the artist of the *Comédie Humaine* is half smothered by the historian. Yet it belongs as well to the matter also to meet the question of whether the historian himself may not be an artist— in which case Balzac's catastrophe would seem to lose its excuse. The answer of course is that the reporter, however philosophic, has one law, and the originator, however substantially fed, has another; so that the two laws can with no sort of harmony or congruity make, for the finer sense, a common household. Balzac's catastrophe—so to name it once again—was in this perpetual conflict and final impossibility, an impossibility that explains his defeat on the classic side and extends so far at times as to make us think of his work as, from the point of view of beauty, a tragic waste of effort.

What it would come to, we judge, is that the irreconcilability of the two kinds of law is, more simply expressed, but the irreconcilability of two different ways of composing one's effect. The principle of composition that his free imagination would have, or certainly might have, handsomely imposed on him is perpetually dislocated by the quite opposite principle of the earnest seeker, the inquirer to a useful end, in whom nothing is free but a born antipathy to his yokefellow. Such a production as *Le Curé de Village*, the wonderful story of Madame Graslin, so nearly a masterpiece yet so ultimately not one, would be, in this connection, could I take due space for it, a perfect illustration. If, as I say, Madame Graslin's creator was confined by his doom to patches and pieces, no piece is finer than the first half of the book in question, the half in which the picture is determined by his unequalled power of putting people on their feet, planting them before us in their habit as they lived—a faculty nourished by observation as much as one will, but with the inner vision all the while wide-awake, the vision for which ideas are as living as facts and assume an equal intensity. This intensity, greatest indeed in the facts, has in Balzac a force all its own, to which none other in any novelist I know can be likened. His touch communicates on the spot to the object, the creature evoked, the hardness and permanence that certain substances, some sorts of stone, acquire by exposure to the air. The hardening medium, for the image soaked

in it, is the air of his mind. It would take but little more
to make the peopled world of fiction as we know it elsewhere affect us by contrast as a world of rather gray
pulp. This mixture of the solid and the vivid is Balzac
at his best, and it prevails without a break, without a
note not admirably true, in *Le Curé de Village*—since
I have named that instance—up to the point at which
Madame Graslin moves out from Limoges to Montégnac
in her ardent passion of penitence, her determination
to expiate her strange and undiscovered association with
a dark misdeed by living and working for others. Her
drama is a particularly inward one, interesting, and in
the highest degree, so long as she herself, her nature,
her behaviour, her personal history and the relations
in which they place her, control the picture and feed our
illusion. The firmness with which the author makes them
play this part, the whole constitution of the scene and of
its developments from the moment we cross the threshold of her dusky stuffy old-time birth-house, is a rare
delight, producing in the reader that sense of local and
material immersion which is one of Balzac's supreme
secrets. What characteristically befalls, however, is that
the spell accompanies us but part of the way—only
until, at a given moment, his attention ruthlessly trans-
fers itself from inside to outside, from the centre of his
subject to its circumference.

This is Balzac caught in the very fact of his monstrous
duality, caught in his most complete self-expression. He
is clearly quite unwitting that in handing over his *data*
to his twin-brother the impassioned economist and surveyor, the insatiate general inquirer and reporter, he is
in any sort betraying our confidence, for his good conscience at such times, the spirit of edification in him,
is a lesson even to the best of us, his rich robust temperament nowhere more striking, no more marked any-

where the great push of the shoulder with which he makes his theme move, overcharged though it may be like a carrier's van. It is not therefore assuredly that he loses either sincerity or power in putting before us to the last detail such a matter as, in this case, his heroine's management of her property, her tenantry, her economic opportunities and visions, for these are cases in which he never shrinks nor relents, in which positively he stiffens and terribly towers—to remind us again of M. Taine's simplifying word about his being an artist doubled with a man of business. Balzac was indeed doubled if ever a writer was, and to that extent that we almost as often, while we read, feel ourselves thinking of him as a man of business doubled with an artist. Whichever way we turn it the oddity never fails, nor the wonder of the ease with which either character bears the burden of the other. I use the word burden because, as the fusion is never complete—witness in the book before us the fatal break of "tone," the one unpardonable sin for the novelist—we are beset by the conviction that but for this strangest of dooms one or other of the two partners might, to our relief and to his own, have been disembarrassed. The disembarrassment, for each, by a more insidious fusion, would probably have conduced to the mastership of interest proceeding from form, or at all events to the search for it, that Balzac fails to embody. Perhaps the possibility of an artist constructed on such strong lines is one of those fine things that are not of this world, a mere dream of the fond critical spirit. Let these speculations and condonations at least pass as the amusement, as a result of the high spirits—if high spirits be the word—of the reader feeling himself again in touch. It was not of our author's difficulties—that is of his difficulty, the great one—that I proposed to speak, but of his immense clear action. Even that is not truly

an impression of ease, and it is strange and striking that
we are in fact so attached by his want of the unity that
keeps surfaces smooth and dangers down as scarce to
feel sure at any moment that we shall not come back
to it with most curiosity. We are never so curious about
successes as about interesting failures. The more reason
therefore to speak promptly, and once for all, of the scale
on which, in its own quarter of his genius, success
worked itself out for him.

It is to that I *should* come back—to the infinite reach
in him of the painter and the poet. We can never know
what might have become of him with less importunity
in his consciousness of the machinery of life, of its furniture and fittings, of all that, right and left, he causes
to assail us, sometimes almost to suffocation, under the
general rubric of *things*. Things, in this sense with him,
are at once our delight and our despair; we pass from
being inordinately beguiled and convinced by them to
feeling that his universe fairly smells too much of them,
that the larger ether, the diviner air, is in peril of finding
among them scarce room to circulate. His landscapes,
his "local colour"—thick in his pages at a time when
it was to be found in his pages almost alone—his towns,
his streets, his houses, his Saumurs, Angoulêmes, Gué-
randes, his great prose Turner-views of the land of the
Loire, his rooms, shops, interiors, details of domesticity
and traffic, are a short list of the terms into which he saw
the real as clamouring to be rendered and into which
he rendered it with unequalled authority. It would be
doubtless more to the point to make our profit of
this consummation than to try to reconstruct a Balzac
planted more in the open. We hardly, as the case stands,
know most whether to admire in such an example as the
short tale of "La Grenadière" the exquisite feeling for
"natural objects" with which it overflows like a brim-

ming wine-cup, the energy of perception and description which so multiplies them for beauty's sake and for the love of their beauty, or the general wealth of genius that can calculate, or at least count, so little and spend so joyously. The tale practically exists for the sake of the enchanting aspects involved—those of the embowered white house that nestles on its terraced hill above the great French river, and we can think, frankly, of no one else with an equal amount of business on his hands who would either have so put himself out for aspects or made them almost by themselves a living subject. A born son of Touraine, it must be said, he pictures his province, on every pretext and occasion, with filial passion and extraordinary breadth. The prime aspect in his scene all the while, it must be added, is the money aspect. The general money question so loads him up and weighs him down that he moves through the human comedy, from beginning to end, very much in the fashion of a camel, the ship of the desert, surmounted with a cargo. "Things" for him are francs and centimes more than any others, and I give up as inscrutable, unfathomable, the nature, the peculiar avidity of his interest in them. It makes us wonder again and again what then is the use on Balzac's scale of the divine faculty. The imagination, as we all know, may be employed up to a certain point in inventing uses for money; but its office beyond that point is surely to make us forget that anything so odious exists. This is what Balzac never forgot; his universe goes on expressing itself for him, to its furthest reaches, on its finest sides, in the terms of the market. To say these things, however, is after all to come out where we want, to suggest his extraordinary scale and his terrible completeness. I am not sure that he does not see character too, see passion, motive, personality, as quite in the order of the "things" we have spoken of. He makes

them no less concrete and palpable, handles them no less
directly and freely. It is the whole business in fine—that
grand total to which he proposed to himself to do high
justice—that gives him his place apart, makes him,
among the novelists, the largest weightiest presence.
There are some of his obsessions—that of the material,
that of the financial, that of the "social," that of the technical, political, civil—for which I feel myself unable to
judge him, judgment losing itself unexpectedly in a particular shade of pity. The way to judge him is to try to
walk all round him—on which we see how remarkably
far we have to go. He is the only member of his order
really monumental, the sturdiest-seated mass that rises in
our path.

1902. From "Honoré de Balzac," in *Notes on
Novelists with Some Other Notes* (1914).

GUSTAVE FLAUBERT:
MADAME BOVARY

One of the things that make [Flaubert] most exhibi-
tional and most describable, so that if we had invented
him as an illustration or a character we would exactly
so have arranged him, is that he was formed intellectually of two quite distinct compartments, a sense of the
real and a sense of the romantic, and that his production, for our present cognizance, thus neatly and vividly
divides itself. The divisions are as marked as the sections
on the back of a scarab, though their distinctness is undoubtedly but the final expression of much inward strife.

M. Faguet[1] indeed, who is admirable on this question of our author's duality, gives an account of the romanticism that found its way for him into the real and of the reality that found its way into the romantic; but he none the less strikes us as a curious splendid insect sustained on wings of a different coloration, the right a vivid red, say, and the left as frank a yellow. This duality has in its sharp operation placed *Madame Bovary* and *L'Éducation* [*sentimentale*] on one side together and placed together on the other *Salammbô* and *La Tentation* [*de Saint-Antoine*]. *Bouvard et Pécuchet* it can scarce be spoken of, I think, as having placed anywhere or anyhow. If it was Flaubert's way to find his subject impossible there was none he saw so much in that light as this last-named, but also none that he appears to have held so important for that very reason to pursue to the bitter end. Posterity agrees with him about the impossibility, but rather takes upon itself to break with the rest of the logic. We may perhaps, however, for symmetry, let *Bouvard et Pécuchet* figure as the tail—if scarabs ever have tails—of our analogous insect. Only in that case we should also append as the very tip the small volume of the *Trois Contes,* preponderantly of the deepest imaginative hue.

His imagination was great and splendid; in spite of which, strangely enough, his masterpiece is not his most imaginative work. *Madame Bovary*, beyond question, holds that first place, and *Madame Bovary* is concerned with the career of a country doctor's wife in a petty

[1] M. Émile Faguet's book *Gustave Flaubert,* published in Paris in 1898 in the series *Les Grands Écrivains français,* was discussed in some detail by James when he wrote this essay on Flaubert (here printed in part) as a critical introduction for an English translation of *Madame Bovary* published in London by William Heinemann in 1902. [*Editor's note.*]

Norman town. The elements of the picture are of the
fewest, the situation of the heroine almost of the mean-
est, the material for interest, considering the interest
yielded, of the most unpromising; but these facts only
throw into relief one of those incalculable incidents that
attend the proceedings of genius. *Madame Bovary* was
doomed by circumstances and causes—the freshness of
comparative youth and good faith on the author's part
being perhaps the chief—definitely to take its position,
even though its subject was fundamentally a negation
of the remote, the splendid and the strange, the stuff
of his fondest and most cultivated dreams. It would have
seemed very nearly to exclude the free play of the
imagination, and the way this faculty on the author's
part nevertheless presides is one of those accidents, ma-
nœuvres, inspirations, we hardly know what to call them,
by which masterpieces grow. He of course knew more
or less what he was doing for his book in making Emma
Bovary a victim of the imaginative habit, but he must
have been far from designing or measuring the total
effect which renders the work so general, so complete
an expression of himself. His separate idiosyncrasies, his
irritated sensibility to the life about him, with the power
to catch it in the fact and hold it hard, and his hunger
for style and history and poetry, for the rich and the
rare, great reverberations, great adumbrations, are here
represented together as they are not in his later writings.
There is nothing of the near, of the directly observed,
though there may be much of the directly perceived and
the minutely detailed, either in *Salammbô* or in *Saint-
Antoine,* and little enough of the extravagance of illusion
in that indefinable last word of restrained evocation and
cold execution *L'Éducation Sentimentale.* M. Faguet
has of course excellently noted this—that the fortune
and felicity of the book were assured by the stroke that

made the central figure an embodiment of helpless romanticism. Flaubert himself but narrowly escaped being
such an embodiment after all, and he is thus able to
express the romantic mind with extraordinary truth.
As to the rest of the matter he had the luck of having
been in possession from the first, having begun so early
to nurse and work up his plan that, familiarity and the
native air, the native soil, aiding, he had finally made
out to the last lurking shade the small sordid sunny dusty
village picture, its emptiness constituted and peopled.
It is in the background and the accessories that the real,
the real of his theme, abides; and the romantic, the romantic of his theme, accordingly occupies the front.
Emma Bovary's poor adventures are a tragedy for the
very reason that in a world unsuspecting, unassisting,
unconsoling, she has herself to distil the rich and the
rare. Ignorant, unguided, undiverted, ridden by the very
nature and mixture of her consciousness, she makes
of the business an inordinate failure, a failure which in
its turn makes for Flaubert the most pointed, the most
told of anecdotes.

There are many things to say about *Madame Bovary*,
but an old admirer of the book would be but half-
hearted—so far as they represent reserves or puzzle-
ments—were he not to note first of all the circumstances
by which it is most endeared to him. To remember it
from far back is to have been present all along at a process of singular interest to a literary mind, a case indeed
full of comfort and cheer. The finest of Flaubert's novels
is to-day, on the French shelf of fiction, one of the first
of the classics; it has attained that position, slowly but
steadily, before our eyes; and we seem so to follow the
evolution of the fate of a classic. We see how the thing
takes place; which we rarely can, for we mostly miss
either the beginning or the end, especially in the case

of a consecration as complete as this. The consecrations
of the past are too far behind and those of the future too
far in front. That the production before us *should* have
come in for the heavenly crown may be a fact to offer
English and American readers a mystifying side; but
it is exactly our ground and a part moreover of the total
interest. The author of these remarks remembers, as with
a sense of the way such things happen, that when a very
young person in Paris he took up from the parental table
the latest number of the periodical in which Flaubert's
then duly unrecognized masterpiece was in course of
publication. The moment is not historic, but it was to
become in the light of history, as may be said, so unforgettable that every small feature of it yet again lives
for him: it rests there like the backward end of the span.
The cover of the old *Revue de Paris* was yellow, if I
mistake not, like that of the new, and *Madame Bovary:
Mœurs de Province,* on the inside of it, was already, on
the spot, as a title, mysteriously arresting, inscrutably
charged. I was ignorant of what had preceded and was
not to know till much later what followed; but present
to me still is the act of standing there before the fire,
my back against the low beplushed and begarnished
French chimney-piece and taking in what I might of
that instalment, taking it in with so surprised an interest,
and perhaps as well such a stir of faint foreknowledge,
that the sunny little salon, the autumn day, the window
ajar and the cheerful outside clatter of the Rue Mon-
taigne are all now for me more or less in the story and
the story more or less in them. The story, however, was
at that moment having a difficult life; its fortune was all
to make; its merit was so far from suspected that, as
Maxime Du Camp—though verily with no excess of
contrition—relates, its cloth of gold barely escaped the
editorial shears. This, with much more, contributes for

us to the course of things to come. The book, on its appearance as a volume, proved a shock to the high propriety of the guardians of public morals under the second Empire, and Flaubert was prosecuted as author of a work indecent to scandal. The prosecution in the event fell to the ground, but I should perhaps have mentioned this agitation as one of the very few, of any public order, in his short list. *Le Candidat* fell at the Vaudeville Theatre, several years later, with a violence indicated by its withdrawal after a performance of but two nights, the first of these marked by a deafening uproar; only if the comedy was not to recover from this accident the misprised lustre of the novel was entirely to reassert itself. It is strange enough at present—so far have we travelled since then—that *Madame Bovary* should in so comparatively recent a past have been to that extent a cause of reprobation; and suggestive above all, in such connections, as to the large unconsciousness of superior minds. The desire of the superior mind of the day—that is the governmental, official, legal—to distinguish a book with such a destiny before it is a case conceivable, but conception breaks down before its design of making the distinction purely invidious. We can imagine its knowing so little, however face to face with the object, what it had got hold of; but for it to have been so urged on by a blind inward spring to publish to posterity the extent of its ignorance, that would have been beyond imagination, beyond everything but pity.

And yet it is not after all that the place the book has taken is so overwhelmingly explained by its inherent dignity; for here comes in the curiosity of the matter. Here comes in especially its fund of admonition for alien readers. The dignity of its substance is the dignity of Madame Bovary herself as a vessel of experience—a question as to which, unmistakably, I judge, we can only depart from the consensus of French critical opinion. M. Faguet for example commends the character of the heroine as one of the most living and discriminated figures of women in all literature, praises it as a field for the display of the romantic spirit that leaves nothing to be desired. Subject to an observation I shall presently make and that bears heavily in general, I think, on Flaubert as a painter of life, subject to this restriction he is right;[1] which is a proof that a work of art may be markedly open to objection and at the same time be rare in its kind, and that when it is perfect to this point nothing else particularly matters. *Madame Bovary* has a perfection that not only stamps it, but that makes it stand almost alone; it holds itself with such a supreme unapproachable assurance as both excites and defies judgment. For it deals not in the least, as to unapproachability, with things exalted or refined; it only confers on its sufficiently vulgar elements of exhibition a final unsurpassable form. The form is in *itself* as interesting, as active, as much of the essence of the subject as the idea, and yet so close is its fit and so inseparable its life

---

[1] The "restriction" which James presently makes in this essay comes in his discussion of *L'Éducation sentimentale*, when he compares that novel's hero, Frédéric Moreau, with Emma Bovary: "Our complaint is that Emma Bovary, in spite of the nature of her consciousness and in spite of her reflecting so much that of her creator, is really too small an affair. . . . She associates herself with Frédéric Moreau in *L'Éducation* to suggest for us a question that can be answered, I hold, only to Flaubert's detriment. . . . Why did Flaubert choose, as special conduits of the life he proposed to depict, such inferior and in the case of Frédéric such abject human specimens? I insist only in respect to the latter, the perfection of Madame Bovary scarce leaving one much warrant for wishing anything better. Even here, however, the general scale and size of Emma, who is small even of her sort, should be a warning to hyperbole." [*Editor's note.*]

that we catch it at no moment on any errand of its own. That verily is to *be* interesting—all round; that is to be genuine and whole. The work is a classic because the thing, such as it is, is ideally *done*, and because it shows that in such doing eternal beauty may dwell. A pretty young woman who lives, socially and morally speaking, in a hole, and who is ignorant, foolish, flimsy, unhappy, takes a pair of lovers by whom she is successively deserted; in the midst of the bewilderment of which, giving up her husband and her child, letting everything go, she sinks deeper into duplicity, debt, despair, and arrives on the spot, on the small scene itself of her poor depravities, at a pitiful tragic end. In especial she does these things while remaining absorbed in romantic intention and vision, and she remains absorbed in romantic intention and vision while fairly rolling in the dust. That is the triumph of the book as the triumph stands, that Emma interests us by the nature of her consciousness and the play of her mind, thanks to the reality and beauty with which those sources are invested. It is not only that they represent *her* state; they are so true, so observed and felt, and especially so shown, that they represent the state, actual or potential, of all persons like her, persons romantically determined. Then her setting, the medium in which she struggles, becomes in its way as important, becomes eminent with the eminence of art; the tiny world in which she revolves, the contracted cage in which she flutters, is hung out in space for her, and her companions in captivity there are as true as herself.

1902. From "Gustave Flaubert" in *Notes on Novelists with Some Other Notes* (1914).

*

HENRY JAMES TO H. G. WELLS

[H. G. Wells was, like Kipling, one of the new English talents of the eighteen-nineties that Henry James—eager to see the novel invigorated by fresh material and imagination, even when these issued from an experience or sensibility unlike his own—saluted with special enthusiasm. A friendship between the two men developed as early as 1898. James told Wells in 1899 that the younger man's work filled him "with wonder and admiration," and in the following years he praised as "extraordinarily and unceasingly interesting" such books of Wells's as *Anticipations, A Modern Utopia, Kipps, Ann Veronica, The New Machiavelli, Tono-Bungay, Marriage, The Passionate Friends.* He sometimes protested against Wells's unbridled habits and all-inclusive verve; he warned him against "that accurst autobiographical form which puts a premium on the loose"; he expressed to Mrs. Humphry Ward his uneasiness at seeing in Wells the combination of "so much talent with so little art, so much life with (so to speak) so little living." But he stuck to his original belief that Wells was a master of social materials and comedy in the tradition of Balzac and Dickens, and in 1912 he wrote him: "I have read you, as I always read you, and as I read no one else, with a complete abdication of all those 'principles of criticism,' canons of form, preconceptions of felicity, references to the idea of method or the sacred laws of composition, which I roam, which I totter, through the pages of others attended in some degree by the fond yet feeble theory of, but which I shake off, as I advance under your spell, with the most cynical inconsistency." In 1914 James summed up his delight and confidence in Wells's gifts in a passage of his essay "The New Novel," in which Wells shared James's attention with Joseph

Conrad, Arnold Bennett, Edith Wharton, Gilbert Cannan, Hugh Walpole, Compton Mackenzie, and (briefly) D. H. Lawrence.

In the summer of 1915 Wells published a book with a long title—*Boon, the Mind of the Race, the Wild Asses of the Devil, and the Last Trump,* purportedly "Being a First Selection from the Literary Remains of George Boon, Appropriate to the Times, Prepared for Publication by Reginald Bliss . . . with An Ambiguous Introduction by H. G. Wells." This was a loose ragbag of a book on literary, social, political, and moral themes, and it included a lengthy attack on James and a parody of the kind of novel he wrote and represented. James was paired with George Moore: "In early life both these men poisoned their minds in studios. . . . But James has never discovered that a novel isn't a picture . . . that life isn't a studio." "James *begins* by taking it for granted that a novel is a work of art that must be judged by its oneness. . . . Some one gave him that idea in the beginning of things and he has never found it out. He doesn't find things out." "He is the culmination of the Superficial type." "He sets himself to pick the straws out of the hair of Life before he paints her. But without the straws she is no longer the mad woman we love." Wells went on to attack James's principle of "selection" as against his own ideal of "saturation." "In practice James's selection becomes just omission and nothing more." "The only living human motives left in the novels of Henry James are a certain avidity and an entirely superficial curiosity. . . . It is like a church lit but without a congregation to distract you, with every light and line focused on the high altar. And on the altar, very reverently placed, intensely there, is a dead kitten, an egg-shell, a bit of string." "Having first made sure that he has scarcely anything left to express, he then sets to work to express it, with an industry, a wealth of intellectual stuff that dwarfs Newton. . . . And all for tales of nothingness. . . . It is leviathan retrieving pebbles. It is a magnificent but painful hippopotamus resolved at any cost, even at the cost of its dignity, upon picking up a pea which has got into a corner of its den. Most things, it insists, are beyond it, but it can, at any rate, modestly, and with an artistic singleness of mind, pick up that pea. . . ."

Wells later admitted that *Boon* had been his retaliation for James's inclusion of him, in the essay on "The New Novel," in "a bundle with a company of young men of questionable quality as one of the Younger Reputations."

James, on receiving and reading *Boon*, wrote to Wells.]

21 Carlyle Mansions,
Cheyne Walk, S.W.
July 6th, 1915.

My dear Wells,

I was given yesterday at a club your volume "Boon, etc.," from a loose leaf in which I learn that you kindly sent it me and which yet appears to have lurked there for a considerable time undelivered. I have just been reading, to acknowledge it intelligently, a considerable number of its pages—though not all; for, to be perfectly frank, I have been in that respect beaten for the first time—or rather for the first time but one—by a book of yours; I haven't found the current of it draw me on and on this time—as, unfailingly and irresistibly, before (which I have repeatedly let you know). However, I shall try again—I hate to lose any scrap of you that *may* make for light or pleasure; and meanwhile I have more or less mastered your appreciation of H. J., which I have found very curious and interesting after a fashion—though it has naturally not filled me with a fond elation. It is difficult of course for a writer to put himself *fully* in the place of another writer who finds him extraordinarily futile and void, and who is moved to publish that to the world—and I think the case isn't easier when he happens to have enjoyed the other writer enormously from far back; because there has then grown up the habit of taking some common meeting-ground between them for granted, and the falling away of this is like the collapse of a bridge which made communication possible. But I am by nature more in dread of any fool's paradise, or at least of any bad misguidedness, than in love with the idea of a security proved, and the fact that a mind as brilliant as yours *can* resolve me into such an unmitigated mistake, can't enjoy me in anything like the degree in which I like to think I may be enjoyed, makes me greatly want to fix myself, for as long as my nerves will stand it, with such a pair of eyes. I am aware of certain things I have, and not less conscious, I believe, of various others that I am simply reduced to wish I did or could have; so I try, for possible light, to enter into the feelings of a critic for whom the deficiencies so preponderate. The difficulty about that effort, however, is that one can't keep it up—one *has* to fall back on one's sense of one's good parts—one's own sense; and I at least should have to do that, I think, even if your picture were painted with a more searching brush. For I should otherwise seem to forget what it is that my poetic and my appeal to experience rest upon. They rest upon *my* measure of fulness—fulness of life and of the projection of it, which seems to you such an emptiness of both. I don't mean to say I don't wish I could do twenty things I can't—many of which you do so livingly; but I confess I ask myself what would become in that case of some of those to which I am most addicted and by which interest seems to me most beautifully producible. I hold that interest may be, *must* be, exquisitely made and created, and that if we don't make it, we who undertake to, nobody and nothing will make it for us; though nothing is more possible, nothing may even be more certain, than that my quest of it, my constant wish to run it to earth, may entail the sacrifice of certain things

that are not on the straight line of it. However, there are
too many things to say, and I don't think your chapter
is really inquiring enough to entitle you to expect all
of them. The fine thing about the fictional form to me
is that it opens such widely different windows of attention; but that is just why I like the window so to frame
the play and the process!

Faithfully yours,

Henry James

[Wells answered the above letter in part as follows, on July
8, 1915: "There is of course a real and very fundamental
difference in our innate and developed attitudes towards
life and literature. To you literature like painting is an end,
to me literature like architecture is a means, it has a use.
Your view was, I felt, altogether too prominent in the world
of criticism and I assailed it in lines of harsh antagonism.
And writing that stuff about you was the first escape I had
from the obsession of this war. *Boon* is just a waste-paper
basket. Some of it was written before I left my home at
Sandgate (1911), and it was while I was turning over some
old papers that I came upon it, found it expressive, and
went on with it last December. I had rather be called a
journalist than an artist, that is the essence of it, and there
was no other antagonist possible than yourself. But since
it was printed I have regretted a hundred times that I did
not express our profound and incurable difference and
contrast with a better grace. . . ." Later, on July 13,
after receiving James's second letter, printed below, Wells
added: "I don't clearly understand your concluding phrases
—which shews no doubt how completely they define our
difference. When you say 'it is art that *makes* life, makes
interest, makes importance,' I can only read sense into it
by assuming that you are using 'art' for every conscious
human activity. I use the word for a research and attainment
that is technical and special. . . ."]

Dictated.

21 Carlyle Mansions,
Cheyne Walk, S.W.
July 10th, 1915.

My dear Wells,

I am bound to tell you that I don't think your letter makes out any sort of case for the bad manners of "Boon," as far as your indulgence in them at the expense of your poor old H. J. is concerned—I say "your" simply because he has *been* yours, in the most liberal, continual, sacrificial, the most admiring and abounding critical way, ever since he began to know your writings: as to which you have had copious testimony. Your comparison of the book to a waste-basket strikes me as the reverse of felicitous, for what one throws into that receptacle is exactly what one doesn't commit to publicity and make the affirmation of one's estimate of one's contemporaries by. I should liken it much rather to the preservative portfolio or drawer in which what is withheld from the basket is savingly laid away. Nor do I feel it anywhere evident that my "view of life and literature," or what you impute to me as such, is carrying everything before it and becoming a public menace—so unaware do I seem, on the contrary, that my products constitute an example in any measurable degree followed or a cause in any degree successfully pleaded: I can't but think that if this were the case I should find it somewhat attested in their circulation—which, alas, I have reached a very advanced age in the entirely defeated hope of. But I *have* no view of life and literature, I maintain, other than that our form of the latter in especial is admirable exactly by its range and variety, its plasticity and liberality, its fairly living on the sincere and shifting experience of the individual practitioner. That is why I have always so admired your so free and strong application of it, the particular rich receptacle of intelligences and impressions emptied out with an energy of its own, that your genius constitutes; and *that* is in particular why, in my letter of two or three days since, I pronounced it curious and interesting that you should find the case I constitute myself only ridiculous and vacuous to the extent of your having to proclaim your sense of it. The curiosity and the interest, however, in this latter connection are of course for my mind those of the break of perception (perception of the veracity of *my* variety) on the part of a talent so generally inquiring and apprehensive as yours. Of course for myself I live, live intensely and am fed by life, and my value, whatever it be, is in my own kind of expression of that. Therefore I am pulled up to wonder by the fact that for you my kind (my sort of sense of expression and sort of sense of life alike) doesn't exist; and that wonder is, I admit, a disconcerting comment on my idea of the various appreciability of our addiction to the novel and of all the personal and intellectual history, sympathy and curiosity, behind the given example of it. It is when that history and curiosity have been determined in the way most different from my own that I want to get at them—precisely *for* the extension of life, which is the novel's best gift. But that is another matter. Meanwhile I absolutely dissent from the claim that there are any differences whatever in the amenability to art of forms of literature aesthetically determined, and hold your distinction between a form that is (like) painting and a form that is (like) architecture for wholly null and void. There is no sense in which architecture is aesthetically "for use" that doesn't leave any other art whatever exactly as much so; and so far from that of literature being irrelevant to the literary report upon life, and to its being made as interesting as possible, I regard it as relevant in a degree that leaves everything else be-hind. It is art that *makes* life, makes interest, makes importance, for our consideration and application of these things, and I know of no substitute whatever for the force and beauty of its process. If I were Boon I should say that any pretence of such a substitute is helpless and hopeless humbug; but I wouldn't be Boon for the world, and am only yours faithfully,

Henry James

IV

PORTRAITS OF PLACES

FOUR CITIES

*

EDITOR'S NOTE

James lived in what today appears as the last great age of romantic travel. The cities and monuments of Europe still stood secure in their appointed places; space had not yet been annihilated by engines, wires, wireless, and air-flight; the sanctity of time and tradition still blessed the holy places of historical and literary pilgrimage; nations lived in comparative amity and mutual respect. James was, moreover, an American in an age when it was one of the duties of every civilized American to rediscover and explore, assess or criticize, his legacy of breed, culture, and tradition in the Old World. Virtually every distinguished American writer—Whitman and Thoreau are the only notable exceptions—made his journey to Europe: Franklin, Adams, and Jefferson, Irving, Cooper, and Emerson, Hawthorne, Melville, and Mark Twain, Howells, Norton, and Henry Adams. James became the archetype of that company, our great exponent of the era of philosophic travel, the explorer on whom almost all his literary followers—Henry B. Fuller, Stephen Crane, Edith Wharton, Willa Cather, Lewis, Dos Passos, Hemingway, Fitzgerald, T. S. Eliot—in some degree modeled their later conquests of Europe.

Europe became part of his life "antecedent to choice."

Long before he went there by preference, long before he became that curious combination of "innocent abroad" and critical cosmopolite who recorded his discoveries in essays and books, he went as a baby in the first year of his life, and presently as a schoolboy. It became, by his father's express design, James's appointed destiny to experience the classic American division between the New and Old Worlds in his own person. He encountered England and Europe in his chosen role of "passionate pilgrim," and he made the encounter, in all its complex and critical ramifications, a major fact in his career and of his work. His models in his travel writings were not only the Americans who preceded him to Europe, but the European masters of this genre—Goethe, Stendhal, Gautier, Heine, Taine, Fromentin, Browning. W. H. Auden has said that "of all possible subjects, travel is the most difficult for an artist, as it is the easiest for the journalist." James as a traveler remains, even at his most casual or journalistic, unmistakably the artist who, "deprived of his most treasured liberty, the freedom to invent," discovers that "successfully to extract importance from historical personal events without ever departing from them, free only to select and never to modify or add, calls for imagination of a very high order."

James published seven books of his travel writings, but a great quantity of his reports remains uncollected in journals and newspapers. The finest distillation of these experiences went into his novels and tales, from *Roderick Hudson, The American,* and *The Portrait of a Lady* to *The Wings of the Dove, The Ambassadors,* and *The Golden Bowl.* From this great sum of material I have chosen four passages on four great cities, three European and one American, as representative of the rest.

The title of this section is borrowed from James's book *Portraits of Places.* "The After-Season in Rome" was first printed in *The Nation* for June 12, 1873, later included in *Transatlantic Sketches* (1875), and revised for *Italian Hours* (1909), from which the present text is taken. "Occasional Paris" was first printed as "Paris Revisited" in *The Galaxy* for January 1878, and later included under its present title in *Portraits of Places* (1883). The picture of London is part of a long essay called "London," which first appeared in *The Century Magazine* for December 1888, later amplified in *Essays in London and Elsewhere* (1893) and in *English Hours* (1905), the text here being taken from the last-named book. The excerpt titled "New York Revisited" is part of a long essay that was written after James's return to America in 1904; it first appeared in *Harper's Magazine* for February, March, and May 1906, and became Chapter II of *The American Scene* (1907).

*

THE AFTER-SEASON IN ROME

One may at the blest end of May say without injustice to anybody that the state of mind of many a *forestiero* in Rome is one of intense impatience for the moment when all other *forestieri* shall have taken themselves off. One may confess to this state of mind and be no misanthrope. The place has passed so completely for the winter months into the hands of the barbarians that that estimable character the passionate pilgrim finds it constantly harder to keep his passion clear. He has a rueful sense of impressions perverted and adulterated; the all-venerable visage disconcerts us by a vain eagerness to see itself mirrored in English, American, German eyes. It isn't simply that you are never first or never alone at the classic or historic spots where you have dreamt of persuading the shy *genius loci* into confidential utterance; it isn't simply that St. Peter's, the Vatican, the Palatine, are for ever ringing with the false note of the languages without style: it is the general oppressive feeling that the city of the soul has become for the time a monstrous mixture of watering-place and curiosity-shop and that its most ardent life is that of the tourists who haggle over false intaglios and yawn through palaces and temples. But you are told of a happy time when these abuses begin to pass away, when Rome becomes Rome again and you may have her all to yourself. "You may like her more or less now," I was assured at the height of the season; "but you must wait till the month of May, when she'll give you *all* she has, to love her. Then the foreigners, or the excess of them, are gone; the galleries and ruins are empty, and the place," said my informant, who was a happy Frenchman of the Académie de France, "*renaît à elle-même.*" Indeed I was haunted all winter by an irresistible prevision of what Rome *must* be in declared spring. Certain charming places seemed to murmur: "Ah, this is nothing! Come back at the right weeks and see the sky above us almost black with its excess of blue, and the new grass already deep, but still vivid, and the white roses tumble in odorous spray and the warm radiant air distil gold for the smelting-pot that the *genius loci* then dips his brush into before making play with it, in his inimitable way, for the general effect of complexion."

A month ago I spent a week in the country, and on my return, the first time I approached the Corso, became conscious of a change. Something delightful had happened, to which at first I couldn't give a name, but which presently shone out as the fact that there were but half as many people present and that these were chiefly the natural or the naturalized. We had been docked of half our irrelevance, our motley excess, and now physically, morally, æsthetically there was elbow-room. In the afternoon I went to the Pincio, and the Pincio was almost dull. The band was playing to a dozen ladies who lay in landaus poising their lace-fringed parasols; but they had scarce more than a light-gloved dandy apiece hanging over their carriage doors. By the parapet to the great terrace that sweeps the city stood but three or four interlopers looking at the sunset and with their Baedekers only just showing in their pockets—the sunsets not being down among the tariffed articles in these precious volumes. I went so far as to hope for them that, like myself, they were, under every precaution, taking some amorous intellectual liberty with the scene.

Practically I violate thus the instinct of monopoly, since it's a shame not to publish that Rome in May is indeed exquisitely worth your patience. I have just been so gratified at finding myself in undisturbed possession for a couple of hours of the Museum of the Lateran that I can afford to be magnanimous. It's almost as if the old all-papal paradise had come back. The weather for a month has been perfect, the sky an extravagance of blue, the air lively enough, the nights cool, nippingly cool, and the whole ancient greyness lighted with an irresistible smile. Rome, which in some moods, especially to new-comers, seems a place of almost sinister gloom, has an occasional art, as one knows her better, of brushing away care by the grand gesture with which some splendid impatient mourning matron—just the Niobe of Nations, surviving, emerging and looking about her again—might pull off and cast aside an oppression of muffling crape. This admirable power still temperamentally to react and take notice lurks in all her darkness and dirt and decay—a something more careless and hopeless than our thrifty northern cheer, and yet more genial and urbane than the Parisian spirit of *blague*. The collective Roman nature is a healthy and hearty one, and you feel it abroad in the streets even when the sirocco blows and the medium of life seems to proceed

more or less from the mouth of a furnace. But who shall
analyse even the simplest Roman impression? It is compounded of so many things, it says so much, it involves
so much, it so quickens the intelligence and so flatters
the heart, that before we fairly grasp the case the imagination has marked it for her own and exposed us to a
perilous likelihood of talking nonsense about it.

The smile of Rome, as I have called it, and its insidious message to those who incline to ramble irresponsibly
and take things as they come, is ushered in with the first
breath of spring, and then grows and grows with the
advancing season till it wraps the whole place in its ten-
fold charm. As the process develops you can do few
better things than go often to Villa Borghese and sit on
the grass—on a stout bit of drapery—and watch its exquisite stages. It has a frankness and a sweetness beyond
any relenting of *our* clumsy climates even when ours
leave off their damnable faces and begin. Nature departs
from every reserve with a confidence that leaves one at
a loss where, as it were, to look—leaves one, as I say,
nothing to do but to lay one's head among the anemones
at the base of a high-stemmed pine and gaze up crest-
ward and skyward along its slanting silvery column. You
may watch the whole business from a dozen of these
choice standpoints and have a different villa for it every
day in the week. The Doria, the Ludovisi, the Medici,
the Albani, the Wolkonski, the Chigi, the Mellini, the
Massimo—there are more of them, with all their sights
and sounds and odours and memories, than you have
senses for. But I prefer none of them to the Borghese,
which is free to all the world at all times and yet never
crowded; for when the whirl of carriages is great in the
middle regions you may find a hundred untrodden spots
and silent corners, tenanted at the worst by a group of
those long-skirted young Propagandists who stalk about

with solemn angularity, each with a book under his arm, like silhouettes from a mediæval missal, and "compose" so extremely well with the still more processional cypresses and with stretches of golden-russet wall overtopped by ultramarine. And yet if the Borghese is good the Medici is strangely charming, and you may stand in the little belvedere which rises with such surpassing oddity out of the dusky heart of the Boschetto at the latter establishment—a miniature presentation of the wood of the Sleeping Beauty—and look across at the Ludovisi pines lifting their crooked parasols into a sky of what a painter would call the most morbid blue, and declare that the place where *they* grow is the most delightful in the world. Villa Ludovisi has been all winter the residence of the lady familiarly known in Roman society as "Rosina," Victor Emmanuel's morganatic wife, the only familiarity, it would seem, that she allows, for the grounds were rigidly closed, to the inconsolable regret of old Roman sojourners. Just as the nightingales began to sing, however, the quasi-august *padrona* departed, and the public, with certain restrictions, have been admitted to hear them. The place takes, where it lies, a princely ease, and there could be no better example of the expansive tendencies of ancient privilege than the fact that its whole vast extent is contained by the city walls. It has in this respect very much the same enviable air of having got up early that marks the great intramural demesne of Magdalen College at Oxford. The stern old ramparts of Rome form the outer enclosure of the villa, and hence a series of "striking scenic effects" which it would be unscrupulous flattery to say you can imagine. The grounds are laid out in the formal last-century manner; but nowhere do the straight black cypresses lead off the gaze into vistas of a melancholy more charged with associations—poetic, romantic, his·

toric; nowhere are there grander, smoother walls of
laurel and myrtle.

I recently spent an afternoon hour at the little Protestant cemetery close to St. Paul's Gate, where the ancient
and the modern world are insidiously contrasted. They
make between them one of the solemn places of Rome—
although indeed when funereal things are so interfused
it seems ungrateful to call them sad. Here is a mixture
of tears and smiles, of stones and flowers, of mourning
cypresses and radiant sky, which gives us the impression
of our looking back at death from the brighter side of
the grave. The cemetery nestles in an angle of the city
wall, and the older graves are sheltered by a mass of
ancient brickwork, through whose narrow loopholes you
peep at the wide purple of the Campagna. Shelley's grave
is here, buried in roses—a happy grave every way for
the very type and figure of the Poet. Nothing could be
more impenetrably tranquil than this little corner in
the bend of the protecting rampart, where a cluster of
modern ashes is held tenderly in the rugged hand of the
Past. The past is tremendously embodied in the hoary
pyramid of Caius Cestius, which rises hard by, half
within the wall and half without, cutting solidly into
the solid blue of the sky and casting its pagan shadow
upon the grass of English graves—that of Keats, among
them—with an effect of poetic justice. It is a wonderful
confusion of mortality and a grim enough admonition
of our helpless promiscuity in the crucible of time. But
the most touching element of all is the appeal of the
pious English inscriptions among all these Roman memories; touching because of their universal expression
of that trouble within trouble, misfortune in a foreign
land. Something special stirs the heart through the fine
Scriptural language in which everything is recorded.
The echoes of massive Latinity with which the atmos-

phere is charged suggest nothing more majestic and monumental. I may seem unduly to refine, but the injunction to the reader in the monument to Miss Bathurst, drowned in the Tiber in 1824, "If thou art young and lovely, build not thereon, for she who lies beneath thy feet in death was the loveliest flower ever cropt in its bloom," affects us irresistibly as a case for tears on the spot. The whole elaborate inscription indeed says something over and beyond all it does say. The English have the reputation of being the most reticent people in the world, and as there is no smoke without fire I suppose they have done something to deserve it; yet who can say that one doesn't constantly meet the most startling examples of the insular faculty to "gush"? In this instance the mother of the deceased takes the public into her confidence with surprising frankness and omits no detail, seizing the opportunity to mention by the way that she had already lost her husband by a most mysterious visitation. The appeal to one's attention and the confidence in it are withal most moving. The whole record has an old-fashioned gentility that makes its frankness tragic. You seem to hear the garrulity of passionate grief.

To be choosing these positive commonplaces of the Roman tone for a theme when there are matters of modern moment going on may seem none the less to require an apology. But I make no claim to your special correspondent's faculty for getting an "inside" view of things, and I have hardly more than a pictorial impression of the Pope's illness and of the discussion of the Law of the Convents. Indeed I am afraid to speak of the Pope's illness at all, lest I should say something egregiously heartless about it, recalling too forcibly that unnatural husband who was heard to wish that his wife would "either" get well—! He had his reasons, and Roman tourists have theirs in the shape of a vague longing for something spectacular at St. Peter's. If it takes the sacrifice of somebody to produce it let somebody then be sacrificed. Meanwhile we have been having a glimpse of the spectacular side of the Religious Corporations Bill. Hearing one morning a great hubbub in the Corso I stepped forth upon my balcony. A couple of hundred men were strolling slowly down the street with their hands in their pockets, shouting in unison "Abbasso il ministero!" and huzzaing in chorus. Just beneath my window they stopped and began to murmur "Al Quirinale, al Quirinale!" The crowd surged a moment gently and then drifted to the Quirinal, where it scuffled harmlessly with half-a-dozen of the king's soldiers. It ought to have been impressive, for what was it, strictly, unless the seeds of revolution? But its carriage was too gentle and its cries too musical to send the most timorous tourist to packing his trunk. As I began with saying: in Rome, in May, everything has an amiable side, even popular uprisings.

1873. From *Transatlantic Sketches* (1875) and, as here printed, *Italian Hours* (1909).

OCCASIONAL PARIS

It is hard to say exactly what is the profit of comparing one race with another, and weighing in opposed groups the manners and customs of neighbouring countries; but it is certain that as we move about the world we constantly indulge in this exercise. This is especially the case if we happen to be infected with the baleful spirit of the cosmopolite—that uncomfortable consequence of seeing many lands and feeling at home in none. To be a cosmopolite is not, I think, an ideal; the ideal should be to be a concentrated patriot. Being a cosmopolite is an accident, but one must make the best of it. If you have lived about, as the phrase is, you have lost that sense of the absoluteness and the sanctity of the habits of your fellow-patriots which once made you so happy in the midst of them. You have seen that there are a great many *patriæ* in the world, and that each of these is filled with excellent people for whom the local idiosyncrasies are the only thing that is not rather barbarous. There comes a time when one set of customs, wherever it may be found, grows to seem to you about as provincial as another; and then I suppose it may be said of you that you have become a cosmopolite. You have formed the habit of comparing, of looking for points of difference and of resemblance, for present and absent advantages, for the virtues that go with certain defects, and the defects that go with certain virtues. If this is poor work compared with the active practice, in the sphere to which a discriminating Providence has assigned you, of the duties of a tax-payer, an elector, a juryman or a diner-out, there is nevertheless something to be said for it. It is good to think well of mankind, and this, on the whole, a cosmopolite does. If you limit your generalisations to the sphere I mentioned just now, there is a danger that your occasional fits of pessimism may be too sweeping. When you are out of humour the whole country suffers, because at such moments one is never discriminating, and it costs you very little bad logic to lump your fellow-citizens together. But if you are living about, as I say, certain differences impose themselves. The worst you can say of the human race is, for instance, that the Germans are a detestable people. They do not represent the human race for you, as in your native town your fellow-citizens do, and your unflattering judgment has a flattering reverse. If the Germans are detestable, you are mentally saying, there are those admirable French, or those charming Americans, or those interesting English. (Of course it is simply by accident that I couple the German name here with the unfavourable adjective. The epithets may be transposed at will.) Nothing can well be more different from anything else than the English from the French, so that, if you are acquainted with both nations, it may be said that on any special point your agreeable impression of the one implies a censorious attitude toward the other, and *vice versâ*. This has rather a shocking sound; it makes the cosmopolite appear invidious and narrow-minded. But I hasten to add that there seems no real reason why even the most delicate conscience should take alarm. The consequence of the cosmopolite spirit is to initiate you into the merits of all peoples; to convince you that national virtues are numerous, though they may be very different, and to make downright preference really very hard. I have, for instance, every disposition to think better of the English race than of any other except my own. There are things which make it natural I should; there are inducements, provocations, temptations, almost bribes. There have been moments when I have almost burned my ships behind me, and declared that, as it simplified matters greatly to pin one's faith to a chosen people, I would henceforth cease to trouble my head about the lights and shades of the foreign character. I am convinced that if I had taken this reckless engagement, I should greatly have regretted it. You may find a room very comfortable to sit in with the window open, and not like it at all when the window has been shut. If one were to give up the privilege of comparing the

English with other people, one would very soon, in a
moment of reaction, make once for all (and most unjustly) such a comparison as would leave the English
nowhere. Compare then, I say, as often as the occasion
presents itself. The result as regards any particular people, and as regards the human race at large, may be pronounced agreeable, and the process is both instructive
and entertaining.

So the author of these observations finds it on returning to Paris after living for upwards of a year in London.
He finds himself comparing, and the results of comparison are several disjointed reflections, of which it may be
profitable to make a note. Certainly Paris is a very old
story, and London is a still older one; and there is no
great reason why a journey across the channel and back
should quicken one's perspicacity to an unprecedented
degree. I therefore will not pretend to have been looking at Paris with new eyes, or to have gathered on the
banks of the Seine a harvest of extraordinary impressions. I will only pretend that a good many old impressions have recovered their freshness, and that there is a
sort of renovated entertainment in looking at the most
brilliant city in the world with eyes attuned to a different pitch. Never, in fact, have those qualities of
brightness and gaiety that are half the stock-in-trade of
the city by the Seine seemed to me more uncontestable.
The autumn is but half over, and Paris is, in common
parlance, empty. The private houses are closed, the
lions have returned to the jungle, the Champs Elysées
are not at all "mondains." But I have never seen Paris
more Parisian, in the pleasantest sense of the word;
better humoured, more open-windowed, more naturally
entertaining. A radiant September helps the case; but
doubtless the matter is, as I hinted above, in a large degree "subjective." For when one comes to the point

there is nothing very particular just now for Paris to rub her hands about. The Exhibition of 1878 is looming up as large as a mighty mass of buildings on the Trocadéro can make it. These buildings are very magnificent and fantastical; they hang over the Seine, in their sudden immensity and glittering newness, like a palace in a fairy-tale. But the trouble is that most people appear to regard the Exhibition as in fact a fairy-tale. They speak of the wonderful structures on the Champ de Mars and the Trocadéro as a predestined monument to the folly of a group of gentlemen destitute of a sense of the opportune. The moment certainly does not seem very well chosen for inviting the world to come to Paris to amuse itself. The world is too much occupied with graver cares—with reciprocal cannonading and chopping, with cutting of throats and burning of homes, with murder of infants and mutilation of mothers, with warding off famine and civil war, with lamenting the failure of its resources, the dulness of trade, the emptiness of its pockets. Rome is burning altogether too fast for even its most irresponsible spirits to find any great satisfaction in fiddling. But even if there is (as there very well may be) a certain scepticism at headquarters as to the accomplishment of this graceful design, there is no apparent hesitation, and everything is going forward as rapidly as if mankind were breathless with expectation. That familiar figure, the Parisian *ouvrier*, with his white, chalky blouse, his attenuated person, his clever face, is more familiar than ever, and I suppose, finding plenty of work to his hand, is for the time in a comparatively rational state of mind. He swarms in thousands, not only in the region of the Exhibition, but along the great thoroughfare—the Avenue de l'Opéra —which has just been opened in the interior of Paris. This is an extremely Parisian creation, and as it is

really a great convenience—it will save a great many
steps and twists and turns—I suppose it should be
spoken of with gratitude and admiration. But I confess
that to my sense it belongs primarily to that order of
benefits which during the twenty years of the Empire
gradually deprived the streets of Paris of nine-tenths of
their ancient individuality. The deadly monotony of the
Paris that M. Haussmann called into being—its huge,
blank, pompous, featureless sameness—sometimes comes
over the wandering stranger with a force that leads
him to devote the author of these miles of architectural commonplace to execration. The new street is
quite on the imperial system; it must make the late
Napoleon III. smile with beatific satisfaction as he looks
down upon it from the Bonapartist corner of Paradise.
It stretches straight away from the pompous façade of
the Opéra to the doors of the Théâtre Français, and it
must be admitted that there is something fine in the
vista that is closed at one end by the great sculptured
and gilded mass of the former building. But it smells
of the modern asphalt; it is lined with great white houses
that are adorned with machine-made arabesques, and
each of which is so exact a copy of all the rest that even
the little white porcelain number on a blue ground,
which looks exactly like all the other numbers, hardly
constitutes an identity. Presently there will be a long
succession of milliners' and chocolate-makers' shops in
the basement of this homogeneous row, and the pretty
bonnets and bonbonnières in the shining windows will
have their ribbons knotted with a *chic* that you must
come to Paris to see. Then there will be little glazed
sentry-boxes at regular intervals along the curbstone,
in which churlish old women will sit selling half a dozen
copies of each of the newspapers; and over the hardened bitumen the young Parisian of our day will con-

stantly circulate, looking rather pallid and wearing very large shirt-cuffs. And the new avenue will be a great success, for it will place in symmetrical communication two of the most important establishments in France— the temple of French music and the temple of French comedy.

I said just now that no two things could well be more unlike than England and France; and though the remark is not original, I uttered it with the spontaneity that it must have on the lips of a traveller who, having left either country, has just disembarked in the other. It is of course by this time a very trite observation, but it will continue to be made so long as Boulogne remains the same lively antithesis of Folkestone. An American, conscious of the family-likeness diffused over his own huge continent, never quite unlearns his surprise at finding that so little of either of these two almost contiguous towns has rubbed off upon the other. He is surprised at certain English people feeling so far away from France, and at all French people feeling so far away from England. I travelled from Boulogne the other day in the same railway-carriage with a couple of amiable and ingenuous young Britons, who had come over to spend ten days in Paris. It was their first landing in France; they had never yet quitted their native island; and in the course of a little conversation that I had with them I was struck with the scantiness of their information in regard to French manners and customs. They were very intelligent lads; they were apparently fresh from a university; but in respect to the interesting country they were about to enter, their minds were almost a blank. If the conductor, appearing at the carriage door to ask for our tickets, had had the leg of a frog sticking out of his pocket, I think their only very definite preconception would have been confirmed. I parted

with them at the Paris station, and I have no doubt that
they very soon began to make precious discoveries;
and I have alluded to them not in the least to throw
ridicule upon their "insularity"—which indeed, being
accompanied with great modesty, I thought a very
pretty spectacle—but because having become, since
my last visit to France, a little insular myself, I was more
conscious of the emotions that attend on an arrival.

The brightness always seems to begin while you are
still out in the channel, when you fairly begin to see the
French coast. You pass into a region of intenser light—
a zone of clearness and colour. These properties brighten
and deepen as you approach the land, and when you
fairly stand upon that good Boulognese quay, among
the blue and red douaniers and soldiers, the small ugly
men in cerulean blouses, the charming fishwives, with
their folded kerchiefs and their crisp cap-frills, their
short striped petticoats, their tightly-drawn stockings,
and their little clicking sabots—when you look about
you at the smokeless air, at the pink and yellow houses,
at the white-fronted café, close at hand, with its bright
blue letters, its mirrors and marble-topped tables, its
white-aproned, alert, undignified waiter, grasping a
huge coffee-pot by a long handle—when you perceive
all these things you feel the additional savour that foreignness gives to the picturesque; or feel rather, I should
say, that simple foreignness may itself make the picturesque; for certainly the elements in the picture I have
just sketched are not especially exquisite. No matter;
you are amused, and your amusement continues—being sensibly stimulated by a visit to the buffet at the
railway-station, which is better than the refreshment-
room at Folkestone. It is a pleasure to have people offering you soup again, of their own movement; it is a
pleasure to find a little pint of Bordeaux standing natu-

rally before your plate; it is a pleasure to have a napkin; it is a pleasure, above all, to take up one of the good long sticks of French bread—as bread is called the staff of life, the French bake it literally in the shape of staves—and break off a loose, crisp, crusty morsel.

There are impressions, certainly, that imperil your good-humour. No honest Anglo-Saxon can like a French railway-station; and I was on the point of adding that no honest Anglo-Saxon can like a French railway-official. But I will not go so far as that; after all I cannot remember any great harm that such a functionary has ever done me—except in locking me up as a malefactor. It is necessary to say, however, that the honest Anglo-Saxon, in a French railway-station, is in a state of chronic irritation—an irritation arising from his sense of the injurious effect upon the genial French nature of the possession of an administrative uniform. I believe that the consciousness of brass buttons on his coat and stripes on his trousers has spoiled many a modest and amiable Frenchman, and the sight of these aggressive insignia always stirs within me a moral protest. I repeat that my aversion to them is partly theoretic, for I have found, as a general thing, that an inquiry civilly made extracts a civil answer from even the most official-looking personage. But I have also found that such a personage's measure of the civility due to him is inordinately large; if he places himself in any degree at your service, it is apparently from the sense that true greatness can afford to unbend. You are constantly reminded that you must not presume. In England these intimations never proceed from one's "inferiors." In France the "administration" is the first thing that touches you; in a little while you get used to it, but you feel somehow that, in the process, you have lost the flower of your self-respect. Of course you are under some obligation to it. It has taken you off the steamer at Boulogne;[1] made you tell your name to a gentleman with a sword, stationed at the farther end of the plank—not a drawn sword, it is true, but still, at the best, a very nasty weapon; marshalled you into the railway-station; assigned you to a carriage—I was going to say to a seat; transported you to Paris, marshalled you again out of the train, and under a sort of military surveillance, into an enclosure containing a number of human sheep-pens, in one of which it has imprisoned you for some half-hour. I am always on the point, in these places, of asking one of my gaolers if I may not be allowed to walk about on parole. The administration at any rate has finally taken you out of your pen, and, through the medium of a functionary who "inscribes" you in a little book, transferred you to a cab selected by a logic of its own. In doing all this it has certainly done a great deal for you; but somehow its good offices have made you feel sombre and resentful. The other day, on arriving from London, while I was waiting for my luggage, I saw several of the porters who convey travellers' impedimenta to the cab come up and deliver over the coin they had just received for this service to a functionary posted *ad hoc* in a corner, and armed with a little book in which he noted down these remittances. The *pourboires* are apparently thrown into a common fund and divided among the guild of porters. The system is doubtless an excellent one, excellently carried out; but the sight of the poor round-shouldered man of burdens dropping his coin into the hand of the official arithmetician was to my fancy but another reminder that the

[1] James's text—*Portraits of Places* (Boston, [1883] 1884) —has "Folkestone" here; obviously it should be "Boulogne." [*Editor's note.*]

individual, as an individual, loses by all that the administration assumes.

After living a while in England you observe the individual in Paris with quickened attention; and I think it must be said that at first he makes an indifferent figure. You are struck with the race being physically and personally a poorer one than that great family of largely-modelled, fresh-coloured people you have left upon the other side of the channel. I remember that in going to England a year ago and disembarking of a dismal, sleety Sunday evening at Folkestone, the first thing that struck me was the good looks of the railway porters —their broad shoulders, their big brown beards, their well-cut features. In like manner, landing lately at Boulogne of a brilliant Sunday morning, it was impossible not to think the little men in numbered caps who were gesticulating and chattering in one's path, rather ugly fellows. In arriving from other countries one is struck with a certain want of dignity in the French face. I do not know, however, whether this is anything worse than the fact that the French face is expressive; for it may be said that, in a certain sense, to express anything is to compromise with one's dignity, which likes to be understood without taking trouble. As regards the lower classes, at any rate, the impression I speak of always passes away; you perceive that the good looks of the French working-people are to be found in their look of intelligence. These people, in Paris, strike me afresh as the cleverest, the most perceptive, and intellectually speaking, the most human of their kind. The Paris *ouvrier*, with his democratic blouse, his expressive, demonstrative, agreeable eye, his meagre limbs, his irregular, pointed features, his sallow complexion, his face at once fatigued and animated, his light, nervous organisation, is a figure that I always encounter again with pleasure. In some cases he looks depraved and perverted, but at his worst he looks refined; he is full of vivacity of perception, of something that one can appeal to.

It takes some courage to say this, perhaps, after reading *L'Assommoir;* but in M. Émile Zola's extraordinary novel one must make the part, as the French say, of the horrible uncleanness of the author's imagination. *L'Assommoir,* I have been told, has had great success in the lower walks of Parisian life; and if this fact is not creditable to the delicacy of M. Zola's humble readers, it proves a good deal in favour of their intelligence. With all its grossness the book in question is essentially a literary performance; you must be tolerably clever to appreciate it. It is highly appreciated, I believe, by the young ladies who live in the region of the Latin Quarter—those young ladies who thirty years ago were called grisettes, and now are called I don't know what. They know long passages by heart; they repeat them with infinite gusto. "Ce louchon d'Augustine"—the horrible little girl with a squint, who is always playing nasty tricks and dodging slaps and projectiles in Gervaise's shop, is their particular favourite; and it must be admitted that "ce louchon d'Augustine" is, as regards reality, a wonderful creation.

If Parisians, both small and great, have more of the intellectual stamp than the people one sees in London, it is striking, on the other hand, that the people of the better sort in Paris look very much less "respectable." I did not know till I came back to Paris how used I had grown to the English *cachet;* but I immediately found myself missing it. You miss it in the men much more than in the women; for the well-to-do Frenchwoman of the lower orders, as one sees her in public, in the streets and in shops, is always a delightfully comfortable and creditable person. I must confess to the highest admiration for her, an admiration that increases with acquaintance. She, at least, is essentially respectable; the neatness, compactness, and sobriety of her dress, the decision of her movement and accent suggest the civic and domestic virtues—order, thrift, frugality, the moral necessity of making a good appearance. It is, I think, an old story that to the stranger in France the women seem greatly superior to the men. Their superiority, in fact, appears to be conceded; for wherever you turn you meet them in the forefront of action. You meet them, indeed, too often; you pronounce them at times obtrusive. It is annoying when you go to order your boots or your shirts, to have to make known your desires to even the most neat-waisted female attendant; for the limitations to the feminine intellect are, though few in number, distinct, and women are not able to understand certain masculine needs. Mr. Worth makes ladies' dresses; but I am sure there will never be a fashionable tailoress. There are, however, points at which, from the commercial point of view, feminine assistance is invaluable. For insisting upon the merits of an article that has failed to satisfy you, talking you over, and making you take it; for defending a disputed bill, for paying the necessary compliments or supplying the necessary impertinence— for all these things the neat-waisted sex has peculiar and precious faculties. In the commercial class in Paris the man always appeals to the woman; the woman always steps forward. The woman always proposes the conditions of a bargain. Go about and look for furnished rooms, you always encounter a concierge and his wife. When you ask the price of the rooms, the woman takes the words out of her husband's mouth, if indeed he have not first turned to her with a questioning look. She takes you in hand; she proposes conditions; she thinks of things he would not have thought of.

What I meant just now by my allusion to the absence of the "respectable" in the appearance of the Parisian population was that the men do not look like gentlemen, as so many Englishmen do. The average Frenchman that one encounters in public is of so different a type from the average Englishman that you can easily believe that to the end of time the two will not understand each other. The Frenchman has always, comparatively speaking, a Bohemian, empirical look; the expression of his face, its colouring, its movement, have not been toned down to the neutral complexion of that breeding for which in English speech we reserve the epithet of "good." He is at once more artificial and more natural; the former where the Englishman is positive, the latter where the Englishman is negative. He takes off his hat with a flourish to a friend, but the Englishman never bows. He ties a knot in the end of a napkin and thrusts it into his shirt-collar, so that, as he sits at breakfast, the napkin may serve the office of a pinafore. Such an operation as that seems to the Englishman as *naïf* as the flourishing of one's hat is pretentious.

I sometimes go to breakfast at a café on the Boulevard, which I formerly used to frequent with considerable regularity. Coming back there the other day, I found exactly the same group of habitués at their little tables, and I mentally exclaimed as I looked at them over my newspaper, upon their unlikeness to the gentlemen who confront you in the same attitude at a London club. Who are they? what are they? On these points I have no information; but the stranger's imagination does not seem to see a majestic social order massing itself behind them as it usually does in London. He goes so far as to suspect that what is behind them is not adapted for exhibition; whereas your Englishmen, whatever may be the defects of their personal character, or the irregularities of their conduct, are pressed upon from the rear by an immense body of private proprieties and comforts, of domestic conventions and theological observances. But it is agreeable all the same to come back to a café of which you have formerly been an habitué. Adolphe or Édouard, in his long white apron and his large patent-leather slippers, has a perfect recollection of "les habitudes de Monsieur." He remembers the table you preferred, the wine you drank, the newspaper you read. He greets you with the friendliest of smiles, and remarks that it is a long time since he has had the pleasure of seeing Monsieur. There is something in this simple remark very touching to a heart that has suffered from that incorruptible dumbness of the British domestic. But in Paris such a heart finds consolation at every step; it is reminded of that most classic quality of the French nature—its sociability; a sociability which operates here as it never does in England, from below upward. Your waiter utters a greeting because, after all, something human within him prompts him; his instinct bids him say something, and his taste recommends that it be agreeable. The obvious reflection is that a waiter must not say too much, even for the sake of being human. But in France the people always like to make the little extra remark, to throw in something above the simple necessary. I stop before a little man who is selling newspapers at a street-corner, and ask him for the *Journal des Débats*. His answer deserves to be literally given: "Je ne l'ai plus, Monsieur; mais je pourrai vous donner quelquechose à peu près dans le même genre—la *République Française*." Even a person of his humble condition must have had a lurking sense of the

comicality of offering anything as an equivalent for the
"genre" of the venerable, classic, academic *Débats*. But
my friend could not bear to give me a naked, mono-
syllabic refusal.

There are two things that the returning observer is
likely to do with as little delay as possible. One is to dine
at some *cabaret* of which he retains a friendly memory;
another is to betake himself to the Théâtre Français. It
is early in the season; there are no new pieces; but I
have taken great pleasure in seeing some of the old
ones. I lost no time in going to see Mademoiselle Sarah
Bernhardt in *Andromaque*. *Andromaque* is not a novelty, but Mademoiselle Sarah Bernhardt has a perennial
freshness. The play has been revived, to enable her to
represent not the great part, the injured and passionate
Hermione, but that of the doleful funereal widow of
Hector. This part is a poor one; it is narrow and monot-
onous, and offers few brilliant opportunities. But the
actress knows how to make opportunities, and she has
here a very sufficient one for crossing her thin white
arms over her nebulous black robes, and sighing forth
in silver accents her dolorous rhymes. Her rendering of
the part is one more proof of her singular intelligence—
of the fineness of her artistic nature. As there is not a
great deal to be done with it in the way of declamation,
she has made the most of its plastic side. She understands the art of motion and attitude as no one else
does, and her extraordinary personal grace never fails
her. Her Andromaque has postures of the most poetic
picturesqueness—something that suggests the broken
stem and drooping head of a flower that had been rudely
plucked. She bends over her classic confidant like the
figure of Bereavement on a bas-relief, and she has a
marvellous manner of lifting and throwing back her

delicate arms, locking them together, and passing them behind her hanging head.

The *Demi-Monde* of M. Dumas *fils* is not a novelty either; but I quite agree with M. Francisque Sarcey that it is on the whole, in form, the first comedy of our day. I have seen it several times, but I never see it without being forcibly struck with its merits. For the drama of our time it must always remain the model. The interest of the story, the quiet art with which it is unfolded, the naturalness and soberness of the means that are used, and by which great effects are produced, the brilliancy and richness of the dialogue—all these things make it a singularly perfect and interesting work. Of course it is admirably well played at the Théâtre Français. Madame d'Ange was originally a part of too great amplitude for Mademoiselle Croizette; but she is gradually filling it out and taking possession of it; she begins to give a sense of the "calme infernal," which George Sand somewhere mentions as the leading attribute of the character. As for Delaunay, he does nothing better, more vividly and gallantly, than Olivier de Jalin. When I say gallantry I say it with qualification; for what a very queer fellow is this M. de Jalin! In seeing the *Demi-Monde* again I was more than ever struck with the oddity of its morality and with the way that the ideal of fine conduct differs in different nations. The *Demi-Monde* is the history of the eager, the almost heroic, effort of a clever and superior woman, who has been guilty of what the French call "faults," to pass from the irregular and equivocal circle to which these faults have consigned her into what is distinctively termed "good society." The only way in which the passage can be effected is by her marrying an honourable man; and to induce an honourable man to marry her, she must suppress the more discreditable facts of her career. Taking her for an honest woman, Raymond de Nanjac falls in love with her, and honestly proposes to make her his wife. But Raymond de Nanjac has contracted an intimate friendship with Olivier de Jalin, and the action of the play is more especially De Jalin's attempt—a successful one—to rescue his friend from the ignominy of a union with Suzanne d'Ange. Jalin knows a great deal about her, for the simple reason that he has been her lover. Their relations have been most harmonious, but from the moment that Suzanne sets her cap at Nanjac, Olivier declares war. Suzanne struggles hard to keep possession of her suitor, who is very much in love with her, and Olivier spares no pains to detach him. It is the means that Olivier uses that excite the wonderment of the Anglo-Saxon spectator. He takes the ground that in such a cause all means are fair, and when, at the climax of the play, he tells a thumping lie in order to make Madame d'Ange compromise herself, expose herself, he is pronounced by the author "le plus honnête homme que je connaisse." Madame d'Ange, as I have said, is a superior woman; the interest of the play is in her being a superior woman. Olivier has been her lover; he himself is one of the reasons why she may not marry Nanjac; he has given her a push along the downward path. But it is curious how little this is held by the author to disqualify him from fighting the battle in which she is so much the weaker combatant. An English-speaking audience is more "moral" than a French, more easily scandalised; and yet it is a singular fact that if the *Demi-Monde* were represented before an English-speaking audience, its sympathies would certainly not go with M. de Jalin. It would pronounce him rather a coward. Is it because such an audience, although it has not nearly such a pretty collection of pedestals to place under the feet of the charming sex, has, after all, in default of this degree of gallantry, a tenderness more fundamental? Madame d'Ange has stained herself, and it is doubtless not at all proper that such ladies should be led to the altar by honourable young men. The point is not that the English-speaking audience would be disposed to condone Madame d'Ange's irregularities, but that it would remain perfectly cold before the spectacle of her ex-lover's masterly campaign against her, and quite fail to think it positively admirable, or to regard the fib by which he finally clinches his victory as a proof of exceptional honesty. The ideal of our own audience would be expressed in some such words as, "I say, that's not fair game. Can't you let the poor woman alone?"

1877 (so dated by James). From *Portraits of Places* (1883).

LONDON

I

There is a certain evening that I count as virtually a first impression,—the end of a wet, black Sunday, twenty years ago, about the first of March. There had been an earlier vision, but it had turned to grey, like faded ink, and the occasion I speak of was a fresh beginning. No doubt I had mystic prescience of how fond of the murky modern Babylon I was one day to become; certain it is that as I look back I find every small circumstance of those hours of approach and arrival still as vivid as if the solemnity of an opening era had breathed upon it. The sense of approach was already almost intolerably strong at Liverpool, where, as I remember, the perception of the English character of everything was as acute as a surprise, though it could only be a surprise without a shock. It was expectation exquisitely gratified, super-abundantly confirmed. There was a kind of wonder indeed that England should be as English as, for my entertainment, she took the trouble to be; but the wonder would have been greater, and all the pleasure absent, if the sensation had not been violent. It seems to sit there again like a visiting presence, as it sat opposite to me at breakfast at a small table in a window of the old coffee-room of the Adelphi Hotel—the unextended (as it then was), the unimproved, the unblushingly local Adelphi. Liverpool is not a romantic city, but that smoky Saturday returns to me as a supreme success, measured by its association with the kind of emotion in the hope of which, for the most part, we betake ourselves to far countries.

It assumed this character at an early hour—or rather, indeed, twenty-four hours before—with the sight, as one looked across the wintry ocean, of the strange, dark, lonely freshness of the coast of Ireland. Better still, before we could come up to the city, were the black steamers knocking about in the yellow Mersey, under a sky so low that they seemed to touch it with their funnels, and in the thickest, windiest light. Spring was already in the air, in the town; there was no rain, but there was still less sun—one wondered what had become, on this side of the world, of the big white splotch in the heavens; and the grey mildness, shading away into black at every pretext, appeared in itself a promise. This was how it hung about me, between the window and the fire, in the coffee-room of the hotel—late in the morning for breakfast, as we had been long disembarking. The other passengers had dispersed, knowingly catching trains for London (we had only been a handful); I had the place to myself, and I felt as if I had an exclusive property in the impression. I prolonged it, I sacrificed to it, and it is perfectly recoverable now, with the very taste of the national muffin, the creak of the waiter's shoes as he came and went (could anything be so English as his intensely professional back? it revealed a country of tradition), and the rustle of the newspaper I was too excited to read.

I continued to sacrifice for the rest of the day; it didn't seem to me a sentient thing, as yet, to enquire into the means of getting away. My curiosity must indeed have languished, for I found myself on the morrow in the slowest of Sunday trains, pottering up to London with an interruptedness which might have been tedious without the conversation of an old gentleman who shared the carriage with me and to whom my alien as well as comparatively youthful character had betrayed itself. He instructed me as to the sights of London and impressed upon me that nothing was more worthy of my attention than the great cathedral of St. Paul. "Have you seen St. Peter's in Rome? St. Peter's is more highly embellished, you know; but you may depend upon it that St. Paul's is the better building of the two." The impression I began with speaking of was, strictly, that of the drive from Euston, after dark, to Morley's Hotel in Trafalgar Square. It was not lovely—it was in fact rather horrible; but as I move again through dusky, tortuous miles, in the greasy four-wheeler to which my luggage had compelled me to commit myself, I recognise the first step in an initiation of which the subsequent stages were to abound in pleasant things. It is a kind of humiliation in a great city not to know where you are going, and Morley's Hotel was then, to my

imagination, only a vague ruddy spot in the general immensity. The immensity was the great fact, and that
was a charm; the miles of housetops and viaducts, the
complication of junctions and signals through which the
train made its way to the station had already given me
the scale. The weather had turned to wet, and we went
deeper and deeper into the Sunday night. The sheep
in the fields, on the way from Liverpool, had shown in
their demeanour a certain consciousness of the day; but
this momentous cab-drive was an introduction to the
rigidities of custom. The low black houses were as inanimate as so many rows of coal-scuttles, save where at
frequent corners, from a gin-shop, there was a flare of
light more brutal still than the darkness. The custom of
gin—that was equally rigid, and in this first impression
the public-houses counted for much.

Morley's Hotel proved indeed to be a ruddy spot;
brilliant, in my recollection, is the coffee-room fire, the
hospitable mohogany, the sense that in the stupendous
city this, at any rate for the hour, was a shelter and a
point of view. My remembrance of the rest of the evening—I was probably very tired—is mainly a remembrance of a vast four-poster. My little bedroom-candle,
set in its deep basin, caused this monument to project
a huge shadow and to make me think, I scarce knew
why, of *The Ingoldsby Legends*. If at a tolerably early
hour the next day I found myself approaching St. Paul's,
it was not wholly in obedience to the old gentleman in
the railway-carriage: I had an errand in the City, and
the City was doubtless prodigious. But what I mainly
recall is the romantic consciousness of passing under the
Temple Bar, and the way two lines of *Henry Esmond*
repeated themselves in my mind as I drew near the
masterpiece of Sir Christopher Wren. "The stout, red-

faced woman" whom Esmond had seen tearing after the stag-hounds over the slopes at Windsor was not a bit like the effigy "which turns its stony back upon St. Paul's and faces the coaches struggling up Ludgate Hill." As I looked at Queen Anne over the apron of my hansom— she struck me as very small and dirty, and the vehicle ascended the mild incline without an effort—it was a thrilling thought that the statue had been familiar to the hero of the incomparable novel. All history appeared to live again, and the continuity of things to vibrate through my mind.

To this hour, as I pass along the Strand, I take again the walk I took there that afternoon. I love the place to-day, and that was the commencement of my passion. It appeared to me to present phenomena, and to contain objects of every kind, of an inexhaustible interest; in particular it struck me as desirable and even indispensable that I should purchase most of the articles in most of the shops. My eyes rest with a certain tenderness on the places where I resisted and on those where I succumbed. The fragrance of Mr. Rimmel's establishment is again in my nostrils; I see the slim young lady (I hear her pronunciation) who waited upon me there. Sacred to me to-day is the particular aroma of the hair-wash that I bought of her. I pause before the granite portico of Exeter Hall (it was unexpectedly narrow and wedge-like), and it evokes a cloud of associations which are none the less impressive because they are vague; coming from I don't know where—from *Punch*, from Thackeray, from volumes of the *Illustrated London News* turned over in childhood; seeming connected with Mrs. Beecher Stowe and *Uncle Tom's Cabin*. Memorable is a rush I made into a glover's at Charing Cross —the one you pass, going eastward, just before you turn into the station; that, however, now that I think of it, must have been in the morning, as soon as I issued from the hotel. Keen within me was a sense of the importance of deflowering, of despoiling the shop.

A day or two later, in the afternoon, I found myself staring at my fire, in a lodging of which I had taken possession on foreseeing that I should spend some weeks in London. I had just come in, and, having attended to the distribution of my luggage, sat down to consider my habitation. It was on the ground floor, and the fading daylight reached it in a sadly damaged condition. It struck me as stuffy and unsocial, with its mouldy smell and its decoration of lithographs and wax-flowers—an impersonal black hole in the huge general blackness. The uproar of Piccadilly hummed away at the end of the street, and the rattle of a heartless hansom passed close to my ears. A sudden horror of the whole place came over me, like a tiger-pounce of homesickness which had been watching its moment. London was hideous, vicious, cruel, and above all overwhelming; whether or no she was "careful of the type," she was as indifferent as Nature herself to the single life. In the course of an hour I should have to go out to my dinner, which was not supplied on the premises, and that effort assumed the form of a desperate and dangerous quest. It appeared to me that I would rather remain dinnerless, would rather even starve, than sally forth into the infernal town, where the natural fate of an obscure stranger would be to be trampled to death in Piccadilly and have his carcass thrown into the Thames. I did not starve, however, and I eventually attached myself by a hundred human links to the dreadful, delightful city. That momentary vision of its smeared face and stony heart has remained memorable to me, but I am happy to say that I can easily summon up others.

II

It is, no doubt, not the taste of every one, but for the real London-lover the mere immensity of the place is a large part of its savour. A small London would be an abomination, as it fortunately is an impossibility, for the idea and the name are beyond everything an expression of extent and number. Practically, of course, one lives in a quarter, in a plot; but in imagination and by a constant mental act of reference the accommodated haunter enjoys the whole—and it is only of him that I deem it worth while to speak. He fancies himself, as they say, for being a particle in so unequalled an aggregation; and its immeasurable circumference, even though unvisited and lost in smoke, gives him the sense of a social, an intellectual margin. There is a luxury in the knowledge that he may come and go without being noticed, even when his comings and goings have no nefarious end. I don't mean by this that the tongue of London is not a very active member; the tongue of London would indeed be worthy of a chapter by itself. But the eyes which at least in some measure feed its activity are fortunately for the common advantage solicited at any moment by a thousand different objects. If the place is big, everything it contains is certainly not so; but this may at least be said—that if small questions play a part there, they play it without illusions about its importance. There are too many questions, small or great; and each day, as it arrives, leads its children, like a kind of mendicant mother, by the hand. Therefore perhaps the most general characteristic is the absence of insistence. Habits and inclinations flourish and fall, but intensity is never one of them. The spirit of the great city is not analytic, and, as they come up, subjects rarely receive at its hands a treatment drearily earnest or tastelessly thorough. There are not many—of those of which London disposes with the assurance begotten of its large experience—that wouldn't lend themselves to a tenderer manipulation elsewhere. It takes a very great affair, a turn of the Irish screw or a divorce case lasting many days, to be fully threshed out. The mind of Mayfair, when it aspires to show what it really can do, lives in the hope of a new divorce case, and an indulgent providence—London is positively in certain ways the spoiled child of the world—abundantly recognises this particular aptitude and humours the whim.

The compensation is that material does arise; that there is a great variety, if not morbid subtlety; and that the whole of the procession of events and topics passes across your stage. For the moment I am speaking of the inspiration there may be in the sense of far frontiers; the London-lover loses himself in this swelling consciousness, delights in the idea that the town which encloses him is after all only a paved country, a state by itself. This is his condition of mind quite as much if he be an adoptive as if he be a matter-of-course son. I am by no means sure even that he need be of Anglo-Saxon race and have inherited the birthright of English speech; though, on the other hand, I make no doubt that these advantages minister greatly to closeness of allegiance. The great city spreads her dusky mantle over innumerable races and creeds, and I believe there is scarcely a known form of worship that has not some temple there (have I not attended at the Church of Humanity, in Lamb's Conduit, in company with an American lady, a vague old gentleman, and several seamstresses?) or any communion of men that has not some club or guild. London is indeed an epitome of the round world, and just as it is a commonplace to say that there is nothing one can't "get" there, so it is equally true that there is nothing one may not study at first hand.

One doesn't test these truths every day, but they form part of the air one breathes (and welcome, says the London-hater,—for there be such perverse reasoners,—to the pestilent compound). They colour the thick, dim distances which in my opinion are the most romantic town-vistas in the world; they mingle with the troubled light to which the straight, ungarnished aperture in one's dull, undistinctive house-front affords a passage and which makes an interior of friendly corners, mysterious tones, and unbetrayed ingenuities, as well as with the low, magnificent medium of the sky, where the smoke and fog and the weather in general, the strangely undefined hour of the day and season of the year, the emanations of industries and the reflection of furnaces, the red gleams and blurs that may or may not be of sunset—as you never see any *source* of radiance, you can't in the least tell—all hang together in a confusion, a complication, a shifting but irremoveable canopy. They form the undertone of the deep, perpetual voice of the place. One remembers them when one's loyalty is on the defensive; when it is a question of introducing as many striking features as possible into the list of fine reasons one has sometimes to draw up, that eloquent catalogue with which one confronts the hostile indictment—the array of *other* reasons which may easily be as long as one's arm. According to these other reasons it plausibly and conclusively stands that, as a place to be happy in, London will never do. I don't say it is necessary to meet so absurd an allegation except for one's personal complacency. If indifference, in so gorged an organism, is still livelier than curiosity, you may avail yourself of your own share in it simply to feel that since such and such a person doesn't care for real richness, so much the worse for such and such a person. But once in a while the best believer recognises the impulse to set his religion in order, to sweep the temple of his thoughts and trim the sacred lamp. It is at such hours as this that he reflects with elation that the British capital is the particular spot in the world which communicates the greatest sense of life.

III

The reader will perceive that I do not shrink even from the extreme concession of speaking of our capital as British, and this in a shameless connection with the question of loyalty on the part of an adoptive son. For I hasten to explain that if half the source of one's interest in it comes from feeling that it is the property and even the home of the human race,—Hawthorne, that best of Americans, says so somewhere, and places it in this sense side by side with Rome,—one's appreciation of it is really a large sympathy, a comprehensive love of humanity. For the sake of such a charity as this one may stretch one's allegiance; and the most alien of the cockneyfied, though he may bristle with every protest at the intimation that England has set its stamp upon him, is free to admit with conscious pride that he has submitted to Londonisation. It is a real stroke of luck for a particular country that the capital of the human race happens to be British. Surely every other people would have it theirs if they could. Whether the English deserve to hold it any longer might be an interesting field of enquiry; but as they have not yet let it slip, the writer of these lines professes without scruple that the arrangement is to his personal taste. For, after all, if the sense of life is greatest there, it is a sense of the life of people of our consecrated English speech. It is the headquarters of that strangely elastic tongue; and I make this remark with a full sense of the terrible way in which the idiom is misused by the populace in general, than whom it has been given to few races to impart to conversation less of the charm of tone. For a man of letters who endeavours to cultivate, however modestly, the medium of Shakespeare and Milton, of Hawthorne and Emerson, who cherishes the notion of what it has achieved and what it may even yet achieve, London must ever have a great illustrative and suggestive value, and indeed a kind of sanctity. It is the single place in which most readers, most possible lovers, are gathered together; it is the most inclusive public and the largest social incarnation of the language, of the tradition. Such a personage may well let it go for this, and leave the German and the Greek to speak for themselves, to express the grounds of *their* predilection, presumably very different.

When a social product is so vast and various, it may be approached on a thousand different sides, and liked and disliked for a thousand different reasons. The reasons of Piccadilly are not those of Camden Town, nor are the curiosities and discouragements of Kilburn the same as those of Westminster and Lambeth. The reasons of Piccadilly—I mean the friendly ones—are those of which, as a general thing, the rooted visitor remains most conscious; but it must be confessed that even these, for the most part, do not lie upon the surface. The absence of style, or rather of the intention of style, is certainly the most general characteristic of the face of London. To cross to Paris under this impression is to find one's self surrounded with far other standards. There everything reminds you that the idea of beautiful and stately arrangement has never been out of fashion, that the art of composition has always been at work or at play. Avenues and squares, gardens and quays, have been distributed for effect, and to-day the splendid city reaps the accumulation of all this ingenuity. The result is not in every quarter interesting, and there is a tiresome monotony of the "fine" and the symmetrical, above all, of the deathly passion for making things "to match." On the other hand the whole air of the place is architectural. On the banks of the Thames it is a tremendous chapter of accidents—the London-lover has to confess to the existence of miles upon miles of the dreariest, stodgiest commonness. Thousands of acres are covered by low black houses of the cheapest construction, without ornament, without grace, without character or even identity. In fact there are many, even in the best quarters, in all the region of Mayfair and Belgravia, of so paltry and inconvenient, especially of so diminutive a type (those that are let in lodgings— such poor lodgings as they make—may serve as an example), that you wonder what peculiarly limited domestic need they were constructed to meet. The great misfortune of London to the eye (it is true that this remark applies much less to the City), is the want of elevation. There is no architectural impression without a certain degree of height, and the London street-vista has none of that sort of pride.

All the same, if there be not the intention, there is at least the accident, of style, which, if one looks at it in a friendly way, appears to proceed from three sources. One of these is simply the general greatness, and the manner in which that makes a difference for the better in any particular spot; so that, though you may often perceive yourself to be in a shabby corner, it never occurs to you that this is the end of it. Another is the atmosphere, with its magnificent mystifications, which flatters and superfuses, makes everything brown, rich, dim, vague, magnifies distances and minimises details, confirms the inference of vastness by suggesting that, as the great city makes everything, it makes its own system of weather and its own optical laws. The last is the congregation of the parks, which constitute an ornament not esewhere to be matched, and give the place a superiority that none of its uglinesses overcome. They spread themselves with such a luxury of space in the centre of the town that they form a part of the impression of any walk, of almost any view, and, with an audacity altogether their own, make a pastoral landscape under the smoky sky. There is no mood of the rich London climate that is not becoming to them—I have seen them look delightfully romantic, like parks in novels, in the wettest winter—and there is scarcely a mood of the appreciative resident to which they have not something to say. The high things of London, which here and there peep over them, only make the spaces vaster by reminding you that you are, after all, not in Kent or Yorkshire; and these things, whatever they be—rows of "eligible" dwellings, towers of churches, domes of institutions—take such an effective grey-blue tint that a clever water-colourist would seem to have put them in for pictorial reasons.

The view from the bridge over the Serpentine has an extraordinary nobleness, and it has often seemed to me that the Londoner, twitted with his low standard, may point to it with every confidence. In all the town-scenery of Europe there can be few things so fine; the only reproach it is open to is that it begs the question by seeming—in spite of its being the pride of five millions of people—not to belong to a town at all. The towers of Notre Dame, as they rise in Paris from the island that divides the Seine, present themselves no more impressively than those of Westminster as you see them looking doubly far beyond the shining stretch of Hyde Park water. Equally delectable is the large river-like manner in which the Serpentine opens away between its wooded shores. Just after you have crossed the bridge (whose very banisters, old and ornamental, of yellowish-brown stone, I am particularly fond of), you enjoy on your left, through the gate of Kensington Gardens as you go towards Bayswater, an altogether enchanting vista—a foot-path over the grass, which loses itself beneath the scattered oaks and elms exactly as if the place were a "chase." There could be nothing less like London in general than this particular morsel, and yet it takes London, of all cities, to give you such an impression of the country.

IV

It takes London to put you in the way of a purely rustic walk from Notting Hill to Whitehall. You may traverse this immense distance—a most comprehensive diagonal —altogether on soft, fine turf, amid the song of birds, the bleat of lambs, the ripple of ponds, the rustle of admirable trees. Frequently have I wished that, for the sake of such a daily luxury and of exercise made romantic, I were a Government clerk living, in snug domestic conditions, in a Pembridge villa,—let me suppose,—and having my matutinal desk in Westminster. I should turn into Kensington Gardens at their northwest limit, and I should have my choice of a hundred pleasant paths to the gates of Hyde Park. In Hyde Park I should follow the water-side, or the Row, or any other fancy of the occasion; liking best, perhaps, after all, the Row in its morning mood, with the mist hanging over the dark-red course, and the scattered early riders taking an identity as the soundless gallop brings them nearer. I am free to admit that in the Season, at the conventional hours, the Row becomes a weariness (save perhaps just for a glimpse once a year, to remind one's self how much it is like Du Maurier); the preoccupied citizen eschews it and leaves it for the most part to the gaping barbarian. I speak of it now from the point of view of the pedestrian; but for the rider as well it is at its best when he passes either too early or too late. Then, if he be not bent on comparing it to its disadvantage with the bluer and boskier alleys of the Bois de Boulogne, it will not be spoiled by the fact that, with its surface that looks like tan, its barriers like those of the ring on which the clown stands to hold up the hoop to the young lady, its empty benches and chairs, its occasional orange-peel, its mounted policemen patrolling at intervals like expectant supernumeraries, it offers points of real contact with a circus whose lamps are out. The sky that bends over it is frequently not a bad imitation of the dingy tent of such an establishment. The ghosts of past cavalcades seem to haunt the foggy arena, and somehow they are better company than the mashers and elongated beauties of current seasons. It is not without interest to remember that most of the salient figures of English society during the present century—and English society means, or rather has hitherto meant, in a large degree, English history—have bobbed in the saddle between Apsley House and Queen's Gate. You may call the roll if you care to, and the air will be thick with dumb voices and dead names, like that of some Roman amphitheatre.

It is doubtless a signal proof of being a London-lover *quand même* that one should undertake an apology for so bungled an attempt at a great public place as Hyde Park Corner. It is certain that the improvements and embellishments recently enacted there have only served to call further attention to the poverty of the elements

and to the fact that this poverty is terribly illustrative
of general conditions. The place is the beating heart of
the great West End, yet its main features are a shabby,
stuccoed hospital, the low park-gates, in their neat but
unimposing frame, the drawing-room windows of Apsley
House and of the commonplace frontages on the little
terrace beside it; to which must be added, of course, the
only item in the whole prospect that is in the least
monumental—the arch spanning the private road beside
the gardens of Buckingham Palace. This structure is
now bereaved of the rueful effigy which used to sur-
mount it—the Iron Duke in the guise of a tin soldier—
and has not been enriched by the transaction as much
as might have been expected.[1] There is a fine view
of Piccadilly and Knightsbridge, and of the noble mansions, as the house-agents call them, of Grosvenor Place,
together with a sense of generous space beyond the
vulgar little railing of the Green Park; but, except for
the impression that there would be room for something
better, there is nothing in all this that speaks to the
imagination: almost as much as the grimy desert of
Trafalgar Square the prospect conveys the idea of an
opportunity wasted.

None the less has it on a fine day in spring an expres-
siveness of which I shall not pretend to explain the
source further than by saying that the flood of life and
luxury is immeasurably great there. The edifices are
mean, but the social stream itself is monumental, and to
an observer not purely stolid there is more excitement
and suggestion than I can give a reason for in the long,
distributed waves of traffic, with the steady policemen
marking their rhythm, which roll together and apart for

[1] The monument in the middle of the square, with Sir
Edgar Boehm's four fine soldiers, had not been set up when
these words were written. [*James's note.*]

so many hours. Then the great, dim city becomes bright and kind, the pall of smoke turns into a veil of haze carelessly worn, the air is coloured and almost scented by the presence of the biggest society in the world, and most of the things that meet the eye—or perhaps I should say more of them, for the most in London is, no doubt, ever the realm of the dingy—present themselves as "well appointed." Everything shines more or less, from the window-panes to the dog-collars. So it all looks, with its myriad variations and qualifications, to one who surveys it over the apron of a hansom, while that vehicle of vantage, better than any box at the opera, spurts and slackens with the current.

It is not in a hansom, however, that we have figured our punctual young man, whom we must not desert as he fares to the southeast, and who has only to cross Hyde Park Corner to find his way all grassy again. I have a weakness for the convenient, familiar, treeless, or almost treeless, expanse of the Green Park and the friendly part it plays as a kind of encouragement to Piccadilly. I am so fond of Piccadilly that I am grateful to any one or anything that does it a service, and nothing is more worthy of appreciation than the southward look it is permitted to enjoy just after it passes Devonshire House—a sweep of horizon which it would be difficult to match among other haunts of men, and thanks to which, of a summer's day, you may spy, beyond the browsed pastures of the foreground and middle distance, beyond the cold chimneys of Buckingham Palace and the towers of Westminster and the swarming river-side and all the southern parishes, the hard modern twinkle of the roof of the Crystal Palace.

If the Green Park is familiar, there is still less of the exclusive in its pendant, as one may call it,—for it literally hangs from the other, down the hill,—the remnant of the former garden of the queer, shabby old palace whose black, inelegant face stares up St. James's Street. This popular resort has a great deal of character, but I am free to confess that much of its character comes from its nearness to the Westminster slums. It is a park of intimacy, and perhaps the most democratic corner of London, in spite of its being in the royal and military quarter and close to all kinds of stateliness. There are few hours of the day when a thousand smutty children are not sprawling over it, and the unemployed lie thick on the grass and cover the benches with a brotherhood of greasy corduroys. If the London parks are the drawing-rooms and clubs of the poor, —that is of those poor (I admit it cuts down the number) who live near enough to them to reach them,— these particular grass-plots and alleys may be said to constitute the very *salon* of the slums.

I know not why, being such a region of greatness,— great towers, great names, great memories; at the foot of the Abbey, the Parliament, the fine fragment of Whitehall, with the quarters of the sovereign right and left,—but the edge of Westminster evokes as many associations of misery as of empire. The neighbourhood has been much purified of late, but it still contains a collection of specimens—though it is far from unique in this—of the low, black element. The air always seems to me heavy and thick, and here more than elsewhere one hears old England—the panting, smoke-stained Titan of Matthew Arnold's fine poem—draw her deep breath with effort. In fact one is nearer to her heroic lungs, if those organs are figured by the great pinnacled and fretted talking-house on the edge of the river. But this same dense and conscious air plays such everlasting tricks to the eye that the Foreign Office, as you see it from the bridge, often looks romantic, and the sheet of water it overhangs poetic—suggests an Indian palace bathing its feet in the Ganges. If our pedestrian achieves such a comparison as this he has nothing left but to go on to his work—which he will find close at hand. He will have come the whole way from the far northwest on the green—which is what was to be demonstrated.

v

I feel as if I were taking a tone almost of boastfulness, and no doubt the best way to consider the matter is simply to say—without going into the treachery of reasons—that, for one's self, one likes this part or the other. Yet this course would not be unattended with danger, inasmuch as at the end of a few such professions we might find ourselves committed to a tolerance of much that is deplorable. London is so clumsy and so brutal, and has gathered together so many of the darkest sides of life, that it is almost ridiculous to talk of her as a lover talks of his mistress, and almost frivolous to appear to ignore her disfigurements and cruelties. She is like a mighty ogress who devours human flesh; but to me it is a mitigating circumstance—though it may not seem so to every one—that the ogress herself is human. It is not in wantonness that she fills her maw, but to keep herself alive and do her tremendous work. She has no time for fine discriminations, but after all she is as good-natured as she is huge, and the more you stand up to her, as the phrase is, the better she takes the joke of it. It is mainly when you fall on your face before her that she gobbles you up. She heeds little what she takes, so long as she has her stint, and the smallest push to the right or the left will divert her wavering bulk from one form of prey to another. It is not to be denied that the heart tends to grow hard in her company; but she is a capital antidote to the morbid, and to live with her successfully is an education of the temper, a consecration of one's private philosophy. She gives one a surface for which in a rough world one can never be too thankful. She may take away reputations, but she forms character. She teaches her victims not to "mind," and the great danger for them is perhaps that they shall learn the lesson too well. . . .

From "London" (1888) in *Essays in London and Elsewhere* (1893) and, as here printed, in *English Hours* (1905).

*

NEW YORK REVISITED

The single impression or particular vision most answering to the greatness of the subject would have been, I think, a certain hour of large circumnavigation that I found prescribed, in the fulness of the spring, as the almost immediate crown of a return from the Far West.[1] I had arrived at one of the transpontine stations of the Pennsylvania Railroad; the question was of proceeding to Boston, for the occasion, without pushing through the terrible town—why "terrible," to my sense, in many ways, I shall presently explain—and the easy and agreeable attainment of this great advantage was to embark on one of the mightiest (as appeared to me) of train-bearing barges and, descending the western waters, pass round the bottom of the city and remount the other current to Harlem; all without "losing touch" of the

[1] James is writing here of his travels during his return visit to the United States in 1904-1905. [*Editor's note.*]

Pullman that had brought me from Washington. This absence of the need of losing touch, this breadth of effect, as to the whole process, involved in the prompt floating of the huge concatenated cars not only without arrest or confusion, but as for positive prodigal beguilement of the artless traveller, had doubtless much to say to the ensuing state of mind, the happily-excited and amused view of the great face of New York. The extent, the ease, the energy, the quantity and number, all notes scattered about as if, in the whole business and in the splendid light, nature and science were joyously romping together, might have been taking on again, for their symbol, some collective presence of great circling and plunging, hovering and perching seabirds, white-winged images of the spirit, of the restless freedom of the Bay. The Bay had always, on other opportunities, seemed to blow its immense character straight into one's face—coming "at" you, so to speak, bearing down on you, with the full force of a thousand prows of steamers seen exactly on the line of their longitudinal axis; but I had never before been so conscious of its boundless cool assurance or seemed to see its genius so grandly at play. This was presumably indeed because I had never before enjoyed the remarkable adventure of taking in so much of the vast bristling promontory from the water, of ascending the East River, in especial, to its upper diminishing expanses.

Something of the air of the occasion and of the mood of the moment caused the whole picture to speak with its largest suggestion; which suggestion is irresistible when once it is sounded clear. It is all, absolutely, an expression of things lately and currently *done*, done on a large impersonal stage and on the basis of inordinate gain—it is not an expression of any other matters whatever; and yet the sense of the scene (which had at

several previous junctures, as well, put forth to my imagination its power) was commanding and thrilling,
was in certain lights almost charming. So it befell, exactly, that an element of mystery and wonder entered
into the impression—the interest of trying to make out,
in the absence of features of the sort usually supposed
indispensable, the reason of the beauty and the joy. It
is indubitably a "great" bay, a great harbour, but no one
item of the romantic, or even of the picturesque, as
commonly understood, contributes to its effect. The
shores are low and for the most part depressingly furnished and prosaically peopled; the islands, though
numerous, have not a grace to exhibit, and one thinks
of the other, the real flowers of geography in this order,
of Naples, of Capetown, of Sydney, of Seattle, of San
Francisco, of Rio, asking how if *they* justify a reputation, New York should seem to justify one. Then, after
all, we remember that there are reputations and reputations; we remember above all that the imaginative response to the conditions here presented may just happen
to proceed from the intellectual extravagance of the
given observer. When this personage is open to corruption by almost any large view of an intensity of life,
his vibrations tend to become a matter difficult even for
him to explain. He may have to confess that the group
of evident facts fails to account by itself for the complacency of his appreciation. Therefore it is that I find
myself rather backward with a perceived sanction, of an
at all proportionate kind, for the fine exhilaration with
which, in this free wayfaring relation to them, the wide
waters of New York inspire me. There is the beauty of
light and air, the great scale of space, and, seen far away
to the west, the open gates of the Hudson, majestic in
their degree, even at a distance, and announcing still
nobler things. But the real appeal, unmistakably, is in

that note of vehemence in the local life of which I have
spoken, for it is the appeal of a particular type of daunt-
less power.

The aspect the power wears then is indescribable; it
is the power of the most extravagant of cities, rejoicing,
as with the voice of the morning, in its might, its fortune, its unsurpassable conditions, and imparting to every object and element, to the motion and expression of
every floating, hurrying, panting thing, to the throb of
ferries and tugs, to the plash of waves and the play
of winds and the glint of lights and the shrill of whistles
and the quality and authority of breeze-borne cries—all,
practically, a diffused, wasted clamour of *detonations*—
something of its sharp free accent and, above all, of its
sovereign sense of being "backed" and able to back.
The universal *applied* passion struck me as shining un-
precedentedly out of the composition; in the bigness
and bravery and insolence, especially, of everything
that rushed and shrieked; in the air as of a great intricate
frenzied dance, half merry, half desperate, or at least
half defiant, performed on the huge watery floor. This
appearance of the bold lacing-together, across the waters, of the scattered members of the monstrous organism
—lacing as by the ceaseless play of an enormous system
of steam-shuttles or electric bobbins (I scarce know
what to call them), commensurate in form with their
infinite work—does perhaps more than anything else to
give the pitch of the vision of energy. One has the
sense that the monster grows and grows, flinging abroad
its loose limbs even as some unmannered young giant at
his "larks," and that the binding stitches must for ever
fly further and faster and draw harder; the future complexity of the web, all under the sky and over the sea,
becoming thus that of some colossal set of clockworks,
some steel-souled machine-room of brandished arms

and hammering fists and opening and closing jaws. The immeasurable bridges are but as the horizontal sheaths of pistons working at high pressure, day and night, and subject, one apprehends with perhaps inconsistent gloom, to certain, to fantastic, to merciless multiplication. In the light of this apprehension indeed the breezy brightness of the Bay puts on the semblance of the vast white page that awaits beyond any other perhaps the black overscoring of science.

Let me hasten to add that its present whiteness is precisely its charming note, the frankest of the signs you recognize and remember it by. That is the distinction I was just feeling my way to name as the main ground of its doing so well, for effect, without technical scenery. There are great imposing ports—Glasgow and Liverpool and London—that have already their page blackened almost beyond redemption from any such light of the picturesque as can hope to irradiate fog and grime, and there are others, Marseilles and Constantinople say, or, for all I know to the contrary, New Orleans, that contrive to abound before everything else in colour, and so to make a rich and instant and obvious show. But memory and the actual impression keep investing New York with the tone, predominantly, of summer dawns and winter frosts, of sea-foam, of bleached sails and stretched awnings, of blanched hulls, of scoured decks, of new ropes, of polished brasses, of streamers clear in the blue air; and it is by this harmony, doubtless, that the projection of the individual character of the place, of the candour of its avidity and the freshness of its audacity, is most conveyed. The "tall buildings," which have so promptly usurped a glory that affects you as rather surprised, as yet, at itself, the multitudinous skyscrapers standing up to the view, from the water, like extravagant pins in a cushion already overplanted, and stuck in as in the dark, anywhere and anyhow, have at least the felicity of carrying out the fairness of tone, of taking the sun and the shade in the manner of towers of marble. They are not all of marble, I believe, by any means, even if some may be, but they are impudently new and still more impudently "novel"—this in common with so many other terrible things in America —and they are triumphant payers of dividends; all of which uncontested and unabashed pride, with flash of innumerable windows and flicker of subordinate gilt attributions, is like the flare, up and down their long, narrow faces, of the lamps of some general permanent "celebration."

.   .   .   .   .

My recovery of impressions, after a short interval, yet with their flush a little faded, may have been judged to involve itself with excursions of memory—memory directed to the antecedent time—reckless almost to extravagance. But I recall them to-day, none the less, for that value in them which ministered, at happy moments, to an artful evasion of the actual. There was no escape from the ubiquitous alien into the future, or even into the present; there was an escape but into the past. I count as quite a triumph in this interest an unbroken ease of frequentation of that ancient end of Fifth Avenue to the whole neighbourhood of which one's earlier vibrations, a very far-away matter now, were attuned. The precious stretch of space between Washington Square and Fourteenth Street had a value, had even a charm, for the revisiting spirit—a mild and melancholy glamour which I am conscious of the difficulty of "rendering" for new and heedless generations. Here again the assault of suggestion is too great; too large, I mean, the number of hares started, before the pursuing imagi-

nation, the quickened memory, by this fact of the felt
moral and social value of this comparatively unimpaired
morsel of the Fifth Avenue heritage. Its reference to a
pleasanter, easier, hazier past is absolutely comparative, just as the past in question itself enjoys as such the
merest courtesy-title. It is all recent history enough,
by the measure of the whole, and there are flaws and
defacements enough, surely, even in its appearance of
decency of duration. The tall building, grossly tall and
grossly ugly, has failed of an admirable chance of distinguished consideration for it, and the dignity of many
of its peaceful fronts has succumbed to the presence of
those industries whose foremost need is to make "a
good thing" of them. The good thing is doubtless being
made, and yet this lower end of the once agreeable street
still just escapes being a wholly bad thing. What held
the fancy in thrall, however, as I say, was the admonition, proceeding from all the facts, that values of this
romantic order are at best, anywhere, strangely relative. It was an extraordinary statement on the subject
of New York that the space between Fourteenth Street
and Washington Square *should* count for "tone," figure
as the old ivory of an overscored tablet.

True wisdom, I found, was to let it, to make it, so
count and figure as much as it would, and charming assistance came for this, I also found, from the young
good-nature of May and June. There had been neither
assistance nor good-nature during the grim weeks of
mid-winter; there had been but the meagre fact of a
discomfort and an ugliness less formidable here than
elsewhere. When, toward the top of the town, circulation, alimentation, recreation, every art of existence, gave
way before the full onset of winter, when the upper
avenues had become as so many congested bottle-necks,
through which the wine of life simply refused to be

decanted, getting back to these latitudes resembled really a return from the North Pole to the Temperate Zone: it was as if the wine of life had been poured for you, in advance, into some pleasant old punch-bowl that would support you through the temporary stress. Your condition was not reduced to the endless vista of a clogged tube, of a thoroughfare occupied as to the narrow central ridge with trolley-cars stuffed to suffocation, and as to the mere margin, on either side, with snow-banks resulting from the cleared rails and offering themselves as a field for all remaining action. Free existence and good manners, in New York, are too much brought down to a bare rigour of marginal relation to the endless electric coil, the monstrous chain that winds round the general neck and body, the general middle and legs, very much as the boa-constrictor winds round the group of the Laocoön. It struck me that when these folds are tightened in the terrible stricture of the snow-smothered months of the year, the New York predicament leaves far behind the anguish represented in the Vatican figures. To come and go where East Eleventh Street, where West Tenth, opened their kind short arms was at least to keep clear of the awful hug of the serpent. And this was a grace that grew large, as I have hinted, with the approach of summer, and that made in the afternoons of May and of the first half of June, above all, an insidious appeal. There, I repeat, was the delicacy, there the mystery, there the wonder, in especial, of the unquenchable intensity of the impressions received in childhood. They are made then once for all, be their intrinsic beauty, interest, importance, small or great; the stamp is indelible and never wholly fades. This in fact gives it an importance when a lifetime has intervened. I found myself intimately recognizing every house my officious tenth year had, in the way of im-

agined adventure, introduced to me—incomparable
master of ceremonies after all; the privilege had been
offered since to millions of other objects that had made
nothing of it, that had gone as they came; so that here
were Fifth Avenue corners with which one's connection
was fairly exquisite. The lowered light of the days'
ends of early summer became them, moreover, exceedingly, and they fell, for the quiet northward perspective,
into a dozen delicacies of composition and tone.

One could talk of "quietness" now, for the shrinkage
of life so marked, in the higher latitudes of the town,
after Easter, the visible early flight of that "society"
which, by the old custom, used never to budge before
June or July, had almost the effect of clearing some of
the streets, and indeed of suggesting that a truly clear
New York might have an unsuspected charm or two
to put forth. An approach to peace and harmony might
have been, in a manner, promised, and the sense of
other days took advantage of it to steal abroad with a
ghostly tread. It kept meeting, half the time, to its discomfiture, the lamentable little Arch of Triumph which
bestrides these beginnings of Washington Square—
lamentable because of its poor and lonely and unsup-
ported and unaffiliated state. With this melancholy
monument it could make no terms at all, but turned its
back to the strange sight as often as possible, helping itself thereby, moreover, to do a little of the pretending
required, no doubt, by the fond theory that nothing
hereabouts was changed. Nothing *was,* it could occasionally appear to me—there was no new note in the
picture, not one, for instance, when I paused before a
low house in a small row on the south side of Waverley
Place and lived again into the queer mediæval costume
(preserved by the daguerreotypist's art) of the very little boy for whom the scene had once embodied the

pangs and pleasures of a dame's small school. The dame
must have been Irish, by her name, and the Irish tradition, only intensified and coarsened, seemed still to possess the place, the fact of the survival, the sturdy sameness, of which arrested me, again and again, to fascination. The shabby red house, with its mere two storeys,
its lowly "stoop," its dislocated ironwork of the forties,
the early fifties, the record, in its face, of blistering summers and of the long stages of the loss of self-respect,
made it as consummate a morsel of the old liquor-
scented, heated-looking city, the city of no pavements,
but of such a plenty of politics, as I could have desired.
And neighbouring Sixth Avenue, overstraddled though
it might be with feats of engineering unknown to the
primitive age that otherwise so persisted, wanted only,
to carry off the illusion, the warm smell of the bakery
on the corner of Eighth Street, a blessed repository of
doughnuts, cookies, cream-cakes and pies, the slow passing by which, on returns from school, must have had
much in common with the experience of the shipmen
of old who came, in long voyages, while they tacked
and hung back, upon those belts of ocean that are
haunted with the balm and spice of tropic islands.

These were the felicities of the backward reach,
which, however, had also its melancholy checks and
snubs; nowhere quite so sharp as in presence, so to
speak, of the rudely, the ruthlessly suppressed birth-
house on the other side of the Square. That was where
the pretence that nearly nothing was changed had most
to come in; for a high, square, impersonal structure, pro-
claiming its lack of interest with a crudity all its own,
so blocks, at the right moment for its own success, the
view of the past, that the effect for me, in Washington
Place, was of having been amputated of half my history.
The grey and more or less "hallowed" University build-

ing—wasn't it somehow, with a desperate bravery, both castellated and gabled?—has vanished from the earth, and vanished with it the two or three adjacent houses, of which the birthplace was one. This was the snub, for the complacency of retrospect, that, whereas the inner sense had positively erected there for its private contemplation a commemorative mural tablet, the very wall that should have borne this inscription had been smashed as for demonstration that tablets, in New York, are unthinkable. And I have had indeed to permit myself this free fantasy of the hypothetic rescued identity of a given house—taking the vanished number in Washington Place as most pertinent—in order to invite the reader to gasp properly with me before the fact that we not only fail to remember, in the whole length of the city, one of these frontal records of birth, sojourn, or death, under a celebrated name, but that we have only to reflect an instant to see any such form of civic piety inevitably and for ever absent. The form is cultivated, to the greatly quickened interest of street-scenery, in many of the cities of Europe; and is it not verily bitter, for those who feel a poetry in the noted passage, longer or shorter, here and there, of great lost spirits, that the institution, the profit, the glory of any such association is denied in advance to communities tending, as the phrase is, to "run" preponderantly to the sky-scraper? Where, in fact, is the point of inserting a mural tablet, at any legible height, in a building certain to be destroyed to make room for a sky-scraper? And from where, on the other hand, in a façade of fifty floors, does one "see" the pious plate recording the honour attached to one of the apartments look down on a responsive people? We have but to ask the question to recognize our necessary failure to answer it as a supremely characteristic local note—a note in the light of which the great city

is projected into its future as, practically, a huge, continuous fifty-floored conspiracy against the very idea
of the ancient graces, those that strike us as having flourished just in proportion as the parts of life and the signs
of character have *not* been lumped together, not been
indistinguishably sunk in the common fund of mere
economic convenience. So interesting, as object-lessons,
may the developments of the American gregarious ideal
become; so traceable, at every turn, to the restless ana-
lyst at least, are the heavy footprints, in the finer
texture of life, of a great commercial democracy seeking
to abound supremely in its own sense and having none
to gainsay it.

.   .   .   .   .   .

Still, as I have already hinted, there was always the
case of the one other rescued identity and preserved
felicity, the happy accident of the elder day still ungrudged and finally legitimated. When I say ungrudged,
indeed, I seem to remember how I had heard that the
divine little City Hall had *been* grudged, at a critical
moment, to within an inch of its life; had but just escaped, in the event, the extremity of grudging. It lives
on securely, by the mercy of fate—lives on in the delicacy of its beauty, speaking volumes again (more volumes, distinctly, than are anywhere else spoken) for
the exquisite truth of the *conferred* value of interesting
objects, the value derived from the social, the civilizing
function for which they have happened to find their
opportunity. It is the opportunity that gives them their
price, and the luck of there being, round about them,
nothing greater than themselves to steal it away from
them. They strike thus, virtually, the supreme note, and
—such is the mysterious play of our finer sensibility!—
one takes this note, one is glad to work it, as the phrase

goes, for all it is worth. I so work the note of the City Hall, no doubt, in speaking of the spectacle there constituted as "divine"; but I do it precisely by reason of the spectacle taken *with* the delightful small facts of the building: largely by reason, in other words, of the elegant, the gallant little structure's situation and history, the way it has played, artistically, ornamentally, its part, · has held out for the good cause, through the long years, alone and unprotected. The fact is it has been the very centre of that assault of vulgarity of which the innumerable mementos rise within view of it and tower, at a certain distance, over it; and yet it has never parted with a square inch of its character, it has forced them, in a manner, to stand off. I hasten to add that in expressing thus its uncompromised state I speak of its outward, its æsthetic character only. So, at all events, it has discharged the civilizing function I just named as inherent in such cases—that of representing, to the community possessed of it, all the Style the community is likely to get, and of making itself responsible for the same.

The consistency of this effort, under difficulties, has been the story that brings tears to the eyes of the hovering kindly critic, and it is through his tears, no doubt, that such a personage reads the best passages of the tale and makes out the proportions of the object. Mine, I recognize, didn't prevent my seeing that the pale yellow marble (or whatever it may be) of the City Hall has lost, by some late excoriation, the remembered charm of its old surface, the pleasant promiscuous patina of time; but the perfect taste and finish, the reduced yet ample scale, the harmony of parts, the just proportions, the modest classic grace, the living look of the type aimed at, these things, with gaiety of detail undiminished and "quaintness" of effect augmented, are all there; and I see them, as I write, in that glow of appreciation which made it necessary, of a fine June morning, that I should some-how pay the whole place my respects. The simplest, in fact the only way, was, obviously, to pass under the charming portico and brave the consequences: this im-punity of such audacities being, in America, one of the last of the lessons the repatriated absentee finds himself learning. The crushed spirit he brings back from Euro-pean discipline never quite rises to the height of the native argument, the brave sense that the public, the civic building is his very own, for any honest use, so that he may tread even its most expensive pavements and staircases (and very expensive, for the American citizen, these have lately become,) without a question asked. This further and further unchallenged penetration begets in the perverted person I speak of a really roman-tic thrill: it is like some assault of the dim seraglio, with the guards bribed, the eunuchs drugged and one's life carried in one's hand. The only drawback to such free-dom is that penetralia it is so easy to penetrate fail a little of a due impressiveness, and that if stationed sentinels are bad for the temper of the freeman they are good for the "prestige" of the building.

Never, in any case, it seemed to me, had any freeman made so free with the majesty of things as I was to make on this occasion with the mysteries of the City Hall—even to the point of coming out into the presence of the Representative of the highest office with which City Halls are associated, and whose thoroughly gracious condonation of my act set the seal of success upon the whole adventure. Its dizziest intensity in fact sprang precisely from the unexpected view opened into the old official, the old so thick-peopled local, municipal world: upper chambers of council and state, delightfully of their nineteenth-century time, as to design and orna-ment, in spite of rank restoration; but replete, above all, with portraits of past worthies, past celebrities and city fathers, Mayors, Bosses, Presidents, Governors, Statesmen at large, Generals and Commodores at large, florid ghosts, looking so unsophisticated now, of years not remarkable, municipally, for the absence of sophistication. Here were types, running mainly to ugliness and all bristling with the taste of their day and the quite touching provincialism of their conditions, as to many of which nothing would be more interesting than a study of New York annals in the light of their personal look, their very noses and mouths and complexions and heads of hair—to say nothing of their waistcoats and neckties; with such colour, such sound and movement would the thick stream of local history then be interfused. Wouldn't its thickness fairly become transparent? since to walk through the collection was not only to see and feel so much that had happened, but to understand, with the truth again and again inimitably pointed, why nothing could have happened otherwise; the whole array thus presenting itself as an unsurpassed demonstration of the real reasons of things. The florid ghosts look out from their exceedingly gilded frames—all that *that* can do is bravely done for them—with the frankest responsibility for everything; their collective presence becomes a kind of copious tell-tale document signed with a hundred names. There are few of these that at this hour, I think, we particularly desire to repeat; but the place where they may be read is, all the way from river to river and from the Battery to Harlem, the place in which there is most of the terrible town. . . .

1906. From Chapter II of *The American Scene* (1907).

V

PASSAGES OF AUTOBIOGRAPHY
AND A JOURNAL

EDITOR'S NOTE

James's three autobiographical memoirs were his major undertaking in the last five years of his life. His last book of tales, *The Finer Grain*, appeared in 1910, and he still had in hand two long-planned novels, *The Sense of the Past* and *The Ivory Tower*, but the completion of these was circumvented by illness, hesitation, and the distressing outbreak of the European war in 1914. Meanwhile his return to the United States in 1904-1905, and again in 1910-11 when he accompanied his ailing brother William back from Europe to New Hampshire and saw him die there, had awakened memories of his youth in New York, Europe, Newport, and Cambridge. After recovering from his grief and the nervous disability that had afflicted him in 1909-11, he saw himself as the last survivor of his immediate family, and he determined to set down his recollections of the events and influences that had shaped his personality and career. *A Small Boy and Others* (1913) deals with the first fifteen years of his life; *Notes of a Son and Brother* (1914) deals with the next ten and particularly with the companionship and shared discoveries of his closest brother, William; *The Middle Years* (unfinished, 1917) shows him in London in 1869 and the early seventies, making his adult entry on the scenes to

which his parents had first introduced him in infancy and
boyhood, and partaking of the "banquet of initiation" which
was to make him a citizen of Europe and a professional
author.

These three memoirs were, however, prepared for by the
fifty years of growing self-awareness and critical self-assess-
ment which had preceded them and which James recorded
not only indirectly in his fiction and essays but more directly
in his letters and journals. Of the letters a selection is given
later in this book. His *Notebooks* are perhaps the richest and
most systematic ever kept by an English-writing novelist.
As published in 1947, they contain not only the plans and
cogitations that went into the making of almost all his
novels and tales but entries of a more intimate character—
summings up of purpose and ambition in his art that show
the conscious design James felt developing out of his experiences. The first three excerpts given here, all taken from
the three above-named memoirs, record from the vantage-
point of his old age three high moments in James's youth.
The titles I have supplied for them derive from James's own
text. "The Sense of Glory" is Chapter XXV of *A Small Boy
and Others,* and tells of James's discovery, in the Louvre in
Paris in 1856 or '57 and at the age of thirteen, of what art
and the "sense of form" were to mean to him. The passage
called "The End of the Civil War: The Mask of Lincoln"
is taken from Chapter XII of *Notes of a Son and Brother,*
and hints of the profound impact which that war, in which
two of his brothers fought, and its national hero made on
James. "The Banquet of Initiation" is Chapter V of *The
Middle Years,* and recounts James's entry into the literary
world of London in the 1870's and his meeting with the
novelist George Eliot, whom he saw as the leading artist and
moral intelligence in Victorian fiction and a model for him in
his own chosen craft. I have particularly included this passage
because I have not been able to include one of James's pieces
on George Eliot among the critical writings in Part III of this
book. "The Voice of Concord" is taken from Chapter VIII
of *The American Scene* (1907). It is not strictly a work of

autobiography, but its basis and reference are personal and it may serve both as a fragment of James's intimate history and as a comment on what Concord and its presiding spirits, Emerson, Thoreau, and Hawthorne, had meant to him in youth and later life. Lastly, the "Journal" which James began in the Brunswick Hotel in Boston in November 1881, continued in Cambridge and London, and finished in Paris in November 1882, is taken from *The Notebooks of Henry James* as edited by F. O. Matthiessen and Kenneth B. Murdock (1947). It is the most extended and significant document of its kind among James's papers—a review of his life at the age of thirty-eight, an assessment of his personal and imaginative assets, and a forecast of the thirty-four years that were to remain to him for the writing of his books and the achievement of success and fame in his chosen career.

THE SENSE OF GLORY

A MEMORY OF PARIS IN YOUTH: THE LOUVRE AND THE GALERIE D'APOLLON

That autumn[1] renewed, I make out, our long and be-guiled walks, my own with W. J. in especial; at the same time that I have somehow the sense of the whole more broken appeal on the part of Paris, the scanter confi-

[1] The autumn to which Henry James here refers (in Chapter XXV of *A Small Boy and Others*) was that of 1856 or 1857. With his family he traveled and lived during the years 1855-58 in Switzerland, England, and France, attending schools in Geneva, Paris (Institution Fezandié), and Boulogne. [*Editor's note.*]

dence and ease it inspired in us, the perhaps more numerous and composite, but obscurer and more baffled
intimations. Not indeed—for all my brother's later vision
of an accepted flatness in it—that there was not some
joy and some grasp; why else were we forever (as I seem
to conceive we were) measuring the great space that
separated us from the gallery of the Luxembourg, every
step of which, either way we took it, fed us with some
interesting, some admirable image, kept us in relation
to something nobly intended? That particular walk was
not prescribed us, yet we appear to have hugged it,
across the Champs-Elysées to the river, and so over the
nearest bridge and the quays of the left bank to the Rue
de Seine, as if it somehow held the secret of our future;
to the extent even of my more or less sneaking off on
occasion to take it by myself, to taste of it with a due
undiverted intensity and the throb as of the finest, which
could only mean the most Parisian, adventure. The further quays, with their innumerable old bookshops and
print-shops, the long cases of each of these commodities,
exposed on the parapets in especial, must have come to
know us almost as well as we knew them; with plot
thickening and emotion deepening steadily, however,
as we mounted the long, black Rue de Seine—*such*
a stretch of perspective, *such* an intensity of tone as it
offered in those days; where every low-browed vitrine
waylaid us and we moved in a world of which the dark
message, expressed in we couldn't have said what sinister way too, might have been "Art, art, art, don't you
see? Learn, little gaping pilgrims, what *that* is!" Oh we
learned, that is we tried to, as hard as ever we could,
and were fairly well at it, I always felt, even by the time
we had passed up into that comparatively short but
wider and finer vista of the Rue de Tournon, which in
those days more abruptly crowned the more compressed

approach and served in a manner as a great outer vestibule to the Palace. Style, dimly described, looked down there, as with conscious encouragement, from the high grey-headed, clear-faced, straight-standing old houses —very much as if wishing to say "Yes, small staring jeune homme, we are dignity and memory and measure, we are conscience and proportion and taste, not to mention strong sense too: for all of which good things take us—you won't find one of them when you find (as you're going soon to begin to at such a rate) vulgarity." This, I admit, was an abundance of remark to such young ears; but it did all, I maintain, tremble in the air, with the sense that the Rue de Tournon, cobbled and a little grass-grown, might more or less have figured some fine old street *de province:* I cherished in short its very name and think I really hadn't to wait to prefer the then, the unmenaced, the inviolate Café Foyot of the left hand corner, the much-loved and so haunted Café Foyot of the old Paris, to its—well, to its roaring successor. The wide mouth of the present Boulevard Saint-Michel, a short way round the corner, had not yet been forced open to the exhibition of more or less glittering fangs; old Paris still pressed round the Palace and its gardens, which formed the right, the sober social antithesis to the "elegant" Tuileries, and which in fine, with these renewals of our young confidence, reinforced both in a general and in a particular way one of the fondest of our literary curiosities of that time, the conscientious study of *Les Français Peints par Eux-Mêmes,* rich in wood-cuts of Gavarni, of Grandville, of Henri-Monnier, which we held it rather our duty to admire and W. J. even a little his opportunity to copy in pen-and-ink. This gilt-edged and double-columned octavo it was that first disclosed to me, forestalling a better ground of acquaintance, the great name of Balzac, who, in common with every other "light" writer of his day, contributed to its pages: hadn't I pored over his exposition there of the contrasted types of "L'Habituée des Tuileries" and "L'Habituée du Luxembourg"?—finding it very *serré,* in fact what I didn't then know enough to call very stodgy, but flavoured withal and a trifle lubricated by Gavarni's two drawings, which had somehow so much, in general, to say.

Let me not however dally by the way, when nothing, at those hours, I make out, so much spoke to us as the animated pictured halls within the Palace, primarily those of the Senate of the Empire, but then also forming, as with extensions they still and much more copiously form, the great Paris museum of contemporary art. This array was at that stage a comparatively (though only comparatively) small affair; in spite of which fact we supposed it vast and final—so that it would have shocked us to foreknow how in many a case, and of the most cherished cases, the finality was to break down. Most of the works of the modern schools that we most admired are begging their bread, I fear, from door to door—that is from one provincial museum or dim back seat to another; though we were on much-subsequent returns to draw a long breath for the saved state of some of the great things as to which our faith had been clearest. It had been clearer for none, I recover, than for Couture's *Romains de la Décadence,* recently acclaimed, at that time, as the last word of the grand manner, but of the grand manner modernised, humanised, philosophised, redeemed from academic death; so that it was to this master's school that the young American contemporary flutter taught its wings to fly straightest, and that I could never, in the long aftertime, face his masterpiece and all its old meanings and marvels without a rush of memories and a stir of ghosts. William Hunt, the New

Englander of genius, the "Boston painter" whose authority was greatest during the thirty years from 1857 or so, and with whom for a time in the early period W. J. was to work all devotedly, had prolonged his studies in Paris under the inspiration of Couture and of Édouard Frère; masters in a group completed by three or four of the so finely interesting landscapists of that and the directly previous age, Troyon, Rousseau, Daubigny, even Lambinet and others, and which summed up for the American collector and in the New York and Boston markets the idea of the modern in the masterly. It was a comfortable time—when appreciation could go so straight, could rise, and rise higher, without critical contortions; when we could, I mean, be both so intelligent and so "quiet." We were in our immediate circle to know Couture himself a little toward the end of his life, and I was somewhat to wonder then where he had picked up the æsthetic hint for the beautiful Page with a Falcon, if I have the designation right, his other great bid for style and capture of it—which we were long to continue to suppose perhaps the rarest of all modern pictures. The feasting Romans were conceivable enough, I mean *as* a conception; no mystery hung about them—in the sense of one's asking one's self whence they had come and by what romantic or roundabout or nobly-dangerous journey; which is that air of the poetic shaken out as from strong wings when great presences, in any one of the arts, appear to alight. What I remember, on the other hand, of the splendid fair youth in black velvet and satin or whatever who, while he mounts the marble staircase, shows off the great bird on his forefinger with a grace that shows *him* off, was that it failed to help us to divine, during that after-lapse of the glory of which I speak, by what rare chance, for the obscured old ex-celebrity we visited, the heavens had once opened.

Poetry had swooped down, breathed on him for an hour and fled. Such at any rate are the see-saws of reputations —which it contributes to the interest of any observational lingering on this planet to have caught so repeatedly in their weird motion; the question of what may happen, under one's eyes, in particular cases, before that motion sinks to rest, whether at the up or at the down end, being really a bribe to one's own non-departure. Especially great the interest of having noted all the rises and falls and of being able to compare the final point— so far as any certainty may go as to that—either with the greatest or the least previous altitudes; since it is only when there have been exaltations (which is what is not commonest), that our attention is most rewarded.

If the see-saw was to have operated indeed for Eugène Delacroix, our next young admiration, though much more intelligently my brother's than mine, that had already taken place and settled, for we were to go on seeing him, and to the end, in firm possession of his crown, and to take even, I think, a harmless pleasure in our sense of having from so far back been sure of it. I was sure of it, I must properly add, but as an effect of my brother's sureness; since I must, by what I remember, have been as sure of Paul Delaroche—for whom the pendulum was at last to be arrested at a very different point. I could see in a manner, for all the queerness, what W. J. meant by that beauty and, above all, that living interest in "La Barque du Dante," where the queerness, according to him, was perhaps what contributed most; see it doubtless in particular when he reproduced the work, at home, from a memory aided by a lithograph. Yet "Les Enfants d'Édouard" thrilled me to a different tune, and I couldn't doubt that the long-drawn odd face of the elder prince, sad and sore and sick, with his wide crimped sidelocks of fair hair and his violet legs

marked by the Garter and dangling from the bed, was
a reconstitution of far-off history of the subtlest and most
"last word" modern or psychologic kind. I had never
heard of psychology in art or anywhere else—scarcely
anyone then had; but I truly felt the nameless force at
play. Thus if I also in my way "subtly" admired, one's
noted practice of that virtue (mainly regarded indeed,
I judge, as a vice) would appear to have at the time
I refer to set in, under such encouragements, once for
all; and I can surely have enjoyed up to then no formal
exhibition of anything as I at one of those seasons enjoyed the commemorative show of Delaroche given,
soon after his death, in one of the rather bleak salles
of the École des Beaux-Arts to which access was had
from the quay. *There* was reconstituted history if one
would, in the straw-littered scaffold, the distracted ladies
with three-cornered coifs and those immense hanging
sleeves that made them look as if they had bath-towels
over their arms; in the block, the headsman, the band-
aged eyes and groping hands, of Lady Jane Grey—not
less than in the noble indifference of Charles the First,
compromised king but perfect gentleman, at his inscrutable ease in his chair and as if on his throne, while
the Puritan soldiers insult and badger him: the thrill
of which was all the greater from its pertaining to that
English lore which the good Robert Thompson had, to
my responsive delight, rubbed into us more than anything else and all from a fine old conservative and
monarchical point of view. Yet of these things W. J.
attempted no reproduction, though I remember his repeatedly laying his hand on Delacroix, whom he found
always and everywhere interesting—to the point of trying effects, with charcoal and crayon, in his manner; and
not less in the manner of Decamps, whom we regarded
as more or less of a genius of the same rare family. They

were touched with the ineffable, the inscrutable, and Delacroix in especial with the incalculable; categories these toward which we had even then, by a happy transition, begun to yearn and languish. We were not yet aware of style, though on the way to become so, but were aware of mystery, which indeed was one of its forms—while we saw all the others, without exception, exhibited at the Louvre, where at first they simply overwhelmed and bewildered me.

It was as if they had gathered there into a vast deafening chorus; I shall never forget how—speaking, that is, for my own sense—they filled those vast halls with the influence rather of some complicated sound, diffused and reverberant, than of such visibilities as one could directly deal with. To distinguish among these, in the charged and coloured and confounding air, was difficult —it discouraged and defied; which was doubtless why my impression originally best entertained was that of those magnificent parts of the great gallery simply not inviting us to distinguish. They only arched over us in the wonder of their endless golden riot and relief, figured and flourished in perpetual revolution, breaking into great high-hung circles and symmetries of squandered picture, opening into deep outward embrasures that threw off the rest of monumental Paris somehow as a told story, a sort of wrought effect or bold ambiguity for a vista, and yet held it there, at every point, as a vast bright gage, even at moments a felt adventure, of experience. This comes to saying that in those beginnings I felt myself most happily cross that bridge over to Style constituted by the wondrous Galerie d'Apollon, drawn out for me as a long but assured initiation and seeming to form with its supreme coved ceiling and inordinately shining parquet a prodigious tube or tunnel through which I inhaled little by little, that is again and again, a general sense of *glory*. The glory meant ever so many things at once, not only beauty and art and supreme design, but history and fame and power, the world in fine raised to the richest and noblest expression. The world there was at the same time, by an odd extension or intensification, the local present fact, to my small imagination, of the Second Empire, which was (for my notified consciousness) new and queer and perhaps even wrong, but on the spot so amply radiant and elegant that it took to itself, took under its protection with a splendour of insolence, the state and ancientry of the whole scene, profiting thus, to one's dim historic vision, confusedly though it might be, by the unparalleled luxury and variety of its heritage. But who shall count the sources at which an intense young fancy (when a young fancy *is* intense) capriciously, absurdly drinks?—so that the effect is, in twenty connections, that of a love-philtre or fear-philtre which fixes for the senses their supreme symbol of the fair or the strange. The Galerie d'Apollon became for years what I can only term a splendid scene of things, even of the quite irrelevant or, as might be, almost unworthy; and I recall to this hour, with the last vividness, what a precious part it played for me, and exactly by that continuity of honour, on my awaking, in a summer dawn many years later, to the fortunate, the instantaneous recovery and capture of the most appalling yet most admirable nightmare of my life. The climax of this extraordinary experience—which stands alone for me as a dream-adventure founded in the deepest, quickest, clearest act of cogitation and comparison, act indeed of life-saving energy, as well as in unutterable fear—was the sudden pursuit, through an open door, along a huge high saloon, of a just dimly-descried figure that retreated in terror before my rush and dash (a glare of inspired reaction from irresistible but shameful dread,) out of the room I had a moment before been desperately, and all the more abjectly, defending by the push of my shoulder against hard pressure on lock and bar from the other side. The lucidity, not to say the sublimity, of the crisis had consisted of the great thought that I, in my appalled state, was probably still more appalling than the awful agent, creature or presence, whatever he was, whom I had guessed, in the suddenest wild start from sleep, the sleep within my sleep, to be making for my place of rest. The triumph of my impulse, perceived in a flash as I acted on it by myself at a bound, forcing the door outward, was the grand thing, but the great point of the whole was the wonder of my final recognition. Routed, dismayed, the tables turned upon him by my so surpassing him for straight aggression and dire intention, my visitant was already but a diminished spot in the long perspective, the tremendous, glorious hall, as I say, over the far-gleaming floor of which, cleared for the occasion of its great line of priceless vitrines down the middle, he sped for *his* life, while a great storm of thunder and lightning played through the deep embrasures of high windows at the right. The lightning that revealed the retreat revealed also the wondrous place and, by the same amazing play, my young imaginative life in it of long before, the sense of which, deep within me, had kept it whole, preserved it to this thrilling use; for what in the world were the deep embrasures and the so polished floor but those of the Galerie d'Apollon of my childhood? The "scene of something" I had vaguely then felt it? Well I might, since it was to be the scene of that immense hallucination.

Of what, at the same time, in those years, were the great rooms of the Louvre almost equally, above and below, not the scene, from the moment they so wrought, stage by stage, upon our perceptions?—literally on al-

most all of these, in one way and another; quite in such
a manner, I more and more see, as to have been educa-
tive, formative, fertilising, in a degree which no other
"intellectual experience" our youth was to know could
pretend, as a comprehensive, conducive thing, to rival.
The sharp and strange, the quite heart-shaking little
prevision had come to me, for myself, I make out, on the
occasion of our very first visit of all, my brother's and
mine, under conduct of the good Jean Nadali, before-
mentioned, trustfully deputed by our parents, in the
Rue de la Paix, on the morrow of our first arrival in Paris
(July 1855) and while they were otherwise concerned.
I hang again, appalled but uplifted, on brave Nadali's
arm—his professional acquaintance with the splendours
about us added for me on the spot to the charm of his
"European" character: I cling to him while I gape at
Géricault's "Radeau de la Méduse," *the* sensation, for
splendour and terror of interest, of that juncture to me,
and ever afterwards to be associated, along with two or
three other more or less contemporary products, Gué-
rin's "Burial of Atala," Prudhon's "Cupid and Psyche,"
David's helmetted Romanisms, Madame Vigée-Lebrun's
"ravishing" portrait of herself and her little girl, with
how can I say what foretaste (as determined by that
instant as if the hour had struck from a clock) of all the
fun, confusedly speaking, that one was going to have,
and the kind of life, always of the queer so-called inward
sort, tremendously "sporting" in its way—though that
description didn't then wait upon it, that one was going
to lead. It came of itself, this almost awful apprehension
in all the presences, under our courier's protection and
in my brother's company—it came just there and so;
there was alarm in it somehow as well as bliss. The bliss
in fact I think scarce disengaged itself at all, but only
the sense of a freedom of contact and appreciation really

too big for one, and leaving such a mark on the very place, the pictures, the frames themselves, the figures within them, the particular parts and features of each, the look of the rich light, the smell of the massively enclosed air, that I have never since renewed the old exposure without renewing again the old emotion and taking up the small scared consciousness. *That,* with so many of the conditions repeated, is the charm—to feel afresh the beginning of so much that was to be. The beginning in short was with Géricault and David, but it went on and on and slowly spread; so that one's stretched, one's even strained, perceptions, one's discoveries and extensions piece by piece, come back, on the great premises, almost as so many explorations of the house of life, so many circlings and hoverings round the image of the world. I have dim reminiscences of permitted independent visits, uncorrectedly juvenile though I might still be, during which the house of life and the palace of art became so mixed and interchangeable— the Louvre being, under a general description, the most peopled of all scenes not less than the most hushed of all temples—that an excursion to look at pictures would have but half expressed my afternoon. I had looked at pictures, looked and looked again, at the vast Veronese, at Murillo's moon-borne Madonna, at Leonardo's almost unholy dame with the folded hands, treasures of the Salon Carré as that display was then composed; but I had also looked at France and looked at Europe, looked even at America as Europe itself might be conceived so to look, looked at history, as a still-felt past and a complacently personal future, at society, manners, types, characters, possibilities and prodigies and mysteries of fifty sorts; and all in the light of being splendidly "on my own," as I supposed it, though we hadn't then that perfection of slang, and of (in especial) going and coming along that interminable and incomparable Seine-side front of the Palace against which young sensibility felt itself almost rub, for endearment and consecration, as a cat invokes the friction of a protective piece of furniture. Such were at any rate some of the vague processes—I see for how utterly vague they must show—of picking up an education; and I was, in spite of the vagueness, so far from agreeing with my brother afterwards that we didn't pick one up and that that never *is* done, in any sense not negligible, and also that an education might, or should, in particular, have picked *us* up, and yet didn't—I was so far dissentient, I say, that I think I quite came to glorify such passages and see them as part of an order really fortunate. If we had been little asses, I seem to have reasoned, a higher intention driving us wouldn't have made us less so—to any point worth mentioning; and as we extracted such impressions, to put it at the worst, from redemptive accidents (to call Louvres and Luxembourgs nothing better) why we weren't little asses, but something wholly other: which appeared all I needed to contend for. Above all it would have been stupid and ignoble, an attested and lasting dishonour, not, with our chance, to have followed our straggling clues, as many as we could and disengaging as we happily did, I felt, the gold and the silver ones, whatever the others might have been—not to have followed them and not to have arrived by them, so far as we were to arrive. Instinctively, for any dim designs we might have nourished, we picked out the silver and the gold, attenuated threads though they must have been, and I positively feel that there were more of these, far more, casually interwoven, than will reward any present patience for my unravelling of the too fine tissue.

From *A Small Boy and Others* (1913), Chapter XXV.

*

THE END OF THE CIVIL WAR

THE MASK OF LINCOLN

Wherever I dip, again, I pull out a plum from under the tooth of time—this at least so to my own rapt sense that had I more space I might pull both freely and at a venture. The strongest savour of the feast—with the fumes of a feast it comes back—was, I need scarce once more insist, the very taste of the War as ending and ended; through which blessing, more and more, the quantity of military life or at least the images of military experience seemed all about us, quite paradoxically, to grow greater. This I take to have been a result, first of the impending, and then of the effective, break-up of the vast veteran Army, swamping much of the scene as with the flow of a monster tide and bringing literally home to us, in bronzed, matured faces and even more in bronzed, matured characters, above all in the absolutely acquired and stored resource of overwhelming reference, reference usually of most substance the less it was immediately explicit, the more in fact it was faded and jaded to indifference, what was meant by having patiently served. The very smell of having so served was somehow, at least to my supersensitive nostril, in the larger and cooler air, where it might have been an emanation, the most masculine, the most communicative as to associated far-off things (according to the nature, ever, of elements vaguely exhaled), from the operation of the general huge gesture of relief—from worn toggery put off, from old army-cloth and other fittings at a discount, from swordbelts and buckles, from a myriad saturated articles now not even lying about but brushed away with an effect upon the passing breeze and all relegated to the dim state of some mere theoretic commemorative panoply that was never in the event to be objectively disposed. The generalisation grew richly or, as it were, quite adorably familiar, that life was ever so handsomely reinforced, and manners, not to say manner at large, refreshed, and personal aspects and types accented, and categories multiplied (no category, for the dreaming painter of things, could our scene afford not to grab at on the chance), just by the fact of the discharge upon society of such an amount of out-of-the-way experience, as it might roughly be termed—such a quantity and variety of possession and assimilation of unprecedented history. It had been unprecedented at least among ourselves, we had had it in our own highly original conditions—or "they," to be more exact, had had it admirably in theirs; and I think I was never to know a case in which his having been directly touched by it, or, in a word, having consistently "soldiered," learnt all about it and exhausted it, wasn't to count all the while on behalf of the happy man for one's own individual impression or attention; call it again, as everything came back to that, one's own need to interpret. The discharge upon "society" is moreover what I especially mean; it being the sense of how society in *our* image of the word was taking it all in that I was most concerned with; plenty of other images figured of course for other entertainers of such. The world immediately roundabout us at any rate bristled with more of the young, or the younger, cases I speak of, cases of "things seen" and felt, and a delectable difference in the man thereby made imputable, than I could begin here to name even had

I kept the record. I think I fairly cultivated the perceiving of it all, so that nothing of it, under some face or other, shouldn't brush my sense and add to my impression; yet my point is more particularly that the body social itself was for the time so permeated, in the light I glance at, that it became to its own consciousness more interesting. As so many existent parts of it, however unstoried yet, to their minor credit, various thrilled persons could inhale the interest to their fullest capacity and feel that they too had been pushed forward—and were even to find themselves by so much the more pushable yet.

I resort thus to the lift and the push as the most expressive figures for that immensely *remonté* state which coincided for us all with the great disconcerting irony of the hour, the unforgettable death of Lincoln. I think of the springtime of '65 as it breathed through Boston streets—my remembrance of all those days is a matter, strangely enough, of the out-of-door vision, of one's constantly dropping down from Beacon Hill, to the brave edge of which we clung, for appreciation of those premonitory gusts of April that one felt most perhaps where Park Street Church stood dominant, where the mouth of the Common itself uttered promises, more signs and portents than one could count, more prodigies than one could keep apart, and where further strange matters seemed to charge up out of the lower districts and of the "business world," generative as never before of news. The streets were restless, the meeting of the seasons couldn't but be inordinately so, and one's own poor pulses matched—at the supreme pitch of that fusion, for instance, which condensed itself to blackness roundabout the dawn of April 15th: I was fairly to go in shame of its being my birthday. These would have been the hours of the streets if none others had been—

when the huge general gasp filled them like a great earth-shudder and people's eyes met people's eyes without the vulgarity of speech. Even this was, all so strangely, part of the lift and the swell, as tragedy has but to be of a pure enough strain and a high enough connection to sow with its dark hand the seed of greater life. The collective sense of what had occurred was of a sadness too noble not somehow to inspire, and it was truly in the air that, whatever we had as a nation produced or failed to produce, we could at least gather round this perfection of a classic woe. True enough, as we were to see, the immediate harvest of our loss was almost too ugly to be borne—for nothing more sharply comes back to me than the tune to which the "esthetic sense," if one glanced but from *that* high window (which was after all one of many too), recoiled in dismay from the sight of Mr. Andrew Johnson perched on the stricken scene. We had given ourselves a figurehead, and the figure-head sat there in its habit as it lived, and we were to have it in our eyes for three or four years and to ask ourselves in horror what monstrous thing we had done. I speak but of aspects, those aspects which, under a certain turn of them, may be all but everything; gathered together they become a symbol of what is behind, and it was open to us to waver at shop-windows exposing the new photograph, exposing, that is, *the* photograph, and ask ourselves what we had been guilty of as a people, when all was said, to deserve the infliction of that form. It was vain to say that we had deliberately invoked the "common" in authority and must drink the wine we had drawn. No countenance, no salience of aspect nor composed symbol, could superficially have referred itself less than Lincoln's mould-smashing mask to any mere matter-of-course type of propriety; but his admirable unrelated head had itself

revealed a type—as if by the very fact that what made
in it for roughness of kind looked out only less than
what made in it for splendid final stamp, in other words
for commanding Style. The result thus determined had
been precious for representation, and above all for fine
suggestional function, in a degree that left behind every
medal we had ever played at striking; whereas before
the image now substituted representation veiled her
head in silence and the element of the suggested was
exactly the direst. What, however, on the further view,
was to be more refreshing than to find that there were
excesses of native habit which truly we couldn't bear?
so that it was for the next two or three years fairly sustaining to consider that, let the reasons publicly given
for the impeachment of the official in question be any
that would serve, the grand inward logic or mystic law
had been that we really couldn't go on offering each
other before the nations the consciousness of such a
presence. That was at any rate the style of reflection to
which the humiliating case reduced me; just this withal
now especially working, I feel, into that image of our
generally quickened activity of spirit, our having by the
turn of events more ideas to apply and even to play
with, that I have tried to throw off. Everything I recover, I again risk repeating, fits into the vast miscellany
—the detail of which I may well seem, however, too
poorly to have handled.

From Chapter XII of *Notes of a Son and Brother* (1914).

*

THE BANQUET OF INITIATION

LONDON AND GEORGE ELIOT

Why, however, should I pick up so small a crumb from that mere brief first course at a banquet of initiation which was in the event to prolong itself through years and years?—unless indeed as a scrap of a specimen, chosen at hazard, of the prompt activity of a process by which my intelligence afterwards came to find itself more fed, I think, than from any other source at all, or, for that matter, from all other sources put together. A hundred more suchlike modest memories breathe upon me, each with its own dim little plea, as I turn to face them, but my idea is to deal somehow more conveniently with the whole gathered mass of my subsequent impressions in this order, a fruitage that I feel to have been only too abundantly stored. Half a dozen of those of a larger and more immediate dignity, incidents more particularly of the rather invidiously so-called social contact, pull my sleeve as I pass; but the long, backward-drawn train of the later life drags them along with it, lost and smothered in its spread—only one of them stands out or remains over, insisting on its place and hour, its felt distinguishability. To this day I feel again *that* roused emotion, my unsurpassably prized admission to the presence of the great George Eliot, whom I was taken to see, by one of the kind door-opening Norton ladies, by whom Mrs. Lewes's guarded portal at North Bank appeared especially penetrable, on a Sunday after-

noon of April '69. Later occasions, after a considerable
lapse, were not to overlay the absolute face-value, as
I may call it, of all the appearances then and there presented me—which were taken home by a young spirit
almost abjectly grateful, at any rate all devoutly prepared, for them. I find it idle even to wonder what
"place" the author of *Silas Marner* and *Middlemarch*
may be conceived to have in the pride of our literature
—so settled and consecrated in the individual range of
view is many such a case free at last to find itself, free
after ups and down, after fluctuations of fame or whatever, which have divested judgment of any relevance
that isn't most of all the relevance of a living and recorded *relation*. It has ceased then to know itself in any
degree as an estimate, has shaken off the anxieties of
circumspection and comparison and just grown happy
to act as an attachment pure and simple, an effect of
life's own logic, but in the ashes of which the wonted
fires of youth need but to be blown upon for betrayal
of a glow. Reflective appreciation may have originally
been concerned; whether at its most or at its least, but
it is well over, to our infinite relief—yes, to our immortal comfort, I think; the interval back cannot again be
bridged. We simply sit with our enjoyed gain, our resid-
ual rounded possession in our lap; a safe old treasure,
which has ceased to shrink, if indeed also perhaps
greatly to swell, and all that further touches it is the
fine vibration set up if the name we know it all by is
called into question—perhaps however little.

It was by George Eliot's name that I was to go on
knowing, was never to cease to know, a great treasure
of beauty and humanity, of applied and achieved art,
a testimony, historic as well as æsthetic, to the deeper
interest of the intricate English aspects; and I now allow
the vibration, as I have called it, all its play—quite

as if I had been wronged even by my own hesitation as
to whether to pick up my anecdote. That scruple wholly
fades with the sense of how I must at the very time have
foreseen that here was one of those associations that
would determine in the far future an exquisite inability
to revise it. *Middlemarch* had not then appeared—we
of the faith were still to enjoy that *saturation,* and *Felix
Holt* the radical was upwards of three years old; the
impetus proceeding from this work, however, was still
fresh enough in my pulses to have quickened the pal-
pitation of my finding myself in presence. I had rejoiced
without reserve in *Felix Holt*—the illusion of reading
which, outstretched on my then too frequently inevitable bed at Swampscott during a couple of very hot
days of the summer of 1866, comes back to me, followed
by that in sooth of sitting up again, at no great ease,
to indite with all promptness a review of the delightful
thing, the place of appearance of which nothing could
now induce me to name, shameless about the general
fact as I may have been at the hour itself: over such a
feast of fine rich natural tone did I feel myself earnestly
bend. Quite unforgettable to me the art and truth with
which the note of this tone was struck in the beautiful
prologue and the bygone appearances, a hundred of the
outward and visible signs of the author's own young
rural and midmost England, made to hold us by their
harmony. The book was not, if I rightly remember, altogether genially greeted, but I was to hold fast to the
charm I had thankfully suffered it, I had been conscious
of absolutely needing it, to work.

Exquisite the remembrance of how it wouldn't have
"done" for me at all, in relation to other inward matters,
not to strain from the case the last drop of its happiest
sense. And I had even with the cooling of the first glow
so little gone back upon it, as we have nowadays learned

to say, had in fact so gone forward, floated by its wave of superlative intended benignity, that, once in the cool quiet drawing-room at North Bank I knew myself steeped in still deeper depths of the medium. G. H. Lewes was absent for the time on an urgent errand; one of his sons, on a visit at the house, had been suddenly taken with a violent attack of pain, the heritage of a bad accident not long before in the West Indies, a suffered onset from an angry bull, I seem to recall, who had tossed or otherwise mauled him, and, though beaten off, left him considerably compromised—these facts being promptly imparted to us, in no small flutter, by our distinguished lady, who came in to us from another room, where she had been with the hapless young man while his father appealed to the nearest good chemist for some known specific. It infinitely moved me to see so great a celebrity quite humanly and familiarly agitated—even with something clear and noble in it too, to which, as well as to the extraordinarily interesting dignity of her whole odd personal conformation, I remember thinking her black silk dress and the lace mantilla attached to her head and keeping company on either side with the low-falling thickness of her dark hair effectively contributed. I have found myself, my life long, attaching value to every noted thing in respect to a great person—and George Eliot struck me on the spot as somehow *illustratively* great; never at any rate has the impression of those troubled moments faded from me, nor that at once of a certain high grace in her anxiety and a frank immediate appreciation of our presence, modest embarrassed folk as we were. It took me no long time to thrill with the sense, sublime in its unexpectedness, that we were perhaps, or indeed quite clearly, helping her to pass the time till Mr. Lewes's return— after which he would again post off for Mr. Paget the pre-eminent surgeon; and I see involved with this the perfect amenity of her assisting us, as it were, to assist her, through unrelinquished proper talk, due responsible remark and report, in the last degree suggestive to me, on a short holiday taken with Mr. Lewes in the south of France, whence they had just returned. Yes indeed, the lightest words of great persons are so little as any words of others are that I catch myself again inordinately struck with her dropping it off-hand that the mistral, scourge of their excursion, had blown them into Avignon, where they had gone, I think, to see J. S. Mill, only to blow them straight out again—the figure put it so before us; as well as with the moral interest, the absence of the *banal,* in their having, on the whole scene, found pleasure further poisoned by the frequency in all those parts of "evil faces: oh the evil faces!" *That* recorded source of suffering enormously affected me—I felt it as beautifully characteristic: I had never heard an *impression de voyage* so little tainted with the superficial or the vulgar. I was myself at the time in the thick of impressions, and it was true that they would have seemed to me rather to fail of life, of their own doubtless inferior kind, if submitting beyond a certain point to be touched with that sad or, as who should say, that grey colour: Mrs. Lewes's were, it appeared, predominantly so touched, and I could at once admire it in them and wonder if they didn't pay for this by some lack of intensity on other sides. Why I didn't more impute to her, or to them, that possible lack is more than I can say, since under the law of moral earnestness the vulgar and the trivial would be then involved in the poor observations of my own making—a conclusion sufficiently depressing.

However, I didn't find myself depressed, and I didn't find the great mind that was so good as to shine upon us at that awkward moment however dimly anything but augumented; what was its sensibility to the evil faces but part of the large old tenderness which the occasion had caused to overflow and on which we were presently floated back into the room she had left?—where we might perhaps beguile a little the impatience of the sufferer waiting for relief. We ventured in our flutter to doubt whether we *should* beguile, we held back with a certain delicacy from this irruption, and if there was a momentary wonderful and beautiful conflict I remember how our yielding struck me as crowned with the finest grace it could possibly have, that of the prodigious privilege of humouring, yes literally humouring so renowned a spirit at a moment when we could really match our judgment with hers. For the injured young man, in the other and the larger room, simply lay stretched on his back on the floor, the posture apparently least painful to him—though painful enough at the best I easily saw on kneeling beside him, after my first dismay, to ask if I could in any way ease him. I see his face again, fair and young and flushed, with its vague little smile and its moist brow; I recover the moment or two during which we sought to make natural conversation in his presence, and my question as to what conversation *was* natural; and then as his father's return still failed my having the inspiration that at once terminated the strain of the scene and yet prolonged the sublime connection. Mightn't *I* then hurry off for Mr. Paget?—on whom, as fast as a cab could carry me, I would wait with the request that he would come at the first possible moment to the rescue. Mrs. Lewes's and our stricken companion's instant appreciation of this offer lent me wings on which I again feel myself borne very much as if suddenly acting as a messenger of the gods—surely I had never come so near to performing in that character. I shook off my fellow visitor for swifter cleaving of the air, and I recall still feeling that I cleft it even in the dull four-wheeler of other days which, on getting out of the house, I recognised as the only object animating, at a distance, the long blank Sunday vista beside the walled-out Regent's Park. I crawled to Hanover Square—or was it Cavendish? I let the question stand—and, after learning at the great man's door that though he was not at home he was soon expected back and would receive my message without delay, cherished for the rest of the day the particular quality of my vibration.

It was doubtless even excessive in proportion to its cause—yet in what else but that consisted the force and the use of vibrations? It was by their excess that one knew them for such, as one for that matter only knew things in general worth knowing. I didn't know what I had expected as an effect of our offered homage, but I had somehow not, at the best, expected a relation—and now a relation had been dramatically determined. It would exist for me if I should never again in all the world ask a feather's weight of it; for myself, that is, it would simply never be able not somehow to act. Its virtue was not in truth at all flagrantly to be put to the proof—any opportunity for that underwent at the best a considerable lapse; but why wasn't it intensely acting, none the less, during the time when, before being in London again for any length of stay, I found it intimately concerned in my perusal of *Middlemarch,* so soon then to appear, and even in that of *Deronda,* its intervention on behalf of which defied any chill of time? And to these references I can but subjoin that they obviously most illustrate the operation of a sense for drama. The process of appropriation of the two fictions was experience, in great intensity, and roundabout the field was drawn the distinguishable ring of something that belonged equally to this condition and that embraced and further vivified the imaged mass, playing in upon it lights of surpassing fineness. So it was, at any rate, that my "relation"—for I didn't go so far as to call it "ours"—helped me to squeeze further values from the intrinsic substance of the copious final productions I have named, a weight of variety, dignity and beauty of which I have never allowed my measure to shrink.

Even this example of a rage for connections, I may also remark, doesn't deter me from the mention here, somewhat out of its order of time, of another of those in which my whole privilege of reference to Mrs. Lewes, such as it remained, was to look to be preserved. I stretch over the years a little to overtake it, and it calls up at once another person, the ornament, or at least the diversion, of a society long since extinct to me, but who, in common with every bearer of a name I yield to the temptation of writing, insists on profiting promptly by the fact of inscription—very much as if first tricking me into it and then proving it upon me. The extinct societies that once were so sure of themselves, how can they *not* stir again if the right touch, that of a hand they actually knew, however little they may have happened to heed it, reaches tenderly back to them? The touch *is* the retrieval, so far as it goes, setting up as it does heaven knows what undefeated continuity. I must have been present among the faithful at North Bank during a Sunday afternoon or two of the winter of '77 and '78— I was to see the great lady alone but on a single occasion before her death; but those attestations are all but lost to me now in the livelier pitch of a scene, as I can only call it, of which I feel myself again, all amusedly, rather as sacrificed witness. I had driven over with Mrs. Greville from Milford Cottage, in Surrey, to the villa George Eliot and George Lewes had not long before built themselves, and which they much inhabited, at Witley—this indeed, I well remember, in no great flush of assurance that my own measure of our intended felicity would be quite that of my buoyant hostess. But here exactly comes, with my memory of Mrs. Greville, from which numberless by-memories dangle, the interesting question that makes for my recall why things happened, under her much-waved wing, not in any too coherent fashion—and this even though it was never once given her, I surmise, to guess that they anywhere fell short. So gently used, all round indeed, was this large, elegant, extremely near-sighted and extremely demonstrative lady, whose genius was all for friendship, admiration, declamation and expenditure, that one doubted whether in the whole course of her career she had ever once been brought up, as it were, against a recognised reality; other at least perhaps than the tiresome cost of the materially agreeable in life and the perverse appearance, at times, that though she "said" things, otherwise recited choice morceaux, whether French or English, with a marked oddity of manner, of "attack," a general incongruity of drawing-room art, the various contributive elements, hour, scene, persuaded patience and hushed attention, were perforce a precarious quantity.

It is in that bygone old grace of the unexploded factitious, the air of a thousand dimmed illusions and more or less early Victorian beatitudes on the part of the blandly idle and the supposedly accomplished, that Mrs. Greville, with her exquisite goodnature and her innocent fatuity, is embalmed for me; so that she becomes in that light a truly shining specimen, almost the image or compendium of a whole side of a social order. Just so she has happy suggestion; just so, whether or no by a twist of my mind toward the enviability of certain complacencies of faith and taste that we would yet neither live back into if we could, nor can catch again if we would, I see my forgotten friend of that moist autumn afternoon of our call, and of another, on the morrow, which I shall not pass over, as having rustled and gushed and protested and performed through her term under a kind of protection by the easy-going gods that is not of this fierce age. Amiabilities and absurdities, harmless serenities and vanities, pretensions and undertakings unashamed, still profited by the mildness of the critical air and the benignity of the social—on the right side at least of the social line. It had struck me from the first that nowhere so much as in England was it fortunate to *be* fortunate, and that against that condition, once it had somehow been handed down and determined, a number of the sharp truths that one might privately apprehend beat themselves beautifully in vain. I say beautifully for I confess without scruple to have found again and again at that time an attaching charm in the general exhibition of enjoyed immunity, paid for as it was almost always by the personal amenity, the practice of all sorts of pleasantness; if it kept the gods themselves for the time in goodhumour, one was willing enough, or at least I was, to be on the side of the gods. Unmistakeable too, as I seem to recover it, was the positive interest of watching and noting, roundabout one, for the turn, or rather for the blest continuity, of their benevolence: such an appeal proceeded, in this, that and the other particular case, from the fool's paradise really rounded and preserved, before one's eyes, for those who were so good as to animate it. There was always the question of how long they would be left to, and the growth of one's fine suspense, not to say one's frank little gratitude, as the miracle repeated itself.

All of which, I admit, dresses in many reflections the small circumstance that Milford Cottage, with its innumerable red candles and candle-shades, had affected me as the most embowered retreat for social innocence that it was possible to conceive, and as absolutely settling the question of whether the practice of pleasantness mightn't quite ideally pay for the fantastic protectedness. The red candles in the red shades have remained with me, inexplicably, as a vivid note of this pitch, shedding their rosy light, with the autumn gale, the averted reality, all shut out, upon such felicities of feminine helplessness as I couldn't have prefigured in advance and as exemplified, for further gathering in, the possibilities of the old tone. Nowhere had the evening curtains seemed so drawn, nowhere the copious service so soft, nowhere the second volume of the new novel, "half-uncut," so close to one's hand, nowhere the exquisite head and incomparable brush of the domesticated collie such an attestation of *that* standard at least, nowhere the harmonies of accident—of intention was more than one could say—so incapable of a wrong deflection. That society would lack the highest finish without some such distributed clusters of the thoroughly gentle, the mildly presumptuous and the inveterately mistaken, was brought home to me there, in fine, to a tune with which I had no quarrel, perverse enough as I had been from an early time to know but the impulse to egg on society to the fullest discharge of any material stirring within its breast and not making for cruelty or brutality, mere baseness or mere stupidity, that would fall into a picture or a scene. The quality of serene anxiety on the part for instance of exquisite Mrs. Thellusson, Mrs. Greville's mother, was by itself a plea for any privilege one should fancy her perched upon; and I scarce know if this be more or be less true because the anxiety

—at least as I culled its fragrance—was all about the most secondary and superfluous small matters alone. It struck me, I remember, as a new and unexpected form of the pathetic altogether; and there was no form of the pathetic, any more than of the tragic or the comic, that didn't serve as another pearl for one's lengthening string. And I pass over what was doubtless the happiest stroke in the composition, the fact of its involving, as all-distinguished husband of the other daughter, an illustrious soldier and servant of his sovereign, of his sovereigns that were successively to be, than against whose patient handsome bearded presence the whole complexus of femininities and futilities couldn't have been left in more tolerated and more contrasted relief; pass it over to remind myself of how, in my particular friend of the three, the comic and the tragic were presented in a confusion that made the least intended of them at any moment take effectively the place of the most. The impression, that is, was never that of the sentiment operating—save indeed perhaps when the dear lady applied her faculty for frank imitation of the ridiculous, which she then quite directly and remarkably achieved; but that she could be comic, that she *was* comic, was what least appeased her unrest, and there were reasons enough, in a word, why her failure of the grand manner or the penetrating note should evoke the idea of their opposites perfectly achieved. She sat, alike in adoration and emulation, at the feet of my admirable old friend Fanny Kemble, the goodnature of whose consent to "hear" her was equalled only by the immediately consequent action of the splendidly corrective spring on the part of that unsurpassed subject of the dramatic afflatus fairly, or, as I should perhaps above all say, contradictiously provoked. Then aspirant and auditor, rash adventurer and shy alarmist, were swept away to-

gether in the gust of magnificent rightness and beauty,
no scrap of the far-scattered prime proposal being left
to pick up.

Which detail of reminiscence has again stayed my
course to the Witley Villa, when even on the way I
quaked a little with my sense of what *generally* most
awaited or overtook my companion's prime proposals.
What had come most to characterise the Leweses to my
apprehension was that there couldn't be a thing in the
world about which they weren't, and on the most conceded and assured grounds, almost scientifically particular; which presumption, however, only added to the
relevance of one's learning how such a matter as their
relation with Mrs. Greville could in accordance with
noble consistencies be carried on. I could trust *her*
for it perfectly, as she knew no law but that of innocent
and exquisite aberration, never wanting and never less
than consecrating, and I fear I but took refuge for the
rest in declining all responsibility. I remember trying to
say to myself that, even such as we were, our visit
couldn't but scatter a little the weight of cloud on the
Olympus we scaled—given the dreadful drenching afternoon we were after all an imaginable short solace there;
and this indeed would have borne me through to the
end save for an incident which, with a quite ideal logic,
left our adventure an approved ruin. I see again our
bland, benign, commiserating hostess beside the fire in
a chill desert of a room where the master of the house
guarded the opposite hearthstone, and I catch once
more the impression of no occurrence of anything at all
appreciable but their liking us to have come, with our
terribly trivial contribution, mainly from a prevision of
how they should more devoutly like it when we departed. It is remarkable, but the occasion yields me no
single echo of a remark on the part of any of us—noth-

ing more than the sense that our great author herself peculiarly suffered from the fury of the elements, and that they had about them rather the minimum of the paraphernalia of reading and writing, not to speak of that of tea, a conceivable feature of the hour, but which was not provided for. Again I felt touched with privilege, but not, as in '69, with a form of it redeemed from barrenness by a motion of my own, and the taste of barrenness was in fact in my mouth under the effect of our taking leave. We did so with considerable flourish till we had passed out to the hall again, indeed to the door of the waiting carriage, toward which G. H. Lewes himself all sociably, *then* above all conversingly, wafted us —yet staying me by a sudden remembrance before I had entered the brougham and signing me to wait while he repaired his omission. I returned to the doorstep, whence I still see him reissue from the room we had just left and hurry toward me across the hall shaking high the pair of blue-bound volumes his allusion to the uninvited, the verily importunate loan of which by Mrs. Greville had lingered on the air after his dash in quest of them; "Ah those books—take them away, please, away, away!" I hear him unreservedly plead while he thrusts them again at me, and I scurry back into our conveyance, where, and where only, settled afresh with my companion, I venture to assure myself of the horrid truth that had squinted at me as I relieved our good friend of his superfluity. What indeed was this superfluity but the two volumes of my own precious "last"—we were still in the blest age of volumes—presented by its author to the lady of Milford Cottage, and by her, misguided votary, dropped with the best conscience in the world into the Witley abyss, out of which it had jumped with violence, under the touch of accident, straight up again into my own exposed face?

The bruise inflicted there I remember feeling for the moment only as sharp, such a mixture of delightful small questions at once salved it over and such a charm in particular for me to my recognising that this particular wrong—inflicted all unawares, which exactly made it sublime—was the only rightness of our visit. Our hosts hadn't so much as connected book with author, or author with visitor, or visitor with anything but the convenience of his ridding them of an unconsidered trifle; grudging as they so justifiedly did the impingement of such matters on their consciousness. The vivid demonstration of one's failure to penetrate there had been in the sweep of Lewes's gesture, which could scarce have been bettered by his actually wielding a broom. I think nothing passed between us in the brougham on revelation of the identity of the offered treat so emphatically declined—I see that I couldn't have laughed at it to the confusion of my gentle neighbour. But I quite recall my grasp of the *interest* of our distinguished friends' inaccessibility to the unattended plea, with the light it seemed to throw on what it was really to *be* attended. Never, never save as attended—by presumptions, that is, far other than any then hanging about one—would one so much as desire *not* to be pushed out of sight. I needn't attempt, however, to supply all the links in the chain of association which led to my finally just qualified beatitude: I had been served right enough in all conscience, but the pity was that Mrs. Greville had been. This I never wanted for her; and I may add, in the connection, that I discover now no grain of false humility in my having enjoyed in my own person adorning such a tale. There was positively a fine high thrill in thinking of persons—or at least of a person, for any fact about Lewes was but derivative— engaged in my own pursuit and yet detached, by what

I conceived, detached by a pitch of intellectual life, from all that made it actual to myself. *There* was the lift of contemplation, there the inspiring image and the big supporting truth; the pitch of intellectual life in the very fact of which we seemed, my hostess and I, to have caught our celebrities sitting in that queer bleak way wouldn't have bullied me in the least if it hadn't been the centre of such a circle of gorgeous creation. It was the fashion among the profane in short either to mis-doubt, before George Eliot's canvas, the latter's back-ing of rich thought, or else to hold that this matter of philosophy, and even if but of the philosophic vocabu-lary, thrust itself through to the confounding of the pic-ture. But with that thin criticism I wasn't, as I have already intimated, to have a moment's patience; I was to become, I was to remain—I take pleasure in repeat-ing—even a very Derondist of Derondists, for my own wanton joy: which amounts to saying that I found the figured, coloured tapestry *always* vivid enough to brave no matter what complication of the stitch.

From *The Middle Years* (1917), Chapter V.

*

THE VOICE OF CONCORD

I felt myself, on the spot,[1] cast about a little for the right expression of it, and then lost any hesitation to say that, putting the three or four biggest cities aside, Con-

[1] James is writing of his return, after an absence of twenty-one years, to America and New England in the autumn of 1904. [*Editor's note.*]

cord, Massachusetts, had an identity more palpable to
the mind, had nestled in other words more successfully
beneath her narrow fold of the mantle of history, than
any other American town. "Compare me with places of
my size, you know," one seemed to hear her plead, with
the modesty that, under the mild autumn sun, so well
became her russet beauty; and this exactly it was that
prompted the emphasis of one's reply, or, as it may even
be called, of one's declaration.

"Ah, my dear, it isn't a question of places of your
'size,' since among places of your size you're too obviously and easily first: it's a question of places, so many
of them, of fifty times your size, and which yet don't
begin to have a fraction of your weight, or your character, or your intensity of presence and sweetness of
tone, or your moral charm, or your pleasant appreciability, or, in short, of anything that is yours. Your 'size'?
Why, you're the biggest little place in America—with
only New York and Boston and Chicago, by what I
make out, to surpass you; and the country is lucky indeed to have you, in your sole and single felicity, for if
it hadn't, where in the world should we go, inane and
unappeased, for the particular communication of which
you have the secret? The country is colossal, and you
but a microscopic speck on the hem of its garment; yet
there's nothing else like you, take you all round, for we
see you complacently, with the naked eye, whereas there
are vast sprawling, bristling areas, great grey 'centres of
population' that spread, on the map, like irremediable
grease-spots, which fail utterly of any appeal to our vision or any control of it, leaving it to pass them by as if
they were not. If you are so thoroughly the opposite of
one of these I don't say it's all your superlative merit; it's
rather, as I have put it, your felicity, your good fortune,
the result of the half-dozen happy turns of the wheel

in your favour. Half-a-dozen such turns, you see, are, for any mortal career, a handsome allowance; and your merit is that, recognizing this, you have not fallen below your state. But it's your fortune, above all, that's your charm. One doesn't want to be patronizing, but you didn't, thank goodness, make yours. That's what the other places, the big ones that are as nothing to you, are trying to do, the country over—to make theirs; and, from the point of view of these remarks, all in vain. Your luck is that you didn't have to; yours had been, just as it shows in you to-day, made *for* you, and you at the most but gratefully submitted to it. It must be said for you, however, that you keep it; and it isn't every place that would have been capable——! You keep the look, you keep the feeling, you keep the air. Your great trees arch over these possessions more protectingly, covering them in as a cherished presence; and you have settled to your tone and your type as to treasures that can now never be taken. Show me the other places in America (of the few that have *had* anything) from which the best hasn't mainly been taken, or isn't in imminent danger of being. There is old Salem, there is old Newport, which I am on my way to see again, and which, if you will, are, by what I hear, still comparatively intact; but their having was never a having like yours, and they adorn, precisely, my little tale of your supremacy. No, I don't want to be patronizing, but your only fault is your tendency to improve—I mean just by your duration as you *are;* which indeed is the only sort of improvement that is not questionable."

Such was the drift of the warm flood of appreciation, of reflection, that Concord revisited could set rolling over the field of a prepared sensibility; and I feel as if I had quite made my point, such as it is, in asking what other American village could have done anything of the sort. I should have been at fault perhaps only in speaking of the interest in question as visible, on that large scale, to the "naked eye"; the truth being perhaps that one wouldn't have been so met half-way by one's impression unless one had rather particularly *known,* and that knowledge, in such a case, amounts to a pair of magnifying spectacles. I remember indeed putting it to myself on the November Sunday morning, tepid and bright and perfect for its use, through which I walked from the station under the constant archway of the elms, as yet but indulgently thinned: would one know, for one's self, what had formerly been the matter here, if one hadn't happened to be able to get round behind, in the past, as it were, and more or less understand? Would the operative elements of the past—little old Concord Fight, essentially, and Emerson and Hawthorne and Thoreau, with the rest of the historic animation and the rest of the figured and shifting "transcendental" company, to its last and loosest ramifications—would even these handsome quantities have so lingered to one's intelligent after-sense, if one had not brought with one some sign by which they too would know; dim, shy spectralities as, for themselves, they must, at the best, have become? Idle, however, such questions when, by the chance of the admirable day, everything, in its own way and order, unmistakably came *out*—every string sounded as if, for all the world, the loose New England town (and I apply the expression but to the relations of objects and places), were a lyre swept by the hand of Apollo. Apollo was the spirit of antique piety, looking about, pausing, remembering, as he moved to his music; and there were glimpses and reminders that of course kept him much longer than others.

Seated there at its ease, as if placidly familiar with pilgrims and quite taking their homage for granted, the place had the very aspect of some grave, refined New England matron of the "old school," the widow of a high celebrity, living on and on in possession of all his relics and properties, and, though not personally addicted to gossip or to journalism, having become, where the great company kept by her in the past is concerned, quite cheerful and modern and responsive. From her position, her high-backed chair by the window that commands most of the coming and going, she looks up intelligently, over her knitting, with no vision of any limit on her part as yet, to this attitude, and with nothing indeed to suggest the possibility of a limit save a hint of that loss of temporal perspective in which we recognize the mental effect of a great weight of years. I had formerly the acquaintance of a very interesting lady, of extreme age, whose early friends, in "literary circles," are now regarded as classics, and who, toward the end of her life, always said, "You know Charles Lamb has produced a play at Drury Lane," or "You know William Hazlitt has fallen in love with such a very odd woman." Her facts were perfectly correct; only death had beautifully passed out of her world—since I don't remember her mentioning to me the demise, which she might have made so contemporary, either of Byron or of Scott. When people were ill she admirably forebore to ask about them—she disapproved wholly of such conditions; and there were interesting invalids round about her, near to her, whose existence she for long years consummately ignored. It is some such quiet backward stride as those of my friend that I seem to hear the voice of old Concord take in reference to her annals, and it is not too much to say that where her soil is most sacred, I fairly caught, on the breeze, the mitigated perfect tense. "You know there has been a fight between our men and the King's"—one wouldn't have

been surprised, that crystalline Sunday noon, where so
little had changed, where the stream and the bridge,
and all nature, and the *feeling*, above all, still so directly
testify, at any fresh-sounding form of such an announcement.

I had forgotten, in all the years, with what thrilling
clearness that supreme site speaks—though anciently,
while so much of the course of the century was still to
run, the distinctness might have seemed even greater.
But to stand there again was to take home this fore-
shortened view, the gained nearness, to one's sensibility; to look straight over the heads of the "American
Weimar" company at the inestimable hour that had so
handsomely set up for them their background. The
Fight had been the hinge—so one saw it—on which the
large revolving future was to turn; or it had been better,
perhaps, the large firm nail, ringingly driven in, from
which the beautiful portrait-group, as we see it to-day,
was to hang. Beautiful exceedingly the local Emerson
and Thoreau and Hawthorne and (in a fainter way)
tutti quanti; but beautiful largely because the fine old
incident down in the valley had so seriously prepared
their effect. That seriousness gave once for all the pitch,
and it was verily as if, under such a value, even with
the seed of a "literary circle" so freely scattered by an
intervening hand, the vulgar note would in that air never
be possible. As I had inevitably, in long absence, let the
value, for immediate perception, rather waste itself, so,
on the spot, it came back most instantly with the extraordinary sweetness of the river, which, under the
autumn sun, like all the American rivers one had seen or
was to see, straightway took the whole case straightway
into its hands. "Oh, you shall tell me of your impression
when you have felt what *I* can do for it: so hang over
me well!"—that's what they all seem to say.

I hung over Concord River then as long as I could, and recalled how Thoreau, Hawthorne, Emerson himself, have expressed with due sympathy the sense of this full, slow, sleepy, meadowy flood, which sets its pace and takes its twists like some large obese benevolent person, scarce so frankly unsociable as to pass you at all. It had watched the Fight, it even now confesses, without a quickening of its current, and it draws along the woods and the orchards and the fields with the purr of a mild domesticated cat who rubs against the family and the furniture. Not to be recorded, at best, however, I think, never to emerge from the state of the inexpressible, in respect to the spot, by the bridge, where one most lingers, is the sharpest suggestion of the whole scene—the power diffused in it which makes it, after all these years, or perhaps indeed by reason of their number, so irresistibly touching. All the commemorative objects, the stone marking the burial-place of the three English soldiers, the animated image of the young belted American yeoman by Mr. Daniel French, the intimately associated element in the presence, not far off, of the old manse, interesting theme of Hawthorne's pen, speak to the spirit, no doubt, in one of the subtlest tones of which official history is capable, and yet somehow leave the exquisite melancholy of everything unuttered. It lies too deep, as it always so lies where the ground has borne the weight of the short, simple act, intense and unconscious, that was to determine the event, determine the future in the way we call immortally. For we read into the scene too little of what we may, unless this muffled touch in it somehow reaches us so that we feel the pity and the irony of the *precluded* relation on the part of the fallen defenders. The sense that was theirs and that moved them we know, but we seem to know better still the sense that wasn't and that couldn't, and that forms

our luxurious heritage as our eyes, across the gulf, seek
to meet their eyes; so that we are almost ashamed of taking so much, such colossal quantity and value, as the
equivalent of their dimly-seeing offer. The huge bargain
they made for us, in a word, made by the gift of the
little all they had—to the modesty of which amount the
homely rural facts grouped there together have appeared to go on testifying—this brilliant advantage
strikes the imagination that yearns over them as unfairly
enjoyed at their cost. Was it delicate, was it decent—
that is *would* it have been—to ask the embattled farm-
ers, simple-minded, unwitting folk, to make us so inordinate a present with so little of the conscious credit
of it? Which all comes indeed, perhaps, simply to the
most poignant of all those effects of disinterested sacrifice
that the toil and trouble of our forefathers produce for
us. The minute-men at the bridge were of course interested intensely, as they believed—but such, too,
was the artful manner in which we see *our* latent, lurking, waiting interest like, a Jew in a dusky back-shop,
providentially bait the trap.

Beyond even such broodings as these, and to another
purpose, moreover, the communicated spell falls, in its
degree, into that pathetic oddity of the small aspect, and
the rude and the lowly, the reduced and humiliated
above all, that sits on so many nooks and corners, objects
and appurtenances, old contemporary things—contemporary with the doings of our race; simplifying our an-
tecedents, our annals, to within an inch of their life,
making us ask, in presence of the rude relics even of
greatness, mean retreats and receptacles, construction-
ally so poor, from what barbarians or from what pigmies we have sprung. There are certain rough black
mementos of the early monarchy, in England and Scotland, there are glimpses of the original humble homes

of other greatness as well, that strike in perfection this grim little note; which has the interest of our being free to take it, for curiosity, for luxury of thought, as that of the real or that of the romantic, and with which, again, the deep Concord rusticity, momentary medium of our national drama, essentially consorts. We remember the small hard facts of the Shakespeare house at Stratford; we remember the rude closet, in Edinburgh Castle, in which James VI of Scotland was born, or the other little black hole, at Holyrood, in which Mary Stuart "sat" and in which Rizzio was murdered. These, I confess, are odd memories at Concord; although the manse, near the spot where we last paused, and against the edge of whose acre or two the loitering river seeks friction in the manner I have mentioned, would now seem to have shaken itself a trifle disconcertingly free of the ornamental mosses scattered by Hawthorne's light hand; it stands there, beyond its gate, with every due similitude to the shrunken historic site in general. To which I must hasten to add, however, that I was much more struck with the way these particular places of visitation resist their pressure of reference than with their affecting us as below their fortune. Intrinsically they are as naught—deeply depressing, in fact, to any impulse to reconstitute, the house in which Hawthorne spent what remained to him of life after his return from the Italy of his Donatello and his Miriam. Yet, in common with everything else, this mild monument benefits by that something in the air which makes us tender, keeps us respectful; meets, in the general interest, waving it vaguely away, any closer assault of criticism.

It is odd, and it is also exquisite, that these witnessing ways should be the last ground on which we feel moved to ponderation of the "Concord school"—to use,

I admit, a futile expression; or rather, I should doubtless say, it *would* be odd if there were not inevitably something absolute in the fact of Emerson's all but lifelong connection with them. We may smile a little as we "drag in" Weimar, but I confess myself, for my part, much more satisfied than not by our happy equivalent, "in American money," for Goethe and Schiller. The money is a potful in the second case as in the first, and if Goethe, in the one, represents the gold and Schiller the silver, I find (and quite putting aside any bimetallic prejudice) the same good relation in the other between Emerson and Thoreau. I open Emerson for the same benefit for which I open Goethe, the sense of moving in large intellectual space, and that of the gush, here and there, out of the rock, of the crystalline cupful, in wisdom and poetry, in Wahrheit and Dichtung; and whatever I open Thoreau for (I needn't take space here for the good reasons) I open him oftener than I open Schiller. Which comes back to our feeling that the rarity of Emerson's genius, which has made him so, for the attentive peoples, the first, and the one really rare, American spirit in letters, couldn't have spent his career in a charming woody, watery place, for so long socially and typically and, above all, interestingly homogeneous, without an effect as of the communication to it of something ineffaceable. It was during his long span his immediate concrete, sufficient world; it gave him his nearest vision of life, and he drew half his images, we recognize, from the revolution of its seasons and the play of its manners. I don't speak of the other half, which he drew from elsewhere. It is admirably, to-day, as if we were still seeing these things *in* those images, which stir the air like birds, dim in the eventide, coming home to nest. If one had reached a "time of life" one had thereby at least heard him lecture; and not a russet leaf fell for me, while I was there, but fell with an Emersonian drop.

From Chapter VIII of The American Scene (1907).

A JOURNAL

BOSTON——CAMBRIDGE——LONDON——PARIS

25 NOVEMBER 1881–11 NOVEMBER 1882

Brunswick Hotel, Boston, November 25th, 1881. If I should write here all that I might write, I should speedily fill this as yet unspotted blank-book, bought in London six months ago, but hitherto unopened. It is so long since I have kept any notes, taken any memoranda, written down my current reflections, taken a sheet of paper, as it were, into my confidence. Meanwhile so much has come and gone, so much that it is now too late to catch, to reproduce, to preserve. I have lost too much by losing, or rather by not having acquired, the note-taking habit. It might be of great profit to me; and now that I am older, that I have more time, that the labour of writing is less onerous to me, and I can work more at my leisure, I ought to endeavour to keep, to a certain extent, a record of passing impressions, of all that comes, that goes, that I see, and feel, and observe. To catch and keep something of life—that's what I mean. Here I am back in America, for instance, after six years of absence, and likely while here to see and learn a great deal that ought not to become mere waste material. Here I am, *da vero*, and here I am likely to be for the next five months.

I am glad I have come—it was a wise thing to do. I needed to see again *les miens,* to revive my relations with them, and my sense of the consequences that these relations entail. Such relations, such consequences, are a part of one's life, and the best life, the most complete, is the one that takes full account of such things. One can only do this by seeing one's people from time to time, by being with them, by entering into their lives. Apart from this I hold it was not necessary I should come to this country. I am 37 [1] years old, I have made my choice, and God knows that I have now no time to waste. My choice is the old world—my choice, my need, my life. There is no need for me today to argue about this; it is an inestimable blessing to me, and a rare good fortune, that the problem was settled long ago, and that I have now nothing to do but to act on the settlement.— My impressions here are exactly what I expected they would be, and I scarcely see the place, and feel the manners, the race, the tone of things, now that I am on the spot, more vividly than I did while I was still in Europe. My work lies there—and with this vast new world, *je n'ai que faire.* One can't do both—one must choose. No European writer is called upon to assume that terrible burden, and it seems hard that I should be. The burden is necessarily greater for an American—for he *must* deal, more or less, even if only by implication, with Europe; whereas no European is obliged to deal in the least with America. No one dreams of calling him less complete for not doing so. (I speak of course of people who do the sort of work that I do; not of economists, of social science people.) The painter of manners who

---

[1] He was actually 38. [Footnote by F. O. Matthiessen and K. B. Murdock in *The Notebooks of Henry James.* The footnotes to this journal are all from this edition.—*Editor's note.*]

neglects America is not thereby incomplete as yet; but a hundred years hence—fifty years hence perhaps—he will doubtless be accounted so. My impressions of America, however, I shall, after all, not write here. I don't need to write them (at least not *à propos* of Boston); I know too well what they are. In many ways they are extremely pleasant; but, Heaven forgive me! I feel as if my time were terribly wasted here! . . .

It is too late to recover all those lost impressions—those of the last six years—that I spoke of in beginning; besides, they are not lost altogether, they are buried deep in my mind, they have become part of my life, of my nature. At the same time, if I had nothing better to do, I might indulge in a retrospect that would be interesting and even fruitful—look back over all that has befallen me since last I left my native shores. I could remember vividly, and I have little doubt I could express happily enough, if I made the effort. I could remember without effort with what an irresistible longing I turned to Europe, with what ardent yet timid hopes, with what indefinite yet inspiring intentions, I took leave of *les miens*. I recall perfectly the maturing of my little plan to get abroad again and remain for years, during the summer of 1875; the summer the latter part of which I spent in Cambridge. It came to me there on my return from New York where I had been spending a bright, cold, unremunerative, uninteresting winter, finishing *Roderick Hudson* and writing for the *Nation*. (It was these two tasks that kept me alive.) I had returned from Europe the year before that, the beginning of September, '74, sailing for Boston with Wendell Holmes and his wife as my fellow passengers. I had come back then to "try New York," thinking it my duty to attempt to live at home before I should grow older, and not take for

AUTOBIOGRAPHY AND JOURNAL

refuge being unable to find quarters at Biarritz. Then late in September I spent a short time at St. Germain, at the Pavillon Louis XIV. I was finishing *The American*. The pleasantest episode (by far) of that summer was [my] visit to the Childes; to whom I had been introduced [by] dear Jane Norton; who had been very kind to me during the winter; and who have remained my very good [frie]nds. Varennes is a little moated *castel* of the most [pict]uresque character, a few miles from Montargis, *au [coeur] de l'ancienne France*. I well recall the impression [of my] arrival—driving over from Montargis with [...]d Childe—in the warm August evening and [...]g the place in the vague twilight, which made it [pr]ecisely like a *décor d'opéra*. I have been back [sin]ce—and it was still delightful; but at that time [...]t had my now very considerable experience of [...]isits in England; I had not seen all those other things. Varennes therefore was an exquisite [...]—a memory I shall never lose. I settled myse[lf in] [Pa]ris—or attempted to do so (I like to ling[er] [...]ris, and to recall them one by one); I h[...] [d]etails, and to recall them one by one); I h[...] of giving it up. But there were difficult[...] [...] Luxembourg—I couldn't get back my [...]ich I had given up during the Summe[r] [...]r what suddenly brought me to the p[...] [...] to; I will try London." I think a l[...] [...]d a good deal to do with it, in whi[...] [...]'t you?—That must be the plac[e] [...] outside often moves one (moves [...] the same word infinitely multip[...] [...]m within. I did try it, and it h[...] [...]y most ardent hopes. As I [...] [...]ve become passionately fo[r] [...]or life. Here I sit scribblin[g] [...] hotel—on a marble-topp[...]

---

granted too much that Europe alone was possible; especially as Europe for me then meant simply Italy, where I had had some very discouraged hours, and which, lovely and desirable though it was, didn't seem as a permanent residence, to lead to anything. I wanted something more active, and I came back and sought it in New York. I came back with a certain amount of scepticism, but with very loyal intentions, and extremely eager to be "interested." As I say, I was interested but imperfectly, and I very soon decided what was the real issue of my experiment. It was by no means equally soon, however, that I perceived how I should be able to cross the Atlantic again. But the opportunity came to me at last—it loomed before me one summer's day, in Quincy St. The best thing I could imagine then was to go and take up my abode in Paris. I went (sailing about October 20th, 1875) and I settled myself in Paris with the idea that I should spend several years there. This was not really what I wanted; what I wanted was London—and Paris was only a stopgap. But London appeared to me then impossible. I believed that I might arrive there in the fulness of years, but there were all sorts of obstacles to my attempting to live there then. I wonder greatly now, in the light of my present knowledge of England, that these obstacles should have seemed so large, so overwhelming and depressing as they did at that time. When a year later I came really to look them in the face, they absolutely melted away. But that year in Paris was not a lost year—on the contrary. On my way thither I spent something like a fortnight in London; lodging at Story's Hotel, in Dover St. It was November—dark, foggy, muddy, rainy—and I knew scarcely a creature in the place. I don't remember calling on anyone but Lady Rose and H. J. W. Coulson, with whom I went out to lunch at Petersham, near Richmond. And yet the great city seemed to me enchanting, and I would have given my little finger to remain there rather than go to Paris. But I went to Paris, and lived for a year at 29 Rue de Luxembourg (now Rue Cambon). I shall not attempt to write the history of that year—further than to say that it was time by no means misspent. I learned to know Paris and French affairs much better than before—I got a certain familiarity with Paris (added to what I had acquired before) which I shall never lose. I wrote letters to the *New York Tribune,* of which, though they were poor stuff, I may say that they were too good for the purpose (of course they didn't succeed). I saw a good deal of Charles Peirce that winter—as to whom his being a man of genius reconciled me to much that was intolerable in him.[1] In the spring, at Madame Turgénieff's, I made the acquaintance of Paul Joukowsky. *Non ragioniam di lui—ma guarda e passa.* I don't speak of Ivan Turgénieff, most delightful and lovable of men, nor of Gustave Flaubert, whom I shall always be so glad to have known; a powerful, serious, melancholy, manly, deeply corrupted, yet not corrupting, nature. There was something I greatly liked in him, and he was very kind to me. He was a head and shoulders above the others, the men I saw at his house on Sunday afternoons—Zola, Goncourt, Daudet,

---

[1] James' reaction to Peirce was summed up in a letter home at the time: "He is a very good fellow—when he is not in ill-humour; then he is intolerable. But, as William says, he is a man of genius. . . ." Peirce wrote to William: "Your brother is looking pretty well, but looks a little serious. . . . He is a splendid fellow. I admire him greatly and have only discovered two faults in him. One is that his digestion isn't quite that of an ostrich and the other is that he isn't as fond of turning over questions as I am, but likes to settle them and have done with them. A manly trait too, but not a philosophic one."

A JOURNAL

etc. (I mean as a man—not as a talker, etc.) I remem in especial one afternoon (a weekday) that I went him and found him alone. I sat with him a lon something led him to repeat to me a little poer Gautier's—*Les Vieux Portraits* (what led him it was that we had been talking of French he had been expressing his preference fo Gautier over Alfred de Musset—*il était* etc.). I went that winter a great deal t Française—though not so much as whe in '72. Then I went every night—or a been a great deal since. I may say tha die Française. Of course I saw a g American "set"—the American *plein Paris.* They were all very pitable, etc; they knew up to a But ineffably tiresome and v had become a kind of obliga with my suddenly decidi indefinite residence, take there as best I could. I re S. made of my doing s as to whom I was perf them the right to ju Nothing is more women than the they assume suc a hundred wa couldn't get o I hated the new quarte nal outsid should s places: and at

—and conscious of a ferocious homesickness—a home-sickness which makes me think of the day when I shall next see the white cliffs of old England loom through their native fog, as one of the happiest of my life! The history of the five years I have spent in London—a pledge, I suppose, of many future years—is too long, and too full to write. I can only glance at it here. I took a lodging at 3 Bolton St., Piccadilly; and there I have remained till today—there I have left my few earthly possessions, to await my return. I have *lived* much there, felt much, thought much, learned much, produced much; the little shabby furnished apartment ought to be sacred to me. I came to London as a complete stranger, and today I know much too many people. *J'y suis absolument comme chez moi.* Such an experience is an education—it fortifies the character and embellishes the mind. It is difficult to speak adequately or justly of London. It is not a pleasant place; it is not agreeable, or cheerful, or easy, or exempt from reproach. It is only magnificent. You can draw up a tremendous list of reasons why it should be insupportable. The fogs, the smoke, the dirt, the darkness, the wet, the distances, the ugliness, the brutal size of the place, the horrible numerosity of society, the manner in which this senseless bigness is fatal to amenity, to convenience, to conversation, to good manners—all this and much more you may expatiate upon. You may call it dreary, heavy, stupid, dull, inhuman, vulgar at heart and tiresome in form. I have felt these things at times so strongly that I have said—"Ah London, you too then are impossible?" But these are occasional moods; and for one who takes it as I take it, London is on the whole the most possible form of life. I take it as an artist and as a bachelor; as one who has the passion of observation and whose business is the study of human life. It is the biggest aggregation of human life—the most complete compendium of the world. The human race is better represented there than anywhere else, and if you learn to know your London you learn a great many things. I felt all this in that autumn of 1876, when I first took up my abode in Bolton St. I had very few friends, the season was of the darkest and wettest; but I was in a state of deep delight. I had complete liberty, and the prospect of profitable work; I used to take long walks in the rain. I took possession of London; I felt it to be the right place. I could get English books: I used to read in the evenings, before an English fire. I can hardly say how it was, but little by little I came to know people, to dine out, etc. I did, I was able to do, nothing at all to bring this state of things about; it came rather of itself. I had very few letters— I was afraid of letters. Three or four from Henry Adams, three or four from Mrs. Wister, of which I only, as I think, presented one (to George Howard). Poor Motley, who died a few months later, and on whom I had no claim of *any* kind, sent me an invitation to the Athenaeum, which was renewed for several months, and which proved an unspeakable blessing. When once one starts in the London world (and one cares enough about it, as I did, to make one's self agreeable, as I did) *cela va de soi;* it goes with constantly increasing velocity. I remained in London all the following summer—till Sept. 1st—and then went abroad and spent some six weeks in Paris, which was rather empty and very lovely, and went a good deal to the theatre. Then I went to Italy, spending almost all my time in Rome (I had a little apartment flooded with sun, in the Capo le Case). I came back to England before Xmas and spent the following nine months or so in Bolton St. The club question had become serious and difficult; a club was indispensable, but I had of course none of my own. I went through Gaskell's (and I think Locker's) kindness for some time to the Travellers'; then after that for a good while to the St. James's, where I could pay a monthly fee. At last, I forget exactly when, I was elected to the Reform; I think it was about April, 1878. (F. H. Hill had proposed, and C. H. Roberts had seconded, me: or vice versa.) This was an excellent piece of good fortune, and the Club has ever since been, to me, a convenience of the first order. I could not have remained in London without it, and I have become extremely fond of it; a deep local attachment. I can now only briefly enumerate the landmarks of the rest of my residence in London. In the autumn of 1878 I went to Scotland, chiefly to stay at Tillypronie. (I afterwards paid a short visit at Gillesbie, Mrs. Rogerson's, in Dumfriesshire.) This was my first visit to Scotland, which made a great impression on me. The following year, 1879, I went abroad again —but only to Paris. I stayed in London during all August, writing my little book on Hawthorne, and on September 1st crossed over to Paris and remained there till within a few days of Xmas. I lodged again in the Rue de Luxembourg, in another house, in a delightful little *entresol entre cour et jardin,* which I had to give up after a few weeks however, as it had been let over my head. Afterwards I went to a hotel in the Rue St. Augustin (de Choiseul et d'Égypte) where I was staying during the great snow-storm of that year, which will long be famous. It was in that October that I went again to Varennes; I had other plans for seeing a little of France which I was unable to carry out. But I did a good deal of work: finished the ill-fated little *Hawthorne,*[1] finished

---

[1] James's *Hawthorne,* printed in 1879, was "ill-fated" in the attacks it provoked. He wrote Elizabeth Boott on 22 February 1880: "The American press, with 2 or 3 exceptions, seems furious over my poor little Hawthorne. It is a melancholy

Confidence, began *Washington Square*, wrote a *Bundle of Letters*. I went that Christmas, as I had been, I think, the Xmas before, to Ch. Milnes Gaskell's (Thorne's). In the spring I went to Italy—partly to escape the "season," which had become a terror to me. I couldn't keep out of it—(I had become a highly-developed diner-out, etc.) and its interruptions, its repetitions, its fatigues, were horribly wearisome, and made work extremely difficult. I went to Florence and spent a couple of months, during which I took a short run down to Rome and to Naples, where I had not been since my first visit to Italy, in 1869. I spent three days with Paul Joukowsky at Posilipo, and a couple of days alone at Sorrento. Florence was divine, as usual, and I was a great deal with the Bootts. At that exquisite Bellosguardo at the Hotel de l'Arno, in a room in that deep recess, in the front, I began the *Portrait of a Lady*[1]—that is, I took up, and worked over, an old beginning, made long before. I returned to London to meet William, who came out in the early part of June, and spent a month with me in Bolton St., before going to the continent. That summer and autumn I worked, *tant bien que mal*, at my novel which began to appear in *Macmillan* in October (1880). I got away from London more or less—to Brighton, detestable in August, to Folkestone, Dover, St. Leonard's, etc. I tried to work hard, and I paid very

revelation of angry vanity, vulgarity and ignorance. I thought they would protest a good deal at my calling New England life unfurnished, but I didn't expect they would lose their heads and their manners at such a rate." A letter to Howells a month earlier refers to some critics of the book as "bloodhounds" eager to besplatter "the decent public" with its author's "gore."

[1] When he wrote the preface to *The Portrait of a Lady* James's memory betrayed him into misdating this visit to the spring of 1879.

few visits. I had a plan of coming to America for the
winter and even took my passage; but I gave it up. William came back from abroad and was with me again for a
few days, before sailing for home. I spent November
and December quietly in London, getting on with the
Portrait, which went steadily, but very slowly, every
part being written twice. About Xmas I went down into
Cornwall, to stay with the John Clarks, who were wintering there, and then to the Pakenhams', who were
(and still are) in the Government House at Plymouth.
(Xmas day, indeed, I spent at the Pakenhams'—a bright,
military dinner at which I took in Elizabeth Thompson
[Mrs. Butler], the military paintress: a gentle, pleasing
woman, very deaf.) Cornwall was charming, and my
dear Sir John drove me far away to Penzance, and then
to the Land's End, where we spent the morning of New
Year's day—a soft moist morning, with the great Atlantic
heaving gently round the outermost point of old England. (I was wrong just above in saying that I went *first*
to the Clarks'. I went on there from Devonport.) I came
back to London for a few weeks, and then, again, I went
abroad. I wished to get away from the London crowd,
the London hubbub, all the entanglements and interruptions of London life; and to quietly bring my novel to a
close. So I planned to betake myself to Venice. I started
about February 10th and I came back in the middle of
July following. I have always to pay toll in Paris—it's
impossible to pass through. I was there for a fortnight,
which I didn't much enjoy. Then I traveled down
through France, to Avignon, Marseilles, Nice, Mentone
and San Remo, in which latter place I spent three charming weeks, during most of which time I had the genial
society of Mrs. Lombard and Fanny L. who came over
from Nice for a fortnight. I worked there capitally, and
it made me very happy. I used in the morning to take

a walk among the olives, over the hills behind the queer little black, steep town. Those old paved roads that rise behind and above San Remo, and climb and wander through the dusky light of the olives, have an extraordinary sweetness. Below and beyond, were the deep ravines, on whose sides old villages were perched, and the blue sea, glittering through the grey foliage. Fanny L. used to go with me—enjoying it so much that it was a pleasure to take her. I went back to the inn to breakfast (that is, lunch), and scribbled for 3 or 4 hours in the afternoon. Then, in the fading light, I took another stroll, before dinner. We went to bed early, but I used to read late. I went with the Lombards, one lovely day, on an enchanting drive—to the strange little old mountain town of Ceriana. I shall never forget that; it was one of the things one remembers; the grand clear hills, among which we wound higher and higher; the long valley, swimming seaward, far away beneath; the bright Mediterranean, growing paler and paler as we rose above it; the splendid stillness, the infinite light, the clumps of olives, the brown villages, pierced by the carriage road, where the vehicle bumped against opposite doorposts. I spent ten days at Milan after that, working at my tale and scarcely speaking to a soul; Milan was cold, dull, and less attractive than it had been to me before. Thence I went straight to Venice, where I remained till the last of June—between three and four months. It would take long to go into that now; and yet I can't simply pass it by. It was a charming time; one of those things that don't repeat themselves; I seemed to myself to grow young again. The lovely Venetian spring came and went, and brought with it an infinitude of impressions, of delightful hours. I became passionately fond of the place, of the life, of the people, of the habits. I asked myself at times whether it wouldn't be a happy thought to take a little *pied-à-terre* there, which one might keep forever. I looked at unfurnished apartments; I fancied myself coming back every year. I *shall* go back; but not every year. Herbert Pratt was there for a month, and I saw him tolerably often; he used to talk to me about Spain, about the East, about Tripoli, Persia, Damascus; till it seemed to me that life would be *manquée* altogether if one shouldn't have some of that knowledge. He was a most singular, most interesting type, and I shall certainly put him into a novel. I shall even make the portrait close and he won't mind. Seeing picturesque lands, simply for their own sake, and without making any use of it—that, with him, is a passion—a passion of which if one lives with him a little (a little, I say; not too much) one feels the contagion. He gave me the nostalgia of the sun, of the south, of colour, of freedom, of being one's own master, and doing absolutely what one pleases. He used to say, "I know such a sunny corner, under the south wall of old Toledo. There's a wild fig tree growing there; I have lain on the grass, with my guitar. There was a musical muleteer, etc." I remember one evening when he took me to a queer little wineshop, haunted only by gondoliers and *facchini,* in an out of the way corner of Venice. We had some excellent muscat wine; he had discovered the place and made himself quite at home there. Another evening I went with him to his rooms—far down on the Grand Canal, overlooking the Rialto. It was a hot night; the cry of the gondoliers came up from the Canal. He took out a couple of Persian books and read me extracts from Firdousi and Saadi. A good deal might be done with Herbert Pratt. He, however, was but a small part of my Venice. I lodged on the Riva, 4161, *quarto piano.* The view from my windows was *una bellezza;* the far-shining lagoon, the pink walls of San Giorgio, the down-

ward curve of the Riva, the distant islands, the movement of the quay, the gondolas in profile. Here I wrote,
diligently every day and finished, or virtually finished,
my novel. As I say, it was a charming life; it seemed to
me, at times, too improbable, too festive. I went out in
the morning—first to Florian's, to breakfast; then to my
bath, at the Stabilimento Chitarin; then I wandered
about, looking at pictures, street life, etc., till noon,
when I went for my real breakfast to the Café Quadri.
After this I went home and worked till six o'clock—or
sometimes only till five. In this latter case I had time for
an hour or two *en gondole* before dinner. The evenings
I strolled about, went to Florian's, listened to the music
in the Piazza, and two or three nights a week went to
Mrs. Bronson's. That was a resource but the milieu was
too American. Late in the spring came Mrs. V.R., from
Rome, who was an even greater resource. I went with
her one day to Torcello and Burano; where we took our
lunch and ate it on a lovely canal at the former place.
Toward the last of April I went down to Rome and
spent a fortnight—during part of which I was laid up
with one of those terrible attacks in my head. But Rome
was very lovely; I saw a great deal of Mrs. V.R.; had
(with her) several beautiful drives. One in particular I
remember; out beyond the Ponte Nomentano, a splendid
Sunday. We left the carriage and wandered into the
fields, where we sat down for some time. The exquisite
stillness, the divine horizon, brought back to me out of
the buried past all that ineffable, incomparable impression of Rome (1869, 1873). I returned to Venice by
Ancona and Rimini. From Ancona I drove to Loreto,
and, on the same occasion, to Recanati, to see the house
of Giacomo Leopardi, whose infinitely touching letters I
had been reading while in Rome. The day was lovely
and the excursion picturesque; but I was not allowed

to enter Leopardi's house. I saw, however, the dreary little hill-town where he passed so much of his life, with its enchanting beauty of site, and its strange, bright loneliness. I saw the streets—I saw the views he looked upon . . . Very little can have changed. I spent only an evening at Rimini, where I made the acquaintance of a most obliging officer, who seemed delighted to converse with a *forestiero,* and who walked me (it was a Sunday evening) all over the place. I passed near *Urbino:* that is, I passed a station, where I might have descended to spend the night, to drive to Urbino the next day. But I didn't stop! If I had been told that a month before, I should have repelled the foul insinuation. But my reason was strong. I was so nervous about my interrupted work that every day I lost was a misery, and I hurried back to Venice and to my MS. But I made another short absence, in June—a 5 days' *giro* to Vicenza, Bassano, Padua. At Vicenza I spent 3 of these days—it was wonderfully sweet; old Italy, and the old feeling of it. Vivid in my memory is the afternoon I arrived, when I wandered into the Piazza and sat there in the warm shade, before a *caffe* with the smooth slabs of the old pavement around me, the big palace and the tall *campanile* opposite, etc. It was so soft, so mellow, so quiet, so genial, so Italian; very little movement, only the waning of the bright day, the approach of the summer night. Before I left Venice the heat became intense, the days and nights alike impossible. I left it at last, and closed a singularly happy episode; but I took much away with me. . . .

I went straight to the Lake of Como and over the Splügen; spent only a lovely evening (with the next morning) at Cadenabbia. I mounted the Splügen under a splendid sky, and I shall never forget the sensation of rising, as night came (I walked incessantly, after we began to ascend) into that cool pure Alpine air, out of the stifling *calidarium* of Italy. I shall always remember a certain glass of fresh milk which I drank that evening, in the gloaming, far up (a woman at a wayside hostel had it fetched from the cow), as the most heavenly draft that ever passed my lips. I went straight to Lucerne, to see Mrs. Kemble, who had already gone to Engelberg. I spent a day on the lake, making the *giro*; it was a splendid day, and Switzerland looked more sympathetic than I had ventured to hope. I went up to Engelberg, and spent nearly a week with Mrs. Kemble and Miss Butler, in that grim, ragged, rather vacuous, but by no means absolutely unbeautiful valley. I spent an enchanting day with Miss Butler—climbing up to the Trübsee, toward the Joch Pass. The Trübsee is a little steel grey tarn, in a high cool valley, at the foot of the Titlis, whose great silver-gleaming snows overhang it and light it up. The whole place was a wilderness of the alpine rose—and the alpine stillness, the splendour of the weather, the beauty of the place, made the whole impression immense. We had a man with us who carried a lunch; and we partook of it at the little cold inn. The whole thing brought back my old Swiss days; I hadn't believed they could revive even to that point. . . .

New York, 115 East 25th St., December 20th, 1881. I had to break off the other day in Boston—the interruptions in the *morning* here are intolerable. That period of the day has none of the social sanctity here that it [has] in England, and which keeps it singularly free from intrusion. People—by which I mean ladies—think nothing of asking you to come and see them before lunch. Of course one can decline, but when many propositions of that sort come, a certain number stick. Besides, I have had all sorts of things to do, chiefly not profitable to recall. I have been three weeks in New York, and all my time has slipped away in mere movement. I try as usual to console myself with the reflection that I am getting impressions. This is very true; I have got a great many. I did well to come over; it was well worth doing. I indulged in some reflections a few pages back which were partly the result of a melancholy mood. I *can* do something here—it is not a mere complication. But it is not of that I must speak first in taking up my pen again—I shall return to those things later. I should like to finish briefly the little retrospect of the past year's doings, which I left ragged on the opposite page. . . . I came back from Switzerland to meet Alice,[1] who had been a month in England, and whom I presently saw at the Star and Garter, at Richmond. I spent two or three days with her, and saw her afterwards at Kew; then I went down to Sevenoaks and to Canterbury for the same purpose, spending a night at each place. I paid during July and August several visits. One to Burford Lodge (Sir Trevor Lawrence's); memorable on which occasion was a certain walk we took (on a Sunday afternoon), through the grounds of the Deepdene, an artificial but to me a most enchanting and most suggestive English place—full of foreign reminiscences; the sort of place that an Englishman of 80 years ago, who had made the grand tour and lingered in Italy, would naturally construct. I went to Leatherhead, and I went twice to Mentmore. (On one of these occasions Mr. Gladstone was there.) I went to Fredk. Macmillan's at Walton-on-Thames, and had some charming moments on the river. Then I went down into Somerset and spent a week at Midelney Place, the Lady Trevilian's. It is the impression of this visit that I wish not wholly to fade

[1] Henry James' sister.

away. Very exquisite it was (not the visit, but the impression of the country); it kept me a-dreaming all the while I was there. It seemed to me very old England; there was a peculiarly mellow and ancient feeling in it all. Somerset is not especially beautiful; I have seen much better English scenery. But I think I have never been more *penetrated*—I have never more loved the land. It was the old houses that fetched me—Montacute, the admirable; Barrington, that superb Ford Abbey, and several smaller ones. Trevilian showed me them all; he has a great care for such things. These delicious old houses, in the long August days, in the south of England air, on the soil over which so much has passed and out of which so much has come, rose before me like a series of visions. I thought of a thousand things; what becomes of the things one thinks of at these times? They are not lost, we must hope; they drop back into the mind again, and they enrich and embellish it. I thought of stories, of dramas, of all the life of the past —of things one can hardly speak of; speak of, I mean, at the time. It is art that speaks of those things; and the idea makes me adore her more and more. Such a house as Montacute, so perfect, with its grey personality, its old-world gardens, its accumulations of expression, of tone—such a house is really, *au fond,* an ineffaceable image; it can be trusted to rise before the eyes in the future. But what we think of with a kind of *serrement de coeur* is the gone-and-left-behind-us emotion with which at the moment we stood and looked at it. The picture may live again; but *that* is part of the past. . . .

Cambridge, December 26th. I came here on the 23d, to spend Xmas, Wilky[1] having come from the West (the first time in several years), to meet me. Here I sit

[1] Henry James' younger brother, Garth Wilkinson.

writing in the old back sitting room which William and
I used to occupy and which I now occupy alone—
or sometimes with poor Wilky, whom I have not seen
in some eleven years, and who is wonderfully unchanged
for a man with whom life has not gone easy. The long
interval of years drops away, and the edges of the chasm
"piece together" again, after a fashion. The feeling of
that younger time comes back to me in which I sat
here scribbling, dreaming, planning, gazing out upon
the world in which my fortune was to seek, and suffering tortures from my damnable state of health. It was
a time of suffering so keen that that fact might [claim?]
to give its dark colour to the whole period; but this is
not what I think of today. When the burden of pain has
been lifted, as many memories and emotions start into
being as the little insects that scramble about when, in
the country, one displaces a flat stone. Ill-health, physical suffering, in one's younger years, is a grievous trial;
but I am not sure that we do not bear it most easily then.
In spite of it we feel the joy of youth; and that is what
I think of today among the things that remind me of the
past. The freshness of impression and desire, the hope,
the curiosity, the vivacity, the sense of the richness and
mystery of the world that lies before us—there is an
enchantment in all that which it takes a heavy dose
of pain to quench and which in later hours, even if
success have come to us, touches us less nearly. Some
of my doses of pain were very heavy; very weary were
some of my months and years. But all that is sacred;
it is idle to write of it today. . . .

What comes back to me freely, delightfully, is the vision
of those untried years. Never did a poor fellow have
more; never was an ingenuous youth more passionately
and yet more patiently eager for what life might bring.

Now that life has brought something, brought a measurable part of what I dreamed of then, it is touching enough to look back. I knew at least what I wanted then —to see something of the world. I have seen a good deal of it, and I look at the past in the light of this knowledge. What strikes me is the definiteness, the unerringness of those longings. I wanted to do very much what I have done, and success, if I may say so, now stretches back a tender hand to its younger brother, desire. I remember the days, the hours, the books, the seasons, the winter skies and darkened rooms of summer. I remember the old walks, the old efforts, the old exaltations and depressions. I remember more than I can say here today. . . .

Again, in New York the other day, I had to break off: I was trying to finish the little history of the past year. There is not much more to be said about it. I came back from Midelney, to find Alice in London, and spent ten days with her there, very pleasantly, at the end of August. Delightful to me is London at that time, after the horrors of the season have spent themselves, and the long afternoons make a cool grey light in the empty West End. Delightful to me, too, it was to see how *she* enjoyed it—how interesting was the impression of the huge, mild city. London is mild then; that is the word. And then I went to Scotland—to Tillypronie, to Cortachy, to Dalmeny, to Laidlawstiel. I was to have wound up, on my way back, with Castle Howard; but I retracted, on account of Lord Airlie's death. I can't go into all this; there were some delightful moments, and Scotland made, as it had made before, a great impression. Perhaps what struck me as much as anything was my drive, in the gloaming, over from Kirriemuir to Cortachy; though, taking the road afterward by daylight, I saw it was commonplace. In the late Scotch twilight, and the keen air, it was romantic; at least it was romantic to ford the river at the entrance to Cortachy, to drive through the dim avenues and up to the great lighted pile of the castle, where Lady A., hearing my wheels on the gravel (I was late) put her handsome head from a window in the clock-tower, asked if it was I, and wished me a bonny good-evening. I was in a Waverly Novel.

Then my drive (with her) to Glamis; and my drive (with Miss Stanley) to Airlie Castle, enchanting spot! Dalmeny is delicious, a magnificent pile of wood beside the Forth, and the weather, while I was there, was the loveliest I have ever known in the British Isles. But the company was not interesting, and there was a good deal of dreariness in the ball we all went to at Hopetoun for the coming of age of the heir. A charming heir he was, however, and a very pretty picture of a young nobleman stepping into his place in society—handsome, well-mannered, gallant, graceful, with 40,000£ a year and the world at his feet. Laidlawstiel, on a bare hill among hills, just above the Tweed, is in the midst of Walter Scott's country. Reay walked with me over to Ashestiel one lovely afternoon; it is only an hour away. The house has been greatly changed since the 'Sheriff's' day;[1] but the place, the country, are the same, and I found the thing deeply interesting. It took one back. While I was at the Reays' I took up one of Scott's novels—*Redgauntlet;* it was years since I had read one. They have always a charm for me—but I was amazed at the badness of R.: *l'enfance de l'art.* . . .

[1] The "Sheriff" was Walter Scott, appointed Sheriff of Selkirkshire in 1799. He rented the house of Ashestiel, on the south bank of the Tweed, near Selkirk, in 1804.

Now and here I have only one feeling—the desire to get at work again. It is nearly six months that I have been resting on my oars—letting the weeks go, with nothing to show for them but these famous "impressions"! Prolonged idleness exasperates and depresses me, and though now that I am here, it is a pity not to move about and (if the chance presents itself) see the country, the prospect of producing nothing for the rest of the winter is absolutely intolerable to me. If it comes to my having to choose between remaining stationary somewhere and getting at work, or making a journey during which I shall be able to do no work, I shall certainly elect for the former. But probably I shall be able to compromise: to see something of the country and yet work a little. My mind is full of plans, of ambitions; they crowd upon me, for these are the productive years of life. I have taken aboard by this time a tremendous quantity of material; I really have never taken stock of my cargo. After long years of waiting, of obstruction, I find myself able to put into execution the most cherished of all my projects—that of beginning to work for the stage. It was one of my earliest—I had it from the first. None has given me brighter hopes—none has given me sweeter emotions. It is strange nevertheless that I should never have done anything—and to a certain extent it is ominous. I wonder at times that the dream should not have faded away. It comes back to me now, however, and I ache with longing to settle down at last to a sustained attempt in this direction. I think there is really reason enough for my not having done so before: the little work at any time that I could do, the uninterrupted need of making money on the spot, the inability to do two things at once, the absence of opportunities, of openings. I may add to this the feeling that I could afford to wait, that, looked at as I look at it, the drama is the ripest of all the arts, the one to which one must bring most of the acquired as well as most of the natural, and that while I was waiting I was studying the art, and clearing off my field. I think I may now claim to have studied the art as well as it can be studied in the contemplative way. The French stage I have mastered; I say that without hesitation. I have it in my pocket, and it seems to me clear that this is the light by which one must work today. I have laid up treasures of wisdom about all that. What interesting hours it has given me— what endless consideration it has led to! Sometimes, as I say, it seems to me simply deplorable that I should not have got at work before. *But it was impossible at the time,* and I knew that my chance would come. Here it is; let me guard it sacredly now. Let nothing divert me from it; but now the loss of time, which has simply been a maturing process, will become an injurious one. *Je me résume,* as George Sand's heroes say. I remember certain occasions; several acute visitations of the purpose of which I write come back to me vividly. Some of them, the earliest, were brought on merely by visits to the theatre—by seeing great actors, etc.—at fortunate hours; or by reading a new piece of Alex. Dumas, of Sardou, of Augier. No, my dear friend, nothing of all that is lost. *Ces emotions-là ne se perdent pas; elles rentrent dans le fonds même de notre nature; elles font partie de notre volonté.* The *volonté* has not expired; it is only perfect today. Two or three of the later occasions of which I speak have been among the things that *count* in the formation of a purpose; they are worth making a note of here. What has always counted, of course, has been the Comédie Française; it is on that, as regards this long day-dream, that I have lived. But there was an evening there that I shall long remember; it was in September, 1877. I had come over from London; I was lodging in the Avenue d'Antin—the house with a *tir* behind it. I went to see *Jean Dacier*, with Coquelin as the hero; I shall certain[ly not] forget that impression. The piece is, on the whole, I suppose, bad; but it contains some very effective scenes, and the two principal parts gave Coquelin and Favart a magnificent chance. It is Coquelin's *great* chance, and he told me afterwards in London that it is the part he values most. He is everything in it by turns, and I don't think I ever followed an actor's creation more intently. It threw me into a great state of excitement; I thought seriously of writing to Coquelin, telling him I had been his school-mate, etc.[1] It held up a glowing light to me—seemed to point to my own path. If I could have sat down to work then I probably should not have stopped soon. But I didn't; I couldn't; I was writing things for which I needed to be paid from month to month. (I like to remind myself of these facts—to justify my innumerable postponements.) I remember how, on leaving the theatre—it was a lovely evening—I walked about a long time under the influence not so much of the piece as of Coquelin's

---

[1] James had been for a time Coquelin's schoolmate at the Collège Communal in Boulogne, as he tells us in *A Small Boy and Others* (1913). When he wrote that book he looked back on Coquelin as "the most interesting and many-sided comedian, or at least the most unsurpassed dramatic *diseur* of the time." As early as 1877, in his essay on "The Théâtre Français" in the *Galaxy* for April, he devoted several appreciative paragraphs to Coquelin, but it was the performance of Lomon's *Jean Dacier* in September that brought his enthusiasm to its peak. The experience proved indeed unforgettable, and ten years later, in his essay on Coquelin in the *Century* for January 1887, James described just as he does here in the notebook his emotional excitement and his late evening walk after leaving the theater. The play, a four-act tragedy in verse, he called Coquelin's "highest flight in the line of rhymed parts."

acting of it, which had made the thing so human, so brilliant, so valuable. I was agitated with what it said to me that I might do—what I ought to attempt; I walked about the Place de la Concorde, along the Seine, up the Champs Elysées. That was nothing, however, to the state I was thrown into by meeting Coquelin at breakfast at Andrew Lang's, when the Comédie Française came to London. The occasion, for obvious reasons, was unpropitious, but I had some talk with him which rekindled and revived all my latent ambitions. At that time, too, my hands were tied; I could do nothing, and the feeling passed away in smoke. But it stirred me to the depths. Coquelin's personality, his talk, the way the *artist* overflowed in him—all this was tremendously suggestive. I could say little to him there—not a tittle of what I wished; I could only listen, and translate to him what *they* said—an awkward task! But I listened to some purpose, and I have never lost what I gained. It excited me powerfully; I shall not forget my walk, afterwards, down from South Kensington to Westminster. I met Jack Gardner, and he walked with me to leave a card at the Speaker's House. All day, and for days afterward, I remained under the impression. It faded away in time, and I had to give myself to other things. But this brings it back to me; and I may say that those two little moments were landmarks. There was a smaller incident, later, which it gives me pleasure to recall, as it gave me extreme pleasure at the time. John Hare asked me (I met him at dinner at the Comyns Carrs')—urged me, I may say—to write a play, and offered me his services in the event of my doing so. I shall take him at his word. When I came back from Scotland in October last I was full of this work; my hands were free; my pocket lined; I would have given a £100 for the liberty to sit down and hammer away. I imagined such a capital winter of work. But I had to come hither instead. If that however involves a loss of part of my time, it needn't involve the loss of all!

February 9th, 1882, 102 Mt. Vernon St., Boston. When I began to make these rather ineffectual records I had no idea that I should have in a few weeks to write such a tale of sadness as today. I came back from Washington on the 30th of last month (reached Cambridge the next day), to find that I should never again see my dear mother. On Sunday, Jan. 29th, as Aunt Kate sat with her in the closing dusk (she had been ill with an attack of bronchial asthma, but was apparently recovering happily), she passed away. It makes a great difference to me! I knew that I loved her—but I didn't know how tenderly till I saw her lying in her shroud in that cold North Room, with a dreary snowstorm outside, and looking as sweet and tranquil and noble as in life. These are hours of exquisite pain; thank Heaven this particular pang comes to us but once. On Sunday evening (at 10 o'clock in Washington) I was dressing to go to Mrs. Robinson's—who has written me a very kind letter—when a telegram came in from Alice (William's): "Your mother exceedingly ill. Come at once." It was a great alarm, but it didn't suggest the loss of all hope; and I made the journey to New York with whatever hope seemed to present itself. In New York at 5 o'clock I went to Cousin H.P.'s—and there the telegram was translated to me. Eliza Ripley was there—and Katie Rodgers— and as I went out I met Lily Walsh. The rest was dreary enough. I went back to the Hoffman House, where I had engaged a room on my way up town and remained there till 9.30, when I took the night-train to Boston. I shall never pass that place in future without thinking of the wretched hours I spent there. At home the worst was

over; I found father and Alice and A.K.[1] extraordinarily
calm—almost happy. Mother seemed still to be there—
so beautiful, so full of all that we loved in her, she
looked in death. We buried her on Wednesday, Feb 1st;
Wilky arrived from Milwaukee a couple of hours before.
Bob[2] had been there for a month—he was devoted to
mother in her illness. It was a splendid winter's day—
the snow lay deep and high. We placed her, for the present, in a temporary vault in the Cambridge cemetery—
the part that lies near the river. When the spring comes
on we shall go and choose a burial place. I have often
walked there in the old years—in those long, lonely
rambles that I used to take about Cambridge, and I had,
I suppose, a vague idea that some of us would some day
lie there, but I didn't see just that scene. It is impossible
for me to say—to begin to say—all that has gone down
into the grave with her. She was our life, she was the
house, she was the keystone of the arch. She held us all
together, and without her we are scattered reeds. She
was patience, she was wisdom, she was exquisite mater-
nity. Her sweetness, her mildness, her great natural beneficence were unspeakable, and it is infinitely touching
to me to write about her here as one that *was*. When
I think of all that she had been, for years—when I think
of her hourly devotion to each and all of us—and that
when I went to Washington the last of December I gave
her my last kiss, I heard her voice for the last time—
there seems not to be enough tenderness in my being
to register the extinction of such a life. But I can reflect,
with perfect gladness, that her work was done—her
long patience had done its utmost. She had had heavy
cares and sorrows, which she had borne without a mur-

---

[1] "A.K." was "Aunt Kate"—James' mother's sister, Kath-
arine Walsh.

[2] Henry James' youngest brother, Robertson.

mur, and the weariness of age had come upon her. I
would rather have lost her forever than see her begin
to suffer as she would probably have been condemned
to suffer, and I can think with a kind of holy joy of her
being lifted now above all our pains and anxieties. Her
death has given me a passionate belief in certain transcendent things—the immanence of being as nobly created as hers—the immortality of such a virtue as that—
the reunion of spirits in better conditions than these.
She is no more of an angel today than she had always
been; but I can't believe that by the accident of her
death all her unspeakable tenderness is lost to the beings
she so dearly loved. She is with us, she is of us—the
eternal stillness is but a form of her love. One can hear
her voice in it—one can feel, forever, the inextinguishable vibration of her devotion. I can't help feeling that
in those last weeks I was not tender enough with her—
that I was blind to her sweetness and beneficence. One
can't help wishing one had only known what was coming, so that one might have enveloped her with the soft-
est affection. When I came back from Europe I was
struck with her being worn and shrunken, and now I
know that she was very weary. She went about her usual
activities, but the burden of life had grown heavy for
her, and she needed rest. There is something inexpressibly touching to me in the way in which, during these
last years, she went on from year to year without it. If
she could only have lived she should have had it, and
it would have been a delight to see her have it. But she
has it now, in the most complete perfection! Summer
after summer she never left Cambridge—it was impossible that father should leave his own house. The country, the sea, the change of air and scene, were an
exquisite enjoyment to her; but she bore with the deepest gentleness and patience the constant loss of such

opportunities. She passed her nights and her days in that dry, flat, hot, stale and odious Cambridge, and had never a thought while she did so but for father and Alice. It was a perfect mother's life—the life of a perfect wife. To bring her children into the world—to expend herself, for years, for their happiness and welfare—then, when they had reached a full maturity and were absorbed in the world and in their own interests—to lay herself down in her ebbing strength and yield up her pure soul to the celestial power that had given her this divine commission. Thank God one knows this loss but once; and thank God that certain supreme impressions remain! . . .

All my plans are altered—my return to England vanishes for the present. I must remain near father; his infirmities make it impossible I should leave him. This means an indefinite detention in this country—a prospect far enough removed from all my recent hopes of departure.

August 3d, 1882, 3 Bolton St. W. From time to time one feels the need of summing-up. I have done it little in the past, but it will be a good thing to do it more in the future. The prevision with which I closed my last entry in these pages was not verified. I sailed from America on the date I had in my mind when I went home— May 10th. Father was materially better and had the strongest wish that I should depart; he and Alice had moved into Boston and were settled very comfortably in a small, pretty house (101 Mt. Vernon St.). Besides, their cottage at Manchester was rapidly being finished; shortly before sailing I went down to see it. Very pretty —bating the American scragginess; with the sea close to the piazzas, and the smell of bayberries in the air.

Rest, coolness, peace, society enough, charming drives; they will have all that.—Very soon after I had got back here my American episode began to fade away, to seem like a dream; a very painful dream, much of it. While I was there, it was Europe, it was England, that was dreamlike—but now all this is real enough. The Season is over, thank God; I came in for as much of it as could crowd itself into June and July. I was out of the mood for it, preoccupied, uninterested, bored, eager to begin work again; but I was obliged, being on the spot, to accommodate myself to the things of the day, and always with my old salve to a perturbed spirit, the idea that I was seeing the world. It seemed to me on the whole a poor world this time; I saw and did very little that was interesting. I am extremely glad to be in London again; I am deeply attached to London; I always shall be; but decidedly I like it best when it is "empty," as during the period now beginning. I know too many people—I have gone in too much for society. . . .

Grand Hôtel, Paris, November 11th. Thanks to "society," which, in the shape of various surviving remnants of the season, and to a succession of transient Americans and to several country visits, continued to mark me for its own during the greater part of the month of August, I had not even time to finish that last sentence written more than three months ago. I can hardly take up at this date the history of these three months: a simple glance must suffice. I remained in England till the 12th of September. Bob, whom I had found reclining on my sofa in Bolton St. when I arrived from America toward the last of May—(I hadn't even time, above, to mention my little disembarkation in Ireland and the few days I spent there)—Bob, who as I say was awaiting me at my lodgings in London—greatly to my surprise, and in a very battered and depressed condition, thanks to his unhappy voyage to the Azores—sailed for home again in the last days of August, after having spent some weeks in London, at Malvern and at Llandudno, in Wales. The last days, before sailing, he spent with me. About the 10th of September William arrived from America, on his way to the Continent to pass the winter. After being with him for a couple of days, I came over to Paris via Folkestone (I came down there and slept, before crossing), while he crossed to Flushing, from Queenborough. All summer I had been trying to work, but my interruptions had been so numerous that it was only during the last weeks that I succeeded, even moderately, in doing something. My record of work for the whole past year is terribly small, and I opened this book, just now, with the intention of taking several solemn vows in reference to the future. But I don't even know whether I shall accomplish that. However, I am not sure that such solemnities are necessary, for God knows I am eager enough to work, and that I am deeply convinced of the need of it, both for fortune and for happiness. . . .

I scarcely even remember the three or four visits to which, in the summer, I succeeded in restricting my "social activity." A pleasant night at Loseley—Rhoda Broughton was there. Another day I went down there to lunch, to take Howells (who spent all August in London) and Bob. Two days at Mentmore; a Saturday-to-Monday episode (very dull) at Miss de Rothschild's, at Wimbledon; a very pleasant day at the Arthur Russells', at Shiere. This last was charming; I think I went nowhere else—having wriggled out of Midelney, from my promised visit to Mrs. Pakenham, and from pledges more or less given to Tillypronie. Toward the last, in

London, I had my time pretty well to myself, and I felt, as I have always felt before, the charm of those long, still days, in the empty time, when one can sit and scribble, without notes to answer or visits to pay. Shall I confess, however, that the evenings had become dull? . . .

I had meant to write some account of my last months in America, but I fear the chance for this has already passed away. I look back at them, however, with a great deal of tenderness. Boston is absolutely nothing to me—I don't even dislike it. I like it, on the contrary; I only dislike to live there. But all those weeks I spent there, after Mother's death, had an exquisite stillness and solemnity. My rooms in Mt. Vernon St. were bare and ugly; but they were comfortable—were, in a certain way, pleasant. I used to walk out, and across the Common, every morning, and take my breakfast at Parker's. Then I walked back to my lodgings and sat writing till four or five o'clock; after which I walked out to Cambridge over that dreary bridge whose length I had measured so often in the past, and, four or five days in the week, dined in Quincy St. with Father and Alice. In the evening, I walked back, in the clear, American starlight. —I got in this way plenty of exercise. It was a simple, serious, wholesome time. Mother's death appeared to have left behind it a soft beneficent hush in which we lived for weeks, for months, and which was full of rest and sweetness. I thought of her, constantly, as I walked to Boston at night along those dark vacant roads, where, in the winter air, one met nothing but the coloured lamps and the far-heard jingle of the Cambridge horse-cars. My work at this time interested me, too, and I look back upon the whole three months with a kind of religious veneration. My work interested me even more than the importance of it would explain—or than the success of it has justified. I tried to write a little play (D[aisy] M[iller]) and I wrote it; but my poor little play has not been an encouragement. I needn't enter into the tiresome history of my ridiculous negotiations with the people of the Madison Square Theatre, of which the Proprietors behaved like asses and sharpers combined; this episode, by itself, would make a brilliant chapter in a realistic novel. It interested me immensely to write the piece, and the work confirmed all my convictions as to the fascination of this sort of composition. But what it has brought [me] to know, both in New York and in London, about the manners and ideas of managers and actors and about the conditions of production on our unhappy English stage, is almost fatally disgusting and discouraging. I have learned, very vividly, that if one attempts to work for it one must be prepared for *disgust*, deep and unspeakable disgust. But though I am disgusted, I do not think I am discouraged. The reason of this latter is that I simply can't afford to be. I have determined to take a year—even two years, if need be— more, in experiments, in studies, in attempts. The dramatic form seems to me the most beautiful thing possible; the misery of the thing is that the baseness of the English-speaking stage affords no setting for it. How I am to reconcile this with the constant solicitation that presses upon me, both from within and from without, to get at work upon another novel, is more than I can say. It is surely the part of wisdom, however, not to begin another novel at once—not to commit myself to a work of *longue haleine*. I must do *short* things, in such measure as I need, which will leave me intervals for dramatic work. I say this rather glibly—and yet I sometimes feel a woeful hunger to sit down to another novel. If I can only *concentrate* myself: this is the great lesson of life. I have hours of unspeakable reaction against my smallness of production; my wretched habits of work—or of un-work; my levity, my vagueness of mind, my perpetual failure to focus my attention, to absorb myself, to look things in the face, to invent, to produce, in a word. I shall be 40 years old in April next: it's a horrible fact! I believe however that I have learned how to work and that it is in moments of forced idleness, almost alone, that these melancholy reflections seize me. When I am really at work, I'm happy, I feel strong, I see many opportunities ahead. It is the only thing that makes life endurable. I must make some great efforts during the next few years, however, if I wish not to have been on the whole a failure. I shall have been a failure unless I do something *great!* . . .

From *The Notebooks of Henry James* (1947).

VI

LETTERS

1869-1915

*

EDITOR'S NOTE

The Letters of Henry James, which Percy Lubbock edited
in two volumes in 1920, is a selection from the immense correspondence of James's lifetime. It remains to the present day
the amplest edition we have of his communications with his
family, his friends, his professional associates and literary
contemporaries. It has been supplemented by several shorter
collections of his letters, the most important being: "A
*Most Unholy Trade": Being Letters on the Drama by Henry
James* (Cambridge, Mass.: Scarab Press, 1923); *Letters of
Henry James to Walter Berry* (Paris: Black Sun Press,
1928); *Henry James: Letters to A. C. Benson and Auguste
Monod,* edited by E. F. Benson (New York: Scribner's,
1930); *Theatre and Friendship: Some Henry James Letters,*
by Elizabeth Robins (New York: Putnam's, 1932); *Henry
James and Robert Louis Stevenson: A Record of Criticism
and Friendship,* by Janet Adam Smith (New York: Macmillan, 1948); "Letters of Henry James to Mr. Justice Holmes,"
edited by M. A. DeWolfe Howe, *Yale Review,* XXXVI, No.
3 (March 1949), pp. 410-33; "Henry James's Letters to
the LaFarges," edited by John LaFarge, Jr., *New England
Quarterly,* XXII (June 1949), pp. 173-92; and Virginia
Harlow's *Thomas Sergeant Perry: A Biography and Letters*

to Perry from William, Henry, and Garth Wilkinson James (Durham, N.C.: Duke University Press, 1950)—the last especially valuable for containing the earliest extant letters of James, as well as his correspondence with a lifelong friend. I have taken all the letters in the following selection from Lubbock's volumes as published in New York by Charles Scribner's Sons.

They cover a space of forty-six years, from 1869, when James made his first adult trip to Europe, to June 1915, in the last year of his life, when he decided to become a British subject. They have been selected to show, however fragmentarily, the drama of his career in America, in Europe, and in literature. They touch on his discovery of England, his "siege of London," his wanderings in Italy and France, his meetings with the literary great in Paris and London, his determined conquest of English society, his fortunes in authorship, the keenly felt losses he suffered in the deaths of his father, mother, sister, and closest brother, his doomed effort to achieve success in the theater, which reached its climax in January 1895 when his *Guy Domville* was jeered by the British public, his discovery of Lamb House at Rye, which he made his last settled home in England, his return to America in 1904-1905, his sense of becoming a survivor of a passing generation, the honors he received on his seventieth birthday in 1913, the profound shock he felt on the coming of war in 1914, and his eventual decision to become a citizen of his adopted country eight months before his death.

His correspondents here are readily recognizable: his father, his mother, his brother William, who became the celebrated Harvard psychologist and philosopher, and his brilliant sister, Alice, who joined him in England in her last invalid years and died there in 1892; William Dean Howells, the American novelist, editor, and critic, foremost and longest-lasting of James's literary contemporaries in America; Grace Norton, his old friend of Cambridge, sister of Charles Eliot Norton of Harvard; Mrs. William James, his sister-in-law; Edmund Gosse, the English critic; Mrs. Henry White, a friend of New York and Paris; Thomas Sergeant Perry of Boston, a friend of James from the time they were youths together at Newport in 1860; Henry Adams, the American editor and historian, author of *The Education of Henry Adams* and *Mont-Saint-Michel and Chartres,* whom James knew in America and Europe over a space of forty years; Howard Sturgis, the American expatriate in England, author of *Belchamber* and other novels, also a friend of many years; Walter Van Rensselaer Berry, another American expatriate, of Paris, friend of James, Mrs. Wharton, and Proust; Edith Wharton, the American novelist and quasi-disciple of James, whom he knew in the last fifteen years of his life in Paris, America, and England; Mrs. W. K. Clifford and Rhoda Broughton, both late Victorian novelists and old friends in England; and his nephew, Henry James, Jr., oldest son of William James, who was eventually to become his uncle's as well as his father's literary executor. These are only a few of the friends and relatives whom James engaged in correspondence from the 1860's to his death.

Here James is glimpsed, writing in London, in Paris, in Italy, in America, in the night watches of Lamb House, in his last flat in London—writing the copious, confiding, lavish, and inimitable letters which, like his travel essays, belong to a different age from ours: pouring them forth in all the intervals of his incessant practice of his craft, until they become a running chronicle of his long life in the world and in his art.

"THE MAGNITUDE OF LONDON":
TO MISS ALICE JAMES

[London]
7 Half Moon St., W.
March 10th [1869].

Ma sœur chérie,

I have half an hour before dinner-time: why shouldn't I begin a letter for Saturday's steamer? . . . I really feel as if I had lived—I don't say a lifetime—but a year in this murky metropolis. I actually believe that this feeling is owing to the singular permanence of the impressions of childhood, to which any present experience joins itself on, without a broken link in the chain of sensation. Nevertheless, I may say that up to this time I have been crushed under a sense of the mere magnitude of London—its inconceivable immensity—in such a way as to paralyse my mind for any appreciation of details. This is gradually subsiding; but what does it leave behind it? An extraordinary intellectual depression, as I may say, and an indefinable flatness of mind. The place sits on you, broods on you, stamps on you with the feet of its myriad bipeds and quadrupeds. In fine, it is anything but a cheerful or a charming city. Yet it is a very splendid one. It gives you here at the west end, and in the city proper, a vast impression of opulence and prosperity. But you don't want a dissertation of commonplaces on London and you would like me to touch on my own individual experience. Well, my dear, since last week it has been sufficient, altho' by no means immense. On Saturday I received a visit from Mr. Leslie Stephen (blessed man) who came unsolicited with the utmost civility in the world and invited me to dine with him the next day. This I did, in company with Miss Jane Norton. His wife made me very welcome and they both appear to much better effect in their own premises than they did in America. After dinner he conducted us by the underground railway to see the beasts in the Regent's Park, to which as a member of the Zoological Society he has admittance 'Sundays.' . . . In the evening I dined with the invaluable Nortons and went with Chas. and Madame, Miss S. and Miss Jane (via underground railway) to hear Ruskin lecture at University College on Greek Myths. I enjoyed it much in spite of

fatigue; but as I am to meet him some day through the
Nortons, I shall reserve comments. On Wednesday evening I dined at the N.'s (toujours Norton, you see) in
company with Miss Dickens—Dickens's only unmarried
daughter—plain-faced, ladylike (in black silk and black
lace,) and the image of her father. I exchanged but ten
words with her. But yesterday, my dear old sister, was
my crowning day—seeing as how I spent the greater
part of it in the house of Mr. Wm. Morris, Poet. Fitly to
tell the tale, I should need a fresh pen, paper and spirits.
A few hints must suffice. To begin with, I breakfasted,
by way of a change, with the Nortons, along with
Mr. Sam Ward, who has just arrived, and Mr. Aubrey
de Vere, *tu sais,* the Catholic poet, a pleasant honest old
man and very much less high-flown than his name. He
tells good stories in a light natural way. After a space
I came home and remained until 4½ p.m., when I had
given rendez-vous to C.N. and ladies at Mr. Morris's
door, they going by appointment to see his shop and C.
having written to say he would bring me. Morris lives
on the same premises as his shop, in Queen's Square,
Bloomsbury, an antiquated ex-fashionable region, smell-
ing strong of the last century, with a hoary effigy of
Queen Anne in the middle. Morris's poetry, you see,
is only his sub-trade. To begin with, he is a manufac-
turer of stained glass windows, tiles, ecclesiastical and
medieval tapestry, altar-cloths, and in fine everything
quaint, archaic, pre-Raphaelite—and I may add, exquisite. Of course his business is small and may be carried on in his house: the things he makes are so handsome, rich and expensive (besides being articles of the
very last luxury) that his *fabrique* can't be on a very
large scale. But everything he has and does is superb
and beautiful. But more curious than anything is himself.
He designs with his own head and hands all the figures

and patterns used in his glass and tapestry, and further-
more works the latter, stitch by stitch, with his own
fingers—aided by those of his wife and little girls. Oh,
ma chère, such a wife! *Je n'en reviens pas*—she haunts
me still. A figure cut out of a missal—out of one of
Rossetti's or Hunt's pictures—to say this gives but a
faint idea of her, because when such an image puts
on flesh and blood, it is an apparition of fearful and
wonderful intensity. It's hard to say whether she's a
grand synthesis of all the pre-Raphaelite pictures ever
made—or they a 'keen analysis' of her—whether she's
an original or a copy. In either case she is a wonder.
Imagine a tall lean woman in a long dress of some dead
purple stuff, guiltless of hoops (or of anything else, I
should say,) with a mass of crisp black hair heaped into
great wavy projections on each of her temples, a thin
pale face, a pair of strange sad, deep, dark Swinburnian
eyes, with great thick black oblique brows, joined in
the middle and tucking themselves away under her hair,
a mouth like the 'Oriana' in our illustrated Tennyson,
a long neck, without any collar, and in lieu thereof some
dozen strings of outlandish beads—in fine complete.
On the wall was a large nearly full-length portrait of her
by Rossetti, so strange and unreal that if you hadn't seen
her you'd pronounce it a distempered vision, but in fact
an extremely good likeness. After dinner (we stayed
to dinner, Miss Grace, Miss S. S. and I,) Morris read
us one of his unpublished poems, from the second series
of his un-'Earthly Paradise', and his wife having a bad
toothache, lay on the sofa, with her handkerchief to her
face. There was something very quaint and remote from
our actual life, it seemed to me, in the whole scene:
Morris reading in his flowing antique numbers a legend
of prodigies and terrors (the story of Bellerophon, it
was), around us all the picturesque bric-a-brac of the

apartment (every article of furniture literally a 'specimen' of something or other,) and in the corner this dark silent medieval woman with her medieval toothache. Morris himself is extremely pleasant and quite different from his wife. He impressed me most agreeably. He is short, burly, corpulent, very careless and unfinished in his dress, and looks a little like B. G. Hosmer, if you can imagine B. G. infinitely magnified and fortified. He has a very loud voice and a nervous restless manner and a perfectly unaffected and business-like address. His talk indeed is wonderfully to the point and remarkable for clear good sense. He said no one thing that I remember, but I was struck with the very good judgment shown in everything he uttered. He's an extraordinary example, in short, of a delicate sensitive genius and taste, saved by a perfectly healthy body and temper. All his designs are quite as good (or rather nearly so) as his poetry: altogether it was a long rich sort of visit, with a strong peculiar flavour of its own. . . . Ouf! what a repulsively long letter! This sort of thing won't do. A few general reflections, a burst of affection (say another sheet), and I must close. . . . Farewell, dear girl, and dear incomparable all—

Your H.

"THIS WONDROUS ENGLAND": ## TO HIS MOTHER

7 Half Moon St., W.
March 26, 1869.

My dearest Mother,

. . . This will have been my fifth weekly bundle since my arrival, and I can't promise—or rather I forbear to threaten—that it shall be as hugely copious as the others. But there's no telling where my pen may take me. You see I am still in what my old landlord never speaks of but as 'this great metropolis'; and I hope you will believe me when I add, moreover, that I am in the best of health and spirits. During the last week I have been knocking about in a quiet way and have deeply enjoyed my little adventures. The last few days in particular have been extremely pleasant. You have perhaps fancied that I have been rather stingy-minded towards this wondrous England, and that I was [not] taking things in quite the magnanimous intellectual manner that befits a youth of my birth and breeding. The truth is that the face of things here throws a sensitive American back on himself—back on his prejudices and national passions, and benumbs for a while the faculty of appreciation and the sense of justice. But with time, if he is worth a copper, the characteristic beauty of the land dawns upon him (just as certain vicious chilblains are now dawning upon my poor feet) and he feels that he would fain plant his restless feet into the rich old soil and absorb the burden of the misty air. If I were in anything like working order now, I should be very sorry to leave England. I should like to settle down for a year and expose my body to the English climate and my mind to English institutions. But a truce to this cheap discursive stuff. I date the moment from which my mind rose erect in impartial might to a little sail I took on the Thames the other day in one of the little penny steamers which shoot along its dirty bosom. It was a grey, raw English day, and the banks of the river, as far as I went, hideous. Nevertheless I enjoyed it. It was too cold to go up to Greenwich. (The weather, by the way, since my arrival has been horribly damp and bleak, and no more like spring than in a Boston

January). The next day I went with several of the Nortons to dine at Ruskin's, out of town. This too was extremely pleasant. Ruskin himself is a very simple matter. In face, in manner, in talk, in mind, he is weakness pure and simple. I use the word, not invidiously, but scientifically. He has the beauties of his defects; but to see him only confirms the impression given by his writing, that he has been scared back by the grim face of reality into the world of unreason and illusion, and that he wanders there without a compass and a guide—or any light save the fitful flashes of his beautiful genius. The dinner was very nice and easy, owing in a great manner to Ruskin's two charming young nieces who live with him—one a lovely young Irish girl with a rich virginal brogue—a creature of a truly delightful British maidenly simplicity—and the other a nice Scotch lass, who keeps house for him. But I confess, cold-blooded villain that I am, that what I most enjoyed was a portrait by Titian—an old doge, a work of transcendent beauty and elegance, such as to give one a new sense of the meaning of art. . . . But, dearest mammy, I must pull up. Pile in scraps of news. Osculate my sister most passionately. Likewise my aunt. Be assured of my sentiments and present them to my father and brother.

Thy Henry jr.

THE AMERICAN IN EUROPE:
TO HIS MOTHER

Florence, Hôtel de l'Europe.
October 13th, 1869.

My darling Mammy,

. . . For the past six weeks that I have been in Italy I've hardly until within a day or two exchanged five

minutes' talk with any one but the servants in the hotels
and the custodians in the churches. As far as meeting
people is concerned, I've not as yet had in Europe a very
brilliant record. Yesterday I met at the Uffizi Miss Anna
Vernon of Newport and her friend Mrs. Carter, with
whom I had some discourse; and on the same morning
I fell in with a somewhat seedy and sickly American,
who seemed to be doing the gallery with an awful
minuteness, and who after some conversation proposed
to come and see me. He called this morning and has just
left; but he seems a vague and feeble brother and I
anticipate no wondrous joy from his acquaintance. The
'hardly' in the clause above is meant to admit two or
three Englishmen with whom I have been thrown for a
few hours. . . . One especially, whom I met at Verona,
won my affections so rapidly that I was really sad at losing him. But he has vanished, leaving only a delightful
impression and not even a name—a man of about 38,
with a sort of quiet perfection of English virtue about
him, such as I have rarely found in another. Willy asked
me in one of his recent letters for an 'opinion' of the English, which I haven't yet had time to give—tho' at times
I have felt as if it were a theme on which I could write
from a full mind. In fact, however, I have very little
right to have any opinion on the matter. I've seen far
too few specimens and those too superficially. The only
thing I'm certain about is that I like them—like them
heartily. W. asked if as individuals they 'kill' the individual American. To this I would say that the Englishmen
I have met not only kill, but bury in unfathomable
depths, the Americans I have met. A set of people less
framed to provoke national self-complacency than the
latter it would be hard to imagine. There is but one word
to use in regard to them—vulgar, vulgar, vulgar. Their
ignorance—their stingy, defiant, grudging attitude to-

wards everything European—their perpetual reference
of all things to some American standard or precedent
which exists only in their own unscrupulous wind-bags
—and then our unhappy poverty of voice, of speech
and of physiognomy—these things glare at you hide-
ously. On the other hand, we seem a people of *character,*
we seem to have energy, capacity and intellectual stuff
in ample measure. What I have pointed at as our vices
are the elements of the modern man with *culture* quite
left out. It's the absolute and incredible lack of *culture*
that strikes you in common travelling Americans. The
pleasantness of the English, on the other side, comes
in a great measure from the fact of their each having
been dipped into the crucible, which gives them a sort
of coating of comely varnish and colour. They have been
smoothed and polished by mutual social attrition. They
have manners and a language. We lack both, but particularly the latter. I have seen very 'nasty' Britons, certainly, but as a rule they are such as to cause your heart
to warm to them. The women are at once better and
worse than the men. Occasionally they are hard, flat,
and greasy and dowdy to downright repulsiveness; but
frequently they have a modest, matronly charm which
is the perfection of womanishness and which makes
Italian and Frenchwomen—and to a certain extent even
our own—seem like a species of feverish highly-developed invalids. You see Englishmen, here in Italy, to a
particularly good advantage. In the midst of these false
and beautiful Italians they glow with the light of the
great fact, that after all they love a bath-tub and they
hate a lie.

16*th, Sunday.* I *have* seen some nice Americans and
I still love my country. I have called upon Mrs. Hunting-
ton and her two daughters—late of Cambridge—whom
I met in Switzerland and who have an apartment here.

The daughters more than reconcile me to the shrill-voiced sirens of New England's rock-bound coast. The youngest is delightfully beautiful and sweet—and the elder delightfully sweet and plain—with a plainness *qui vaut bien des beautés.* . . .

Maman de mon âme, farewell. I have kept my letter three days, hoping for news from home. I hope you are not paying me back for that silence of six weeks ago. Blessings on your universal heads.

Thy lone and loving exile,
H. J. jr.

SUNDAY AT MME. VIARDOT'S:
TO HIS FATHER

[Paris]
29 Rue du Luxembourg.
April 11th [1876].

Dear Father,

. . . The slender thread of my few personal relations hangs on, without snapping, but it doesn't grow very stout. You crave chiefly news, I suppose, about Ivan Sergeitch [Turgenev], whom I have lately seen several times. I spent a couple of hours with him at his room, some time since, and I have seen him otherwise at Mme. Viardot's. The latter has invited me to her musical parties (Thursdays) and to her Sundays *en famille.* I have been to a couple of the former and (as yet only) one of the latter. She herself is a most fascinating and interesting woman, ugly, yet also very handsome or, in the French sense, *très-belle.* Her musical parties are rigidly musical and to me, therefore, rigidly boresome, especially as she herself sings very little. I stood the

other night on my legs for three hours (from 11 till 2)
in a suffocating room, listening to an interminable fiddling, with the only consolation that Gustave Doré,
standing beside me, seemed as bored as myself. But
when Mme. Viardot does sing, it is superb. She sang
last time a scene from Gluck's *Alcestis,* which was the
finest piece of musical declamation, of a grandly tragic
sort, that I can conceive. Her Sundays seem rather
dingy and calculated to remind one of Concord 'historical games' etc. But it was both strange and sweet to see
poor Turgenev acting charades of the most extravagant
description, dressed out in old shawls and masks, going
on all fours etc. The charades are their usual Sunday evening occupation and the good faith with which
Turgenev, at his age and with his glories, can go into
them is a striking example of that spontaneity which
Europeans have and we have not. Fancy Longfellow,
Lowell, or Charles Norton doing the like, and every Sunday evening! I am likewise gorged with music at Mme.
de Blocqueville's, where I continue to meet Émile
Montégut, whom I don't like so well as his writing, and
don't forgive for having, à l'avenir, spoiled his writing a
little for me. Calling the other day on Mme. de B. I
found with her M. Caro, the philosopher, a man in the
expression of whose mouth you would discover depths
of dishonesty, but a most witty and agreeable personage.
I had also the other day a very pleasant call upon Flaubert, whom I like personally more and more each time
I see him. But I think I easily—more than easily—see all
round him intellectually. There is something wonderfully
simple, honest, kindly, and touchingly inarticulate about
him. He talked of many things, of Théo. Gautier among
others, who was his intimate friend. He said nothing
new or rare about him, except that he thought him after
the Père Hugo the greatest of French poets, much above

Alfred de Musset; but Gautier in his extreme perfection was unique. And he recited some of his sonnets in a way to make them seem the most beautiful things in the world. Find in especial (in the volume I left at home) one called *Les Portraits Ovales.* . . . I went down to Chartres the other day and had a charming time—but I won't speak of it as I have done it in the Tribune.[1] The American papers over here are *accablants,* and the vulgarity and repulsiveness of the Tribune, whenever I see it, strikes me so violently that I feel tempted to stop my letter. But I shall not, though of late there has been a painful dearth of topics to write about. But soon comes the *Salon.* . . . I am very glad indeed that Howells is pleased with my new tale; I am now actively at work upon it. I am well pleased that the *Atlantic* has obtained it. His own novel I have not read, but he is to send it to me.

Your home news has all been duly digested. Tell Willy that I will answer his most interesting letter specifically; and say to my dearest sister that if she will tell me which—black or white—she prefers I will send her gratis a fichu of écru lace, which I am told is the proper thing for her to have.

Ever, dearest daddy, your loving son,

H. James jr.

[1] James was at this time contributing a series of reports on French life and art to the *New York Tribune.* [*Editor's note.*]

ENGLISH SPLENDORS: TO HIS MOTHER

> Mentmore, Leighton Buzzard,
> November 28th, 1880.

Dearest mammy,

. . . This is a pleasant Sunday, and I have been spending it (from yesterday evening) in a very pleasant place. 'Pleasant' is indeed rather an odd term to apply to this gorgeous residence, and the manner of life which prevails in it; but it is that as well as other things beside. Lady Rosebery (it is her enviable dwelling) asked me down here a week ago, and I stop till tomorrow a.m. There are several people here, but no one very important, save John Bright and Lord Northbrook, the last Liberal Viceroy of India. Millais, the painter, has been here for a part of the day, and I took a walk [with him] this afternoon back from the stables, where we had been to see three winners of the Derby trotted out in succession. This will give you an idea of the scale of Mentmore, where everything is magnificent. The house is a huge modern palace, filled with wonderful objects accumulated by the late Sir Meyer de Rothschild, Lady R.'s father. All of them are precious and many are exquisite, and their general Rothschildish splendour is only equalled by their profusion. . . .

I have spent a good part of the time in listening to the conversation of John Bright, whom, though I constantly see him at the Reform Club, I had never met before. He has the repute of being often "grumpy"; but on this occasion he has been in extremely good form and has discoursed uninterruptedly and pleasantly. He gives one an impression of sturdy, honest, vigorous,

English middle-class liberalism, accompanied by a certain infusion of genius, which helps one to understand how his name has become the great rallying-point of that sentiment. He reminds me a good deal of a superior New Englander—with a fatter, damper nature, however, than theirs. . . . They are at afternoon tea downstairs in a vast, gorgeous hall, where an upper gallery looks down like the colonnade in Paul Veronese's pictures, and the chairs are all golden thrones, belonging to ancient Doges of Venice. I have retired from the glittering scene, to meditate by my bedroom fire on the fleeting character of earthly possessions, and to commune with my mammy, until a supreme being in the shape of a dumb footman arrives, to ventilate my shirt and turn my stockings inside out (the beautiful red ones imparted by Alice—which he must admire so much, though he doesn't venture to show it,) preparatory to my dressing for dinner. Tomorrow I return to London and to my personal occupation, always doubly valued after 48 hours passed among *ces gens-ci,* whose chief effect upon me is to sharpen my desire to distinguish myself by personal achievement, of however limited a character. It is the only answer one can make to their atrocious good fortune. Lord Rosebery, however, with youth, cleverness, a delightful face, a happy character, a Rothschild wife of numberless millions to distinguish and demoralize him, wears them with such tact and bonhomie that you almost forgive him. He is extremely nice with Bright, draws him out, defers to him etc., with a delicacy rare in an Englishman. But, after all, there is much to say—more than can be said in a letter— about one's relations with these people. You may be interested, by the way, to know that Lord R. said this morning at lunch that his ideal of the happy life was that of Cambridge, Mass., "living like Longfellow." You may imagine that at this the company looked awfully vague, and I thought of proposing to him to exchange Mentmore for 20 Quincy Street.

I have little other personal news than this, which I have given you in some detail, for entertainment's sake. . . . I embrace you, dearest mother, and also your two companions.

Ever your fondest

H. James, jr.

THE DEATH OF THE FATHER:
TO WILLIAM JAMES

131 Mt. Vernon St.,
Boston.
Dec. 26th, '82.

My dear William—

You will already have heard the circumstances under which I arrived at New York on Thursday 21st, at noon, after a very rapid and prosperous, but painful passage. Letters from Alice and Katherine L. were awaiting me at the dock, telling me that dear father was to be buried that morning. I reached Boston at 11 that night; there was so much delay in getting up-town. I found Bob at the station here. He had come on for the funeral only, and returned to Milwaukee the next morning. Alice, who was in bed, was very quiet and A. K. was perfect. They told me everything—or at least they told me a great deal—before we parted that night, and what they told me was deeply touching, and yet not at all literally painful. Father had been so tranquil, so painless, had died so easily and, as it were, deliberately, and there had been none—not the least—of that anguish and confusion which we imagined in London. . . . He simply, after the "improvement" of which we were written before I sailed, had a sudden relapse—a series of swoons—after which he took to his bed not to rise again. He had no visible malady—strange as it may seem. The "softening of the brain" was simply a gradual refusal of food, because he *wished* to die. There was no dementia except a sort of exaltation of his belief that he had entered into "the spiritual life." Nothing could persuade him to eat, and yet he never suffered, or gave the least sign of suffering, from inanition. All this will seem strange and incredible to you, but told with all the details, as Aunt Kate has told it to me, it becomes real—taking father as he was—almost natural. He prayed and longed to die. He ebbed and faded away, though in spite of his strength becoming continually less, he was able to see people and talk. He wished to see as many people as he could, and he talked with them without effort. He saw F. Boott and talked much two or three days before he died. Alice says he said the most picturesque and humorous things. He knew I was coming and was glad, but not impatient. He was delighted when he was told that you would stay in my rooms in my absence, and seemed much interested in the idea. He had no belief apparently that he should live to see me, but was perfectly cheerful about it. He slept a great deal, and as A. K. says there was "so little of the sick-room" about him. He lay facing the windows, which he would never have darkened—never pained by the light. . . . 27th a.m. Will send this now and write again tonight. All our wish here is that you should remain abroad the next six months.

                                        Ever your
                                        H. James

"THE VOICE OF STOICISM"—"THE GIFT OF LIFE": TO GRACE NORTON

131 Mount Vernon St., Boston.
July 28th [1883].

My dear Grace,

Before the sufferings of others I am always utterly powerless, and your letter reveals such depths of suffering that I hardly know what to say to you. This indeed is not my last word—but it must be my first. You are not isolated, verily, in such states of feeling as this— that is, in the sense that you appear to make all the misery of all mankind your own; only I have a terrible sense that you give all and receive nothing—that there is no reciprocity in your sympathy—that you have all the affliction of it and none of the returns. However— I am determined not to speak to you except with the voice of stoicism. I don't know *why* we live—the gift of life comes to us from I don't know what source or for what purpose; but I believe we can go on living for the reason that (always of course up to a certain point) life is the most valuable thing we know anything about, and it is therefore presumptively a great mistake to surrender it while there is any yet left in the cup. In other words consciousness is an illimitable power, and though at times it may seem to be all consciousness of misery, yet in the way it propagates itself from wave to wave, so that we never cease to feel, and though at moments we appear to, try to, pray to, there is something that holds one in one's place, makes it a standpoint in the universe which it is probably good not to forsake. You are right in your consciousness that we are all echoes and reverberations of the *same*, and you are noble when your interest and pity as to everything that surrounds you, appears to have a sustaining and harmonizing power. Only don't, I beseech you, *generalize* too much in these sympathies and tendernesses—remember that every life is a special problem which is not yours but another's, and content yourself with the terrible algebra of your own. Don't melt too much into the universe, but be as solid and dense and fixed as you can. We all live together, and those of us who love and know, live so most. We help each other—even unconsciously, each in our own effort, we lighten the effort of others, we contribute to the sum of success, make it possible for others to live. Sorrow comes in great waves—no one can know that better than you—but it rolls over us, and though it may almost smother us it leaves us on the spot, and we know that if it is strong we are stronger, inasmuch as it passes and we remain. It wears us, uses us, but we wear it and use it in return; and it is blind, whereas we after a manner see. My dear Grace, you are passing through a darkness in which I myself in my ignorance see nothing but that you have been made wretchedly ill by it; but it is only a darkness, it is not an end, or *the* end. Don't think, don't feel, any more than you can help, don't conclude or decide—don't do anything but *wait*. Everything will pass, and serenity and *accepted* mysteries and disillusionments, and the tenderness of a few good people, and new opportunities and ever so much of life, in a word, will remain. You will do all sorts of things yet, and I will help you. The only thing is not to *melt* in the meanwhile. I insist upon the necessity of a sort of mechanical condensation—so that however fast the horse may run away there will, when he pulls up, be a somewhat agitated but perfectly identical G. N. left in the saddle. Try not to be ill—that is all; for in that there is a failure.

You are marked out for success, and you must not fail.
You have my tenderest affection and all my confidence.
Ever your faithful friend—

Henry James

AFTER *Guy Domville:*
TO WILLIAM JAMES

34 De Vere Gardens, W.
Jan 9th, 1895.

My dear William,

I never cabled to you on Sunday 6th (about the first
night of my play,)[1] because, as I daresay you will have
gathered from some despatches or newspapers (if there
have been any, and you have seen them,) the case was
too complicated. Even now it's a sore trial to me to have
to write about it—weary, bruised, sickened, disgusted
as one is left by the intense, the cruel ordeal of a first
night that—after the immense labour of preparation
and the unspeakable tension of suspense—has, in a few
brutal moments, not gone well. In three words the delicate, picturesque, extremely human and extremely ar-

[1] *Guy Domville* was the most ambitious of the plays James
wrote in the years 1890-95. It was produced by George
Alexander at St. James's Theatre, London, on January 5,
1895. James, in a great state of agitation and suspense, stayed
away from the opening night (he attended Oscar Wilde's
An Ideal Husband at the Haymarket instead). When he
went to St. James's to take the final curtain call he was
greated by the mingled applause of his admirers and the
noisy jeers of the gallery. A vivid account of this famous
disaster among London first nights is given by Leon Edel in
his edition of *The Complete Plays of Henry James* (1949).
pp. 465-83. [*Editor's note.*]

tistic little play was taken profanely by a brutal and ill-disposed gallery which had shown signs of malice prepense from the first and which, held in hand till the end, kicked up an infernal row at the fall of the curtain. There followed an abominable quarter of an hour during which all the forces of civilization in the house waged a battle of the most gallant, prolonged and sustained applause with the hoots and jeers and catcalls of the roughs, whose *roars* (like those of a cage of beasts at some infernal "zoo") were only exacerbated (as it were) by the conflict. It was a cheering scene, as you may imagine, for a nervous, sensitive, exhausted author to face—and you must spare my going over again the horrid hour, or those of disappointment and depression that have followed it; from which last, however, I am rapidly and resolutely, thank God, emerging. The "papers" have, into the bargain, been mainly ill-natured and densely stupid and vulgar; but the only two dramatic critics who count, W. Archer and Clement Scott, have done me more justice. Meanwhile all *private* opinion is apparently one of extreme admiration—I have been flooded with letters of the warmest protest and assurance. . . . Everyone who was there has either written to me or come to see me—I mean every one I know and many people I don't. Obviously the little play, which I strove to make as broad, as simple, as clear, as British, in a word, as possible, is over the heads of the *usual* vulgar theatre-going London public—and the chance of its going for a while (which it is too early to measure) will depend wholly on its holding on long enough to attract the *unusual*. I was there the second night (Monday, 7th) when, before a full house—a remarkably good "money" house, Alexander told me—it went singularly well. But it's soon to see or to say, and I'm prepared for the worst. The thing fills me with horror for the abysmal vulgarity and brutality of the theatre and its regular public, which God knows I have had intensely even when working (from motives as "pure" as pecuniary motives *can* be) against it; and I feel as if the simple freedom of mind thus begotten to return to one's legitimate form would be simply by itself a divine solace for everything. Don't worry about me: I'm a Rock. If the play has no life on the stage I shall publish it; it's altogether the best thing I've done. You would understand better the elements of the case if you had seen the thing it followed (*The Masqueraders*) and the thing that is now succeeding at the Haymarket—the thing of Oscar Wilde's. On the basis of *their* being plays, or successes, my thing is necessarily neither. Doubtless, moreover, the want of a roaring actuality, simplified to a few big *familiar* effects, in my subject—an episode in the history of an old English Catholic family in the last century— militates against it, with all usual theatrical people, who don't want plays (from variety and nimbleness of fancy) of different *kinds*, like books and stories, but only of one kind, which their stiff, rudimentary, clumsily-working vision recognizes as the kind they've had before. And yet I had tried so to meet them! But you can't make a sow's ear out of a silk purse.—I can't write more— and don't ask for more details. This week will probably determine the fate of the piece. If there is increased advance-booking it will go on. If there isn't, it will be withdrawn, and with it all my little hope of profit. The time one has given to such an affair from the very first to the very last represents in all—so inconceivably great, to the uninitiated, is the amount—a pitiful, tragic bankruptcy of hours that might have been rendered retroactively golden. But I am not plangent—one must take the thick with the thin—and I have such possibilities of another and better sort before me. I am only sorry for your and Alice's having to be so sorry for yours forever,

Henry

"A GREAT CHANGE IN MY LIFE": TO W. D. HOWELLS

34 De Vere Gardens, W.

January 22d, 1895.

My dear Howells,

. . . I am indebted to you for your most benignant letter of December last. It lies open before me and I read it again and am soothed and cheered and comforted again. You put your finger sympathetically on the place and spoke of what I wanted you to speak of. I *have* felt, for a long time past, that I have fallen upon evil days—every sign or symbol of one's being in the least *wanted*, anywhere or by any one, having so utterly failed. A new generation, that I know not, and mainly prize not, has taken universal possession. The sense of being utterly out of it weighed me down, and I asked myself what the future would be. All these melancholies were qualified indeed by one redeeming reflection—the sense of how little, for a good while past (for reasons very logical, but accidental and temporary,) I had been producing. I *did* say to myself "Produce again—produce; produce better than ever, and all will yet be well"; and there was sustenance in that so far as it went. But it has meant much more to me since *you* have said it—for it *is,* practically, what you admirably say. It is exactly, moreover, what I meant to admirably do—and have meant, all along, about this time to get into the motion of. The whole thing, however, represents a great change in my life, inasmuch as what is clear is that periodical publication is practically closed to me—I'm the last hand that the magazines, in this country or in the U.S., seem to want. I won't afflict you with the now accumulated (during all these past years) evidence on which this induction rests—and I have spoken of it to no creature till, at this late day, I speak of it to you. . . . All this, I needn't say, is for your *segretissimo* ear. What it means is that "production" for me, as aforesaid, means production of the little *book,* pure and simple—independent of any antecedent appearance; and, truth to tell, now that I wholly *see* that, and have at last accepted it, I am, incongruously, not at all sorry. I am indeed very serene. I have always hated the magazine form, magazine conditions and manners, and much of the magazine company. I hate the hurried little subordinate part that one plays in the catchpenny picture-book—and the negation of all literature that the insolence of the picture-book imposes. The money-difference will be great—but not so great after a bit as at first; and the other differences will be so all to the good that even from the economic point of view they will tend to make up for that and perhaps finally even completely do so. It is about the distinctness of one's *book-position* that you have so substantially reassured me; and I mean to do far better work than ever I have done before. I have, potentially, improved immensely and am bursting with ideas and subjects—though the act of composition is with me more and more slow, painful and difficult. I shall never again write a *long* novel; but I hope to write six immortal short ones—and some tales of the same quality. Forgive, my dear Howells, the cynical egotism of these remarks—the fault of which is in your own sympathy. Don't fail me this summer. I shall probably not, as usual, absent myself from these islands—

not be beyond the Alps as I was when you were here last. That way Boston lies, which is the deadliest form of madness. I sent you only last night messages of affection by dear little "Ned" Abbey, who presently sails for N.Y. laden with the beautiful work he has been doing for the new Boston public library. I hope you will see him—he will speak of me competently and kindly. I wish all power to your elbow. Let me hear as soon as there is a sound of packing. Tell Mildred I rejoice in the memory of her. Give my love to your wife, and believe me, my dear Howells, yours in all constancy,

Henry James

THE DISCOVERY OF LAMB HOUSE: TO MRS. WILLIAM JAMES

Dictated.

34 De Vere Gardens, W.
1st December, 1897.

Dearest Alice,

It's too hideous and horrible, this long time that I have not written you and that your last beautiful letter, placed, for reminder, well within sight, has converted all my emotion on the subject into a constant, chronic blush. The reason has been that I have been driving very hard for another purpose this inestimable aid to expression, and that, as I have a greater loathing than ever for the mere manual act, I haven't, on the one side, seen my way to inflict on you a written letter, or on the other had the virtue to divert, till I should have finished my little book, to another stream any of the valued and expensive industry of my amanuensis. I *have*, at last, finished my little book—that is *a* little book, and so have two or three mornings of breathing time before I begin another. Le plus clair of this small interval "I consecrate to thee!"

I am settled in London these several weeks and making the most of that part of the London year—the mild, quiet, grey stretch from the mid-October to Christmas —that I always find the pleasantest, with the single defect of its only not being long enough. We are having, moreover, a most creditable autumn; no cold to speak of and almost no rain, and a morning-room window at which, this December 1st, I sit with my scribe, admitting a radiance as adequate as that in which you must be actually bathed, and probably more mildly golden. I have no positive plan save that of just ticking the winter swiftly away on this most secure basis. There are, however, little doors ajar into a possible brief absence. I fear I have just closed one of them rather ungraciously indeed, in pleading a "non possumus" to a most genial invitation from John Hay to accompany him and his family, shortly after the new year, upon a run to Egypt and a month up the Nile; he having a boat for that same —I mean for the Nile part—in which he offers me the said month's entertainment. It is a very charming opportunity, and I almost blush at not coming up to the scratch; especially as I shall probably never have the like again. But it isn't so simple as it sounds; one has on one's hands the journey to Cairo and back, with whatever seeing and doing by the way two or three irresistible other things, to which one would feel one might never again be so near, would amount to. (I mean, of course, then or never, on the return, Athens, Corfu, Sicily the never-seen, etc., etc.) It would all "amount" to too much this year, by reason of a particular little complication— most pleasant in itself, I hasten to add—that I haven't, all this time, mentioned to you. Don't be scared—I haven't accepted an "offer." I have only taken, a couple of months ago, a little old house in the country—for the rest of my days!—on which, this winter, though it is, for such a commodity, in exceptionally good condition, I shall have to spend money enough to make me quite concentrate my resources. The little old house you will at no distant day, I hope, see for yourself and inhabit and even, I trust, temporarily and gratuitously possess —for half the fun of it, in the coming years, will be occasionally to lend it to you. I marked it for my own two years ago at Rye—so perfectly did it, the first instant I beheld it, offer the solution of my long-unassuaged desire for a calm retreat between May and November. It is the very calmest and yet cheerfullest that I could have dreamed—*in* the little old, cobble-stoned, grass-grown, red-roofed town, on the summit of its mildly pyramidal hill and close to its noble old church—the chimes of which will sound sweet in my goodly old red-walled garden.

The little place is so rural and tranquil, and yet discreetly animated, that its being within the town is, for convenience and immediate accessibility, purely to the good; and the house itself, though modest and unelaborate, full of a charming little stamp and dignity of its period (about 1705) without as well as within. The next time I go down to see to its "doing up," I will try to have a photograph taken of the pleasant little old-world town-angle into which its nice old red-bricked front, its high old Georgian doorway and a most delightful little old architectural garden-house, perched alongside of it on its high brick garden-wall—into which all these pleasant features together so happily "compose." Two years ago, after I had lost my heart to it—walking over from Point Hill to make sheep's eyes at it (the more so that it is called Lamb House!)—there was no appearance whatever that one could ever have it; either that its fond proprietor would give it up or that if he did it would come at all within one's means. So I simply sighed and renounced; tried to think no more about it; till at last, out of the blue, a note from the good local ironmonger, to whom I had whispered at the time my hopeless passion, informed me that by the sudden death of the owner and the preference (literal) of his son for Klondyke, it might perhaps drop into my lap. Well, to make a long story short, it *did* immediately drop and, more miraculous still to say, on terms, for a long lease, well within one's means—terms quite deliciously moderate. The result of these is, naturally, that they will "do" nothing to it: but, on the other hand, it has been so well lived in and taken care of that the doing —off one's own bat—is reduced mainly to sanitation and furnishing—which latter includes the peeling off of old papers from several roomfuls of pleasant old top-to-toe wood panelling. There are two rooms of complete old oak—one of them a delightful little parlour, opening by one side into the little vista, church-ward, of the small old-world street, where not one of the half-dozen wheeled vehicles of Rye ever passes; and on the other straight into the garden and the approach, from that quarter, to the garden-house aforesaid, which is simply the making of a most commodious and picturesque detached study and workroom. Ten days ago Alfred Parsons, best of men as well as best of landscape-painters-and-gardeners, went down with me and revealed to me the most charming possibilities for the treatment of the tiny out-of-door part—it amounts to about an acre of garden and lawn, all shut in by the peaceful old red wall aforesaid, on which the most flourishing old espaliers, apricots, pears, plums and figs, assiduously grow. It appears that it's a glorious little growing exposure, air, and soil—and all the things that were still flourishing out of doors (November 20th) were a joy to behold. There went with me also a good friend of mine, Edward Warren, a very distingué architect and loyal spirit, who is taking charge of whatever is to be done. So I hope to get in, comfortably enough, early in May. In the meantime one must "pick up" a sufficient quantity of ancient mahogany-and-brass odds and ends —a task really the more amusing, here, where the resources are great, for having to be thriftily and cannily performed. The house is really quite charming enough in its particular character, and as to the stamp of its period, not to do violence to by rash modernities; and I am developing, under its influence and its inspiration, the most avid and gluttonous eye and most infernal watching patience, in respect of lurking "occasions" in not too-delusive Chippendale and Sheraton. The "King's Room" will be especially treated with a preoccupation of the comfort and aesthetic sense of cherished sisters-in-law; King's Room so-called by reason of George Second having passed a couple of nights there and so stamped it for ever. (He was forced ashore, at Rye, on a progress somewhere with some of his ships, by a tempest, and accommodated at Lamb House as at the place in the town then most consonant with his grandeur. It would, for that matter, quite correspond to this description still. Likewise the Mayors of Rye have usually lived there! Or the persons usually living there have usually *become* mayors! That was conspicuously the case with the late handsome old Mr. Bellingham, whose son is my landlord. So you see the ineluctable dignity in store for me.) But enough of this swagger. I have been copious to copiously amuse you.

Your beautiful letter, which I have just read over again is full of interest about you all; causing me spe-

cial joy as to what it says of William's present and prospective easier conditions of work, relinquishment of
laboratory, refusal of outside lectures, etc., and of the
general fine performance, and promise, all round, of the
children. What you say of each makes me want to see
that particular one most. . . . I had a very great pleasure the other day in a visit, far too short—only six hours
—from dear old Howells, who did me a lot of good in
an illuminating professional (i.e. commercial) way, and
came, in fact, at quite a psychological moment. I hope
you may happen to see him soon enough to get from him
also some echo of *me*—such as it may be. But, my dear
Alice, I must be less interminable. Please tell William
that I have two Syracuse "advices," as yet gracelessly
unacknowledged—I mean to him—to thank him for. It's
a joy to find these particular months less barren than
they used to be. I embrace you tenderly all round and
am yours very constantly,

Henry James

AMERICA REVISITED: TO EDMUND GOSSE

The Mount,
Lenox, Mass.
October 27th, 1904.

My dear Gosse,

   The weeks have been many and crowded since I received, not very many days after my arrival, your inci-
sive letter from the depths of the so different world
(from this here;) but it's just because they have been so
animated, peopled and pervaded, that they have rushed
by like loud-puffing motor-cars, passing out of my sight
before I could step back out of the dust and the noise

long enough to dash you off such a response as I could fling after them to be carried to you. And during my first three or four here my postbag was enormously—appallingly—heavy: I almost turned tail and re-embarked at the sight of it. And then I wanted above all, before writing you, to make myself a notion of how, and where, and even *what*, I was. I have turned round now a good many times, though still, for two months, only in this corner of a corner of a corner, that is round New England; and the postbag has, happily, shrunken a good bit (though with liabilities, I fear, of re-expanding,) and this exquisite Indian summer day sleeps upon these really admirable little Massachusetts mountains, lakes and woods, in a way that lulls my perpetual sense of precipitation. I have moved from my own fireside for long years so little (have been abroad, till now, but once, for ten years previous) that the mere quantity of movement remains something of a terror and a paralysis to me—though I am getting to brave it, and to like it, as the sense of adventure, of holiday and romance, and above all of the great so visible and observable world that stretches before one more and more, comes through and makes the tone of one's days and the counterpoise of one's homesickness. I am, at the back of my head and at the bottom of my heart, transcendently homesick, and with a sustaining private reference, all the while (at every moment, verily,) to the fact that I have a tight anchorage, a definite little downward burrow, in the ancient world—a secret consciousness that I chink in my pocket as if it were a fortune in a handful of silver. But, with this, I have a most charming and interesting time, and [am] seeing, feeling, how agreeable it is, in the maturity of age, to revisit the long neglected and long unseen land of one's birth—especially when that land affects one as such a living and breathing and feeling and moving great monster as this one is. It is all very interesting and quite unexpectedly and almost uncannily delightful and sympathetic—partly, or largely from my intense impression (all this glorious golden autumn, with weather like tinkling crystal and colours like molten jewels) of the sweetness of the country itself, this New England rural vastness, which is all that I've seen. I've been only in the country—shamelessly visiting and almost only old friends and scattered relations—but have found it far more beautiful and amiable than I had ever dreamed, or than I ventured to remember. I had seen too little, in fact, of old, *to* have anything, to speak of, to remember—so that seeing so many charming things for the first time I quite thrill with the romance of elderly and belated discovery. Of Boston I haven't even had a full day—of N. Y. but three hours, and I have seen nothing whatever, thank heaven, of the "littery" world. I have spent a few days at Cambridge, Mass., with my brother, and have been greatly struck with the way that in the last 25 years Harvard has come to mass so much larger and to have gathered about her such a swarm of distinguished specialists and such a big organization of learning. This impression is increased this year by the crowd of foreign experts of sorts (mainly philosophic etc.) who have been at the St. Louis congress and who appear to be turning up overwhelmingly under my brother's roof—but who will have vanished, I hope, when I go to spend the month of November with him—when I shall see something of the goodly Boston. The blot on my vision and the shadow on my path is that I have contracted to write a book of Notes[1]—without which contraction I simply

---

[1] The book which James had contracted to write about his trip to America appeared as *The American Scene* in 1907. [*Editor's note.*]

couldn't have come; and that the conditions of life, time, space, movement etc. (really to *see*, to get one's material,) are such as to threaten utterly to frustrate for me any prospect of simultaneous work—which is the rock on which I may split altogether—wherefore my alarm is great and my project much disconcerted; for I have as yet scarce dipped into the great Basin at all. Only a large measure of Time can help me—to do anything as decent as I want: wherefore pray for me constantly; and all the more that if I can only arrive at a means of application (for I see, already, from here, my *Tone*) I shall do, verily, a lovely book. I am interested, up to my eyes—at least I think I am! But you will fear, at this rate, that I am trying the book on you already. I *may* have to return to England only as a saturated sponge and wring myself out there. I hope meanwhile that your own saturations, and Mrs. Nelly's, prosper, and that the Pyrenean, in particular, continued rich and ample. If you are having the easy part of your year now, I hope you are finding in it the lordliest, or rather the *un*lordliest leisure. . . . I commend you all to felicity and am, my dear Gosse, yours always,

Henry James

BROTHER TO BROTHER:
TO WILLIAM JAMES

Lamb House, Rye
November 23rd, 1905.

Dearest William,

. . . I mean (in response to what you write me of your having read the *Golden B[owl]*) to try to produce some uncanny form of thing, in fiction, that will gratify you, as Brother—but let me say, dear William, that I shall greatly be humiliated if you *do* like it, and thereby lump it, in your affection, with things, of the current age, that I have heard you express admiration for and that I would sooner descend to a dishonoured grave than have written. Still I *will* write you your book, on that two-and-two-make-four system on which all the awful truck that surrounds us is produced, and *then* descend to my dishonoured grave—taking up the art of the slate pencil instead of, longer, the art of the brush (vide my lecture on Balzac). But it is, seriously, too late at night, and I am too tired, for me to express myself on this question—beyond saying that I'm always sorry when I hear of your reading anything of mine, and always hope you won't—you seem to me so constitutionally unable to "enjoy" it, and so condemned to look at it from a point of view remotely alien to mine in writing it, and to the conditions out of which, *as* mine, it has inevitably sprung—so that all the intentions that have been its main reason for being (with *me*) appear never to have reached you at all—and you appear even to assume that the life, the elements forming its subject-matter, deviate from felicity in not having an impossible analogy with the life of Cambridge. I see nowhere about me done or dreamed of the things that alone for me constitute the *interest* of the doing of the novel—and yet it is in a sacrifice of them on their very own ground that the thing you suggest to me evidently consists. It shows how far apart and to what different ends we have had to work out (very naturally and properly!) our respective intellectual lives. And yet I can read *you* with rapture—having three weeks ago spent three or four days with Manton Marble at Brighton and found in his hands ever so many of your recent papers and discourses, which, having margin of mornings in my room, through both breakfasting and lunching there (by the habit of the house,) I found time to read several of— with the effect of asking you, earnestly, to address me some of those that I so often, in Irving St., saw you address to others who were not your brother. I had no time to read them there. Philosophically, in short, I am "with" you, almost completely, and you ought to take account of this and get me over altogether. . . .

But oh, fondly, good-night!

Ever your

Henry

WINTER MIDNIGHT AT LAMB HOUSE:
TO MRS. HENRY WHITE

Lamb House, Rye.
Dec. 29, 1908.

Dearest Margaret White,

I sit here to-night, I quite crouch by my homely little fireside, muffled in soundless snow—where the loud tick of the clock is the *only* sound—and give myself up to the charmed sense that in your complicated career, amid all the more immediate claims of the *bonne année*, you have been moved to this delightful sign of remembrance of an old friend who is on the whole, and has always been, condemned to lose so much more of you (through divergence of ways!) than he has been privileged to enjoy. Snatches, snatches, and happy and grateful moments—and then great empty yearning intervals only—and under all the great ebbing, melting, and irrecoverableness of life! But this is almost a happy and grateful moment—almost a *real* one, I mean— though again with bristling frontiers, long miles of land

and water, doing their best to make it vain and fruitless. You live on the crest of the wave, and I deep down in the hollow—and your waves seem to be all crests, just as mine are only concave formations! I feel at any rate very much in the hollow these winter months—when great adventures, like Paris, look far and formidable, and I see a domestic reason for sitting tight wherever I turn my eyes. That reads as if I had thirteen children—or thirty wives—instead of being so lone and lorn; but what it means is that I have, in profusion, modest, backward labours. We have been having here lately the great and glorious pendulum in person, Mrs. Wharton, on her return oscillation, spending several weeks in England, for almost the first time ever and having immense success—so that I think she might fairly fix herself here—if she could stand it! But she is to be at 58 Rue de Varenne again from the New Year and you will see her and she will give you details. *My* detail is that though she has kindly asked me to come to them again there this month or spring I have had to plead simple abject terror—terror of the pendulous life. I am a *stopped* clock—and I strike (that is I caper about) only when very much wound up. Now I don't have to be wound up at all to tell you what a yearning I have to see you all back *here*—and what a kind of sturdy faith that I absolutely shall. Then your crest will be much nearer my hollow, and vice versa, and you will be able to look down quite *straight* at me, and we shall be almost together again—as we really must manage to be for these interesting times to come. I don't want to miss any more Harry's freshness of return from the great country—with the golden apples of his impression still there on the tree. I have always only tasted them plucked by other hands and—baked! I want to munch these *with* you—en famille. Therefore I confidently await and evoke you. I delight in these proofs of strength of your own and am yours always and ever,

Henry James

THE DEATH OF WILLIAM JAMES:
TO THOMAS SERGEANT PERRY

[William James, in failing health, had gone to Nauheim in Germany in the spring of 1910 to seek a cure. Henry James, himself in ill health at the time, joined him there with Mrs. James, and in August returned with them to America, where William James died at his summer home in New Hampshire on August 26, 1910.—*Editor's note.*]

Chocorua, N.H.
Sept. 2nd, 1910.

My dear old Thomas,

I sit heavily stricken and in darkness—for from far back in dimmest childhood he had been my ideal Elder Brother, and I still, through all the years, saw in him, even as a small timorous boy yet, my protector, my backer, my authority and my pride. His extinction changes the face of life for me—besides the mere missing of his inexhaustible company and personality, originality, the whole unspeakably vivid and beautiful presence of him. And his noble intellectual vitality was still but at its climax—he had two or three ardent purposes and plans. He had cast them away, however, at the end —I mean that, dreadfully suffering, he wanted only to die. Alice and I had a bitter pilgrimage with him from far off—he sank here, on his threshold; and then it went horribly fast. I cling for the present to *them*—and so try to stay here through this month. After that I shall be with them in Cambridge for several more—we shall cleave more together. I should like to come and see you for a couple of days much, but it would have to be after the 20th, or even October 1st, I think; and I fear you may not then be still in *villeggiatura*. *If so I will* come. You knew him—among those living now—from furthest back with me. Yours and Lilla's all faithfully,

Henry James

THANKS FOR A GIFT:
TO WALTER V. R. BERRY

[H. J. never at any time received presents easily, and the difficulty seems to have reached a climax over one recently sent him by Mr. Berry. It may not be obvious that the gift in question was a leather dressing-case.—*Note by Percy Lubbock.*]

Lamb House, Rye.
February 8th, 1912.

Très-cher et très-grand ami!

How you must have wondered at my silence! But it has been, alas, inevitable and now is but feebly and dimly broken. Just after you passed through London— or rather even *while* you were passing through it—I began to fall upon evil days again; a deplorable bout of unwellness which, making me fit for nothing, gave me a sick struggle, first, in those awkward Pall Mall conditions, and then reduced me to scrambling back here as best I might, where I have been these several days but a poor ineffectual rag. I shall get better here if I can still further draw on my sadly depleted store of time and patience; but meanwhile I am capable but of this weak and appealing grimace—so deeply discouraged am I to feel that there are still, and after I have travelled so far, such horrid little deep holes for me to tumble into. (This has been a deeper one than for many months, though I am, I believe, slowly scrambling out; and blest to me has been the resource of crawling to cover here— for better aid and comfort.) . . . The case has really and largely been, however, all the while, dearest Walter, that of my having had to yield, just after your glittering passage in town, to that simply overwhelming *coup de massue* of your—well, of your you know what. It was *that* that knocked me down—when I was just trembling for a fall; it was that that laid me flat.

February 14th. Well, dearest Walter, it laid me after all so flat that I broke down, a week ago, in the foregoing attempt to do you, and your ineffable procédé, some manner of faint justice; I wasn't then apt for any sort of right or worthy approach to you, and there was nothing for me but resignedly to intermit and *me re-coucher.* You had done it with your own mailed fist— mailed in glittering gold, speciously glazed in polished, inconceivably and indescribably sublimated, leather, and I had rallied but too superficially from the stroke. It claimed its victim afresh, and I have lain the better part of a week just languidly heaving and groaning as a result *de vos œuvres*—and forced thereby quite to neglect and ignore all letters. I am a little more on my feet again, and if this continues shall presently be able to return to town (Saturday or Monday;) where, how- ever, the monstrous object will again confront me. That is the grand fact of the situation—that is the tawny lion, portentous creature, in my path. I can't get past him, I can't get round him, and on the other hand he stands glaring at me, refusing to give way and practically blocking all my future. I can't live with him, you see; be- cause I can't live *up* to him. His claims, his pretensions, his dimensions, his assumptions and consumptions,

above all the manner in which he causes every surrounding object (on my poor premises or within my
poor range) to tell a dingy or deplorable tale—all this
makes him the very scourge of my life, the very blot on
my scutcheon. He doesn't regild that rusty metal—he
simply takes up an attitude of gorgeous swagger, straight
in front of all the rust and the rubbish, which makes me
look as if I had stolen *somebody else's* (re-garnished
blason) and were trying to palm it off as my own. Cher
et bon Gaultier, I simply can't *afford* him, and that is the
sorry homely truth. *He is out of the picture*—out of
mine; and behold me condemned to live forever with
that canvas turned to the wall. Do you know what that
means?—to have to give up going about at all, lest
complications (of the most incalculable order) should
ensue from its being seen what I go about *with*. Bonne
renommée vaut mieux que sac-de-voyage doré, and
though I may have had weaknesses that have brought
me a little under public notice, my modest hold-all
(which has accompanied me in most of my voyage
through life) has at least, so far as I know, never *fait
jaser*. All this I have to think of—and I put it candidly
to you while yet there is time. That you shouldn't have
counted the cost—to yourself—that is after all perhaps
conceivable (quoiqu'à peine!) but that you shouldn't
have counted the cost to *me,* to whom it spells ruin:
that ranks you with those great lurid, though lovely,
romantic and historic figures and charmers who have
scattered their affections and lavished their favours
only (as it has presently appeared) to consume and
to destroy! More prosaically, dearest Walter (if one of
the most lyric acts recorded in history—and one of the
most finely aesthetic, and one stamped with the most
matchless grace, *has* a prosaic side,) I have been truly
overwhelmed by the princely munificence and generos-

ity of your procédé, and I have gasped under it while
tossing on the bed of indisposition. For a beau geste,
c'est le plus beau, by all odds, of any in all my life ever
esquissé in my direction, and it *has,* as such, left me
really and truly panting helplessly after—or rather quite
intensely *before*—it! What is a poor man to do, mon
prince, mon bon prince, mon grand prince, when so
prodigiously practised upon? There is *nothing,* you see:
for the proceeding itself swallows at a gulp, with its
open crimson jaws (*such* a rosy mouth!) like Carlyle's
Mirabeau, "all formulas." One doesn't "thank," I take it,
when the heavens open—that is when the whale of
Mr. Allen's-in-the-Strand celestial shopfront does—and
discharge straight into one's lap the perfect compendium, the very burden of the song, of just what the
Angels have been raving about ever since we first heard
of them. Well *may* they have raved—but I can't, you
see; I have to take the case (the incomparable suit-
case) in abject silence and submission. Ah, Walter,
Walter, why do you do these things? they're magnificent, but they're not—well, discussable or permissible or
forgiveable. At least not all at once. It will take a long,
long time. Only little by little and buckle-hole by
buckle-hole, shall I be able to look, with you, even one
strap in the face. As yet a sacred horror possesses me,
and I must ask you to let me, please, though writing you
at such length, not so much as mention the subject. It's
better so. Perhaps your conscience will tell you why—
tell you, I mean, that great supreme *gestes* are only fair
when addressed to those who can themselves gesticulate.
I can't—and it makes me feel so awkward and graceless and poor. I go about trying—so as to hurl it (something or other) back on you; but it doesn't come off—
practice *doesn't* make perfect; you are victor, winner,
master, oh irresistible one—you've done it, you've

brought it off and got me down forever, and I must just feel your weight and bear your might to bless your name—even to the very end of the days of yours, dearest Walter, all too abjectly and too touchedly,

Henry James

ON HIS SEVENTIETH BIRTHDAY:
TO 270 FRIENDS

[On James's seventieth birthday—April 15, 1913—a group of 270 friends sent him a letter, a piece of plate ("a really splendid 'golden bowl' of the highest interest and most perfect taste"), and a request that he sit for his portrait to John Singer Sargent (the portrait is now in the National Portrait Gallery, London). This is James's letter of thanks; at the end he wrote the names of the friends who had offered him tribute.—*Editor's note*.]

21 Carlyle Mansions,
Cheyne Walk, S.W.
April 21st, 1913.

Dear Friends All,

Let me acknowledge with boundless pleasure the singularly generous and beautiful letter, signed by your great and dazzling array and reinforced by a correspondingly bright material gage, which reached me on my recent birthday, April 15th. It has moved me as brave gifts and benedictions can only do when they come as signal surprises. I seem to wake up to an air of breathing good will the full sweetness of which I had never yet tasted; though I ask myself now, as a second thought, how the large kindness and hospitality in which I have so long and so consciously lived among you could fail to act itself out according to its genial nature and by some inspired application. The perfect grace with which it has embraced the just-past occasion for its happy thought affects me, I ask you to believe, with an emotion too deep for stammering words. I was drawn to London long years ago as by the sense, felt from still earlier, of all the interest and association I should find here, and I now see how my faith was to sink deeper foundations than I could presume ever to measure—how my justification was both stoutly to grow and wisely to wait. It is so wonderful indeed to me as I count up your numerous and various, your dear and distinguished friendly names, taking in all they recall and represent, that I permit myself to feel at once highly successful and extremely proud. I had never in the least understood that I was the one or signified that I was the other, but you have made a great difference. You tell me together, making one rich tone of your many voices, almost the whole story of my social experience, which I have reached the right point for living over again, with all manner of old times and places renewed, old wonderments and pleasures reappeased and recaptured—so that there is scarce one of your ranged company but makes good the particular connection, quickens the excellent relation, lights some happy train and flushes with some individual colour. I pay you my very best respects while I receive from your two hundred and fifty pair of hands, and more, the admirable, the inestimable bowl, and while I engage to sit, with every accommodation, to the so markedly indicated "one of you," my illustrious friend Sargent. With every accommodation, I say, but with this one condition that you yourselves, in your strength and goodness, remain guardians of the result of his labour—even as I remain all faithfully and gratefully yours,

Henry James

P.S. And let me say over your names.

"WE ARE LONE SURVIVORS":
TO HENRY ADAMS

21 Carlyle Mansions
Cheyne Walk, S.W.
March 21, 1914.

My dear Henry,

I have your melancholy outpouring of the 7th, and I know not how better to acknowledge it than by the full recognition of its unmitigated blackness. *Of course* we are lone survivors, of course the past that was our lives is at the bottom of an abyss—if the abyss *has* any bottom; of course, too, there's no use talking unless one particularly *wants* to. But the purpose, almost, of my printed divagations was to show you that one *can*, strange to say, still want to—or at least can behave as if one did.[1] Behold me therefore so behaving—and apparently capable of continuing to do so. I still find my consciousness interesting—under *cultivation* of the interest. Cultivate it *with* me, dear Henry—that's what I hoped to make you do—to cultivate yours for all that it has in common with mine. *Why* mine yields an interest I don't know that I can tell you, but I don't challenge or quarrel with it—I encourage it with a ghastly grin. You see I still, in presence of life (or of what you deny to be such,) have reactions—as many as possible —and the book I sent you is a proof of them. It's, I suppose, because I am that queer monster, the artist, an obstinate finality, an inexhaustible sensibility. Hence

---

[1] James had sent Henry Adams a copy of his second autobiographical memoir, *Notes of a Son and Brother,* recently published. [*Editor's note.*]

the reactions—appearances, memories, many things, go on playing upon it with consequences that I note and "enjoy" (grim word!) noting. It all takes doing—and I *do*. I believe I shall do yet again—it is still an act of life. But you perform them still yourself—and I don't know what keeps me from calling your letter a charming one! There we are, and it's a blessing that you understand— I admit indeed alone—your all-faithful

Henry James

THE COMING OF THE WAR: 1914

TO HOWARD STURGIS

Lamb House, Rye.
[Continuing a letter of
August 4th, 1914.]

Dearly beloved Howard!

. . . *August 5th*. The taper went out last night, and I am afraid I now kindle it again to a very feeble ray— for it's vain to try to talk as if one weren't living in a nightmare of the deepest dye. How can what is going on not be to one as a huge horror of blackness? Of course that is what it is to you, dearest Howard, even as it is to your infinitely sickened inditer of these lines. The plunge of civilization into this abyss of blood and darkness by the wanton feat of those two infamous autocrats is a thing that so gives away the whole long age during which we have supposed the world to be, with whatever abatement, gradually bettering, that to have to take it all now for what the treacherous years were all the while really making for and *meaning* is too tragic for any words. But one's reflections don't really bear being ut-

tered—at least we each make them enough for our individual selves and I didn't mean to smother you under
mine in addition to your own. . . .

But good-night again—my lamp now is snuffed out.
Have I mentioned to you that I am not here alone?—
having with me my niece Peggy and her younger brother
—both "caught" for the time, in a manner; though willing, even glad, as well as able, to bear their poor old appalled Uncle the kindest company—very much the
same sort as William bears you. I embrace you, and him
too, and am ever your faithfullest old

H. J.

TO MISS RHODA BROUGHTON

Lamb House, Rye.
August 10th, 1914.

Dearest Rhoda!

It is not a figure of speech but an absolute truth that
even if I had not received your very welcome and sympathetic script I should be writing to you this day. I
have been on the very edge of it for the last week—so
had my desire to make you a sign of remembrance and
participation come to a head; and verily I must—or
may—almost claim that this all but "crosses" with your
own. The only blot on our unanimity is that it's such
an unanimity of woe. Black and hideous to me is the
tragedy that gathers, and I'm sick beyond cure to have
lived to see it. You and I, the ornaments of our generation, should have been spared this wreck of our belief
that through the long years we had seen civilization
grow and the worst become impossible. The tide that
bore us along was then all the while moving to *this* as its

grand Niagara—yet what a blessing we didn't know it.
It seems to me to *undo* everything, everything that
was ours, in the most horrible retroactive way—but I
avert my face from the monstrous scene!—you can hate
it and blush for it without my help; we can each do
enough of that by ourselves. The country and the season here are of a beauty of peace, and loveliness of
light, and summer grace, that make it inconceivable that
just across the Channel, blue as *paint* today, the fields of
France and Beligum are being, or about to be, given up
to unthinkable massacre and misery. One is ashamed to
admire, to enjoy, to take any of the normal pleasure, and
the huge shining indifference of Nature strikes a chill to
the heart and makes me wonder of what abysmal mystery, or villainy indeed, such a cruel smile is the expression. In the midst of it all at any rate we walked, this
strange Sunday afternoon (9th), my niece Peggy, her
youngest brother and I, about a mile out, across the
blessed grass mostly, to see and have tea with a genial
old Irish friend (Lady Mathew, who has a house here
for the summer,) and came away an hour later bearing
with us a substantial green volume, by an admirable
eminent hand, which our hostess had just read with such
a glow of satisfaction that she overflowed into easy lending. I congratulate you on having securely put it forth
before this great distraction was upon us—for I am utterly pulled up in the midst of a rival effort by finding
that my job won't at all consent to be done in the face
of it. The picture of little private adventures simply
fades away before the great public. I take great comfort in the presence of my two young companions, and
above all in having caught my nephew by the coat-tail
only *just* as he was blandly starting for the continent
on Aug. 1st. Poor Margaret Payson is trapped somewhere in France—she *having* then started, though not

for Germany, blessedly; and we remain wholly without news of her. Peggy and Aleck have four or five near maternal relatives lost in Germany—though as Americans they may fare a little less dreadfully there than if they were English. And I have numerous friends—we all have, haven't we?—inaccessible and unimaginable there; it's becoming an anguish to think of them. Nevertheless I do believe that we shall be again gathered into a blessed little Chelsea drawing-room—it will be like the reopening of the salons, so irrepressibly, after the French revolution. So only sit tight, and invoke your heroic soul, dear Rhoda, and believe me more than ever all-faithfully yours,

Henry James

TO MRS. W. K. CLIFFORD

Lamb House, Rye.
August 22nd, 1914.

Dearest Lucy,

I have, I know, been quite portentously silent—your brief card of distress to-night (Saturday p. m.—) makes me feel it—but you on your side will also have felt the inevitability of this absence of mere vain and vague remark in the presence of such prodigious realities. My overwhelmed sense of them has simply left me nothing to say—the rupture with all the blest old proportion of things has been so complete and utter, and I've felt as if most of my friends (from very few of whom I have heard at all) were so wrapped in gravities and dignities of silence that it wasn't fair to write to them simply to make *them* write. And so it has gone—the whole thing defying expression so that one has just stared at the horror and watched it grow. But I am not writing now, dearest old friend, to express either alarm or despair—and this mainly by reason of there being so high a decency in *not* doing so. I hate not to possess my soul—and oh I should like, while I am *about* that, to possess yours for you too. One doesn't possess one's soul unless one squares oneself a good deal, in fact very hard indeed, for the purpose; but in proportion as one succeeds that means preparation, and preparation means confidence, and confidence means force, and that is as far as we need go for the moment. Your few words express a bad apprehension which I don't share—and which even our straight outlook here over the blue channel of all these amazing days, toward the unthinkable horrors of its almost other edge, doesn't *make* me share. I don't in the least believe that the Germans will be "here"—with us generally—because I don't believe—I don't admit—that anything so abject as the allowance of it by our overwhelming Fleet, in conditions making it so tremendously difficult for them (the G.'s), is in the least conceivable. Things are not going to be so easy for them as that—however uneasy they may be for ourselves. I *insist* on a great confidence—I cultivate it as resolutely as I can, and if we were only nearer together I think I should be able to help you to some of the benefit of it. I have been very thankful to be on this spot all these days—I mean in this sympathetic little old house, which has somehow assuaged in a manner the nightmare. One invents *arts* for assuaging it—of which some work better than others. The great sore sense I find the futility of talk—*about* the cataclysm: this is so impossible that I can really almost talk about other things! . . . I am supposing you see a goodish many people—since one hears that there are so many in town, and I am glad for you of that: solitude in these

conditions being grim, even if society is bleak! I try to
read and I rather succeed, and also even to write, and
find the effort of it greatly pays. Lift up your heart,
dearest friend—I believe we shall meet to embrace and
look back and tell each other how appallingly interesting
the whole thing "was." I gather in all of you right affectionately and am yours, in particular, dearest Lucy, so
stoutly and tenderly,

                                        Henry James

TO MRS. WHARTON

                                    Lamb House, Rye.
                                    September 21st, 1914.

Dearest Edith,

   Rheims is the most unspeakable and immeasurable
horror and infamy—and what is appalling and heart-
breaking is that it's *"for ever and ever."* [1] But no words
fill the abyss of it—nor touch it, nor relieve one's heart
nor light by a spark the blackness; the ache of one's
howl and the anguish of one's execration aren't mitigated by a shade, even as one brands it as the most hideous crime ever perpetrated against the mind of man.
There it *was*—and now all the tears of rage of all the
bereft millions and all the crowding curses of all the
wondering ages will never bring a stone of it back! Yet
one tries—even now—tries to get something from saying that the measure is so full as to overflow at last in

---

[1] It will be remembered that the first news of the bombard-
ment of Rheims Cathedral suggested greater destruction than
was the fact at that time. The wreckage was of course carried much further before the end of the war. [*Note by Percy
Lubbock.*]

a sort of vindictive deluge (though for all the stones
that *that* will replace!) and that the arm of final retributive justice becomes by it an engine really in some degree proportionate to the act. I positively do think it
helps me a little, to think of how they can be made to
wear the shame, in the pitiless glare of history, forever
and ever—and not even to get rid of it when they are
maddened, literally, by the weight. And for that the
preparations must have already at this hour begun: how
can't they be as a tremendous force fighting on the side,
fighting in the very fibres, of France? I think too somehow—though I don't know *why*, practically—of how
nothing conceivable could have so damned and dished
them forever in our great art-loving country!

. . . All homage and affection to you, dearest Edith,
from your desolate and devoted old

H. J.

"CIVIS BRITANNICUS SUM": TO HENRY JAMES, JUNIOR

[Henry James was to become naturalized as a British subject
on July 26, 1915. On that day he wrote Edmund Gosse:
"since 4.30 this afternoon I have been able to say Civis Bri-
tannicus sum!" The present letter to his nephew anticipated
the event by a month.—*Editor's note.*]

Dictated

21 Carlyle Mansions,
Cheyne Walk, [London], S.W.
June 24th, 1915.

Dearest Harry,

I am writing to you in this fashion even although I
am writing you "intimately"; because I am not at the

present moment in very good form for any free play of hand, and this machinery helps me so much when there is any question of pressure and promptitude, or above all of particular clearness. That *is* the case at present—at least I feel I ought to lose no more time.

You will wonder what these rather portentous words refer to—but don't be too much alarmed! It is only that my feeling about my situation here has under the stress of events come so much to a head that, certain particular matters further contributing, I have arranged to seek technical (legal) advice no longer hence than this afternoon as to the exact modus operandi of my becoming naturalised in this country. This state of mind probably won't at all surprise you, however; and I think I can assure you that it certainly wouldn't if you were now on the scene here with me and had the near vision of all the circumstances. My sense of how everything more and more makes for it has been gathering force ever since the war broke out, and I have thus waited nearly a whole year; but my feeling has become acute with the information that I can only go down to Lamb House now on the footing of an Alien under Police supervision—an alien friend of course, which is a very different thing from an alien enemy, but still a definite technical outsider to the whole situation here, in which my affections and my loyalty are so intensely engaged. I feel that if I take this step I shall simply rectify a position that has become inconveniently and uncomfortably false, making my civil status merely agree not only with my moral, but with my material as well, in every kind of way. Hadn't it been for the War I should certainly have gone on as I was, taking it as the simplest and easiest and even friendliest thing: but the circumstances are utterly altered now, and to feel with the country and the cause as absolutely and ardently as I feel, and not offer them my moral support with a perfect consistency (my material is too small a matter), affects me as standing off or wandering loose in a detachment of no great dignity. I have spent here all the best years of my life—they practically have *been* my life: about a twelvemonth hence I shall have been domiciled uninterruptedly in England for forty years, and there is not the least possibility, at my age, and in my state of health, of my ever returning to the U. S. or taking up any relation with it as a country. My practical relation has been to this one for ever so long, and now my "spiritual" or "sentimental" quite ideally matches it. I am telling you all this because I can't not want exceedingly to take you into my confidence about it—but again I feel pretty certain that you will understand me too well for any great number of words more to be needed. The real truth is that in a matter of this kind, under such extraordinarily special circumstances, one's own intimate feeling must speak and determine the case. Well, without haste and without rest, mine has done so, and with the prospect of what I have called the rectification, a sense of great relief, a great lapse of awkwardness, supervenes.

I think that even if by chance your so judicious mind should be disposed to suggest any reserves—I think, I say, that I should then still ask you not to launch them at me unless they should seem to you so important as to balance against my own argument and, frankly speaking, my own absolute need and passion here; which the whole experience of the past year has made quite unspeakably final. I can't imagine at all what these objections should be, however—my whole long relation to the country having been what it is. Regard my proceeding as a simple act and offering of allegiance and devotion, recognition and gratitude (for long years and

innumerable relations that have meant so much to me,)
and it remains perfectly simple. Let me repeat that I
feel sure I shouldn't in the least have come to it without this convulsion, but one is *in* the convulsion (I
wouldn't be out of it either!) and one must act accordingly. I feel all the while too that the tide of American identity of consciousness with our own, about the
whole matter, rises and rises, and will rise still more before it rests again—so that every day the difference of
situation diminishes and the immense fund of common
sentiment increases. However, I haven't really meant so
much to expatiate. What I am doing this afternoon is,
I think, simply to get exact information—though I am
already sufficiently aware of the question to know that
after my long existence here the process of naturalisation
is very simple and short. . . . My last word about the
matter, at any rate, has to be that my decision is absolutely tied up with my innermost personal feeling. I
think that will only make you glad, however, and I add
nothing more now but that I am your all-affectionate
old Uncle,

Henry James

✳

BIBLIOGRAPHY

I: THE FURTHER READING OF HENRY JAMES

James himself once gave advice on the reading of his novels. On September 14, 1913, he wrote his old friend Mrs. G. W. Prothero, who had appealed to him to supply her friend, a "young man from Texas," Mr. Stark Young, with guidance in the study of his books. James made two lists of his major novels, "all on the basis of the Scribner's (or [London] Macmillan's) collective and revised and prefaced edition" of his fiction. The first list contained *Roderick Hudson** (1876), *The Portrait of a Lady** (1881), *The Princess Casamassima** (1886), *The Wings of the Dove** (1902), *The Golden Bowl** (1904). The second list, which he called "the more 'advanced,'" also included five novels: *The American** (1877), *The Tragic Muse** (1890), *The Wings of the Dove** (1902), *The Ambassadors** (1903), and *The Golden Bowl** (1904).

These two lists are useful to readers wishing to trace James's progress as a novelist, but both of them lack certain novels of major importance which no serious reader will want to miss: *The Europeans* (1878), *Washington Square* (1881), *The Bostonians* (1886), *The Spoils of Poynton** (1897), *What Maisie Knew** (1897), *In the Cage** (1898), and *The Awkward Age** (1899). For more specialized readers there remain the early novels *Watch and Ward* (1878) and *Confidence* (1880); *The Other House* (1896) and *The Sacred Fount* (1901); and two unfinished novels, *The Ivory Tower* (1917) and *The Sense of the Past* (1917).

James's shorter fiction ranges from short stories to long tales or *nouvelles*. These run to over a hundred titles. As a supplement to the fiction included in this book I offer the following suggestions for reading. I list them under several convenient categories. I omit stories included in the present volume, and I asterisk titles revised by James in the New York Edition. The dates here are of first publication, usually in magazines, sometimes in book collections of his tales. The first book publication of all these tales is given in the *Chronology* on pages 29-36.

---

* Asterisks indicate that titles so marked were revised and included by James in the New York Edition of his fiction, 1907-1909, but the dates given are those of first book publication.

Beginnings: Early Tales. "The Story of a Year" (1865), "Poor Richard" (1867), "A Most Extraordinary Case" (1868)—these three dealing with the Civil War; "A Landscape Painter" (1866), "The Romance of Certain Old Clothes" (1868), "DeGrey: A Romance" (1868), "Gabrielle de Bergerac" (1869), "Travelling Companions" (1870).

The International Theme. "A Passionate Pilgrim" * (1871), "Madame de Mauves" * (1875), "An International Episod_ * (1878), *Daisy Miller* (1878), "A Bundle of Letters" * (1879), "The Pension Beaurepas" * (1879), "The Point of View" * (1882), "The Siege of London" * (1883), "A London Life" * (1888), *The Reverberator* (1888), " 'Europe' " * (1899), "Miss Gunton of Poughkeepsie" * (1900), "Fordham Castle" * (1904).

The Comedy and Tragedy of Society. "Eugene Pickering" (1874), "Lady Barbarina" * (1884), "Georgina's Reasons" (1885), "Louisa Pallant" * (1888), "The Liar" * (1888), "The Patagonia" * (1888), "Mrs. Temperley" (1889), "The Solution" (1889), "Brooksmith" * (1891), "The Chaperon" * (1891), "The Wheel of Time" (1892), "Lord Beaupré" (1893), "The Two Faces" * (1901), "The Beldonald Holbein" * (1901), "Mrs. Medwin" * (1901), "Flickerbridge" * (1902), "The Special Type" (1903), *Julia Bride* (1908), "Crapy Cornelia" (1909), "Mora Montravers" (1909).

Stories of Writers and Artists. "The Madonna of the Future" * (1873), "The Author of Beltraffio" * (1884), "The Aspern Papers" * (1888), "The Lesson of the Master" * (1888), "The Private Life" * (1892), "The Middle Years" * (1893), "Sir Dominick Ferrand" (1893), "The Death of the Lion" * (1894), "The Coxon Fund" * (1894), "The Next Time" * (1895), "The Figure in the Carpet" * (1896), "John Delavoy" (1898), "Broken Wings" * (1900), "The Abasement of the Northmores" * (1900), "The Tone of Time" (1900), "The Story in It" * (1903), "The Velvet Glove" (1909). A good collection of the tales on this theme is *Stories of Writers and Artists* by Henry James, edited by F. O. Matthiessen (1946).

Ghostly Tales. "Sir Edmund Orme" * (1892), "The Private Life" * (1892), "Owen Wingrave" * (1893), "The Altar of the Dead" * (1895), "The Friends of the Friends" * ([1896] 1909), "The Turn of the Screw" * (1898), "The Great Good Place" * (1900), "The Real Right Thing" * (1900), "Maud-Evelyn" (1900), "The Third Person" (1900), "The Jolly Corner" * (1908). For all of James's stories of this kind, see Leon Edel's excellent edition of *The Ghostly Tales of Henry James* (1948).

James's major writings in criticism are contained in the book collections he himself made of his critical essays. The little book on *Hawthorne* (1879) is of first importance. His other books of criticism and the essays of special importance in them are: *French Poets and Novelists* (1878)—"Théophile Gautier," "Charles Baudelaire," "Honoré de Balzac," "Balzac's Letters," "George Sand," "Ivan Turgénieff," "The Théâtre Français." *Partial Portraits* (1888)—"Emerson," "The Life of George Eliot," "Anthony Trollope," "Robert Louis Stevenson," "Alphonse Daudet," "Guy de Maupassant," "Ivan Turgénieff," "The Art of Fiction." *Essays in London and Elsewhere* (1893)—"James Russell Lowell," "Gustave Flaubert," "Pierre Loti," "Henrik Ibsen," "Criticism." *The Question of Our Speech / The Lesson of Balzac* (1905). *Notes on Novelists with Some Other Notes* (1914)—"Robert Louis Stevenson," "Émile Zola," "Gustave Flaubert," "Honoré de Balzac" (two essays), "George Sand" (three essays), "Gabriele D'Annunzio," "The New Novel, 1914," "The Novel in *The Ring and the Book*." Of the early criticisms collected by LeRoy Phillips in *Views and Reviews* (1908), those particularly interesting are "The Novels of George Eliot," "Swinburne's Essays," "Matthew Arnold's Essays," "Mr. Walt Whitman," "The Limitations of Dickens," "Tennyson's Drama," and "Mr. Kipling's Early Stories." Pierre de Chaignon la Rose's edition of other early *Notes and Reviews* (1921) shows James as a critic and reviewer of books from 1864 to 1886. James's single collection of his writings on art is *Picture and Text* (1893). His writings on drama, theater, and acting have been admirably collected by Allan Wade under the title *The Scenic Art* (1948). In all these fields of criticism of literature, art, and drama, James wrote much that remains uncollected; most of this work is listed in LeRoy Phillips's *Bibliography of the Writings of Henry James* (New York: Coward-McCann, 1930).

James's memoir of *William Wetmore Story and His Friends* (1903) is a book of great charm and fascination, and a major document on James's own relations with Europe.

His dramas may now be read in Leon Edel's definitive edition of *The Complete Plays of Henry James* (1949), with their copious biographical, textual, and critical annotations.

His writings on travel, cultures, societies, are best followed in the series of these he himself published in book form: *Transatlantic Sketches* (1875), *Foreign Parts* (1883), *Portraits of Places* (1883), *A Little Tour of France* (1885), the essay on "London" in *Essays in London and Elsewhere* (1893), *English Hours* (1905), *The American Scene* (1907)—his major work of this kind—and *Italian Hours* (1909). Here again a great quantity of James's writing remains uncollected and must be traced in Phillips's *Bibliography*.

Phillips gives the basic facts on the complex details of the editions and publishers of James's books in England and America (such details have not been included above), but his work is importantly supplemented by I. R. Brussel's *Anglo-American First Editions* (London and New York: Bowker Co., 1935-36), indispensable to students of James's bibliography.

II: BIOGRAPHY AND CRITICISM

Biography. No full biography of Henry James has yet appeared, but a life, detailed and authorized, is in preparation by Leon Edel. James' own three autobiographical memoirs are indispensable: *A Small Boy and Others* (1913), *Notes of a Son and Brother* (1914), and *The Middle Years* (1917). Percy Lubbock's edition of *The Letters of Henry James* (New York: Scribner's, 1920) contains a sketch of his life as well as the valuable letters themselves. For other collections of letters, see the Editor's Note to Part VI of this book. F. W. Dupee's *Henry James* in the American Men of Letters Series (New York: William Sloane Associates, 1951) gives an account of the life as well as critical interpretation of the works. Much additional material on Henry James is included in the records of his family:

James, Henry, Jr., *The Letters of William James* (Boston: Atlantic Monthly Press, 1920).

Grattan, C. Hartley, *The Three Jameses: A Family of Minds* (New York: Longmans, Green, 1932).

Warren, Austin, *The Elder Henry James* (New York: Macmillan, 1934).

Burr, Anna Robeson, *Alice James: Her Brothers, Her Journal* (New York: Dodd, Mead, 1934).

Perry, Ralph Barton, *The Thought and Character of William James* (Boston: Little, Brown & Co., 1935).

Matthiessen, F. O., *The James Family, Including Selections from the Writings of Henry James Senior, William, Henry, and Alice James* (New York: Alfred A. Knopf, 1947).

The personality and legend of Henry James are strikingly presented in:

Bosanquet, Theodora, *Henry James at Work* (London: Hogarth Press, 1924). An essay by his last secretary.

Nowell-Smith, Simon, *The Legend of the Master* (New York: Scribner's, 1948). A compilation of reports and anecdotes of H.J. by those who knew him; the best guide to the many contemporary memoirs and biographies which include accounts of James.

Fundamental to the study of James's life, as well as his art, are:
James, Henry, *The Art of the Novel: Critical Prefaces* (New

York: Scribner's, 1935), with a preface by R. P. Blackmur.
James's prefaces for the New York Edition of his fiction.
Matthiessen, F. O., and Kenneth B. Murdock, editors, *The
Notebooks of Henry James* (New York: Oxford University Press, 1947). This contains the plans, sketches, and
"germs" of his fiction and includes much autobiographical material.

The crucial years that James spent writing for the theater
are dealt with in the following books and editions, which
contain much additional biographical material:

Edel, Leon, *Henry James: Les Années Dramatiques* (Paris:
Jouve et Cie., 1931).
Robins, Elizabeth, *Theatre and Friendship: Some Henry
James Letters* (New York: Putnam's, 1932).
Wade, Allan, ed., *The Scenic Art: Notes on Acting and the
Drama, 1872-1901,* by Henry James (New Brunswick,
N. J.: Rutgers University Press, 1948).
Edel, Leon, ed., *The Complete Plays of Henry James*
(Philadelphia: J. B. Lippincott, 1949).

Criticism. Interpretation and evaluation of James's art is
voluminous. Essays and discussions in books on fiction cannot
be listed fully here. A lengthy bibliography up to 1941 is
included in *Henry James: Representative Selections,* edited by
Lyon P. Richardson (Cincinnati: American Book Co., 1941),
and this is reproduced in *The Question of Henry James,* a
symposium of Jamesian criticism, edited by F. W. Dupee (New
York: Henry Holt, 1945). It has been extended to include the
years 1941-48 by Eunice C. Hamilton in *American Literature,*
XX (1948-49), pp. 424-35. The following are the principal
books that have been written on James; titles of special value
are indicated by an asterisk:

Andreas, Osborn, *Henry James and the Expanding Horizon*
(Seattle: University of Washington Press, 1948).
* Beach, Joseph Warren, *The Method of Henry James* (New
Haven: Yale University Press, 1918). An early study but
still one of the soundest general treatments.
Brooks, Van Wyck, *The Pilgrimage of Henry James* (New
York: E. P. Dutton and Co., 1925). Notable as an extreme
argument against James's expatriation from America and
its effect on his work.
Cary, Elizabeth Luther, *The Novels of Henry James* (New
York: Putnam's, 1906). The earliest book on James.
* Dupee, F. W., *Henry James* (New York: William Sloane

Associates, 1951). A valuable work combining biography and criticism.

Edel, Leon, *The Prefaces of Henry James* (Paris: Jouve et Cie., 1931).

Edgar, Pelham, *Henry James: Man and Author* (London: Grant Richards; Boston: Houghton Mifflin, 1927). General and descriptive chiefly.

Garnier, Marie-Reine, *Henry James et la France* (Paris: Honoré Champion, 1927).

Hueffer [Ford], Ford Madox, *Henry James: A Critical Study* (New York: Dodd, Mead, 1916). Personal and eccentric, but stimulating as a study of craft and style.

* Kelly, Cornelia Pulsifer, *The Early Development of Henry James* (Urbana: University of Illinois, 1930). Documented, scrupulous, sound; especially valuable for its study of James's European literary affiliations.

* Matthiessen, F. O., *Henry James: The Major Phase* (New York: Oxford University Press, 1944). A study of the period 1895-1910.

Milano, Paolo, *Henry James: o Il Proscritto Volontario* (Milan: Arnoldo Mondadori, 1948).

* Roberts, Morris, *Henry James's Criticism* (Cambridge: Harvard University Press, 1929). The fullest study of James as critic.

Snell, Edwin Marion, *The Modern Fables of Henry James* (Cambridge: Harvard University Press, 1935). Short but perceptive.

* Stevenson, Elizabeth, *The Crooked Corridor: A Study of Henry James* (New York: Macmillan, 1949). A limited but sensitive introductory study of James.

West, Rebecca, *Henry James* (London: Nisbet and Co., 1916). A short early study; opinionated but stimulating.

No effort is made here to list recent reprints or collections of James's work, but the following should be mentioned because of the biographical or critical material they include:

Auden, W. H., ed., *The American Scene* by Henry James (New York: Scribner's, 1946).

Edel, Leon, ed., *The Ghostly Tales of Henry James* (New Brunswick, N. J.: Rutgers University Press, 1948).

Fadiman, Clifton, ed., *The Short Stories of Henry James* (New York: Random House, 1945).

Kenton, Edna, ed., *Eight Uncollected Tales of Henry James* (New Brunswick, N. J.: Rutgers University Press, 1950).

Matthiessen, F. O., ed., *Henry James: Stories of Writers and Artists* (New York: New Directions, 1946).

Matthiessen, F. O., ed., *The American Novels and Stories of Henry James* (New York: Alfred A. Knopf, 1947).

Rahv, Philip, ed., *The Great Short Novels of Henry James* (New York: Dial Press, 1944).

Richardson, Lyon P., ed., *Henry James: Representative Selections* (Cincinnati: American Book Company, 1941).

A number of critical symposia on Henry James have been published, the most notable being:

The Little Review, Henry James Number, Vol. V, No. 4 (August 1918), pp. 1-64. Prepared by Ezra Pound, with essays by Ethel Colburn Mayne, Ezra Pound, T. S. Eliot, John Rodker, Theodora Bosanquet.

The Hound and Horn, "Homage to Henry James," Vol. VII, No. 3 (April-June 1934), pp. 361-562. Edited by Lincoln Kirstein. With essays by Marianne Moore, Lawrence Leighton, Edmund Wilson, Francis Fergusson, Stephen Spender, Newton Arvin, R. P. Blackmur, Alice Boughton, John Wheelwright, Robert Cantwell, Edna Kenton, H. R. Hays, Glenway Wescott.

The New Republic, Memorial Issue on William and Henry James, Vol. CVIII, issue of February 15, 1943. With essays by Alfred Kazin, Jacques Barzun, Irwin Edman, William Troy, Philip Rahv.

The Kenyon Review, Henry James Number, Vol. V, No. 4 (Autumn 1943), pp. 481-617. Edited by Robert Penn Warren. With essays by Katherine Anne Porter, Francis Fergusson, Jacques Barzun, John L. Sweeney, F. O. Matthiessen, Austin Warren, David Daiches, Eliseo Vivas, R. P. Blackmur.

The Question of Henry James, edited by F. W. Dupee (New York: Henry Holt and Co., 1945). With essays by Thomas Wentworth Higginson, William Dean Howells, Frank Moore Colby, Herbert Croly, Max Beerbohm, Joseph Conrad, Ford Madox Ford, Percy Lubbock, Stuart P. Sherman, Joseph Warren Beach, Thomas Beer, T. S. Eliot, Van Wyck Brooks, Vernon Louis Parrington, Edna Kenton, Constance Rourke, Edmund Wilson, R. P. Blackmur, Morton Dauwen Zabel, F. O. Matthiessen, Stephen Spender, W. H. Auden, André Gide, Jacques Barzun, William Troy, Philip Rahv.

The books and critical collections previously listed will illustrate for the reader much of the best Jamesian criticism and the characteristic "approaches" of the past several decades. Certain other essays on James have special value in dealing with fundamental, sometimes controversial, aspects of his work. The following are some of the most important:

Anderson, Quentin, "Henry James and the New Jerusalem," *Kenyon Review*, VIII (Autumn 1946), pp. 515-66. An inquiry into the influence of his father's religious and philosophic ideas on James's art and thought.

Bewley, Marius, "James's Debt to Hawthorne," *Scrutiny* (Cambridge, England), XVI (September 1949), pp. 178-195, and (Winter 1949), pp. 301-317; XVII (Spring 1950), pp. 14-31. A detailed study of a major influence on James.

Bewley, Marius, "Appearance and Reality in Henry James," *Scrutiny*, XVII (Summer 1950), pp. 90-114.

Blackmur, Richard P., "Henry James," in *Literary History of the United States,* Vol. II (New York: Macmillan, 1948). A sound general account and estimation.

Eliot, T. S., "In Memory" and "The Hawthorne Aspect," *The Little Review*, V (August 1918), pp. 44-53. Reprinted in Edmund Wilson's anthology *The Shock of Recognition* (New York: Doubleday, 1943) and in F. W. Dupee's *The Question of Henry James* (New York: Holt, 1945). Eliot's most important writings on James; important as the view of a continuator.

Kenton, Edna, "Henry James to the Ruminant Reader: *The Turn of the Screw,*" *The Arts*, VI (November 1924), pp. 245-55. A pioneer essay on psychological elements in James.

Leavis, F. R., "Henry James," in *The Great Tradition* (New York: George W. Stewart, 1949). Acute and essential; one of the most valuable among recent critical treatments.

Leavis, F. R., "James's *What Maisie Knew:* A Disagreement," *Scrutiny*, XVII (Summer 1950), pp. 115-27.

Lubbock, Percy, *The Craft of Fiction* (New York: Scribner's, 1921). Includes several analyses of James's novels by a disciple of his critical method.

Pound, Ezra, "Henry James," in *Make It New* (New Haven: Yale University Press, 1935). Program notes and commentary on the work in general.

Rahv, Philip, "The Heiress of All the Ages" and "Attitudes Toward Henry James," in *Image and Idea: Fourteen Essays on Literary Themes* (New York: New Directions, 1949).

Rosenzweig, Saul, "The Ghost of Henry James: A Study in Thematic Apperception," in *Character and Personality* (Duke University Press), XIII, No. 2 (December 1943); reprinted in *Partisan Review,* XI (Fall 1944), pp. 436-55. Perhaps the most notable psychological inquiry into James's personality and fiction.

Rourke, Constance, "The American," in *American Humor: A Study of the National Character* (New York: Harcourt, Brace, 1931). A brilliant essay on humor and native satire in James.

Spender, Stephen, "Part One: Henry James," in *The Destructive Element: A Study of Modern Writers and Beliefs* (Boston: Houghton Mifflin, 1935).

Trilling, Lionel, "Introduction" to *The Princess Casamassima* (New York: Macmillan, 1948); reprinted in *The Liberal Imagination* by Lionel Trilling (New York: Viking Press, 1950).

Wilson, Edmund, "The Ambiguity of Henry James," in *The Triple Thinkers* (New York: Harcourt, Brace, 1938; but revised and expanded: New York: Oxford University Press, 1948). A notable, Freudian, and provocative interpretation of *The Turn of the Screw*, but also a suggestive review of the whole body of James's work; one of the most stimulating of recent interpretations. The view it presents has been variously opposed or debated; see, for instance, Robert B. Heilman's "The Freudian Reading of *The Turn of the Screw*," *Modern Language Notes*, LXII (November 1947), pp. 433-45, and "*The Turn of the Screw* as Poem," *University of Kansas City Review*, XIV (Summer 1948), pp. 277-89; also A. J. A. Waldock's "Mr. Edmund Wilson and *The Turn of the Screw*," *Modern Language Notes*, LXII (May 1947), pp. 331-34; E. E. Stoll's "Symbolism in Coleridge," *Publications of the Modern Language Association*, LXIII (March 1948), pp. 214-33; Francis X. Roellinger's "Psychical Research and *The Turn of the Screw*," *American Literature*, XX (1948-49), pp. 401-412; Glenn A. Reed's "Another Turn on James's *Turn of the Screw*," *American Literature*, XX (1948-49), pp. 413-23; and further, "The 'Hallucination' Theory of *The Turn of the Screw*" in *A Treatise on the Novel* by Robert Liddell (London: Cape, 1947), pp. 138-145, and Leon Edel in his *Ghostly Tales of Henry James* (New Brunswick, N. J.: Rutgers University Press, 1948).

Winters, Yvor, "Maule's Well, or Henry James and the Relation of Morals to Manners," in *Maule's Curse: Seven Studies in the History of American Obscurantism* (Norfolk, Conn.: New Directions, 1938); now reprinted in Winters' *In Defense of Reason* (New York: Swallow Press and William Morrow, 1947; and University of Denver, Alan Swallow, 1950). A basic and radical study of moral and social elements in James.

It must finally be emphasized again that Henry James was an author who subjected much of his fiction to revision, not only for the 24 volumes of the New York Edition (Scribner's, 1907-1909), but even in earlier transitions from serialized to book form and frequently from edition to edition in book form (*The American* is a notable example of this). Sometimes such revision, of a more incidental kind, appeared in successive editions of his critical, travel, and other writings. The serious reader must consequently be aware of what version of a text he is reading.

The New York Edition, now out of print, was published by Scribner in New York and by Macmillan in London; and to its 24 original volumes of novels and tales the unfinished novels *The Ivory Tower* and *The Sense of the Past* were added in 1917, the *Letters* in 1920. These are revised texts and sometimes reappear in recent reprintings or anthologies. (The present volume reproduces the texts of its fiction from the New York Edition.) Critical opinion as to the wisdom of James's revisions has naturally differed. In the 35 volumes of *The Novels and Stories of Henry James* which Macmillan published in London in 1921-23, the editor, Percy Lubbock, included, besides the texts and prefaces of the New York Edition, eleven further volumes of novels and tales which James did not have room for in the New York Edition or chose to omit from it; only a few works, like "Covering End," *The Other House,* and *The Outcry,* which James converted into or novelized from his plays, were omitted. This invaluable edition is also, regrettably, out of print at present. The nonfictional writing of James has never been collected in a uniform edition. Editions of his early uncollected work that have been made by various editors since his death are listed in the *Chronology* of the present volume. Current reprint editions of James's work should, but do not always, indicate which version of their text they employ. Phillips's *Bibliography* and I. R. Brussel's *Anglo-American First Editions*, both mentioned above, are basic equipment for investigating the complex conditions of James's texts and editions.

(For further bibliographical material added to the 1956 edition, see Addenda, 1956, pp. 37-38.)